NONLINEAR AND DYNAMIC PROGRAMMING

NONLINEAR AND DYNAMIC PROGRAMMING

by

G. HADLEY

ADDISON-WESLEY PUBLISHING COMPANY
Reading, Massachusetts · Menlo Park, California · London · Sydney · Manila

THIS BOOK IS AN ADDISON-WESLEY
WORLD STUDENT SERIES EDITION

FIRST PRINTING 1970

Library of Congress Catalog Card No. 64-15564

PREFACE

This work is intended as a sequel to the author's *Linear Programming*, and it concentrates on a study of the theory and computational aspects of nonlinear programming problems. The first chapter surveys in simple terms those features of nonlinear programming problems which make them much more difficult to solve than linear ones. Chapter 2 attempts to summarize the most important mathematical background needed and introduces the notation to be used throughout the text. By the inclusion of this chapter it is hoped that the current work can be used independently of the author's *Linear Programming* or *Linear Algebra* text. Chapter 3 concentrates on classical optimization methods based on the calculus, mainly the method of Lagrange multipliers. It also develops the most important properties of convex and concave functions that will be needed in the remainder of the text. No attempt is made to study the calculus of variations in this chapter since an entire book would be required to develop this subject adequately. Indeed, the only references to the calculus of variations which appear in this text are brief sections in the chapters on dynamic programming. Chapter 4 discusses approximate methods for finding either a local or global optimum (depending on the nature of the problem) for nonlinear programming problems. Chapter 5 is devoted to stochastic programming problems and Chapter 6 to the Kuhn-Tucker theory. In Chapter 7 quadratic programming problems are studied and in Chapter 8 integer linear programming is discussed. Chapter 9 is concerned with gradient methods for solving programming problems, and the remaining two chapters deal with dynamic programming.

The subject matter of nonlinear programming is much broader and much more difficult to unify than is that concerned only with linear programming. For this reason, the current text may appear to be somewhat lacking in cohesiveness and may seem to be concerned with a set of somewhat unrelated special methods for solving particular types of problems. This is true to a considerable extent, because there does not at present exist any unifying theory for all of what might be considered nonlinear programming and because, in addition, computational algorithms exist only for solving very special types of problems. The development of these algorithms depends in a crucial way on the special characteristics of the problems. A very large number of computational schemes have been suggested for solving a variety of the problems considered here. It was out of the question to discuss every method that has been proposed for solving a particular type of problem, and hence the author was forced to make a choice in selecting the ones to be discussed. In many cases, this had to be done on an arbitrary basis, because no data exist for comparing the computational efficiency of various schemes. In some cases, a method may have been omitted simply because the author was not aware of its existence. The field of nonlinear programming is currently in a state of rapid change. In selecting material for this text, an attempt was made to include those methods which would be more or less of lasting relevance. However, it is quite possible that many of the computational algorithms discussed will be superseded by improved ones in the not too distant future.

The mathematical background needed for a study of this work varies considerably from chapter to chapter. For most of the chapters a rudimentary knowledge of linear algebra and linear programming is needed (say, roughly, the first eight or nine chapters of the author's *Linear Programming*). However, a large part of the material on dynamic programming could be read without a knowledge of either linear algebra or linear programming. Some knowledge of calculus is needed in Chapters 3 and 6, but not elsewhere to any significant extent. Chapter 2 attempts to summarize most of the necessary mathematical background referred to above. There remains one background area which Chapter 2 does not attempt to summarize. This is the subject matter of elementary probability theory. Discussions involving the use of probability theory appear in Chapters 3, 5, 10, and 11.

The author is indebted once again to Jackson E. Morris, who has so generously supplied the excellent quotations appearing at the beginning of each chapter. The reviewers, Robert Dorfman and Stuart Dreyfus, provided a number of useful suggestions for which the author is grateful. The Graduate School of Business, University of Chicago, generously provided the secretarial assistance for having the manuscript typed and reproduced.

Bogotá, Colombia G.H.
June 1964

CONTENTS

Chapter 4. Approximate Methods for Solving Problems Involving Separable Functions

Chapter 5. Stochastic Programming

Chapter 6. Kuhn-Tucker Theory

Chapter 7. Quadratic Programming

CHAPTER 1

INTRODUCTION

Each venture
Is a new beginning, a raid on the inarticulate
With shabby equipment always deteriorating.

T. S. Eliot, *East Coker*

1–1 Programming problems. Any problem which seeks to maximize or minimize a numerical function of one or more variables (or functions) when the variables (or functions) can be independent or related in some way through the specification of certain constraints may be referred to as an optimization problem. Optimization problems have long been of interest to mathematicians, physical scientists, and engineers. The possibility of using the methods of the differential calculus and the calculus of variations to solve certain types of optimization problems arising in geometry and physics has been known and applied since the middle of the eighteenth century. In the last fifteen years there has been a remarkable growth of interest in a new class of optimization problems, often referred to as programming problems, which are usually not amenable to solution by the classical methods of the calculus. Programming problems can frequently be classified in a broad context as problems in economics, rather than problems in geometry or physics as were the classical optimization problems. Often a programming problem can be considered to be one concerned with the allocation of scarce resources—men, machines, and raw materials—to the manufacture of one or more products in such a way that the products meet certain specifications, while at the same time some objective function such as profit or cost is maximized or minimized. Programming problems have attracted such wide interest because they do not occur in theoretical economics only, but also arise, in the form of important practical problems, in industry, commerce, government, and the military.

The general programming problem can be formulated as follows. It is desired to determine values for n variables $x_1, \ldots, x_n$ which satisfy the m inequalities or equations

$$g_i(x_1, \ldots, x_n)\{\leq, =, \geq\}b_i, \qquad i = 1, \ldots, m, \tag{1–1}$$

and, in addition, maximize or minimize the function

$$z = f(x_1, \ldots, x_n). \tag{1–2}$$

The restrictions (1–1) are called the *constraints*, and (1–2) is called the *objective function*. In (1–1) the $g_i(x_1, \ldots, x_n)$ are assumed to be specified functions, and the b_i are assumed to be known constants. Furthermore, in (1–1), one and only one of the signs $\leq, =, \geq$ holds for each constraint, but the sign may vary from one constraint to another. The values of m and n need not be related in any way, that is, m can be greater than, less than, or equal to n. We shall allow m to be zero, so that we include cases where there are no constraints (1–1). Usually, some or all of the variables are restricted to be non-negative. In addition, it may be required that some or all of the variables are allowed to take on only certain discrete values, such as integral values. Unless otherwise specified, (1–1) and (1–2) will be interpreted as a problem in which it is desired to find numerical values for the n variables $x_1, \ldots, x_n$ which optimize (1–2) subject to (1–1) and any non-negativity and/or integrality requirements. In certain cases, however, the variables x_j will be functions of one or more parameters, and the problem will then be one of determining a set of functions $x_1, \ldots, x_n$ which optimize (1–2) subject to (1–1) and any non-negativity and/or integrality requirements on the x_j.

The real impetus for the growth of interest in and the practical applications of programming problems came in 1947, when George Dantzig devised the simplex algorithm for solving the general linear programming problem. If in (1–1) and (1–2),

$$g_i(x_1, \ldots, x_n) = \sum_{j=1}^{n} a_{ij}x_j, \quad i = 1, \ldots, m, \tag{1–3}$$

and

$$f(x_1, \ldots, x_n) = \sum_{j=1}^{n} c_j x_j, \tag{1–4}$$

where the a_{ij} and c_j are known constants, the programming problem is said to be linear provided that there are no other restrictions except perhaps the requirement that some or all variables must be non-negative. Usually, in the formulation of the general linear programming problem, it is specified that *each* variable must be non-negative, i.e.,

$$x_j \geq 0, \quad j = 1, \ldots, n, \tag{1–5}$$

since this form is most convenient when making numerical computations. Any problem in which some of the variables are unrestricted in sign may easily be transformed to one in which all variables are non-negative. Thus a linear programming problem seeks to determine non-negative values of the n variables x_j which satisfy the m constraints

$$\textstyle\sum_j a_{ij}x_j\{\leq, =, \geq\}b_i,$$

and which maximize or minimize the linear function $z = \sum_j c_j x_j$. We shall not consider a problem of the above form to be linear unless all x_j values which satisfy the constraints and the non-negativity restrictions are allowable, i.e., it is not permissible to impose an additional restriction, for example, that the variables can only assume integral values. All programming problems that are not linear in the sense defined above will be called nonlinear.

In this text we shall be concerned almost exclusively with the solution of nonlinear programming problems. It will be assumed that the reader is familiar with linear programming to the extent covered in the first nine chapters of the author's *Linear Programming* [13].* This is an essential prerequisite, since many of the techniques for the solution of nonlinear problems involve in one way or another the use of a simplex-type algorithm. Unfortunately, nonlinear programming problems are almost always much more difficult to solve than linear ones. Indeed, computational procedures have been devised for solving only a very small subset of all nonlinear programming problems. We shall study those that can be solved and the techniques available for solving them. No attempt will be made to study in detail the great variety of practical problems that can be formulated as nonlinear programming problems. It might be noted, however, that most practical problems which have been formulated as linear programming problems are in reality nonlinear ones for which the nonlinearities were ignored or approximated in some way. Although no attempt will be made to cover formally the applications of nonlinear programming to practical situations, a number of practical applications will be considered in the discussion of examples and in the problems.

1–2 Special cases of interest. Most of the following chapters will either be concerned with a study of techniques for solving very specialized types of nonlinear programming problems, or will be devoted to examining the types of nonlinear programming problems that can be solved with some particular computational technique. It seems desirable at the outset to review briefly the special types of nonlinear programming problems that will receive the greatest attention, and the general types of computational techniques that have been found useful in solving such problems. This section will deal with the special types of problems to be considered in detail later, and the next section will be concerned with computational techniques. In the discussion to follow it will be assumed that the variables are *not* restricted to integral or, more generally, discrete values unless it is indicated specifically that they are so restricted.

---

* Numbers in brackets refer to bibliographical references.

The class of nonlinear programming problems which has been studied most extensively is that where the constraints are linear and the objective function is nonlinear. The general problem of this kind can be written in the abbreviated format

$$\sum_{j=1}^{n} a_{ij}x_j \{\leq, =, \geq\} b_i, \qquad i = 1, \ldots, m, \tag{1–6}$$

$$x_j \geq 0, \qquad j = 1, \ldots, n, \tag{1–7}$$

$$\max \text{ or } \min z = f(x_1, \ldots, x_n). \tag{1–8}$$

Equations (1–6) through (1–8) should be read: Find non-negative values of the n variables x_j which satisfy the constraints (1–6) and which maximize or minimize the objective function $z = f(x_1, \ldots, x_n)$. For convenience, the variables were required to be non-negative in the above formulation. Problems in which some or all variables are allowed to be unrestricted in sign may be easily reduced to this case by a simple transformation that will be introduced later.

Even when attention is restricted to problems involving linear constraints, computational techniques for finding optimal solutions have not been devised except in cases where the objective function has very special properties. There are two special cases of (1–6) through (1–8) that will be of particular interest to us. In the first, the objective function can be written as a sum of n functions, each of which is a function of only a single variable, i.e.,

$$z = f(x_1, \ldots, x_n) = f_1(x_1) + f_2(x_2) + \cdots + f_n(x_n). \tag{1–9}$$

To guarantee that an optimal solution can be found, additional restrictions must be placed on the $f_j(x_j)$. These will be discussed later. When the objective function can be written in the form (1–9), it is said to be separable. Occasionally, when studying problems with separable objective functions and a very small number of linear constraints, we shall also consider cases where the variables are restricted to taking on only integral values.

In the second case, the objective function can be written as the sum of a linear form plus a quadratic form, so that

$$\begin{aligned} z = f(x_1, \ldots, x_n) &= \sum_{j=1}^{n} c_j x_j + \sum_{i=1}^{n}\sum_{j=1}^{n} d_{ij}x_ix_j \\ &= c_1x_1 + \cdots + c_nx_n + d_{11}x_1^2 + d_{12}x_1x_2 + \cdots + d_{1n}x_1x_n \\ &\qquad + \cdots + d_{nn}x_n^2. \end{aligned} \tag{1–10}$$

Such a nonlinear programming problem is referred to as a quadratic programming problem. To be certain that an optimal solution can be found in this case, the d_{ij} must satisfy certain restrictions which need not be considered now. An entire chapter, Chapter 7, will be devoted to studying the theory of, and techniques for, solving quadratic programming problems.

For a variety of reasons that will become clear later, problems with nonlinear constraints tend to be much more difficult to solve than those with linear constraints. We shall devote parts of several chapters to studying problems in which the constraints may be nonlinear. Most of our attention will be limited, however, to cases in which the constraints are separable. This means that the $g_i(x_1, \ldots, x_n)$ in (1–1) must be capable of being written

$$g_i(x_1, \ldots, x_n) = g_{i1}(x_1) + \cdots + g_{in}(x_n). \tag{1–11}$$

To ensure that we can obtain an optimal solution to problems with nonlinear constraints of the form (1–11), very stringent restrictions must be placed both on the $g_{ij}(x_j)$ and on the objective function. Although it is profitable to study the special case of a nonseparable objective function which is the sum of a linear and a quadratic form, this is not true in the corresponding case for nonseparable constraints, and we shall not attempt to do so.

There is one other class of problems which may have nonlinear constraints that we shall spend some time studying. Problems in this class are referred to as classical optimization problems. To obtain the form of this kind of problem, let us return to the general nonlinear programming problem (1–1) and (1–2) and imagine that (1) no inequalities appear in the constraints, (2) there are no non-negativity or discreteness restrictions on the variables, (3) $m < n$, and (4) the functions $g_i(x_1, \ldots, x_n)$ and $f(x_1, \ldots, x_n)$ are continuous and possess partial derivatives at least through second order. Such a programming problem can be represented as

$$\begin{gathered} g_i(x_1, \ldots, x_n) = b_i, \qquad i = 1, \ldots, m, \\ \max \text{ or } \min z = f(x_1, \ldots, x_n). \end{gathered} \tag{1–12}$$

A problem of this kind will be called a *classical optimization problem*. Problems such as (1–12) can be solved, at least in principle, by means of the classical optimization techniques based on the calculus. While there are problems (1–12) which can actually be solved numerically in this manner, one usually encounters computational difficulties of such a magnitude that it becomes mandatory to attempt some other method of solution. Indeed, we shall not even classify the classical techniques as computational devices, but instead as theoretical tools. It is important, however, to have some familiarity with the classical techniques, because in many areas they form the basis for the theoretical analyses employed. For example, much of the standard theory of production and consumer behavior in economics is based on classical optimization methods. Our main reason, then, for studying problems of the form (1–12) as a special class will be to develop the theory of classical optimization methods rather than to develop numerical procedures for solving problems of this type. Classical optimization techniques will be studied in Chapter 3.

The classical techniques can be generalized to handle cases in which the variables are required to be non-negative and the constraints may be inequalities, but again these generalizations are primarily of theoretical value and do not usually constitute computational procedures. Nonetheless, we shall see that these theoretical results will be very useful. In one particular case, that of quadratic programming, they will indirectly provide a computational method, i.e., they will provide another problem (which can be solved by the methods to be considered in the next section) whose solution yields an optimal solution to the quadratic programming problem. Chapter 6 will be devoted to a study of these theoretical generalizations of classical optimization techniques.

Another class of nonlinear programming problems that will be of interest to us is obtained from the general linear programming problem by imposing the additional requirement that the variables can take on only integral values. Such problems are frequently referred to as integer linear programming problems. They can be represented mathematically as

$$\sum_{j=1}^{n} a_{ij}x_j \{\leq, =, \geq\} b_i, \qquad i = 1, \ldots, m,$$

$$x_j \geq 0, \qquad j = 1, \ldots, n; \qquad \text{some or all } x_j \text{ integers}, \tag{1–13}$$

$$\max \text{ or } \min z = \sum_{j=1}^{n} c_j x_j.$$

If all x_j are required to be integers, the problem is called an all integer problem. Otherwise, we shall refer to it as a mixed integer-continuous variable problem. Chapter 8 will be concerned entirely with developing means for solving integer linear programming problems and showing that a wide variety of interesting problems can be formulated in this manner.

One other special type of nonlinear programming problem will be studied in some detail. This will be a type of stochastic sequential decision problem which is frequently encountered in production planning and inventory control. We shall not attempt to provide its mathematical form now. It will, however, exemplify the case where the variables x_j are functions of other parameters so that, instead of determining a set of numerical values for the x_j, one must determine a set of functions.

This completes the summary of the special types of problems that will occupy most of our attention in the remainder of this work. Other kinds of programming problems will be considered, but they will not be discussed as extensively as the special classes of problems considered in this section. We must restrict ourselves in large measure to special classes of problems, because the computational procedures for finding optimal solutions rely heavily on the special features and structures of the problems.

1-3 Computational procedures. The simplex algorithm for solving the general linear programming problem is an iterative procedure which yields an exact optimal solution in a finite number of steps. For the nonlinear programming problems to be studied in this text, we shall not always be able to devise computational procedures which yield exactly an optimal solution in a finite number of steps. One must often settle for procedures which provide only an approximate optimal solution or which may require an infinite number of steps for convergence.

One of the most powerful techniques for solving nonlinear programming problems is to transform the problem by some means into a form which permits application of the simplex algorithm (or one of the simplex-type algorithms). Thus the simplex algorithm turns out to be one of the most powerful computational devices for solving nonlinear programming problems as well as for solving linear programming problems. The nature of the "transformation" required to change a nonlinear programming problem into a form permitting the use of the simplex method varies widely with the type of problem being studied. In certain cases no approximations are needed to obtain a problem to which the simplex method can be applied, whereas in others approximations must be made. However, these approximations may be made as accurate as one desires (at the expense of increased computational effort).

Another useful computational technique for solving certain types of nonlinear programming problems is *dynamic programming*. The title of this text might suggest that dynamic programming refers to a special class of programming problems that are in some way distinct from nonlinear ones. Indeed there is some justification in this assumption, since the term dynamic programming is often used to refer to programming problems where changes occur over time and hence time must be considered explicitly. We shall not use dynamic programming in this sense. Instead, we shall take dynamic programming to mean the computational method involving recurrence relations which has been developed to a considerable extent by Richard Bellman. This technique evolved as a result of studying programming problems in which changes over time were important, and this is why it was given the name "dynamic programming." However, the technique can be applied to problems in which time is in no way relevant. Hence a different name would be desirable, but the term "dynamic programming" has now become so firmly established that change would prove difficult.

It should be pointed out that we are using the term "dynamic programming" in a rather narrow sense, although one will frequently find it used to describe a special type of computational procedure. The analysis of a very broad class of functional equations is also often considered to be a part of dynamic programming, in which case the procedure becomes an analytical as well as a computational tool. Indeed, we shall even discuss briefly the analysis of certain functional equations in our discussion of dynamic programming, so that we are not treating it as a strictly computational technique. Basically, however, we shall consider the term to refer to a special kind of computational procedure.

The final computational algorithm which will be used is referred to as the *gradient method*. Like the simplex method, it is an iterative technique in which we move at each step from one feasible solution to another in such a way that the value of the objective function is improved. It differs from the simplex method in that it is not an adjacent extreme point technique. In general, gradient methods may require an infinite number of iterations for convergence.

1–4 Difficulties introduced by nonlinearities. Before entering into a detailed discussion of any particular class of nonlinear programming problems, we shall examine some of the characteristics of nonlinear phenomena that can make it much more difficult to solve nonlinear programming problems than it is to solve linear ones. Recall that linear programming problems have the following properties:

(a) The set of feasible solutions [i.e., the set of all n-tuples $[x_1, \ldots, x_n]$ which satisfy the constraints (1–6) and the non-negativity restrictions (1–7)] is a convex set. This convex set has a finite number of corners which are usually referred to as extreme points.

(b) The set of all n-tuples $[x_1, \ldots, x_n]$ which yield a specified value of the objective function is a hyperplane. Furthermore, the hyperplanes corresponding to different values of the objective function are parallel.

(c) A local maximum or minimum is also the absolute (global) maximum or minimum of the objective function over the set of feasible solutions, i.e., there do not exist local optima of the objective function different from the global optimum. A feasible solution yields the absolute maximum of the objective function if the value of z for this feasible solution is at least as great as that for any other feasible solution, whereas, roughly speaking, a feasible solution yields a local maximum of the objective function if the value of z for this feasible solution is greater than the value of z for nearby feasible solutions.

(d) If the optimal value of the objective function is bounded, at least one of the extreme points of the convex set of feasible solutions will be an optimal solution. Furthermore, starting at any extreme point of the con-

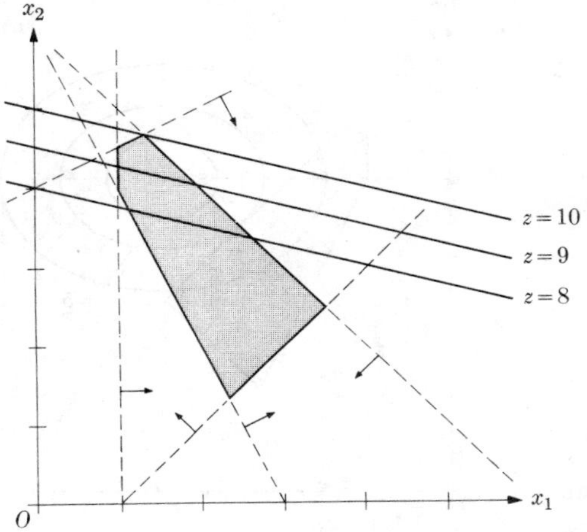

FIGURE 1–1

vex set of feasible solutions, it is possible to reach an optimal extreme point in a series of steps such that at each step one moves only to an adjacent extreme point. Finally, a given extreme point is optimal if and only if the value of the objective function at that extreme point is at least as great as the value of the objective function at each adjacent extreme point.

For any given nonlinear programming problem, some or all of these features which characterize linear programming problems may be violated.

Programming problems involving only two variables can easily be solved graphically. We shall now present several such graphical examples to illustrate more vividly the differences between linear and nonlinear programming problems. Consider first the following linear programming problem:

$$\begin{aligned} x_1 + x_2 &\leq 6, \\ x_1 - x_2 &\leq 1, \\ 2x_1 + x_2 &\geq 6, \\ 0.5x_1 - x_2 &\geq -4, \\ x_1 \geq 1, \quad x_2 &\geq 0, \\ \max z &= 0.5x_1 + 2x_2. \end{aligned} \tag{1–14}$$

The graphical solution is shown in Fig. 1–1. The region of feasible solutions is shaded. Note that the optimum does occur at an extreme point. In this case, the values of the variables that yield the maximum value of the objective function are unique and are the point of intersection of the lines $x_1 + x_2 = 6$, $0.5x_1 - x_2 = -4$ so that the optimal values of the variables, x_1^* and x_2^*, are $x_1^* = \frac{4}{3}$, $x_2^* = \frac{14}{3}$. The maximum value of the objective function is $z^* = 10$.

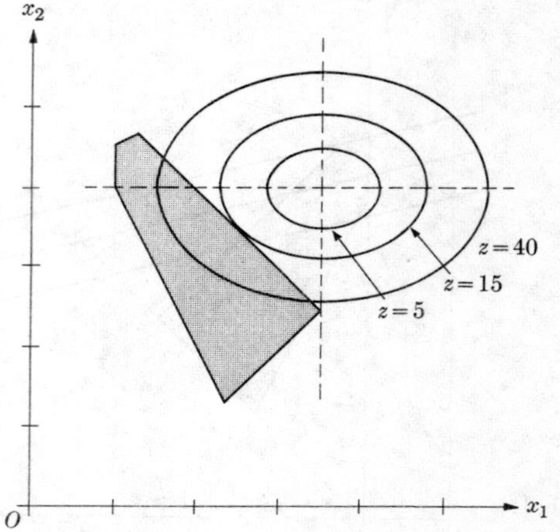

FIGURE 1–2

Consider now a nonlinear programming problem which differs from the linear programming problem only in that the objective function is

$$z = 10(x_1 - 3.5)^2 + 20(x_2 - 4)^2. \tag{1–15}$$

Imagine that it is desired to minimize the objective function. Observe that here we have a separable objective function, and the problem to be solved is of the form of (1–6) through (1–9). The graphical solution of this problem is given in Fig. 1–2. The region representing the feasible solutions is, of course, precisely the same as that for the linear programming problem of Fig. 1–1. Here, however, the curves of constant z are ellipses with centers at the point (3.5, 4). The optimal solution is that point at which an ellipse is tangent to one side of the convex set. If the optimal values of the variables are x_1^* and x_2^*, and the minimum value of the objective function is z^*, then from Fig. 1–2, $x_1^* + x_2^* = 6$, and $z^* = 10(x_1^* - 3.5)^2 + 20(x_2^* - 4)^2$. Furthermore the slope of the curve $z^* = 10(x_1 - 3.5)^2 + 20(x_2 - 4)^2$ evaluated at (x_1^*, x_2^*) must be -1 since this is the slope of $x_1 + x_2 = 6$. Thus we have the additional equation $(x_2^* - 4) = 0.5(x_1^* - 3.5)$. We have obtained three equations involving x_1^*, x_2^*, and z^*. The unique solution is $x_1^* = 2.50$, $x_2^* = 3.50$, and $z^* = 15$. Now the point which yields the optimal value of the objective function lies on the boundary of the convex set of feasible solutions, but it is not an extreme point of this set. Consequently, any computational procedure for solving problems of this type cannot be one which examines only the extreme points of the convex set of feasible solutions.

By a slight modification of the objective function studied above the minimum value of the objective function can be made to occur at an

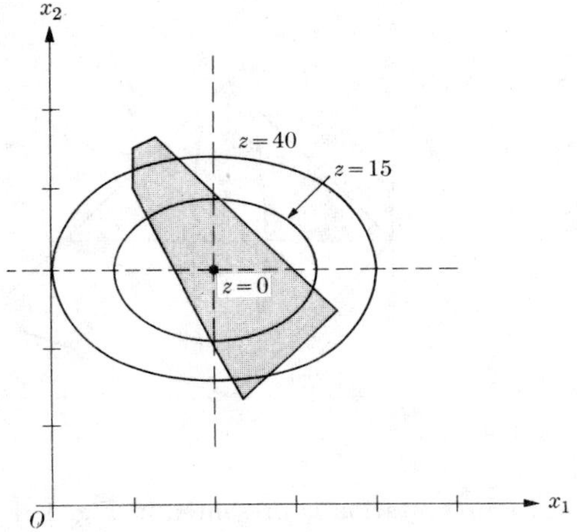

FIGURE 1-3

interior point of the convex set of feasible solutions. Suppose, for example, that the objective function is

$$z = 10(x_1 - 2)^2 + 20(x_2 - 3)^2, \tag{1-16}$$

and that the convex set of feasible solutions is the same as that considered above. This case is illustrated graphically in Fig. 1-3. The optimal values of x_1, x_2, and z are $x_1^* = 2$, $x_2^* = 3$, and $z^* = 0$. Thus it is not even necessary that the optimizing point lie on the boundaries. Note that in this case, the minimum of the objective function in the presence of the constraints and non-negativity restrictions is the same as the minimum in the absence of any constraints or non-negativity restrictions. In such situations we say that the constraints and non-negativity restrictions are inactive, since the same optimum is obtained whether or not the constraints and non-negativity restrictions are included.

Each of the examples presented thus far has had the property that a local optimum was also a global optimum. It is easy, however, to devise examples where this is not the case. Consider the following problem with linear constraints and a separable objective function:

$$\begin{aligned} x_1 + x_2 &\geq 2, \\ x_1 - x_2 &\geq -2, \\ x_1 + x_2 &\leq 6, \\ x_1 - 3x_2 &\leq 2, \\ x_1, x_2 &\geq 0, \\ \max z = 25(x_1 - 2)^2 &+ (x_2 - 2)^2. \end{aligned} \tag{1-17}$$

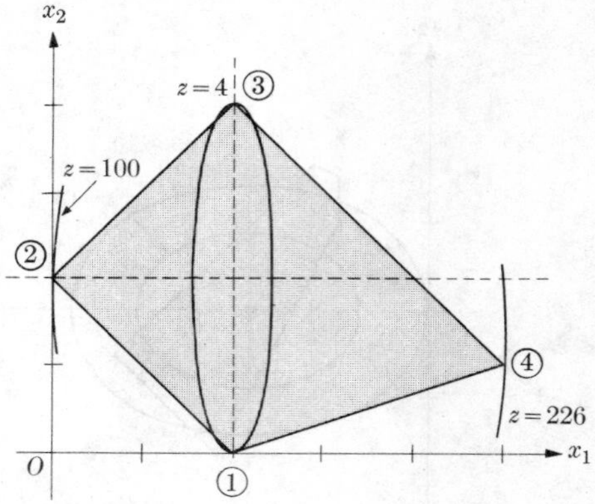

FIGURE 1–4

The graphical representation is presented in Fig. 1–4. Note that extreme point 4 yields the global maximum of the objective function. However, extreme point 2 yields a relative maximum of the objective function different from the global maximum. Note, in fact, that the value of the objective function at extreme point 2 is greater than the value of the objective function at either of its adjacent extreme points 1 and 3.

Here we have a case where the global maximum value of the objective function was taken on at an extreme point of the convex set of feasible solutions; in addition, there existed a different extreme point which yielded a relative maximum with respect to its adjacent extreme points that was different from the global maximum. For problems of this sort, one might know that the global optimum does occur at an extreme point; however, it would not be possible to use a computational technique of the simplex type (based on moving from one extreme point to an adjacent one) which terminated once an extreme point was found that yielded a relative optimum of the objective function with respect to all adjacent extreme points. Such a technique would lead to a relative optimum, but not necessarily the global optimum.

When a programming problem contains nonlinear constraints, it need no longer be true that the region of feasible solutions is convex. In fact, the region may even consist of several disconnected parts. Suppose, for example, that the constraints of a particular problem are

$$\begin{aligned} (x_1 - 1)x_2 &\leq 1, \\ x_1 + x_2 &\geq 3.5, \end{aligned} \tag{1–18}$$

and that the variables must be non-negative. The set of feasible solutions consists of the shaded regions in Fig. 1–5. The set of feasible solutions consists of two disjoint parts, neither of which is convex. When the set of

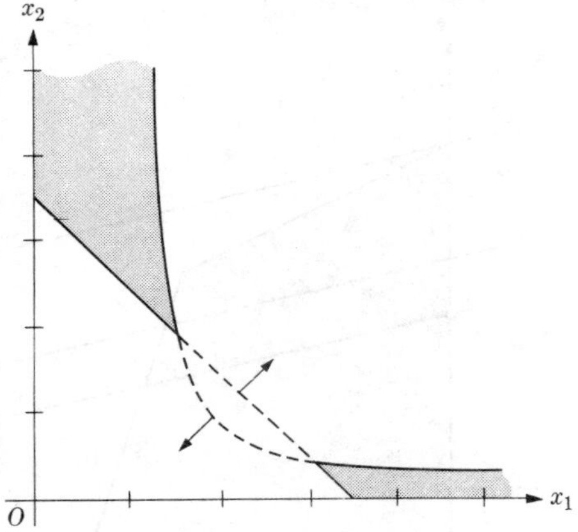

FIGURE 1-5

feasible solutions is not convex, there can exist local optima different from the global optimum even though the objective function is linear.

For nonlinear programming problems which may have local optima different from the global optimum, most of the computational techniques we shall consider can do no better than find a point which yields a local optimum of the objective function. They will not, in general, give any indication as to whether or not the solution so obtained provides the global optimum. Nonetheless, methods for finding local optima are often very useful in practice, because the determination of even a local optimum gives useful information. The one computational technique which will always yield a global optimum regardless of how many local optima there are is dynamic programming. Consequently, if a problem can be solved by dynamic programming, it will be possible to determine the global optimum irrespective of the existence of local optima.

As a final example, we shall examine an integer linear programming problem. Let us solve the problem

$$\begin{aligned} 0.5x_1 + x_2 &\le 1.75, \\ x_1 + 0.30x_2 &\le 1.50, \\ x_1, x_2 \ge 0, \qquad & x_1, x_2 \text{ integers}, \\ \max z &= 0.25x_1 + x_2. \end{aligned} \tag{1-19}$$

The situation is illustrated geometrically in Fig. 1-6. The shaded region would be the convex set of feasible solutions in the absence of the integrality requirements. When the x_j are required to be integers, there are only four feasible solutions which are represented by circles in Fig. 1-6. If we solve the problem as a linear programming problem, ignoring the integrality

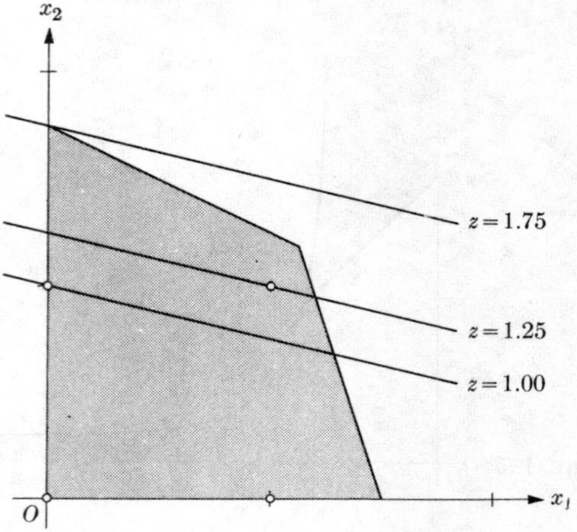

FIGURE 1–6

requirements, the optimal solution is $x_1^* = 0$, $x_2^* = 1.75$, and $z^* = 1.75$. However, it is clear that when it is required that the x_j be integers, the optimal solution is $x_1^* = 1$, $x_2^* = 1$, and $z^* = 1.25$. Note that this is not the solution that would be obtained by solving the problem as a linear programming problem and rounding the results to the nearest integers which satisfy the constraints (this would give $x_1 = 0$, $x_2 = 1$, and $z = 1$).

1–5 Brief historical sketch. It has already been noted that it was the discovery in 1947 of a practical numerical procedure for solving linear programming problems which provided the real spark for the phenomenal growth of interest in the theory and application of programming problems which has occurred since then. The numerical procedure for solving linear programming problems, called the simplex method, was devised by George Dantzig while he was a member of a group which, under the direction of Marshall Wood, was working on certain types of programming problems for the United States Air Force. Although the simplex method was developed in 1947, it was not generally available until 1951, when it was published in the Cowles Commission Monograph No. 13, edited by T. Koopmans [16].

Interest in nonlinear programming problems developed simultaneously with the growing interest in linear programming. In 1951, H. W. Kuhn and A. W. Tucker [17] published an important paper, "Nonlinear Programming," dealing with necessary and sufficient conditions for optimal solutions to programming problems, which laid the foundations for a great deal of later work in nonlinear programming. Some generalizations of their theoretical work by other authors appeared later in the book, *Studies in Linear and Nonlinear Programming* [1], edited by K. J. Arrow, L. Hurwicz, and H. Uzawa, and published in 1958.

In 1954, A. Charnes and C. Lemke [6] published an approximation method of treating problems which have as an objective the minimization of a separable function, subject to linear constraints, when each of the separable functions has a property which we shall later refer to as convexity. An alternative formulation of this problem was given by Dantzig [7]. Later the technique was generalized by C. Miller [21] to include separable constraints. Beginning in 1955, a number of papers by different authors dealing with quadratic programming began to appear. These include the works of E. Barankin and R. Dorfman [2] (1955), E. M. L. Beale [3] (1955), M. Frank and P. Wolfe [10] (1956), H. Markowitz [19] (1956), C. Hildreth [14] (1957), H. Houthakker [15] (1957), and P. Wolfe [23] (1959). Additional papers have appeared since 1959. Except for the paper by Barankin and Dorfman, each of the articles cited presents a computational technique for solving quadratic programming problems. All the techniques differ slightly. The one suggested by Wolfe [23] is the best known and has the great advantage that it reduces the task of solving a quadratic programming problem to a form permitting application of the simplex method. This is the technique which will be discussed in detail in Chapter 7.

Interest in integer solutions to linear programming problems arose early in the development of the field. One of the first papers to be concerned with the subject was that published by Dantzig, Fulkerson, and Johnson [8] in 1954. A later paper by Markowitz and Manne [20] discussed numerical techniques and, in addition, some types of nonlinear programming problems which could be solved by integer linear programming. Although the above papers presented computational techniques for solving integer linear programming problems, Gomory [11, 12] was the first to set forth a systematic computational technique for which it could be proved that convergence would be obtained in a finite number of iterations. This was done in 1958 for the all integer case and in 1960 for the mixed integer-continuous variable case.

The history of dynamic programming is intimately associated with the name of Richard Bellman, who in fact made the major original contribution to the development of the subject and published his results in about 100 papers throughout the 1950's. A summary of this work is contained in his book, *Dynamic Programming* [4], published in 1957, and in the book, *Applied Dynamic Programming* [5], co-authored with S. Dreyfus and published in 1962.

Gradient techniques have long been of interest in mathematics and physics. However, it was the theoretical work appearing in the book, *Studies in Linear and Nonlinear Programming* [1], referred to above which drew attention to the potentialities of this technique for solving nonlinear programming problems. J. B. Dennis [9] seems to have been one of the first to set down the elements needed for a computational algorithm, although he did not study the subject in any detail. Later, somewhat different detailed algorithms were developed by G. Zoutendijk [24] and J. Rosen [22]. More papers have appeared on this subject recently.

The above history brings us to about 1962. We have made no attempt to trace the origins of classical optimization techniques, which began to be developed early in the eighteenth century; many great mathematicians, including Newton, Lagrange, the Bernoullis, Hamilton, and Weierstrass, contributed to their development.

This very brief historical survey has emphasized only what seems at the present time to have been the most important contributions. It should be pointed out, however, that nonlinear programming is still in a state of flux, and a history written several years from now might emphasize quite different things. This also implies, of course, that some or all of the computational techniques presented in this text may be superseded by more efficient ones in the not too distant future.

1–6 The road ahead. In the next chapter we review some of the topics from linear algebra, linear programming, and analysis which will be needed in our further work. The main purpose of this chapter is to introduce notation and to serve as a brief reference. In most instances, no proofs are given, since it is assumed that the reader is more or less familiar with this material. Chapter 3 treats classical optimization techniques. The properties of convex and concave functions are also developed here.

Chapter 4 is devoted to the study of nonlinear programming problems with separable objective functions and constraints. In Chapter 5 we consider stochastic programming problems, that is, problems for which certain parameters are random variables. Chapter 6 is devoted to Kuhn and Tucker's work on the generalization of classical optimization conditions to problems in which the constraints may involve inequalities and the variables may be required to be non-negative. In Chapter 7 the theory developed in Chapter 6 is applied to quadratic programming problems to obtain Wolfe's method for solving such problems. Other computational methods which have been developed are surveyed briefly. We shall also discuss duality as applied to quadratic programming. Chapter 8 deals with integer linear programming and develops Gomory's algorithms for solving the all integer and mixed integer-continuous variable problems. It also illustrates how a number of interesting nonlinear programming problems may be formulated as integer linear ones. In Chapter 9 we study several types of gradient methods for solving nonlinear programming problems. Chapters 10 and 11 are devoted to dynamic programming.

Since dynamic programming refers to a computational technique rather than to a specific type of programming problem, problems with widely varying features will be studied. It will be found that dynamic programming can, at least in theory, be used to solve a great variety of nonlinear programming problems. We shall see, however, that there are severe limitations on the kinds of problems which can be solved numerically.

References

1. Arrow, K. J., L. Hurwicz, and H. Uzawa, *Studies in Linear and Nonlinear Programming.* Stanford, California: Stanford University Press, 1958.

2. Barankin, E. W., and R. Dorfman, *Towards Quadratic Programming.* Office of Naval Research Logistics Projects at Columbia University and University of California, Berkeley, 1955.

3. Beale, E. M. L., "On Minimizing a Convex Function Subject to Linear Inequalities," *Journal of the Royal Statistical Society* (*B*), **17,** 1955, pp. 173–184.

4. Bellman, R., *Dynamic Programming.* Princeton, N. J.: Princeton University Press, 1957.

5. Bellman, R., and S. Dreyfus, *Applied Dynamic Programming.* Princeton, N. J.: Princeton University Press, 1962.

6. Charnes, A., and C. Lemke, "Minimization of Nonlinear Separable Convex Functionals," *Naval Research Logistics Quarterly,* **1,** 1954, pp. 301–312.

7. Dantzig, G. B., "Recent Advances in Linear Programming," *Management Science,* **2,** 1956, pp. 131–144.

8. Dantzig, G. B., D. R. Fulkerson, and S. Johnson, "Solution of a Large-Scale Traveling-Salesman Problem," *Journal of the Operations Research Society of America,* **2,** 1954, pp. 393–410.

9. Dennis, J. B., *Mathematical Programming and Electrical Networks.* Cambridge, Massachusetts: Technology Press, 1959.

10. Frank, M., and P. Wolfe, "An Algorithm for Quadratic Programming," *Naval Research Logistics Quarterly,* **3,** 1956, pp. 95–110.

11. Gomory, R., "Essentials of an Algorithm for Integer Solutions to Linear Programs," *Bulletin American Mathematical Society,* **64,** 1958, pp. 275–278.

12. Gomory, R., "An Algorithm for the Mixed Integer Problem," *RM-2597,* The RAND Corp., 1960.

13. Hadley, G., *Linear Programming.* Reading, Mass.: Addison-Wesley, 1962.

14. Hildreth, C., "A Quadratic Programming Procedure," *Naval Research Logistics Quarterly,* **14,** 1957, pp. 79–85.

15. Houthakker, H., "The Capacity Method of Quadratic Programming," *Econometrica,* **28,** 1960, pp. 62–87.

16. Koopmans, T. (ed.), *Activity Analysis of Production and Allocation.* New York: Wiley, 1951.

17. Kuhn, H. W., and A. W. Tucker, "Nonlinear Programming," *Proceedings Second Berkeley Symposium on Mathematical Statistics and Probability,* 1951, pp. 481–492.

18. LEMKE, C., "The Constrained Gradient Method of Linear Programming," *Journal of the Society for Industrial and Applied Mathematics*, **9**, 1961, pp. 1–17.

19. MARKOWITZ, H., "The Optimization of a Quadratic Function Subject to Linear Constraints," *Naval Research Logistics Quarterly*, **3**, 1956, pp. 111–133.

20. MARKOWITZ, H., and A. S. MANNE, "On the Solution to Discrete Programming Problems," *Econometrica*, **25**, 1957, pp. 84–110.

21. MILLER, C. E., "The Simplex Method for Local Separable Programming," in *Recent Advances in Mathematical Programming*, R. Graves and P. Wolfe, editors. New York: McGraw-Hill, 1963.

22. ROSEN, J., "The Gradient Projection Method for Nonlinear Programming. Part I. Linear Constraints," *Journal of the Society for Industrial and Applied Mathematics*, **9**, 1960, pp. 181–217.

23. WOLFE, P., "The Simplex Method for Quadratic Programming," *Econometrica*, **27**, 1959, pp. 382–398.

24. ZOUTENDIJK, G., "Maximizing a Function in a Convex Region," *Journal of the Royal Statistical Society* (*B*), **21**, 1959, pp. 338–355.

PROBLEMS

Solve the following nonlinear programming problems, and illustrate them geometrically.

1–1.
$$\begin{aligned} 0.5x_1 + x_2 &\le 4, \\ 3x_1 + x_2 &\le 15, \\ x_1 + x_2 &\ge 1, \\ x_1, x_2 &\ge 0, \\ \min z = 4(x_1 - 6)^2 &+ 6(x_2 - 2)^2. \end{aligned}$$

1–2.
$$\begin{aligned} 0.5x_1 + x_2 &\le 4, \\ 3x_1 + x_2 &\le 15, \\ x_1 + x_2 &\ge 1, \\ x_1, x_2 &\ge 0, \\ \max z = 3(x_1 - 1.5)^2 &+ 6(x_2 - 1.5)^2. \end{aligned}$$

1–3.
$$\begin{aligned} x_1 - x_2 &\ge 0, \\ x_1 + x_2 &\le 4, \\ x_1 &\le 3, \\ \min z = 2x_1 + 3x_2 &+ 4x_1^2 + 2x_1x_2 + x_2^2. \end{aligned}$$

1–4.
$$\begin{aligned} x_1 - x_2 &\ge 0, \\ x_1 + x_2 &\le 4, \\ x_1 &\le 3, \\ \max z = 2x_1 + 3x_2 &+ 4x_1^2 + 2x_1x_2 + x_2^2. \end{aligned}$$

1–5.
$$(x_1 - 2)^2 + (x_2 - 1)^2 \leq 9,$$
$$x_1, x_2 \geq 0,$$
$$\max z = 3x_1 + 2x_2.$$

1–6.
$$x_1x_2 \geq 1,$$
$$x_1^2 + x_2^2 \leq 9,$$
$$\min z = 7(x_1 - 6)^2 + 3(x_2 - 4)^2.$$

1–7.
$$x_1x_2 \geq 1,$$
$$x_1^2 + x_2^2 \leq 9,$$
$$x_1 \leq 2,$$
$$x_1, x_2 \geq 0,$$
$$\max z = 8x_1^2 + 2x_2^2.$$

1–8.
$$(x_1 - 1)(x_2 - 1) \leq 1,$$
$$x_1 + x_2 \geq 3,$$
$$x_1, x_2 \geq 0,$$
$$\min z = 6(x_1 - 5)^2 + (x_2 - 4)^2.$$

1–9.
$$3x_1 + 2x_2 \leq 9,$$
$$0.5x_1 + x_2 \leq 4,$$
$$x_1, x_2 \geq 0,$$
$$\max z = x_1x_2.$$

1–10.
$$(x_1 - 3)(x_2 - 3) \geq 1,$$
$$x_1, x_2 \geq 0,$$
$$\min z = (x_1 - 2.5)^2 + (x_2 - 3.5)^2.$$

1–11.
$$(x_1 - 3)(x_2 - 3) \geq 1,$$
$$x_1, x_2 \geq 0,$$
$$\max z = (x_1 - 2.5)^2 + (x_2 - 3.5)^2.$$

1–12.
$$(x_1 - 3)(x_2 - 3) \leq 1,$$
$$x_1, x_2 \geq 0,$$
$$\min z = (x_1 - 6)^2 + (x_2 - 8)^2.$$

1–13.
$$x_1 + x_2 \leq 5,$$
$$0.3x_1 + x_2 \leq 3,$$
$$x_1, x_2 \geq 0,$$
$$\min z = 5x_1^2 + 3x_1 - 4x_2.$$

1–14.
$$x_1 + x_2 \leq 5,$$
$$0.3x_1 + x_2 \leq 3,$$
$$x_1, x_2 \geq 0,$$
$$\max z = 5x_1^2 + 3x_1 - 4x_2.$$

1–15.
$$2x_1 - x_2 \geq 0,$$
$$0.5x_1 - x_2 \leq 0,$$
$$x_1 + x_2 \leq 5,$$
$$x_1, x_2 \geq 0, \quad \text{and} \quad x_1, x_2 \text{ integers},$$
$$\max z = 4x_1 + 3x_2.$$

1–16.
$$2x_1 - x_2 \geq 0,$$
$$0.5x_1 - x_2 \leq 0,$$
$$x_1 + x_2 \leq 5,$$
$$x_1, x_2 \geq 0,$$
$$x_1 \text{ an integer}, \quad x_2 \text{ continuous},$$
$$\max z = 4x_1 + 3x_2.$$

CHAPTER 2

MATHEMATICAL BACKGROUND

. . . what's past is prologue, what to come
In yours and my discharge.

Shakespeare, *The Tempest*

2–1 Matrices and vectors. The background material from linear algebra and linear programming which will be reviewed in this chapter is covered in detail in the author's texts, *Linear Algebra* [3] and *Linear Programming* [4]. Frequent reference will be made to these works. We shall do so by listing the appropriate chapter and section in abbreviated form: thus {LA 3–6} will mean Chapter 3, Section 6 of the *Linear Algebra* text; the letters LP instead of LA will refer to the *Linear Programming* text.

We define a *matrix* to be a rectangular array of real numbers. The numbers are called the *elements* of the matrix. Usually, upper-case boldface letters, that is, **A**, **B**, etc., will be used to represent matrices. The elements will be represented by italicized lower-case letters, having a double subscript, for example, a_{ij}, b_{ij}, when specific numbers are not used. Thus we can write

$$\mathbf{A} = \|a_{ij}\| = \begin{bmatrix} a_{11} & a_{12} \cdots a_{1n} \\ a_{21} & a_{22} \cdots a_{2n} \\ \vdots & \vdots \\ a_{m1} & a_{m2} \cdots a_{mn} \end{bmatrix}. \tag{2–1}$$

When we wish to represent a matrix by showing the general element, we use $\|a_{ij}\|$. The matrix **A** of (2–1) is called an m by n (written $m \times n$) matrix since it has m rows and n columns. The first subscript of the element a_{ij} indicates the row and the second subscript specifies the column where the element appears in the matrix. If $m = n$, the matrix is said to be square and is called an *nth-order matrix*.

Two matrices **A**, **B** are said to be equal, written $\mathbf{A} = \mathbf{B}$, if and only if the corresponding elements are equal, that is, $a_{ij} = b_{ij}$, all i, j. To add two $m \times n$ matrices, we simply add the corresponding elements; the *sum* of **A** and **B** will be written $\mathbf{A} + \mathbf{B}$. Note that matrix addition obeys the associative and commutative laws:

$$\mathbf{A} + \mathbf{B} + \mathbf{C} = (\mathbf{A} + \mathbf{B}) + \mathbf{C} = \mathbf{A} + (\mathbf{B} + \mathbf{C}) \quad \text{and} \quad \mathbf{A} + \mathbf{B} = \mathbf{B} + \mathbf{A}.$$

We shall frequently refer to a real number as a *scalar*. The *product* of a matrix **A** and a scalar λ, written $\lambda\mathbf{A}$ or $\mathbf{A}\lambda$, is obtained by multiplying each element of **A** by λ:

$$\lambda\mathbf{A} = \|\lambda a_{ij}\|.$$

Note that $\mathbf{A} + \mathbf{A} = 2\mathbf{A}$, and if $\mathbf{A} = \mathbf{B}$, then $\lambda\mathbf{A} = \lambda\mathbf{B}$. Subtraction of matrices can be defined in terms of concepts already introduced as

$$\mathbf{A} - \mathbf{B} = \mathbf{A} + (-1)\mathbf{B}.$$

The *product* **AB** of two matrices **A** and **B** is defined if and only if the number of columns in **A** is equal to the number of rows in **B**. If **A** is $m \times r$ and **B** is $r \times n$, then $\mathbf{C} = \mathbf{AB}$ is $m \times n$ and $c_{ij} = \sum_{k=1}^{r} a_{ik}b_{kj}$. Although matrix multiplication is associative,

$$\mathbf{ABC} = (\mathbf{AB})\mathbf{C} = \mathbf{A}(\mathbf{BC}),$$

it is not in general commutative, so that **AB** and **BA** need not be the same. In fact, it need not even be true that **AB** and **BA** are both defined.

A matrix is said to be a *null* or *zero matrix* if all its elements are zero. The null matrix is denoted by the symbol **0**. When the operations are defined,

$$\mathbf{A} + \mathbf{0} = \mathbf{A} = \mathbf{0} + \mathbf{A} \quad \text{and} \quad \mathbf{A0} = \mathbf{0A} = \mathbf{0}.$$

In general, the equation $\mathbf{AB} = \mathbf{0}$ does not necessarily imply that $\mathbf{A} = \mathbf{0}$ or $\mathbf{B} = \mathbf{0}$. There exist non-null matrices whose product is the null matrix. A square matrix **A** is said to be *diagonal* if $a_{ij} = 0$, where $i \neq j$; the elements a_{ii} lie on what is called the *main diagonal* of the matrix (which runs from the upper left-hand corner to the lower right-hand corner). A diagonal matrix with each a_{ii} being the same, so that $a_{ii} = \lambda$, is called a *scalar matrix*. Let the symbol δ_{ij} (called the *Kronecker delta*) be defined to be zero if $i \neq j$, and unity if $i = j$. Then a diagonal matrix can be written $\|a_{ii}\delta_{ij}\|$ and a scalar matrix can be written $\|\lambda\delta_{ij}\|$. There is a complete equivalence between the set of all nth-order scalar matrices $\|\lambda\delta_{ij}\|$ and the set of all real numbers λ. The square matrix $\mathbf{I} = \|\delta_{ij}\|$ is called the *identity matrix*. Frequently, it is convenient to place a subscript on **I**, for example $\mathbf{I}_n$, to indicate the order of **I**. The only elements of an identity matrix which are different from zero are those on the main diagonal; these have the value unity. Thus

$$\mathbf{I}_3 = \begin{bmatrix} 1 & 0 & 0 \\ 0 & 1 & 0 \\ 0 & 0 & 1 \end{bmatrix}.$$

If **A** is $m \times n$, then $\mathbf{I}_m\mathbf{A} = \mathbf{A}\mathbf{I}_n = \mathbf{A}$. Also $\mathbf{II} = \mathbf{I}$.

The *transpose* of an $m \times n$ matrix $\mathbf{A}$ is an $n \times m$ matrix obtained from $\mathbf{A}$ by interchanging rows and columns so that the first row of $\mathbf{A}$ becomes the first column of the transpose, etc.. The transpose of $\mathbf{A}$ is written $\mathbf{A}'$. If $\mathbf{A}' = \|a'_{ij}\|$, then $a'_{ij} = a_{ji}$. The following properties are sometimes useful:

$$(\mathbf{A} + \mathbf{B})' = \mathbf{A}' + \mathbf{B}',$$

$$(\mathbf{A}')' = \mathbf{A}, \qquad (\mathbf{AB})' = \mathbf{B}'\mathbf{A}'.$$

Note that the transpose of the product is the product of the transposes in the reverse order {LA 3–7}. A square matrix $\mathbf{A}$ is said to be symmetric if $\mathbf{A} = \mathbf{A}'$, that is, $a_{ij} = a_{ji}$. A square matrix $\mathbf{A}$ is said to be *skew-symmetric* if $\mathbf{A} = -\mathbf{A}'$, that is, $a_{ij} = -a_{ji}$, $i \neq j$, $a_{ii} = 0$.

If we delete all but t rows and u columns of an $m \times n$ matrix $\mathbf{A}$, the resulting $t \times u$ matrix is called a *submatrix* of $\mathbf{A}$. On occasions, either to exhibit some particular structure of a matrix or to simplify multiplication, it will be convenient to partition a matrix into submatrices. This is done by drawing partitioning lines between certain selected rows and columns. For example, one possible partitioning of a 4×4 matrix is

$$\mathbf{A} = \left[\begin{array}{ccc|c} a_{11} & a_{12} & a_{13} & a_{14} \\ \hline a_{21} & a_{22} & a_{23} & a_{24} \\ a_{31} & a_{32} & a_{33} & a_{34} \\ a_{41} & a_{42} & a_{43} & a_{44} \end{array}\right] = \begin{bmatrix} \mathbf{A}_{11} & \mathbf{A}_{12} \\ \mathbf{A}_{21} & \mathbf{A}_{22} \end{bmatrix}.$$

The resulting submatrices are denoted by $\mathbf{A}_{ij}$, as shown. If the product $\mathbf{AB}$ of two partitioned matrices $\mathbf{A}$ and $\mathbf{B}$ is defined, the product can be computed by block multiplication, provided that the columns of $\mathbf{A}$ and the rows of $\mathbf{B}$ are partitioned in the same way. It does not matter how the rows of $\mathbf{A}$ or the columns of $\mathbf{B}$ are partitioned. For example, if $\mathbf{AB}$ is defined, the columns of $\mathbf{A}$ are partitioned in the same way as the rows of $\mathbf{B}$, and

$$\mathbf{A} = \begin{bmatrix} \mathbf{A}_{11} & \mathbf{A}_{12} & \mathbf{A}_{13} \\ \mathbf{A}_{21} & \mathbf{A}_{22} & \mathbf{A}_{23} \end{bmatrix}, \qquad \mathbf{B} = \begin{bmatrix} \mathbf{B}_{11} \\ \mathbf{B}_{21} \\ \mathbf{B}_{31} \end{bmatrix},$$

then

$$\mathbf{AB} = \begin{bmatrix} \mathbf{A}_{11}\mathbf{B}_{11} + \mathbf{A}_{12}\mathbf{B}_{21} + \mathbf{A}_{13}\mathbf{B}_{31} \\ \mathbf{A}_{21}\mathbf{B}_{11} + \mathbf{A}_{22}\mathbf{B}_{21} + \mathbf{A}_{23}\mathbf{B}_{31} \end{bmatrix}.$$

Partitioning is discussed in more detail in {LA 3–9}.

Matrices having a single row or column are often referred to as *vectors*. A matrix having a single row is called a *row vector*, and a matrix having a single column is called a *column vector*. Vectors will generally be symbolized by lower-case boldface letters. Row vectors will be written $\mathbf{a} = (a_1, \ldots a_n)$ and column vectors will be written $\mathbf{a} = [a_1, \ldots, a_n]$. It is usually inconvenient to print a column of numbers, and hence a column vector is printed as a row and enclosed by brackets rather than parentheses. The vectors $(a_1, \ldots, a_n)$ or $[a_1, \ldots, a_n]$ are called n-component vectors, and a_i is called the ith-component or coordinate of $\mathbf{a}$. We shall need column vectors more frequently than row vectors, and hence we shall suppose that any vector is a column vector unless it is specifically defined to be a row vector. Frequently we shall find it desirable to partition an $m \times n$ matrix $\mathbf{A}$ in such a way that each submatrix becomes a column of $\mathbf{A}$, that is, $\mathbf{A}$ is partitioned into a row of column vectors. If $\mathbf{a}_j = [a_{1j}, \ldots, a_{mj}]$, then $\mathbf{A} = (\mathbf{a}_1, \ldots, \mathbf{a}_n)$. The columns of $\mathbf{A}$ will be written $\mathbf{a}_j$. Similarly, $\mathbf{A}$ can be partitioned into a column of row vectors. If $\mathbf{a}^i = (a_{i1}, \ldots, a_{in})$, then $\mathbf{A} = [\mathbf{a}^1, \ldots, \mathbf{a}^m]$. The rows of $\mathbf{A}$ will be written $\mathbf{a}^i$.

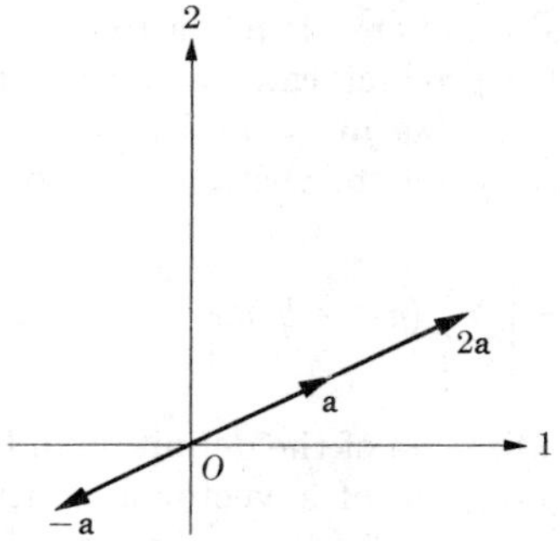

FIGURE 2–1

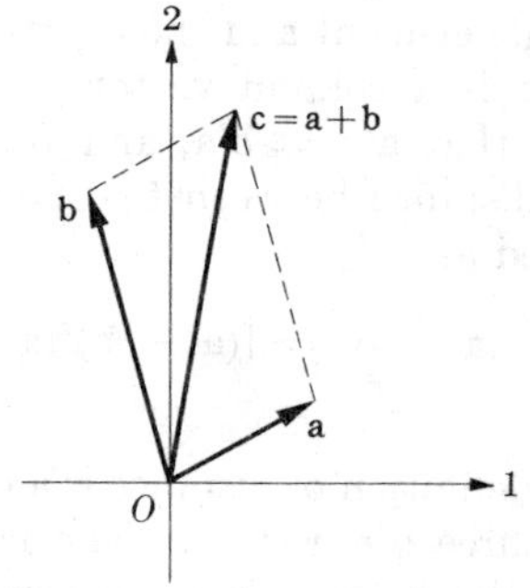

FIGURE 2–2

It is often convenient to think of an n-component vector as a point in an n-dimensional space. Thus the geometrical interpretation of a vector is a point. Geometrically, we do not distinguish between row and column vectors. When using geometrical language, we shall often refer to vectors as points. Frequently, it is convenient to represent vectors geometrically in two and three dimensions by means of a directed line segment drawn from the origin to the point which characterizes the vector. In this way, it is easy to illustrate operations on vectors, such as multiplication by a scalar (Fig. 2–1) and addition (Fig. 2–2).

For the n-dimensional space which is the collection of all n-tuples $[a_1, \ldots, a_n]$ to have properties similar to those of the familiar two- and three-dimensional spaces of analytical geometry, we must introduce a *coordinate system* and the *notion of distance*. To do this, we first introduce n n-component vectors

$$\mathbf{e}_1 = [1, 0, \ldots, 0], \quad \mathbf{e}_2 = [0, 1, 0, \ldots, 0], \quad \ldots, \quad \mathbf{e}_n = [0, 0, \ldots, 0, 1],$$

called the *unit vectors*. Note that any n-component vector $\mathbf{a}$ can be written

$$\mathbf{a} = [a_1, \ldots, a_n] = a_1\mathbf{e}_1 + a_2\mathbf{e}_2 + \cdots + a_n\mathbf{e}_n. \tag{2-2}$$

Given a set of vectors $\mathbf{a}_1, \ldots, \mathbf{a}_k$, a vector $\mathbf{a}$ is said to be a linear combination of these vectors if there exist scalars λ_j such that $\mathbf{a} = \sum_{j=1}^{k} \lambda_j\mathbf{a}_j$. Equation (2-2) shows that every n-component vector can be written as a linear combination of the unit vectors. We then use the unit vectors to define a coordinate system by imagining that a coordinate axis is drawn from the origin $\mathbf{0} = [0, 0, \ldots, 0]$ through each point $\mathbf{e}_j$. The two unit vectors which define the coordinate system in Fig. 2-2 are illustrated.

The *scalar product* of two n-component vectors $\mathbf{a}$ and $\mathbf{b}$ is defined to be the number $\sum_{j=1}^{n} a_jb_j$. If $\mathbf{a}, \mathbf{b}$ are column vectors this number is the matrix product $\mathbf{a}'\mathbf{b}$ (it is unnecessary to distinguish between matrices containing a single element and the corresponding real number). If $\mathbf{a}$ is a row vector and $\mathbf{b}$ is a column vector, then the scalar product can be written $\mathbf{ab}$. Note that $\mathbf{a}'\mathbf{b} = \mathbf{b}'\mathbf{a}$, and for any scalar λ, $(\lambda\mathbf{a}')\mathbf{b} = \mathbf{a}'(\lambda\mathbf{b}) = \lambda(\mathbf{a}'\mathbf{b})$. The distance between two points (vectors) $\mathbf{a}$ and $\mathbf{b}$, written $|\mathbf{a} - \mathbf{b}|$, is defined as

$$|\mathbf{a} - \mathbf{b}| = [(\mathbf{a} - \mathbf{b})'(\mathbf{a} - \mathbf{b})]^{1/2} = \left[\sum_{j=1}^{n} (a_j - b_j)^2\right]^{1/2} \cdot \tag{2-3}$$

This definition of distance is a direct generalization of the definition in two and three dimensions. The length or magnitude of a vector $\mathbf{a}$, written $|\mathbf{a}|$, is the distance from the origin to $\mathbf{a}$: $|\mathbf{a}| = |\mathbf{a} - \mathbf{0}|$. The collection of all n-component vectors $[a_1, \ldots, a_n]$, with distance defined by (2-3), will be called an *n-dimensional Euclidean space* and will be represented by the symbol E^n. The symbols E^2 and E^3 denote the familiar two- and three-dimensional spaces of analytic geometry.

For any two n-component vectors $\mathbf{a}$ and $\mathbf{b}$, it is true that $|\mathbf{a}'\mathbf{b}| \leq |\mathbf{a}|\,|\mathbf{b}|$, where $|\mathbf{a}'\mathbf{b}|$ is the absolute value of the scalar product. This is called the *Schwarz inequality*. If $\mathbf{a}, \mathbf{b} \neq \mathbf{0}$, the angle θ between $\mathbf{a}$ and $\mathbf{b}$ is computed from

$$\cos\theta = \frac{\mathbf{a}'\mathbf{b}}{|\mathbf{a}|\,|\mathbf{b}|} \cdot \tag{2-4}$$

By the Schwarz inequality, $|\cos\theta| \leq 1$, and we can always determine an angle θ such that $0 \leq \theta \leq \pi$. In E^2 and E^3, θ is the angle between the two vectors $\mathbf{a}$ and $\mathbf{b}$ represented as directed line segments {LA 2-3}.

Two vectors $\mathbf{a}$ and $\mathbf{b}$ are said to be *orthogonal* if $\mathbf{a}'\mathbf{b} = 0$. Thus if $\mathbf{a}, \mathbf{b} \neq \mathbf{0}$, they are orthogonal, provided the angle between them is $\pi/2$. Note that the unit vectors are orthogonal: $\mathbf{e}_i'\mathbf{e}_j = 0$, $i \neq j$. The coordinate system defined by the unit vectors is thus an orthogonal coordinate system.

By $\mathbf{a} \geq \mathbf{b}$ we mean $a_j \geq b_j$, $j = 1, \ldots, n$, and by $\mathbf{a} > \mathbf{b}$ we mean $a_j > b_j$, $j = 1, \ldots, n$.

A set of vectors $\mathbf{a}_1, \ldots, \mathbf{a}_k$ is said to be *linearly dependent* if there exist scalars λ_j not all zero such that

$$\sum_{j=1}^{k} \lambda_j \mathbf{a}_j = \mathbf{0}. \tag{2-5}$$

Otherwise the vectors are said to be linearly independent. If the vectors are linearly independent, the only set of λ_j for which (2-5) holds is $\lambda_j = 0$, $j = 1, \ldots, k$. A finite set of two or more vectors is linearly dependent if and only if some one vector can be written as a linear combination of the others {LA 2-7}. If a set of k vectors is linearly independent, any subset of this set is also linearly independent. We say that the maximum number of linearly independent vectors in a set is r if there exists at least one subset of r linearly independent vectors, and if there exists no subset containing $r + 1$ linearly independent vectors. The null vector is linearly dependent on all other vectors, and no linearly independent set contains $\mathbf{0}$. The unit vectors are linearly independent since $\sum_{j=1}^{n} \lambda_j \mathbf{e}_j = [\lambda_1, \ldots, \lambda_n] = \mathbf{0}$ implies $\lambda_j = 0$, $j = 1, \ldots, n$.

A set of vectors $\mathbf{a}_1, \ldots, \mathbf{a}_r$ from E^n is said to *span* E^n if every vector in E^n can be represented as a linear combination of $\mathbf{a}_1, \ldots, \mathbf{a}_r$. A *basis* for E^n is a linearly independent subset of vectors from E^n which spans the entire space. From the preceding discussion it follows that the unit vectors are a basis for E^n. Any set of basis vectors can be thought of as defining a coordinate system (not necessarily orthogonal) for E^n. The representation of any vector in terms of a set of basis vectors is unique {LA 2-8}. An important operation in linear programming is that of changing a basis by replacing a single vector in the basis to yield a new basis. Given a set of basis vectors $\mathbf{a}_1, \ldots, \mathbf{a}_r$ for E^n and any other vector $\mathbf{d} \neq \mathbf{0}$, consider $\mathbf{d} = \sum_{j=1}^{r} \alpha_j \mathbf{a}_j$. If any vector $\mathbf{a}_j$ for which $\alpha_j \neq 0$ is removed from the set of basis vectors and is replaced by $\mathbf{d}$, the new collection of r vectors is also a basis for E^n {LA 2-9}. Given that $\mathbf{x}$ is any vector in E^n, and that $\mathbf{x} = \sum_{j=1}^{r} \lambda_j \mathbf{a}_j$, then, if $\mathbf{d}$ replaces $\mathbf{a}_k$, we have, in terms of the new set of basis vectors,

$$\mathbf{x} = \sum_{\substack{j=1 \\ j \neq k}}^{r} \left(\lambda_j - \frac{\alpha_j}{\alpha_k} \lambda_k \right) \mathbf{a}_j + \frac{\lambda_k}{\alpha_k} \mathbf{d}. \tag{2-6}$$

This result is obtained simply by solving for $\mathbf{a}_k$ in $\mathbf{d} = \sum \alpha_j \mathbf{a}_j$ and substituting the result into $\mathbf{x} = \sum \lambda_j \mathbf{a}_j$. If $\mathbf{d}$ replaces a vector $\mathbf{a}_j$ with $\alpha_j = 0$, the new set of vectors is linearly dependent and is not a basis.

Every basis for E^n contains precisely n vectors. Furthermore, any set of n linearly independent vectors from E^n is a basis for E^n. Hence any $n + 1$ or more vectors from E^n are linearly dependent. Any $m < n$ linearly independent vectors from E^n form part of a basis for E^n. Thus there exists an infinite number of bases for E^n. These results are proved in {LA 2–10}. The maximum number of linearly independent vectors in E^n is n. Frequently, it is desirable to define the dimension of a space as the maximum number of linearly independent vectors in the space instead of associating dimension with the number of components in the vectors that comprise the space.

A *subspace* S of E^n is defined to be a subset of vectors from E^n which is closed under the operations of addition and multiplication by a scalar. The dimension of the subspace is defined to be the maximum number of linearly independent vectors in the subspace. Note that every subspace must contain the origin since it is closed under multiplication by a scalar. Intuitively, a subspace of E^n is simply a Euclidean space of dimension less than or equal to n in E^n, which contains the origin of E^n. The subspaces of E^3 are the origin (dimension zero), lines through the origin, planes through the origin, and E^3 itself. The set of all linear combinations of m vectors from E^n is a subspace of E^n {LA 2–13}.

Given two subspaces S_1 and S_2 of E^n, the sum $S_1 + S_2$ of these subspaces is the collection of all vectors $\mathbf{u} + \mathbf{v}$, $\mathbf{u}$ in S_1 and $\mathbf{v}$ in S_2. The set $S_1 + S_2$ is also a subspace, and if $\mathbf{0}$ is the only vector common to S_1 and S_2, the dimension of $S_1 + S_2$ is the sum of the dimensions of S_1 and S_2. If S is a subspace of E^n, the *orthogonal complement* of S, written $O(S)$, is a subspace each of whose vectors is orthogonal to every vector in S. The dimension of $S + O(S)$ is n, that is, $E^n = S + O(S)$. Every vector $\mathbf{x}$ in E^n can then be written uniquely as $\mathbf{x} = \mathbf{u} + \mathbf{v}$, where $\mathbf{u}$ is in S and $\mathbf{v}$ in $O(S)$.

The *rank* of a matrix $\mathbf{A}$ is defined to be the maximum number of linearly independent columns in $\mathbf{A}$. The maximum number of linearly independent rows in $\mathbf{A}$ is equal to the maximum number of linearly independent columns, and hence the rank of $\mathbf{A}$ can equally well be defined as the maximum number of linearly independent rows in $\mathbf{A}$ {LA 4–4}. We shall denote the rank of $\mathbf{A}$ by $r(\mathbf{A})$. The rank of $\mathbf{AB}$ is not uniquely determined by $r(\mathbf{A})$ and $r(\mathbf{B})$; however, $r(\mathbf{AB}) \leq \min [r(\mathbf{A}), r(\mathbf{B})]$ {LA 4–3}.

A matrix $\mathbf{A}$ is said to have an *inverse* if there exists a matrix $\mathbf{B}$ such that $\mathbf{BA} = \mathbf{AB} = \mathbf{I}$. It follows from this requirement that only square matrices have inverses. An nth-order matrix $\mathbf{A}$ will have an inverse if and only if $r(\mathbf{A}) = n$ {LA 4–4}. If $r(\mathbf{A}) = n$, $\mathbf{A}$ is called nonsingular. A square matrix $\mathbf{A}$ is nonsingular if and only if its determinant $|\mathbf{A}|$ is different from zero.

Such a matrix $\mathbf{A}$ has the property that its columns form a basis for E^n, and so do its rows. If $\mathbf{A}$ has no inverse, it is said to be singular. The inverse of a matrix $\mathbf{A}$ is usually written $\mathbf{A}^{-1}$. The inverse is unique {LA 3-18}. If $\mathbf{A}$ and $\mathbf{B}$ are nonsingular nth-order matrices, $\mathbf{AB}$ is also nonsingular and $(\mathbf{AB})^{-1} = \mathbf{B}^{-1}\mathbf{A}^{-1}$ {LA 3-19}. Also, $(\mathbf{A}^{-1})^{-1} = \mathbf{A}$ and $(\mathbf{A}')^{-1} = (\mathbf{A}^{-1})'$. If $\mathbf{A}$ is nonsingular, then $r(\mathbf{AB}) = r(\mathbf{B})$. Let $\mathbf{B} = (\mathbf{b}_1, \ldots, \mathbf{b}_n)$ be a nonsingular matrix. Let $\mathbf{B}_a$ be formed from $\mathbf{B}$ by replacing $\mathbf{b}_r$ by the vector $\mathbf{a}$. It is possible to compute $\mathbf{B}_a^{-1}$ (if it exists) in terms of $\mathbf{B}^{-1}$ as follows. Compute $\mathbf{y} = \mathbf{B}^{-1}\mathbf{a}$ and

$$\boldsymbol{\eta} = \left[-\frac{y_1}{y_r}, \ldots, -\frac{y_{r-1}}{y_r}, \frac{1}{y_r}, -\frac{y_{r+1}}{y_r}, \ldots, -\frac{y_n}{y_r}\right].$$

Next form the matrix $\mathbf{E}$ by replacing the rth column of $\mathbf{I}_n$ by $\boldsymbol{\eta}$. Then $\mathbf{B}_a^{-1} = \mathbf{E}\mathbf{B}^{-1}$. $\mathbf{B}_a^{-1}$ exists if and only if $y_r \neq 0$ {LA 3-21}.

If the nonsingular matrix $\mathbf{M}$ can be partitioned as

$$\mathbf{M} = \begin{bmatrix} \boldsymbol{\alpha} & \boldsymbol{\beta} \\ \boldsymbol{\gamma} & \boldsymbol{\delta} \end{bmatrix},$$

where $\boldsymbol{\delta}$ is nonsingular, then $\mathbf{M}^{-1}$ can be partitioned in the same way:

$$\mathbf{M}^{-1} = \begin{bmatrix} \mathbf{A} & \mathbf{B} \\ \mathbf{C} & \mathbf{D} \end{bmatrix},$$

and {LA 3-20}

$$\begin{aligned} \mathbf{A} &= (\boldsymbol{\alpha} - \boldsymbol{\beta}\,\boldsymbol{\delta}^{-1}\boldsymbol{\gamma})^{-1}, & \mathbf{B} &= -\mathbf{A}\boldsymbol{\beta}\,\boldsymbol{\delta}^{-1}, \\ \mathbf{C} &= -\boldsymbol{\delta}^{-1}\boldsymbol{\gamma}\mathbf{A}, & \mathbf{D} &= \boldsymbol{\delta}^{-1} - \boldsymbol{\delta}^{-1}\boldsymbol{\gamma}\mathbf{B}. \end{aligned} \tag{2-7}$$

2-2 Simultaneous linear equations. A system of m linear equations in n unknowns x_j, $j = 1, \ldots, n$, can be written $\mathbf{Ax} = \mathbf{b}$ or $\sum_{j=1}^{n} a_{ij}x_j = b_i$, $i = 1, \ldots, m$. Such a system of equations may have (a) no solution, (b) a unique solution, or (c) an infinite number of solutions. Consider the matrix $\mathbf{A}_b = (\mathbf{A}, \mathbf{b})$, called the *augmented matrix* of the system. Note that either $r(\mathbf{A}_b) = r(\mathbf{A})$ or $r(\mathbf{A}_b) > r(\mathbf{A})$. If $r(\mathbf{A}_b) = r(\mathbf{A}) = k$, there exist k linearly independent columns of $\mathbf{A}$ such that every column of $\mathbf{A}_b$, and in particular $\mathbf{b}$, can be written as a linear combination of these k columns. Hence in this case, the system of equations $\mathbf{Ax} = \mathbf{b}$ has at least one solution. On the other hand, if $r(\mathbf{A}_b) > r(\mathbf{A})$ and $r(\mathbf{A}_b) = k$, every set of k linearly independent columns from $\mathbf{A}_b$ must contain $\mathbf{b}$, and therefore $\mathbf{b}$ cannot be written as a linear combination of the columns of $\mathbf{A}$. In this case, the system $\mathbf{Ax} = \mathbf{b}$ has no solution.

If for a system of m equations in n unknowns, $\mathbf{Ax} = \mathbf{b}$, we have $r(\mathbf{A}) = r(\mathbf{A}_b) = k < n$, then there exists an infinite number of solutions such that $n - k$ of the variables may be given arbitrary values. If $r(\mathbf{A}) = r(\mathbf{A}_b) = n$, there is a unique solution to the system of equations. When $r(\mathbf{A}) = r(\mathbf{A}_b) = k < m$, then $m - k$ of the equations are redundant. Any $\mathbf{x}$ satisfying k equations for which the corresponding rows of $\mathbf{A}$ are linearly independent will satisfy all m equations. To generate all possible solutions, select a nonsingular submatrix from $\mathbf{A}$ of order k. If $k < m$, drop all equations not associated with the rows of $\mathbf{A}$ appearing in this submatrix. Given any values for the $n - k$ variables not associated with the columns of $\mathbf{A}$ that appear in the kth-order submatrix, one can solve uniquely for the k variables associated with the columns of $\mathbf{A}$ that appear in the submatrix, since the submatrix has an inverse. The resulting n-tuple will be a solution to $\mathbf{Ax} = \mathbf{b}$. By allowing the $n - k$ variables referred to above to take on all possible values, all solutions to the system of equations are generated. If $\mathbf{b} = \mathbf{0}$, the system of equations is called *homogeneous*. The set of solutions to $\mathbf{Ax} = \mathbf{0}$ is a subspace of E^n of dimension $n - k$ if $r(\mathbf{A}) = k$. (The proofs of the material in this paragraph are given in {LA 5–5} and {LA 5–6}.) Note that $\mathbf{x} = \mathbf{0}$ is always a solution to $\mathbf{Ax} = \mathbf{0}$; $\mathbf{x} = \mathbf{0}$ is called a *trivial solution*. There exist nontrivial solutions if and only if $r(\mathbf{A}) < n$, n being the number of variables.

Consider a system of m equations in n unknowns for which $r(\mathbf{A}) = r(\mathbf{A}_b) = m$. Select an mth-order submatrix from $\mathbf{A}$; call it $\mathbf{B}$. Let $\mathbf{x}_B$ be a vector containing the variables associated with the columns of $\mathbf{B}$. Also, let $\mathbf{x}_R$ contain the remaining variables and let $\mathbf{R}$ be the matrix containing the columns of $\mathbf{A}$ associated with these variables. Then for any $\mathbf{x}_R$, a solution to the system will be obtained if $\mathbf{x}_B = \mathbf{B}^{-1}\mathbf{b} - \mathbf{B}^{-1}\mathbf{R}\mathbf{x}_R$. A solution $\mathbf{x}_R = \mathbf{0}$ and $\mathbf{x}_B = \mathbf{B}^{-1}\mathbf{b}$ is called a *basic solution*. A basic solution has no more than m variables different from zero. The variables in $\mathbf{x}_B$ are called the *basic variables;* the other variables are called the *nonbasic* variables. The nonbasic variables are by definition zero. A basic solution is said to be *degenerate* if one or more of the basic variables also is zero. The maximum possible number of basic solutions one can obtain to the system $\mathbf{Ax} = \mathbf{b}$ is $n!/m!(n - m)!$, corresponding to the number of different combinations of m columns from $\mathbf{A}$ which can be selected to form $\mathbf{B}$. Not all basic solutions need exist, because not every set of m columns from $\mathbf{A}$ is necessarily linearly independent.

If $\mathbf{A}$ is an $m \times n$ matrix and $\mathbf{x}$ is a point in E^n, then $\mathbf{y} = \mathbf{Ax}$ can be thought of as a point in E^m. For each point in E^n, there is a corresponding unique point $\mathbf{y} = \mathbf{Ax}$ in E^m. The point $\mathbf{y}$ is called the image of $\mathbf{x}$. The matrix $\mathbf{A}$ is said to *map* E^n into all or part of E^m. The collection of points $\mathbf{y}$ obtained by allowing $\mathbf{x}$ to range over all of E^n is a subspace of E^m {LA 4–2}. The matrix $\mathbf{A}$ is said to *map* or *transform* E^n into a subspace of E^m.

A matrix transformation is often referred to as a linear transformation. It preserves addition and multiplication by a scalar, i.e., if $\mathbf{y}_1 = \mathbf{A}\mathbf{x}_1$ and $\mathbf{y}_2 = \mathbf{A}\mathbf{x}_2$, then if $\mathbf{y} = \mathbf{y}_1 + \mathbf{y}_2$, it follows that $\mathbf{y} = \mathbf{A}(\mathbf{x}_1 + \mathbf{x}_2)$. Similarly, if $\mathbf{y} = \mathbf{A}\mathbf{x}$, then $\lambda\mathbf{y}$ is the image of $\lambda\mathbf{x}$.

2-3 Linear programming. The general linear programming problem seeks to determine non-negative values of n variables x_j which satisfy m linear constraints $\sum_{j=1}^{n} a_{ij}x_j\{\leq, =, \geq\}b_i$, $i = 1, \ldots, m$, and maximize or minimize the linear objective function $z = \sum c_jx_j$. We shall now review the simplex procedure for solving numerically any linear programming problem. This method requires that each $b_i \geq 0$. We shall assume this to be the case. If in the original formulation any $b_i < 0$, we multiply that constraint by -1 (and thereby change the direction of the inequality if it is not an equation). Given that each $b_i \geq 0$, the first step is to convert the constraints into a set of simultaneous linear equations. This is easily done by adding slack and surplus variables {LP 3-2}. Imagine that the constraints are numbered so that those with a $\leq$ sign come first, then those with a $\geq$ sign, and finally, the equations. If constraint i is of the form $\sum_j a_{ij}x_j \leq b_i$, then we define a new variable, called a *slack variable*, by

$$x_{n+i} = b_i - \sum_{j=1}^{n} a_{ij}x_j \quad \text{or} \quad \sum_{j=1}^{n} a_{ij}x_j + x_{n+i} = b_i. \tag{2-8}$$

For any set of x_j, $j = 1, \ldots, n$, which satisfy this constraint, $x_{n+i} \geq 0$. When a constraint is of the form $\sum_j a_{ij}x_j \geq b_i$, we define a new variable x_{n+i}, called a *surplus variable*:

$$x_{n+i} = \sum_{j=1}^{n} a_{ij}x_j - b_i \quad \text{or} \quad \sum_{j=1}^{n} a_{ij}x_j - x_{n+i} = b_i. \tag{2-9}$$

For any set of x_j which satisfy this constraint, $x_{n+i} \geq 0$. Thus the constraints can be converted into a system of m linear equations in N unknowns, $\mathbf{A}\mathbf{x} = \mathbf{b}$, where N satisfies $n \leq N \leq n + m$. The number of slack and surplus variables added will be $N - n$. The definition of slack and surplus variables ensures that they will always be non-negative for any set of x_j, $j = 1, \ldots, n$, satisfying the original constraints. The columns of $\mathbf{A}$ are referred to as *activity vectors*. The activity vector corresponding to a slack variable will be a unit vector, and the activity vector corresponding to a surplus variable will be (-1) times a unit vector. There is a one-to-one correspondence between the sets of solutions to the original constraints having $x_j \geq 0$, $j = 1, \ldots, n$, and the solutions with $\mathbf{x} \geq \mathbf{0}$ to the system $\mathbf{A}\mathbf{x} = \mathbf{b}$ obtained by the addition of slack and surplus variables to the original constraints. Solutions with $\mathbf{x} \geq \mathbf{0}$ will be called *feasible* solutions. If the price of a slack or surplus variable is taken to be zero

(c_j in the objective function will be referred to as the *price* of x_j), then the value of z for any feasible solution to $\mathbf{Ax} = \mathbf{b}$ will be the same as that of the corresponding feasible solution to the original constraints, and vice versa. Thus by addition of slack and surplus variables, any linear programming problem can be converted to the equivalent problem $\mathbf{Ax} = \mathbf{b}$, $\mathbf{x} \geq \mathbf{0}$, max or min $z = \mathbf{cx}$, where $\mathbf{c} = (c_1, \ldots, c_N)$. This is the standard form used in the simplex method. In the future, instead of using both n and N, as was done above, we shall find it convenient always to use n for the number of variables in any programming problem, whether or not the constraints contain inequalities. This will not cause any confusion.

It should be observed that whenever the constraints are linear, they can be converted to a system of linear equations by the addition of slack and surplus variables, regardless of the nature of the objective function. Thus problems of the form (1–6) through (1–9) with linear constraints and a nonlinear objective function can be converted to the equivalent form

$$\mathbf{Ax} = \mathbf{b}, \qquad \mathbf{x} \geq \mathbf{0}, \qquad \text{max or min } z = f(x_1, \ldots, x_n). \tag{2–10}$$

Slack and surplus variables can also be introduced into the constraints of integer programming problems. Here, however, even though the original variables are integers, it is not necessarily true that the slack and surplus variables defined by (2–8) and (2–9), respectively, will be integral if the a_{ij} and the b_i are not integers. Thus, in general, introduction of slack and surplus variables converts an all integer problem into a mixed integer-continuous variable problem. However, it is possible to make sure that the slack and surplus variables are integers to an arbitrarily accurate approximation. This is accomplished by choosing the physical dimensions of the a_{ij} and b_i in such a way that to the accuracy specified, the a_{ij} and b_i are integers. This may require that time be measured in seconds instead of hours, for example, or that the availability of a raw material be expressed in pounds rather than tons, etc. Thus to an arbitrarily good approximation, an all integer linear programming problem can be converted to the form $\mathbf{Ax} = \mathbf{b}$, $\mathbf{x} \geq \mathbf{0}$, all variables integers, max or min $z = \mathbf{cx}$. In this formulation, the slack and surplus variables are also integers.

Let us now turn to the simplex method itself. This method is an iterative procedure which reaches an optimal solution in a finite number of steps or provides an indication that there is an unbounded solution. As a matter of convention, unbounded solutions will not be called optimal. If the problem has an optimal solution, the optimum value of z must be finite. Let us assume that the linear programming problem has been converted to the standard form $\mathbf{Ax} = \mathbf{b}$, $\mathbf{x} \geq \mathbf{0}$, max $z = \mathbf{cx}$. It is only necessary to study maximization problems, since a minimization problem can be converted into a maximization problem by changing the signs of the prices, that is, $\min z = \mathbf{cx} = -(-\mathbf{cx}) = -\max \bar{z}, \bar{z} = (-\mathbf{c})\mathbf{x}$ {LP 4-9}. Then ({LP 3-6} through {LP 3-8}):

(a) If the problem has an optimal solution, at least one basic feasible solution to $\mathbf{Ax} = \mathbf{b}$ will be optimal.

(b) If we have a basic feasible solution which is not optimal, it is possible to reach an optimal basic solution in a finite number of steps by changing just one of the basic variables at each step, or to obtain ultimately an indication of an unbounded solution.

It will be assumed that $r(\mathbf{A}) = r(\mathbf{A}_b) = m$. (We shall see shortly that this assumption does not lead to a loss in generality.) Then a basic feasible solution will never have more than m positive variables. Let $\mathbf{B}$ be a matrix containing any m linearly independent columns of $\mathbf{A}$. The corresponding basic (but not necessarily feasible) solution can be written $\mathbf{x}_B = \mathbf{B}^{-1}\mathbf{b}$, where all nonbasic variables are zero. The value of the objective function for this solution is $z = \mathbf{c}_B\mathbf{x}_B$, where $\mathbf{c}_B = (c_{B1}, \ldots, c_{Bm})$ contains the prices of the basic variables. Let $\mathbf{a}_j$ be any activity vector (i.e., any column of $\mathbf{A}$). Write $\mathbf{y}_j = [y_{1j}, \ldots, y_{mj}] = \mathbf{B}^{-1}\mathbf{a}_j$, and $z_j = \mathbf{c}_B\mathbf{y}_j$. Assume now that we have a basic feasible solution $\mathbf{x}_B = \mathbf{B}^{-1}\mathbf{b}$ and that we have computed the $\mathbf{y}_j$ and z_j for all $\mathbf{a}_j$. The following possibilities exist:

(a) $z_j - c_j \geq 0$, $j = 1, \ldots, n$. In this case, the basic feasible solution is optimal.

(b) For a particular j, $z_j - c_j < 0$ and $y_{ij} \leq 0$, $i = 1, \ldots, m$. In this case, there is an unbounded solution.

(c) One or more $z_j - c_j < 0$, and for each such j, at least one $y_{ij} > 0$, $i = 1, \ldots, m$. In this case, there exists another basic feasible solution with the value of objective function at least as large as the current value. In fact, if the current basic feasible solution is not degenerate, it is possible to increase the value of the objective function by changing just one vector in $\mathbf{B}$, i.e., changing one of the basic variables.

These results are proved in {LP 3-6} through {LP 3-8}.

The simplex method begins with a basic feasible solution and proceeds by changing one vector in the basis at each iteration. The rules for changing vectors in the basis are as follows:

(1) *Vector to enter basis.* Compute

$$z_k - c_k = \min_j (z_j - c_j), \qquad z_j - c_j < 0.$$

Then $\mathbf{a}_k$ enters the basis at the next iteration. If the minimum computed is not unique, select from among the tied values the vector with the smallest index j.

(2) *Vector to leave basis.* Compute

$$x_{Br}/y_{rk} = \min_i (x_{Bi}/y_{ik}) \qquad \text{for} \quad y_{ik} > 0$$

(if all $y_{ik} \leq 0$ there is an unbounded solution). Then column r of $\mathbf{B}$ is removed and replaced by $\mathbf{a}_k$. If there is a tie, choose the vector for which y_{ik} is greatest; if this does not break the tie choose from among the remaining vectors the one with the smallest index i.

The new values of the $\mathbf{y}_j$, $z_j - c_j$, $\mathbf{x}_B$, and z, which will be written $\hat{\mathbf{y}}_j$, $\hat{z}_j - c_j$, $\hat{\mathbf{x}}_B$, $\hat{z}$, may be computed from the current values as follows. Let $\mathbf{x}_B = \mathbf{y}_0$, $z_j - c_j = y_{m+1,j}$, $z = y_{m+1,0}$. Then

$$\hat{y}_{ij} = y_{ij} - \frac{y_{ik}}{y_{rk}} y_{rj}, \quad i = 1, \ldots, m+1, \quad i \neq r; \quad \hat{y}_{rj} = \frac{y_{rj}}{y_{rk}}, \quad j = 0, 1, \ldots, n. \tag{2-11}$$

These results are obtained in {LP 4–1} through {LP 4–4}.

Consider now the problem of obtaining an initial basic feasible solution. If an identity matrix appears in $\mathbf{A}$ (this will be true if a slack variable was added to each constraint), we immediately have the basic feasible solution $\mathbf{B} = \mathbf{I}$, $\mathbf{x}_B = \mathbf{b}$, $\mathbf{y}_j = \mathbf{a}_j$, $z_j - c_j = \mathbf{c}_B\mathbf{a}_j - c_j$, $z = \mathbf{c}_B\mathbf{b}$. If an identity matrix is not present in $\mathbf{A}$, we annex sufficient unit vectors to $\mathbf{A}$ to yield an identity matrix. The additional activity vectors are called *artificial vectors,* and the corresponding variables are called *artificial variables* (written x_{ai}). The original variables will be referred to as *legitimate variables* to distinguish them from artificial variables. To obtain a feasible solution to the original problem, the values of the artificial variables must be driven to zero. One way of accomplishing this is to assign a price of $-M$ to each artificial variable, where M is taken to be a very large positive number. For hand computation the value of M need not be made explicit. The artificial variables can be driven to zero if there is a feasible solution. If no unit vectors were present in $\mathbf{A}$, one would, after having annexed artificial

TABLE 2–1

TABLEAU FORMAT FOR SIMPLEX METHOD

	c_j		c_1		c_n
$\mathbf{c}_B$	Basic variables	$\mathbf{b}$	$\mathbf{a}_1$	$\cdots$	$\mathbf{a}_n$
c_{B1}	x_{B1}	$x_{B1} = y_{10}$	y_{11}	$\cdots$	y_{1n}
$\vdots$					$\vdots$
c_{Bm}	x_{Bm}	$x_{Bm} = y_{m0}$	y_{m1}	$\cdots$	y_{mn}
		$z = y_{m+1,0}$	$z_1 - c_1 = y_{m+1,1}$	$\cdots$	$z_n - c_n = y_{m+1,n}$

variables, begin with the following linear programming problem:

$$\mathbf{Ax} + \mathbf{Ix}_a = \mathbf{b}, \quad \mathbf{x} \geq \mathbf{0}, \quad \mathbf{x}_a \geq \mathbf{0}, \quad \max z = \mathbf{cx} - M\mathbf{1x}_a, \tag{2-12}$$

where $\mathbf{x}_a = [x_{a1}, \ldots, x_{am}]$, $\mathbf{1} = (1, 1, \ldots, 1)$. Then for the initial basic feasible solution to (2–12), $\mathbf{x}_B = \mathbf{b}$, $\mathbf{y}_j = \mathbf{a}_j$, $z = -M\mathbf{1b}$, and $z_j - c_j = -M\mathbf{1a}_j - c_j$. When a unit vector $\mathbf{e}_k$ is present in $\mathbf{A}$, it is unnecessary to add an artificial vector $\mathbf{e}_k$. Artificial variables are discussed in detail in {LP 4–5} and {LP 4–6}.

The tableau format of Table 2–1 is useful for simplex hand computations. A new tableau is constructed at each iteration by means of (2–11). Columns for artificial variables need not be included since an artificial vector which has been removed from the basis will never be reinserted.

2–4 The revised simplex method. Generally, when linear programming problems are solved on digital computers, the revised simplex method is used rather than the simplex method discussed above. Instead of transforming all the $\mathbf{y}_j$ at each iteration, the revised simplex method transforms only $\mathbf{B}^{-1}$, $\mathbf{c}_B\mathbf{B}^{-1}$, $\mathbf{x}_B$, and z. The $z_j - c_j$ and $\mathbf{y}_k$ are computed directly from their definitions by means of $z_j - c_j = (\mathbf{c}_B\mathbf{B}^{-1})\mathbf{a}_j - c_j$, $\mathbf{y}_k = \mathbf{B}^{-1}\mathbf{a}_k$. Furthermore, artificial variables are treated by what is known as the two-phase method rather than by the $-M$ pricing technique. It is convenient to discuss the computational aspects of the revised simplex algorithm in two parts, depending on whether or not it is necessary to add artificial vectors. Let us develop first the case where artificial vectors are not needed. Assume that, as usual, we wish to solve the problem $\mathbf{Ax} = \mathbf{b}$, $\mathbf{x} \geq \mathbf{0}$, $\max z = \mathbf{cx}$. Consider a basic feasible solution described by the basis matrix $\mathbf{B}$. If we write $z = \mathbf{c}_B\mathbf{x}_B$ as $z - \mathbf{c}_B\mathbf{x}_B = 0$ and consider this to be another equation, we can summarize the basic feasible solution in matrix form as

$$\begin{bmatrix} 1 & -\mathbf{c}_B \\ \mathbf{0} & \mathbf{B} \end{bmatrix} \begin{bmatrix} z \\ \mathbf{x}_B \end{bmatrix} = \begin{bmatrix} 0 \\ \mathbf{b} \end{bmatrix} \quad \text{or} \quad \mathbf{x}_B^{(1)} = \begin{bmatrix} z \\ \mathbf{x}_B \end{bmatrix} = \begin{bmatrix} 1 & \mathbf{c}_B\mathbf{B}^{-1} \\ \mathbf{0} & \mathbf{B}^{-1} \end{bmatrix} \begin{bmatrix} 0 \\ \mathbf{b} \end{bmatrix}. \tag{2-13}$$

Note also that

$$\mathbf{y}_j^{(1)} = \begin{bmatrix} z_j - c_j \\ \mathbf{y}_j \end{bmatrix} = \begin{bmatrix} 1 & \mathbf{c}_B\mathbf{B}^{-1} \\ \mathbf{0} & \mathbf{B}^{-1} \end{bmatrix} \begin{bmatrix} -c_j \\ \mathbf{a}_j \end{bmatrix}. \tag{2-14}$$

Denote the columns of the $(m + 1) \times m$ matrix

$$\begin{bmatrix} \mathbf{c}_B\mathbf{B}^{-1} \\ \mathbf{B}^{-1} \end{bmatrix}$$

TABLE 2–2

TABLEAU FORMAT FOR REVISED SIMPLEX METHOD

Basic variables	$\boldsymbol{\beta}_1$	$\cdots$	$\boldsymbol{\beta}_m$	$\mathbf{x}_B^{(1)}$	$\mathbf{y}_k^{(1)}$
z	β_{01}	$\cdots$	β_{0m}	z	$z_k - c_k$
x_{B1}	β_{11}	$\cdots$	β_{1m}	x_{B1}	y_{1k}
$\vdots$		$\cdots$			$\vdots$
x_{Bm}	β_{m1}	$\cdots$	β_{mm}	x_{Bm}	y_{mk}

by $\boldsymbol{\beta}_1, \ldots, \boldsymbol{\beta}_m$. The tableau format which is convenient for carrying out the computations is shown in Table 2–2.

The computational procedure is as follows: Suppose that we are given a tableau such as Table 2–2 for a basic feasible solution, except that no entries are in the $\mathbf{y}_k^{(1)}$-column. We must now determine whether or not the solution is optimal, and if not, which vector should enter the basis at the next iteration. To do this, compute the $z_j - c_j$ for the nonbasic variables by taking the scalar product of the first row of the tableau with $\mathbf{a}_j$ and subtracting c_j from the result. If all $z_j - c_j \geq 0$, the solution is optimal. If not, select the vector $\mathbf{a}_k$ to enter the basis, using the procedure adopted in the simplex method. To determine the vector to leave the basis, we need $\mathbf{y}_k$. Compute y_{ik}, $i = 1, \ldots, m$, by taking the scalar product of row $i + 1$ of the tableau with $\mathbf{a}_k$. Thus fill in the $\mathbf{y}_k^{(1)}$-column of the tableau. Determine the column r to be removed from the basis as is done in the simplex method. The transformation formulas are then applied to obtain a new tableau. Write $z_k - c_k = y_{0k}$; $[z, \mathbf{x}_B] = \boldsymbol{\beta}_{m+1}$. The transformation formulas are (with carets denoting the new values):

$$\hat{\beta}_{ij} = \beta_{ij} - \frac{y_{ik}}{y_{rk}}\,\beta_{rj}, \quad i \neq r; \qquad \hat{\beta}_{rj} = \frac{\beta_{rj}}{y_{rk}}, \quad j = 1, \ldots, m + 1. \tag{2–15}$$

Consider now the case where one or more artificial variables are needed. Here the problem is solved in two parts. In Phase I, the artificial variables are driven to zero. This is done by assigning a price of zero to the legitimate variables (regardless of the actual price) and a price of -1 to the artificial variables. In Phase II we determine an optimal basic feasible solution. For Phase II, the legitimate variables are assigned their actual prices, and any artificial variables remaining in the basis (at a zero level) are assigned a price of zero. To be specific, we shall assume that it is necessary to add m artificial variables. In Phase I we wish to maximize $z_a = -x_{a1} - x_{a2} - \cdots - x_{am}$, whereas in Phase II we maximize $z = \mathbf{cx}$. In Phase II artificial variables are assigned a price of zero; hence if any such variables appear in the basis at a zero level when Phase I ends, an extra constraint must be introduced to maintain these artificial variables in the basis at a zero level. This extra constraint is $z_a + x_{a1} + \cdots + x_{am} = 0$; $z_a = 0$ at the end of Phase I if there is a feasible solution, and hence it can be included in the constraint in Phase II, since it will remain zero if it is treated like another artificial variable (and assigned a price of zero). It is convenient to include z_a in this way. For any basis matrix $\mathbf{B}$ for the augmented system of constraints including the artificial variables, let $\mathbf{c}_B$ contain the prices appropriate to Phase II and $\mathbf{c}_{B1}$ the prices appropriate to Phase I (these will be 0 or -1). In Phase I it is desirable to transform $\mathbf{c}_B\mathbf{B}^{-1}$ as well as $\mathbf{c}_{B1}\mathbf{B}^{-1}$. Hence a basic feasible solution with the associated values of z and z_a can be conveniently represented as

$$\begin{bmatrix} 1 & 0 & -\mathbf{c}_B \\ 0 & 1 & -\mathbf{c}_{B1} \\ \mathbf{0} & \mathbf{0} & \mathbf{B} \end{bmatrix} \begin{bmatrix} z \\ z_a \\ \mathbf{x}_B \end{bmatrix} = \begin{bmatrix} 0 \\ 0 \\ \mathbf{b} \end{bmatrix} \quad \text{or} \quad \begin{bmatrix} z \\ z_a \\ \mathbf{x}_B \end{bmatrix} = \begin{bmatrix} 1 & 0 & \mathbf{c}_B\mathbf{B}^{-1} \\ 0 & 1 & \mathbf{c}_{B1}\mathbf{B}^{-1} \\ \mathbf{0} & \mathbf{0} & \mathbf{B}^{-1} \end{bmatrix} \begin{bmatrix} 0 \\ 0 \\ \mathbf{b} \end{bmatrix}. \tag{2-16}$$

Also, if $z_{j1} - c_{j1}$ are the $z_j - c_j$ for Phase I, we have

$$\begin{bmatrix} z_j - c_j \\ z_{j1} - c_{j1} \\ \mathbf{y}_j \end{bmatrix} = \begin{bmatrix} 1 & 0 & \mathbf{c}_B\mathbf{B}^{-1} \\ 0 & 1 & \mathbf{c}_{B1}\mathbf{B}^{-1} \\ \mathbf{0} & \mathbf{0} & \mathbf{B}^{-1} \end{bmatrix} \begin{bmatrix} -c_j \\ -c_{j1} \\ \mathbf{a}_j \end{bmatrix}. \tag{2-17}$$

If $\mathbf{a}_j$ is a legitimate vector, $c_{j1} = 0$, and if $\mathbf{a}_j$ is an artificial vector, $c_j = 0$, and $c_{j1} = -1$.

A convenient tableau format for solving the problem is again that shown in Table 2-2. Now, however, there will be an additional row. Furthermore, it is desirable to insert an additional column $\boldsymbol{\beta}_0$ corresponding in Phase I to z_a. Although the column will always remain $\mathbf{e}_2$ in Phase I, we shall see that it may change in Phase II, and hence it should be included. In Phase I we determine the vector to enter the basis by first taking the scalar product of the second row of the tableau with the vector $[0, \mathbf{a}_j]$ for each legitimate vector to yield $z_{j1} - c_{j1}$ and then applying the usual simplex criterion. The vector to be removed is also determined according to the usual simplex criterion. Phase I ends when $z_a = 0$ (or if there is no feasible solution when all $z_{j1} - c_{j1} \geq 0$ and $z_a < 0$). In Phase II we have $m + 1$ constraints and deal with bases of order $m + 1$. Interestingly enough, we were able to arrange things so that the final tableau for Phase I serves as the initial tableau for Phase II. To initiate Phase II, we compute the $z_j - c_j$ for each legitimate vector not in the basis by taking the scalar product of the first row of the tableau with $[0, \mathbf{a}_j]$ and subtract c_j. We then determine the vector to enter the basis in the usual way. The vector to leave the basis is also determined in the usual way. Now, however, we must also allow for the possibility that the first column of the tableau, i.e., the column corresponding to z_a in Phase I, may be replaced. The transformation formulas again have the form (2–15). The revised simplex method is discussed in {LP 7–1} through {LP 7–9}.

2–5 Duality. Given any linear programming problem $\mathbf{Ax} = \mathbf{b}, \mathbf{x} \geq \mathbf{0}$, $\max z = \mathbf{cx}$, there is another linear programming problem $\mathbf{A'w} \geq \mathbf{c'}$, $\min Z = \mathbf{b'w}$ which is called the *dual* of the given problem. The given problem is referred to as the *primal* problem. The primal and dual problems have the following properties: (1) If either problem has an optimal solution, then so does the other, and furthermore, $\max z = \min Z$, i.e., the optimal values of the objective functions are equal. If one problem has an unbounded solution, the other has no solution. (2) If $\mathbf{x}_B^* = \mathbf{B}^{-1}\mathbf{b}$ is an optimal basic feasible solution to the primal with $z^* = \mathbf{c}_B\mathbf{x}_B^*$, then $\mathbf{w}^{*\prime} = \mathbf{c}_B\mathbf{B}^{-1}$ is an optimal solution to the dual. Conversely, if $\mathbf{w}_B^* = \mathbf{B}_D^{-1}\mathbf{c}'$ is an optimal basic solution to the dual with $Z^* = \mathbf{b}'_B\mathbf{w}_B^*$, then $\mathbf{x}^{*\prime} = \mathbf{b}'_B\mathbf{B}_D^{-1}$ is an optimal solution to the primal. Note that the dual variables are not required to be non-negative. Also, if $\mathbf{x}$ is any feasible solution to the primal and $\mathbf{w}$ is any solution to the dual, then $\mathbf{cx} \leq \mathbf{b'w}$. These results are proved in {LP 8–1} through {LP 8–7}.

Note that the number of variables in the primal problem is equal to the number of constraints in the dual. Thus, if we have a linear programming problem with many constraints (this would require a large basis matrix) but not many variables, it is more efficient to solve the dual problem by the simplex or revised simplex methods and then obtain an optimal solution to the primal as discussed in the previous paragraph. It follows from the previous paragraph that if the primal problem is solved by the revised simplex method, an optimal solution to the dual will be found in the first row of the tableau giving an optimal solution to the primal. Conversely, if the dual is solved by the revised simplex method, an optimal solution to the primal will be contained in the first row of the tableau giving an optimal solution to the dual. An optimal solution to the dual when the primal is solved by the simplex method (or an optimal solution to the primal when the dual is solved by the simplex method) can be obtained from the final simplex tableau. To do this, look under the columns corresponding to those that formed the identity matrix for the initial basis. Imagine that the primal was solved by the simplex method. Then, if $\mathbf{a}_j = \mathbf{e}_i$ in the original basis was a slack vector, the number entered in the $z_j - c_j$

position of the final tableau is w_i^*. If $\mathbf{e}_i$ was an artificial vector, then $z_j - c_j - M = w_i^*$ (note that in order to determine the dual variables, the $z_j - c_j$ for the artificial vectors must be included in the tableau and must be transformed at each iteration). Precisely the same procedure is used to find an optimal solution to the primal if the dual is solved by the simplex method.

Note that there is a dual variable associated with every primal constraint, and a primal variable associated with every dual constraint. If a slack variable was added to the ith primal constraint, then $w_i \geq 0$, whereas if a surplus variable was added to the ith primal constraint, $w_i \leq 0$. If x_j is unrestricted in sign, then the jth dual constraint must hold as a strict equality. If $\mathbf{x}$ is any optimal solution to the primal, and $\mathbf{w}_s$ contains the surplus variables for any optimal solution to the dual, then it must be true that $\mathbf{x}'\mathbf{w}_s = 0$ {LP 8–5}. This is referred to as the complementary slackness principle.

By applying the simplex method to the dual problem one can obtain a new algorithm, called the *dual simplex method*, for solving the primal. Let us assume that we have a basic but nonfeasible solution to the primal, with the property that $z_j - c_j \geq 0$ for all j. If we obtain new basic solutions by changing just a single basic variable at a time, in such a way that all $z_j - c_j \geq 0$ for each such solution, then any feasible basic solution obtained will be an optimal solution. The rules for making a change of basis are: (1) the variable to leave the basis is the most negative x_{Bi}; call it x_{Br}. (2) The variable x_k enters the basis, where k is determined by means of

$$\frac{z_k - c_k}{y_{rk}} = \max_j \frac{z_j - c_j}{y_{rj}}, \qquad y_{rj} < 0.$$

If no $y_{rj} < 0$, there is no feasible solution. The dual simplex method is useful mainly for making certain kinds of changes after an optimal solution has been obtained, since it is usually not easy to get a basic nonfeasible solution with all $z_j - c_j \geq 0$. The dual simplex algorithm is discussed in {LP 8–7, 8–8}.

2–6 Convex sets. Collections of points in E^n will be referred to as *point sets.* Upper-case letters, for example X, S, etc., will be used to denote point sets. If $\mathbf{x}$ is an element of the set X, we write $\mathbf{x} \in X$. The intersection of two sets X and Y, written $X \cap Y$, is the collection of all points common to X and Y. The union of X and Y ,written $X \cup Y$, is the set of all points in either X or Y (or both). A set with no elements is called the *null set.* A point set is often defined by some property or properties satisfied by its elements. If X is the collection of all points $\mathbf{x}$ with the property or properties $\boldsymbol{\rho}(\mathbf{x})$, we write $X = \{\mathbf{x}|\boldsymbol{\rho}(\mathbf{x})\}$. For a given point $\mathbf{a}$ and any $\epsilon > 0$, the collection of points $X = \{\mathbf{x}|\ |\mathbf{x} - \mathbf{a}| = \epsilon\}$ is called a *hypersphere* in

E^n with center at $\mathbf{a}$ and radius ϵ. The set $X = \{\mathbf{x} | |\mathbf{x} - \mathbf{a}| < \epsilon\}$ is called the *inside of the hypersphere*. An ϵ-neighborhood of a point $\mathbf{a}$ is the inside of a hypersphere with center at $\mathbf{a}$ and with radius ϵ. A point $\mathbf{a}$ is called an *interior point* of a set if there exists an ϵ-neighborhood about $\mathbf{a}$ which contains only points of the set. A point $\mathbf{a}$ is called a *boundary point* if *every* ϵ-neighborhood about $\mathbf{a}$ contains points which are in the set and points which are not in the set. A set which contains all its boundary points is said to be *closed*. A set which does not contain any of its boundary points is said to be *open*. An ϵ-neighborhood of a point $\mathbf{a}$ is an open set. This material is discussed in more detail in {LA 6–1} through {LA 6–3}.

The *line* passing through two different points $\mathbf{x}_1$ and $\mathbf{x}_2$ in E^n is defined to be the set of points

$$X = \{\mathbf{x} | \mathbf{x} = \lambda \mathbf{x}_2 + (1 - \lambda)\mathbf{x}_1, \text{all } \lambda\}. \tag{2–18}$$

If λ is restricted to $0 \leq \lambda \leq 1$, then the set (2–18) represents the *line segment* joining $\mathbf{x}_1$ and $\mathbf{x}_2$. For a specified λ, $0 \leq \lambda \leq 1$, the point $\mathbf{x} = \lambda \mathbf{x}_2 + (1 - \lambda)\mathbf{x}_1$ is called a *convex combination* of $\mathbf{x}_1$ and $\mathbf{x}_2$. A *hyperplane* in E^n is the collection of points $X = \{\mathbf{x} | \mathbf{c}\mathbf{x} = z\}$, where $\mathbf{c} \neq \mathbf{0}$ is a specified row vector and z is a specified scalar. The vector $\mathbf{c}$ is called a normal to the hyperplane; $\lambda \mathbf{c}$ is also a normal to the hyperplane for any $\lambda \neq 0$. Two hyperplanes $\mathbf{c}_1 \mathbf{x} = z_1$ and $\mathbf{c}_2 \mathbf{x} = z_2$ are said to be parallel if $\mathbf{c}_1 = \lambda \mathbf{c}_2$ for some λ. The sets $X = \{\mathbf{x} | \mathbf{c}\mathbf{x} < z\}$ and $X = \{\mathbf{x} | \mathbf{c}\mathbf{x} > z\}$ are called *open half-spaces*. Similarly, the sets $X = \{\mathbf{x} | \mathbf{c}\mathbf{x} \leq z\}$ and $X = \{\mathbf{x} | \mathbf{c}\mathbf{x} \geq z\}$ are called *closed half-spaces*. Hyperplanes and closed half-spaces are closed sets. A set X is said to be strictly bounded if for each $\mathbf{x} \in X$ there exists an $r > 0$ such that $|\mathbf{x}| < r$, that is, X lies inside a hypersphere with its center at the origin and radius r. A set X is said to be bounded from below if there exists a vector $\mathbf{a}$ such that for each $\mathbf{x} \in X$, $\mathbf{a} \leq \mathbf{x}$. Similarly, X is bounded from above if there exists a vector $\mathbf{a}$ such that for each $\mathbf{x} \in X$, $\mathbf{x} \leq \mathbf{a}$. The material in this paragraph is covered in detail in {LA 6–3}.

A set is said to be *convex* if for any points $\mathbf{x}_1$ and $\mathbf{x}_2$ in the set, every convex combination of $\mathbf{x}_1, \mathbf{x}_2$ is also in the set, i.e., the line segment joining $\mathbf{x}_1, \mathbf{x}_2$ is also in the set. A set consisting of a single point is considered to be convex. The point $\mathbf{x}$ in a convex set is said to be an *extreme point* if and only if there do not exist two different points $\mathbf{x}_1, \mathbf{x}_2$ in the set such that $\mathbf{x} = \lambda \mathbf{x}_2 + (1 - \lambda)\mathbf{x}_1, 0 < \lambda < 1$. An extreme point must be a boundary point. However, not all boundary points are necessarily extreme points since some boundary points may be between two extreme points. The set of points $\mathbf{x} \geq \mathbf{0}$ is called the *non-negative orthant* and is a closed convex set. Hyperplanes and closed half-spaces are closed convex sets. Furthermore, the intersection of two or more convex sets is convex. Also, the intersection of closed sets is closed. Note that the set of points $\mathbf{x}$ satisfying

$\mathbf{Ax} = \mathbf{b}$, $\mathbf{x} \geq \mathbf{0}$, can be looked upon as the intersection of m hyperplanes and n closed half-spaces. Hence, if there is a point satisfying these conditions, the set of points is a closed convex set. Therefore, if there is a feasible solution to a linear programming problem, the set of feasible solutions is a closed convex set. A basic feasible solution to $\mathbf{Ax} = \mathbf{b}$ will be an extreme point of the convex set of feasible solutions, and conversely, every extreme point is a basic feasible solution. Hence, if the optimal value of the objective function is bounded, at least one extreme point of the convex set will be optimal. A linear transformation $\mathbf{y} = \mathbf{Ax}$ with $\mathbf{A}$ an $m \times n$ matrix maps a convex set in E^n into a convex set in E^m. Furthermore, a nonsingular linear transformation (i.e., one with $\mathbf{A}$ nonsingular) takes an extreme point into an extreme point. See {LA 6–4} and {LP 3–10} for proofs of the material in this paragraph.

Given a closed convex set X, a point $\mathbf{v}$ either is an element of X or there exists a hyperplane which contains $\mathbf{v}$ such that all of X is contained in one open half-space produced by the hyperplane. This is called the theorem of separating hyperplanes. Let $\mathbf{w}$ be a boundary point of a convex set X. Then $\mathbf{cx} = z$ is called a supporting hyperplane at $\mathbf{w}$ if $\mathbf{cw} = z$ and if all of X lies in one closed half-space produced by the hyperplane. For every boundary point $\mathbf{w}$ of X, there exists at least one supporting hyperplane at $\mathbf{w}$. If the closed convex set X is bounded from below, from above, or strictly bounded, then the intersection of any supporting hyperplane with X contains at least one extreme point of X. The line joining two distinct extreme points of a convex set is called an edge if it is the intersection of the set with a supporting hyperplane. Two extreme points are called adjacent if the line segment joining them is an edge of the convex set. In the simplex method, one moves at each iteration from an extreme point to an adjacent extreme point. The proofs of the theorems presented here are given in {LA 6–6} through {LA 6–8}.

A closed, strictly bounded convex set with a finite number of extreme points is called a *convex polyhedron*. Any point in a convex polyhedron can be written as a convex combination of the extreme points of the polyhedron {LA 6–8}. If the intersection of a finite number of half-spaces and perhaps some hyperplanes is not empty, and is strictly bounded, then the intersection is a convex polyhedron.

2–7 Characteristic values and quadratic forms. The problem of finding vectors $\mathbf{x} \neq \mathbf{0}$ and scalars λ such that for a given square matrix $\mathbf{A}$,

$$\mathbf{Ax} = \lambda\mathbf{x} \tag{2–19}$$

is called a *characteristic value* problem. Clearly $\mathbf{x} = \mathbf{0}$ satisfies (2–19) for any λ. However, if $\mathbf{x} \neq \mathbf{0}$ satisfies (2–19), then $(\mathbf{A} - \lambda\mathbf{I})\mathbf{x} = \mathbf{0}$. This can be possible only if $\mathbf{A} - \lambda\mathbf{I}$ is singular, so that $|\mathbf{A} - \lambda\mathbf{I}| = 0$. Thus, there will exist $\mathbf{x} \neq \mathbf{0}$ satisfying (2–19) if and only if λ satisfies $f(\lambda) = |\mathbf{A} - \lambda\mathbf{I}| = 0$; $f(\lambda)$ is an nth-degree polynomial in λ. Now $f(\lambda) = 0$ has n roots (which may be real or complex) if a root is counted a number of times equal to its multiplicity. Hence there exist no more than n different values of λ for which there are $\mathbf{x} \neq \mathbf{0}$ satisfying (2–19). The roots of $f(\lambda) = 0$ are called the *characteristic values* or *eigenvalues* of the matrix $\mathbf{A}$. When λ in (2–19) is a characteristic value of $\mathbf{A}$, there exists at least one linearly independent $\mathbf{x} \neq \mathbf{0}$ satisfying (2–19); such an $\mathbf{x}$ is called a *characteristic vector* or *eigenvector* of $\mathbf{A}$. The number of linearly independent $\mathbf{x}$ satisfying (2–19) is $n - r(\mathbf{I} - \lambda\mathbf{A})$, where n is the order of $\mathbf{A}$ and λ is set equal to the characteristic value under consideration. The polynomial $f(\lambda)$ is called the *characteristic polynomial* of $\mathbf{A}$, and $f(\lambda) = 0$ is called the *characteristic equation* for the matrix $\mathbf{A}$. If $\mathbf{S}$ is a nonsingular matrix, then $\mathbf{S}^{-1}\mathbf{AS}$ has the same characteristic values as $\mathbf{A}$. The matrix $\mathbf{S}^{-1}\mathbf{AS}$ is said to be *similar* to $\mathbf{A}$.

We shall now restrict our attention to the case where $\mathbf{A}$ is a symmetric matrix. This is the situation which is usually of interest to us. If $\mathbf{A}$ is symmetric, the characteristic values of $\mathbf{A}$ are real, and characteristic vectors corresponding to different characteristic values are orthogonal. If a characteristic value has multiplicity m, it is possible to determine m mutually orthogonal characteristic vectors corresponding to this characteristic value. Hence for a symmetric matrix of order n, there always exist n mutually orthogonal characteristic vectors for $\mathbf{A}$. Usually, the magnitude of a characteristic vector is not of importance, and hence we shall assume that the characteristic vectors have been normalized so that their magnitude is unity; such characteristic vectors will be denoted by $\mathbf{u}_j, j = 1, \ldots, n$. Note that $\mathbf{u}_i'\mathbf{u}_j = \delta_{ij}$. Non-null vectors which are mutually orthogonal are linearly independent. Hence a set of n mutually orthogonal eigenvectors for $\mathbf{A}$ of unit length form a basis for E^n. Such a basis is called an orthonormal basis, and the vectors $\mathbf{u}_j$ are called an orthonormal set.

Consider a matrix $\mathbf{Q} = (\mathbf{u}_1, \ldots, \mathbf{u}_n)$ whose columns are a set of orthonormal eigenvectors for $\mathbf{A}$. Then $\mathbf{Q}'\mathbf{Q} = \mathbf{I}$ or $\mathbf{Q}^{-1} = \mathbf{Q}'$. The matrix $\mathbf{Q}$ is called an *orthogonal* matrix. Now observe that

$$\begin{aligned}\mathbf{Q}^{-1}\mathbf{AQ} &= \mathbf{Q}'\mathbf{AQ} = \mathbf{Q}'(\mathbf{Au}_1, \ldots, \mathbf{Au}_n)\\ &= \mathbf{Q}'(\lambda_1\mathbf{u}_1, \ldots, \lambda_n\mathbf{u}_n) = \|\lambda_j\delta_{ij}\|. \qquad (2\text{–}20)\end{aligned}$$

Thus any symmetric matrix $\mathbf{A}$ is similar to a diagonal matrix whose elements on the main diagonal are the characteristic values of $\mathbf{A}$. Furthermore, the matrix $\mathbf{Q}$ used to diagonalize $\mathbf{A}$ is an orthogonal matrix whose columns are an orthonormal set of characteristic vectors for $\mathbf{A}$. For any nonsingular matrix $\mathbf{Q}$, the matrix $\mathbf{Q}'\mathbf{AQ}$ is said to be congruent to $\mathbf{A}$.

Thus every symmetric matrix is congruent to a diagonal matrix whose diagonal elements are the characteristic values of **A**.

A *quadratic form* in n variables $x_1, \ldots, x_n$ is a numerical function of these variables which can be written $z = \sum_{j=1}^{n} \sum_{i=1}^{n} a_{ij}x_ix_j$. If $\mathbf{A} = \|a_{ij}\|$, $\mathbf{x} = [x_1, \ldots, x_n]$, then in matrix notation, $z = \mathbf{x}'\mathbf{A}\mathbf{x}$. It will be noted that when $i \neq j$, the coefficient of x_ix_j is $a_{ij} + a_{ji}$. From this it follows immediately that **A** can always be assumed to be a symmetric matrix, because, if it is not, we can uniquely define new coefficients

$$b_{ij} = b_{ji} = \frac{a_{ij} + a_{ji}}{2}, \qquad \text{all } i,j,$$

so that $b_{ij} + b_{ji} = a_{ij} + a_{ji}$ and $\mathbf{B} = \|b_{ij}\|$ is symmetric. This redefinition of the coefficients does not change the value of z for any **x**. In the future, we shall always assume that a matrix associated with a quadratic form is symmetric.

A quadratic form $\mathbf{x}'\mathbf{A}\mathbf{x}$ is called *positive definite* if $\mathbf{x}'\mathbf{A}\mathbf{x} > 0$ for every $\mathbf{x}$ except $\mathbf{x} = \mathbf{0}$; $\mathbf{x}'\mathbf{A}\mathbf{x}$ is called *positive semidefinite* if $\mathbf{x}'\mathbf{A}\mathbf{x} \geq 0$ for every $\mathbf{x}$ and there exist $\mathbf{x} \neq \mathbf{0}$ for which $\mathbf{x}'\mathbf{A}\mathbf{x} = 0$. A form $\mathbf{x}'\mathbf{A}\mathbf{x}$ is called *negative definite* (*negative semidefinite*) if $-\mathbf{x}'\mathbf{A}\mathbf{x}$ is positive definite (positive semidefinite). The form $\mathbf{x}'\mathbf{A}\mathbf{x}$ is said to be *indefinite* if it is positive for some points **x** and negative for others. Consider the following quadratic forms in two variables. Observe that $z = x_1^2 + 2x_1x_2 + x_2^2 = (x_1 + x_2)^2$ is positive definite, $z = x_1^2 - 2x_1x_2 + x_2^2 = (x_1 - x_2)^2$ is positive semidefinite since it is never negative but is zero whenever $x_1 = x_2$, and $z = x_1^2 - 2x_1x_2 - x_2^2$ is indefinite since $z > 0$ when $x_1 = 5$, $x_2 = 0$, and $z < 0$ when $x_1 = 0$, $x_2 = 5$.

Sometimes it is possible to simplify a quadratic form $z = \mathbf{x}'\mathbf{A}\mathbf{x}$ by a transformation of variables $\mathbf{x} = \mathbf{S}\mathbf{y}$, where **S** is a nonsingular matrix. In terms of the new variables, $z = \mathbf{y}'\mathbf{S}'\mathbf{A}\mathbf{S}\mathbf{y} = \mathbf{y}'\mathbf{B}\mathbf{y}$, where **B** is congruent to **A**. When **x** is allowed to vary over all of E^n, the set of values taken on by z is called the range of the quadratic form. Under a change of variables $\mathbf{x} = \mathbf{S}\mathbf{y}$, **S** nonsingular, the *range* of a quadratic form remains unchanged. Furthermore, a positive (negative) definite form remains positive (negative) definite. If **S** in the above transformation of variables is taken to be the matrix **Q** whose columns consist of an orthonormal set of eigenvectors for **A**, then in terms of the y_j variables, $z = \sum_{j=1}^{n} \lambda_j y_j^2$, where the λ_j are the characteristic values of **A**. When a quadratic form involves only the square of the variables, it is said to be in diagonal form. Every quadratic form can be diagonalized by an orthogonal similarity transformation, and in addition, the diagonal form has the property that the coefficients of the y_j^2 are the characteristic values of **A**. From this it follows that a quadratic form will be positive (negative) definite if and only if each characteristic value of **A** is positive (negative). Similarly a form

$\mathbf{x'Ax}$ is positive (negative) semidefinite if and only if each characteristic value of $\mathbf{A}$ is non-negative (nonpositive) and at least one characteristic value is zero. A form is indefinite if and only if $\mathbf{A}$ has both positive and negative eigenvalues. The material presented in this section is covered in detail in {LA 7–1} through {LA 7–10}.

2–8 Function of *n* variables. Recall that a *function* of two variables is simply a rule which associates with each point $\mathbf{x} = [x_1, x_2]$ in E^2 or each point in some subset X of E^2 a unique number z. The usual notation for such a function is $z = f(x_1, x_2)$. A function of two variables can frequently be thought of geometrically as describing a surface in three dimensions. However, we can equally well describe the function by plotting its level curves in E^2. For a fixed value of z, $z = f(x_1, x_2)$ provides a relation between x_1 and x_2 which is normally a curve in the x_1x_2-plane. Such a curve is called a level curve. It describes the shape of the surface for a fixed value of z. For example, $z = x_1^2 + x_2^2$ is a paraboloid of revolution, and the level curves are circles with center at the origin and radii $z^{1/2}$. Similarly, a function of n variables is a rule which associates with each point $\mathbf{x}$ in E^n or each point in some subset of X of E^n a unique number z. A function of n variables is often symbolized by $z = f(x_1, \ldots, x_n)$ or more simply $z = f(\mathbf{x})$. When no confusion will result, we merely use f or z. Usually $z = f(\mathbf{x})$ can be imagined to describe a surface in E^{n+1}. Such a surface is referred to as an n-dimensional surface or hypersurface since each of the n variables (components of $\mathbf{x}$) can be varied independently of the others (i.e., there are n degrees of freedom). For a fixed value of z, $z = f(\mathbf{x})$ represents a relation among the n components of $\mathbf{x}$ which usually can be thought of as representing a surface (of dimension $n - 1$) in E^n, called a level surface of $z = f(\mathbf{x})$.

The functions of n variables which will be of interest to us will usually have the property that they are continuous. Intuitively, $z = f(\mathbf{x})$ is *continuous* at the point $\mathbf{x}_0$ if $f(\mathbf{x}_0)$ exists, and for each $\mathbf{x}$ in a δ ($\delta > 0$) neighborhood of $\mathbf{x}_0$, $f(\mathbf{x})$ can be made arbitrarily close to $f(\mathbf{x}_0)$ if δ is chosen small enough. More rigorously, $z = f(\mathbf{x})$ is said to be continuous at the point $\mathbf{x}_0$ if, given *any* $\epsilon > 0$, however small, it is possible to find a $\delta > 0$ (which depends on ϵ) such that for all $\mathbf{x}$ satisfying $|\mathbf{x} - \mathbf{x}_0| < \delta$, it is true that $|f(\mathbf{x}) - f(\mathbf{x}_0)| < \epsilon$. Linear functions $z = \mathbf{cx}$ and quadratic forms $z = \mathbf{x'Ax}$ are continuous at every point in E^n.

Sums and products of continuous functions are continuous functions. The quotient of two continuous functions is continuous at all points where the denominator does not vanish. If $f(\mathbf{x})$ is continuous at $\mathbf{x}_0$, and if $f(\mathbf{x}_0) > 0$, then there exists a $\delta > 0$ such that $f(\mathbf{x}) > 0$ for all $\mathbf{x}$, $|\mathbf{x} - \mathbf{x}_0| < \delta$. This follows immediately from the definition of continuity since, if $f(\mathbf{x}_0) = \gamma > 0$, then by the definition of continuity there exists a δ such that for all $\mathbf{x}$, $|\mathbf{x} - \mathbf{x}_0| < \delta$, it is true that $|f(\mathbf{x}) - f(\mathbf{x}_0)| \leq \gamma/2$, that is, $f(\mathbf{x}) > 0$ for such $\mathbf{x}$.

2-9 Partial derivatives. The *derivative* of a function $f(x)$ of a single variable at the point x_0, written $df(x_0)/dx$ or $f'(x_0)$, is defined in terms of a limiting process as

$$f'(x_0) = \lim_{x \to x_0} \left[\frac{f(x) - f(x_0)}{x - x_0}\right] = \lim_{h \to 0} \left[\frac{f(x_0 + h) - f(x_0)}{h}\right], \tag{2-21}$$

provided that the limit exists. By $\lim_{x \to x_0} g(x) = a$ we mean that, given any $\epsilon > 0$, there exists a δ such that if $0 < |x - x_0| < \delta$, it is true that $|g(x) - a| < \epsilon$. Geometrically, $f'(x_0)$ is the slope of the curve $z = f(x)$ at x_0. Hence the derivative provides information about the rate of change of the function at x_0.

For a function of n variables it is possible to define n *partial derivatives* which provide information about the rate of change of the function at any given point in the direction of each of the n coordinate axes. The partial derivative of f with respect to x_j at the point $\mathbf{x}_0 = [x_1^0, \ldots, x_n^0]$ is defined to be

$$\lim_{h \to 0} \left[\frac{f(x_1^0, \ldots, x_{j-1}^0, x_j^0 + h, x_{j+1}^0, \ldots, x_n^0) - f(\mathbf{x}_0)}{h}\right]$$
$$= \lim_{h \to 0} \left[\frac{f(\mathbf{x}_0 + h\mathbf{e}_j) - f(\mathbf{x}_0)}{h}\right], \tag{2-22}$$

provided the limit exists. We shall usually represent the partial derivative of f with respect to x_j at $\mathbf{x}_0$ by $\partial f(\mathbf{x}_0)/\partial x_j$. Other notations frequently used are $(\partial f/\partial x_j)_0$, $(\partial z/\partial x_j)_0$, or $D_j f(\mathbf{x}_0)$. When we are not interested in specifying a particular point at which the partial derivative is to be evaluated, we shall simply write $\partial f/\partial x_j$ or $\partial z/\partial x_j$. Note that each of the n partial derivatives of f can also be considered to be a function of n variables. To obtain the partial derivative of f with respect to x_j, we simply determine the ordinary derivative treating all variables except x_j as constants. Usually, we shall assume that at each point in E^n where f is defined, all n partial derivatives of f with respect to the x_j exist and are continuous. To indicate that a function f is continuous over some subset of E^n we write $f \in C$, and if f and all its first derivatives are continuous, we write $f \in C^1$. We say that $f(\mathbf{x})$ is differentiable at $\mathbf{x}_0$ if $f \in C^1$ at $\mathbf{x}_0$. When $f \in C^1$ over some subset of E^n, then for each point $\mathbf{x}$ in this subset, we can define an n-component row vector ∇f by

$$\nabla f = \left(\frac{\partial f}{\partial x_1}, \ldots, \frac{\partial f}{\partial x_n}\right). \tag{2-23}$$

The vector ∇f is called the *gradient vector* of f; the symbol ∇f is read "del f." If we wish to indicate that each component of ∇f is to be evaluated at a particular point $\mathbf{x}_0$, we shall write $\nabla f(\mathbf{x}_0)$.

Since each of the partial derivatives of f with respect to x_j, $j = 1, \ldots, n$, is a function of n variables, we can form n partial derivatives of each of these functions if they exist. The resulting functions are referred to as the second partial derivatives of f and are written $\partial^2 f/\partial x_i\, \partial x_j$ or $\partial^2 z/\partial x_i\, \partial x_j$ or $D_{ij}^2 f$. There are n^2 such second partial derivatives. If the second partial derivatives of f exist and are continuous, we write $f \in C^2$. When $f \in C^2$, then

$$\frac{\partial^2 f}{\partial x_i\, \partial x_j} = \frac{\partial^2 f}{\partial x_j\, \partial x_i}, \quad \text{all } i, j, \tag{2–24}$$

i.e., the order of differentiation can be interchanged, and the same result will be obtained. We shall not prove this fact (see References 1 or 2), but it will always be assumed to be true when we need the second partial derivatives of a function. The n^2 second partial derivatives of f can be considered to be the elements of an $n \times n$ matrix $\mathbf{H}_f = \|\partial^2 f/\partial x_i\, \partial x_j\|$. $\mathbf{H}_f$ is called the *Hessian matrix* for f; from (2–24), it follows that $\mathbf{H}_f$ is a symmetric matrix. By $\mathbf{H}_f(\mathbf{x}_0)$ we shall mean that each element of $\mathbf{H}_f$ is evaluated at the point $\mathbf{x}_0$. On taking partial derivatives of the second partial derivatives of f one obtains partial derivatives of higher order. We shall have no need for these.

Let us now imagine that each variable x_j in the function f is itself a function of m variables y_i, that is, $x_j = \phi_j(y_1, \ldots, y_m)$. In this case we refer to f as a compound function. In reality $z = f(x_1, \ldots, x_n)$ is a function of $y_1, \ldots, y_m$ and can be written

$$z = f[\phi_1(y_1, \ldots, y_m), \ldots, \phi_n(y_1, \ldots, y_m)] = g(y_1, \ldots, y_m). \tag{2–25}$$

If $f \in C^1$ and $\phi_j \in C^1$, $j = 1, \ldots, n$, then $\partial z/\partial y_i$, $i = 1, \ldots, m$, exists and is given by the chain rule formula

$$\frac{\partial z}{\partial y_i} = \sum_{j=1}^{n} \frac{\partial f}{\partial x_j} \frac{\partial x_j}{\partial y_i}, \qquad i = 1, \ldots, m, \tag{2–26}$$

where in computing $\partial f/\partial x_j$ we treat f as a function of $x_1, \ldots, x_n$. We shall not prove this result; the proof can be found in [1] or [2]. By use of the chain rule, it is possible to differentiate very complicated functions, making use only of our knowledge of the rules for differentiating simple well-known functions.

The partial derivatives of f provide information only about the rate of change of the function in the directions of the coordinate axes. One can, however, define a derivative of f in any direction desired. A direction in space is defined by a non-null vector $\mathbf{r}$, the direction being that of the directed line from the origin to $\mathbf{r}$. Let us now select a direction $\mathbf{r}$; for convenience we shall assume that $|\mathbf{r}| = 1$. Then the derivative of f in the direction $\mathbf{r}$ evaluated at the point $\mathbf{x}_0$, written $D_{\mathbf{r}}f(\mathbf{x}_0)$, is defined to be

$$D_{\mathbf{r}}f(\mathbf{x}_0) = \lim_{h\to 0} \frac{f(\mathbf{x}_0 + h\mathbf{r}) - f(\mathbf{x}_0)}{h} \tag{2–27}$$

when the limit exists. Such a derivative is referred to as a *directional derivative*. We shall see later that when $f \in C^1$, then it is possible to express $D_{\mathbf{r}}f(\mathbf{x}_0)$ as a linear combination of the partial derivatives of f evaluated at $\mathbf{x}_0$.

EXAMPLES. 1. Let f be the quadratic form

$$f(\mathbf{x}) = \mathbf{x}'\mathbf{A}\mathbf{x} = \sum_{i=1}^{n}\sum_{j=1}^{n} a_{ij}x_ix_j = \sum_{j=1}^{n} a_{jj}x_j^2 + 2\sum_{j>i} a_{ij}x_ix_j.$$

Then

$$\frac{\partial f}{\partial x_j} = 2\sum_{i=1}^{n} a_{ij}x_i, \qquad j = 1, \ldots, n, \tag{2–28}$$

and

$$\nabla f = 2\mathbf{x}'\mathbf{A}. \tag{2–29}$$

Also

$$\frac{\partial^2 f}{\partial x_i\,\partial x_j} = 2a_{ij} \qquad \text{or} \qquad \mathbf{H}_f = 2\mathbf{A}. \tag{2–30}$$

In particular, when $n = 3$, then

$$f(\mathbf{x}) = a_{11}x_1^2 + a_{22}x_2^2 + a_{33}x_3^2 + 2a_{12}x_1x_2 + 2a_{13}x_1x_3 + 2a_{23}x_2x_3,$$

and

$$\frac{\partial f}{\partial x_1} = 2a_{11}x_1 + 2a_{12}x_2 + 2a_{13}x_3 = 2(a_{11}x_1 + a_{21}x_2 + a_{31}x_3),$$

since $a_{ij} = a_{ji}$. Also

$$\begin{aligned}\frac{\partial f}{\partial x_2} &= 2a_{12}x_1 + 2a_{22}x_2 + 2a_{23}x_3\\ &= 2(a_{12}x_1 + a_{22}x_2 + a_{32}x_3),\\ \frac{\partial f}{\partial x_3} &= 2a_{13}x_1 + 2a_{23}x_2 + 2a_{33}x_3\\ &= 2(a_{13}x_1 + a_{23}x_2 + a_{33}x_3).\end{aligned}$$

2. Suppose that $f = x_1^3 x_2^{-1/2} \ln x_3$. Then

$$\frac{\partial f}{\partial x_1} = 3x_1^2 x_2^{-1/2} \ln x_3; \qquad \frac{\partial f}{\partial x_2} = -\tfrac{1}{2} x_1^3 x_2^{-3/2} \ln x_3;$$

$$\frac{\partial f}{\partial x_3} = x_1^3 x_2^{-1/2} x_3^{-1};$$

$$\frac{\partial}{\partial x_2}\left[\frac{\partial f}{\partial x_1}\right] = -\tfrac{3}{2} x_1^2 x_2^{-3/2} \ln x_3; \qquad \frac{\partial}{\partial x_1}\left[\frac{\partial f}{\partial x_2}\right] = -\tfrac{3}{2} x_1^2 x_2^{-3/2} \ln x_3,$$

and

$$\frac{\partial^2 f}{\partial x_2\, \partial x_1} = \frac{\partial^2 f}{\partial x_1\, \partial x_2}.$$

2–10 Taylor's theorem. A frequently useful result in analysis is known as Taylor's theorem. This theorem states that if $f(\mathbf{x}) \in C^1$ over an open convex set X in E^n, then for any two points $\mathbf{x}_1$ and $\mathbf{x}_2 = \mathbf{x}_1 + \mathbf{y}$ in X, it follows that there exists a θ, $0 \leq \theta \leq 1$, such that

$$f(\mathbf{x}_2) = f(\mathbf{x}_1) + \nabla f[\theta\mathbf{x}_1 + (1 - \theta)\mathbf{x}_2]\mathbf{y}. \tag{2–31}$$

Furthermore, if $f(\mathbf{x}) \in C^2$ over X, then there exists a θ, $0 \leq \theta \leq 1$, such that

$$f(\mathbf{x}_2) = f(\mathbf{x}_1) + \nabla f(\mathbf{x}_1)\mathbf{y} + \tfrac{1}{2}\mathbf{y}'\mathbf{H}_f[\theta\mathbf{x}_1 + (1 - \theta)\mathbf{x}_2]\mathbf{y}. \tag{2–32}$$

In (2–31), $\nabla f[\theta\mathbf{x}_1 + (1 - \theta)\mathbf{x}_2]$ is the gradient vector of f evaluated at $\theta\mathbf{x}_1 + (1 - \theta)\mathbf{x}_2$, and in (2–32), $\mathbf{H}_f[\theta\mathbf{x}_1 + (1 - \theta)\mathbf{x}_2]$ is the Hessian matrix of f evaluated at $\theta\mathbf{x}_1 + (1 - \theta)\mathbf{x}_2$. Taylor's theorem can be extended to the case of $f \in C^k$, $k > 2$, but we shall not need these results. The proof of Taylor's theorem can be found in [1] or [2].

If $f(\mathbf{x}) \in C^1$, we can use Taylor's theorem to express the directional derivative of f, (2–27), in terms of the partial derivatives of f. By (2–31),

$$\frac{f(\mathbf{x}_0 + h\mathbf{r}) - f(\mathbf{x}_0)}{h} = \nabla f[\theta\mathbf{x}_0 + (1 - \theta)(\mathbf{x}_0 + h\mathbf{r})]\mathbf{r}.$$

Thus

$$D_{\mathbf{r}} f(\mathbf{x}_0) = \nabla f(\mathbf{x}_0)\mathbf{r} = \sum_{j=1}^{n} \frac{\partial f(\mathbf{x}_0)}{\partial x_j}\, r_j, \tag{2–33}$$

so that if the partial derivatives of f are continuous, the directional derivative is simply a linear combination of the partial derivatives.

Let $f \in C^1$ at $\mathbf{x}_0$. Write $z_0 = f(\mathbf{x}_0)$. Then the hyperplane

$$z - z_0 = \nabla f(\mathbf{x}_0)(\mathbf{x} - \mathbf{x}_0) \quad \text{or} \quad \nabla f(\mathbf{x}_0)\mathbf{x} - z = \nabla f(\mathbf{x}_0) - z_0 \tag{2–34}$$

is called the *tangent hyperplane* to the surface $z = f(\mathbf{x})$ at $\mathbf{x}_0$. Note that the vector $(\nabla f(\mathbf{x}_0), -1)$ is a normal to the hyperplane (2–34); this vector is also said to be normal to the surface $z = f(\mathbf{x})$ at $\mathbf{x}_0$, and is often referred to as a normal vector.

The hyperplane (2–34) is a hyperplane in E^{n+1} and is a tangent hyperplane to the n-dimensional surface $z = f(\mathbf{x})$ at $\mathbf{x}_0$ in E^{n+1}. Suppose now that we select a specific value of z, say z_1, and consider the $(n - 1)$-dimensional level surface in E^n described by the relation $z_1 = f(\mathbf{x})$. Let $\mathbf{x}_1$ be any point in E^n such that $z_1 = f(\mathbf{x}_1)$. Then the hyperplane

$$\nabla f(\mathbf{x}_1)(\mathbf{x} - \mathbf{x}_1) = 0 \quad \text{or} \quad \nabla f(\mathbf{x}_1)\mathbf{x} = \nabla f(\mathbf{x}_1)\mathbf{x}_1 \tag{2–35}$$

in E^n is called the tangent hyperplane to the $(n - 1)$-dimensional surface at $\mathbf{x}_1$. The vector $\nabla f(\mathbf{x}_1)$ is normal to the hyperplane and is also called a normal to the level surface at $\mathbf{x}_1$. Note that the original n-dimensional hypersurface can be thought of as a level surface for the $(n + 1)$-dimensional surface $\hat{z} = f(\mathbf{x}) - z$ having $\hat{z} = 0$. Thought of in these terms, the tangent hyperplane at the point $[\mathbf{x}_0, z_0]$ should be

$$(\nabla f(\mathbf{x}_0), -1)[\mathbf{x}, z] = (\nabla f(\mathbf{x}_0), -1)[\mathbf{x}_0, z_0], \tag{2–36}$$

which is precisely what we had above.

2–11 The implicit function theorem. Recall that if we have a set of m linear equations in n unknowns $\mathbf{A}\mathbf{x} = \mathbf{b}$ and $r(\mathbf{A}) = m$, then if we select any nonsingular submatrix $\mathbf{B}$ of order m from $\mathbf{A}$, we can solve uniquely for the m variables associated with the columns of $\mathbf{B}$ in terms of the remaining $n - m$ variables. For example, if the submatrix of order m formed from the first m columns of $\mathbf{A}$ is nonsingular, we can write

$$x_i = \beta_i + \sum_{j=m+1}^{n} \alpha_{ij}x_j, \qquad i = 1, \ldots, m; \tag{2–37}$$

also, for any arbitrary values which we may assign to x_j, $j = m + 1, \ldots, n$, if x_i, $i = 1, \ldots, m$, is computed from (2–37), the resulting $\mathbf{x}$ is a solution to $\mathbf{A}\mathbf{x} = \mathbf{b}$. Equation (2–37) expresses x_i as a function of the x_j, $j = m + 1, \ldots, n$.

Suppose now that instead of a set of linear equations, we have a set of m equations in n variables,

$$g_i(\mathbf{x}) = 0, \qquad i = 1, \ldots, m, \tag{2–38}$$

which may in general be nonlinear. We would like to know whether it is possible to select some m variables, say $x_1, \ldots, x_m$, and express these as functions of the remaining variables. In other words, we would like to know whether there exist functions

$$x_i = \phi_i(x_{m+1}, \ldots, x_n), \qquad i = 1, \ldots, m, \tag{2-39}$$

such that if we assign arbitrary values to $x_{m+1}, \ldots, x_n$ and compute the x_i, $i = 1, \ldots, m$ by means of (2-39), the resulting $\mathbf{x}$ will satisfy the equations (2-38). If the functions ϕ_i exist, we often say that we can solve for the x_i, $i = 1, \ldots, m$, in terms of $x_{m+1}, \ldots, x_n$. However, knowing that the functions ϕ_i exist does not tell us how to solve explicitly for the x_i, $i = 1, \ldots, m$. In general, this may be not only a very difficult task, but an impossible one to carry out in terms of elementary functions.

A theorem from analysis known as the implicit function theorem answers the question of when the functions ϕ_i exist. Before stating the theorem, we shall introduce some notation. For each function g_i of (2-38), we can determine n first partial derivatives $\partial g_i/\partial x_j$, $j = 1, \ldots, n$, if they exist. For the m functions g_i we obtain a total of mn first-order partial derivatives. These can be arranged into an $m \times n$ matrix $\mathbf{G} = \|\partial g_i/\partial x_j\|$. From this matrix we can form $n!/m!(n - m)!$ different submatrices of order m. A typical submatrix of this kind can be written

$$\mathbf{J}_{\mathbf{x}}(j_1, \ldots, j_m) = \begin{bmatrix} \dfrac{\partial g_1}{\partial x_{j_1}} \cdots \dfrac{\partial g_1}{\partial x_{j_m}} \\ \vdots \qquad \vdots \\ \dfrac{\partial g_m}{\partial x_{j_1}} \cdots \dfrac{\partial g_m}{\partial x_{j_m}} \end{bmatrix}. \tag{2-40}$$

Such a matrix is called the *Jacobian matrix* of the functions g_i with respect to the variables $x_{j_1}, \ldots, x_{j_m}$. The subscript $\mathbf{x}$ on $\mathbf{J}$ indicates the point in E^n at which the elements in the Jacobian matrix are to be evaluated. Let $k_1, \ldots, k_{n-m}$ be the set of indicies from $1, \ldots, n$ not appearing in the set $j_1, \ldots, j_m$. The implicit function theorem can then be stated as follows.

Let $\mathbf{x}_0 = [x_1^0, \ldots, x_n^0]$ be a point in E^n with the following properties:

(1) The functions $g_i(\mathbf{x}) \in C^1$, $i = 1, \ldots, m$, in some δ-neighborhood of $\mathbf{x}_0$.

(2) $g_i(\mathbf{x}_0) = 0$, $i = 1, \ldots, m$.

(3) $\mathbf{J}_{\mathbf{x}_0}(j_1, \ldots, j_m)$ is nonsingular.

If these conditions hold, then there exists an ϵ-neighborhood ($\epsilon > 0$) of

$\hat{\mathbf{x}}_0 = [x_{k_1}^0, \ldots, x_{k_{n-m}}^0]$ in E^{n-m} such that for every point

$$\hat{\mathbf{x}} = [x_{k_1}, \ldots, x_{k_{n-m}}]$$

in this ϵ-neighborhood there exists a set of functions

$$x_{j_i} = \phi_i(x_{k_1}, \ldots, x_{k_{n-m}}), \qquad i = 1, \ldots, m,$$

which are single-valued and continuous functions of $\hat{\mathbf{x}}$ and which have the properties:

(a) $x_{j_i}^0 = \phi_i(\hat{\mathbf{x}}_0), \qquad i = 1, \ldots, m.$

(b) For any $\hat{\mathbf{x}}$ in the ϵ-neighborhood of $\hat{\mathbf{x}}_0$, the values of x_{j_i}, $i = 1, \ldots, m$, computed from (2–41), along with $\hat{\mathbf{x}}$, yield an $\mathbf{x}$ which satisfies (2–38).

(c) In an ϵ-neighborhood of $\hat{\mathbf{x}}_0$, the functions $\phi_i(\hat{\mathbf{x}})$ are differentiable, and for a given k_r, $r = 1, \ldots, m - n$, the derivatives $\partial \phi_i / \partial x_{k_r}$, $i = 1, \ldots, m$, are the unique solutions to the set of linear equations

$$\sum_{u=1}^{m} \frac{\partial g_i}{\partial x_{j_u}} \frac{\partial \phi_u}{\partial x_{k_r}} = -\frac{\partial g_i}{\partial x_{k_r}}, \qquad i = 1, \ldots, m. \tag{2–41}$$

As stated, the implicit function theorem says something only about the existence of the ϕ_i "in the small," i.e., in an ϵ-neighborhood of $\hat{\mathbf{x}}_0$. The value of ϵ for which the ϕ_i exist may be very small. The task of determining the largest value of ϵ for which the ϕ_i exist can be a very difficult one.

The condition just stated, which guarantees that one can solve explicitly for m of the variables in (2–38), may be given an interesting interpretation. If we think of each equation $g_i(\mathbf{x}) = 0$ as representing an $(n - 1)$-dimensional surface in E^n, then if the hypotheses of the implicit function theorem are satisfied, this surface has a tangent plane at $\mathbf{x}_0$ which, by (2–35), is

$$\nabla g_i(\mathbf{x}_0)\mathbf{x} = \nabla g_i(\mathbf{x}_0)\mathbf{x}_0, \qquad i = 1, \ldots, m. \tag{2–42}$$

Now (2–42) represents a set of m tangent hyperplanes, one corresponding to each of the m surfaces. Let us now consider points $\mathbf{x}$ which lie on all m hyperplanes simultaneously and are therefore solutions to the set of m linear equations (2–42). The condition that we can solve explicitly for the variables $x_{i_1}, \ldots, x_{i_m}$ in terms of the remaining variables is precisely the condition that the Jacobian matrix (2–40) be nonsingular at $\mathbf{x}_0$. Thus we can solve (2–38) explicitly for m variables in a neighborhood of $\mathbf{x}_0$ if we can solve explicitly for the corresponding variables in the set of m linear equations in m unknowns representing the tangent hyperplanes to the surfaces $g_i(\mathbf{x}) = 0$ at $\mathbf{x}_0$.

Proofs of the implicit function theorem can be found in [1] and [2].

References

1. Apostol, T. M., *Mathematical Analysis*. Reading, Mass.: Addison-Wesley, 1957.

2. Courant, R., *Differential and Integral Calculus, Vol. II*. New York: Interscience, 1936.

3. Hadley, G., *Linear Algebra*. Reading, Mass.: Addison-Wesley, 1961.

4. Hadley, G., *Linear Programming*. Reading, Mass.: Addison-Wesley, 1962.

Problems

2–1. Compute **AB** and **BA** (when they are defined) in the following cases:

(a) $\mathbf{A} = \begin{bmatrix} -1 & 3 \\ 2 & 5 \end{bmatrix}; \quad \mathbf{B} = \begin{bmatrix} 4 & 0 \\ 7 & 6 \end{bmatrix}$

(b) $\mathbf{A} = [2, 1, 3]; \quad \mathbf{B} = (-2, 4, 5)$

(c) $\mathbf{A} = \begin{bmatrix} 3 & -5 \\ -6 & 2 \end{bmatrix}; \quad \mathbf{B} = \begin{bmatrix} 4 & 1 \\ 0 & 7 \\ 2 & 9 \end{bmatrix}$

(d) $\mathbf{A} = \begin{bmatrix} 3 & 0 & 0 \\ 0 & 2 & 0 \\ 0 & 0 & 1 \end{bmatrix}; \quad \mathbf{B} = \begin{bmatrix} -1 & 6 & 11 \\ 9 & 2 & 5 \\ 0 & 3 & 7 \end{bmatrix}$

2–2. Compute the transpose of each of the matrices given in Problem 2–1, and for part (a) of Problem 2–1 show that $(\mathbf{AB})' = \mathbf{B}'\mathbf{A}'$.

2–3. Let **AB** be defined and write **B** as a row of column vectors, that is, $\mathbf{B} = (\mathbf{b}_1, \ldots, \mathbf{b}_n)$. Show that

$$\mathbf{AB} = (\mathbf{Ab}_1, \mathbf{Ab}_2, \ldots, \mathbf{Ab}_n).$$

2–4. Consider the nonsingular matrix

$$\mathbf{M} = \begin{bmatrix} \mathbf{A} & \mathbf{B} \\ \mathbf{C} & \mathbf{D} \end{bmatrix},$$

where **A** is $k \times k$ and **D** is $r \times r$. Assume that $\mathbf{A}^{-1}$ exists, and determine the inverse of **M** in terms of **A**, **B**, **C**, and **D**. [*Hint:* Partition the inverse in the same way as **M**.]

2–5. Show that $n - 1$ linearly independent vectors in E^n uniquely determine a hyperplane through the origin. Thus show that any hyperplane through the origin is a subspace of dimension $n - 1$.

2–6. Find all existing basic solutions to the following set of equations:

$$\begin{aligned} 3x_1 + 2x_2 - 9x_3 + x_4 &= 16, \\ 7x_1 - 3x_2 + 5x_3 - 9x_4 &= 8. \end{aligned}$$

2–7. Solve the following linear programming problems graphically and by the simplex method:

$$3x_1 + 2x_2 \leq 6,$$
$$x_1 + 4x_2 \leq 4,$$
$$x_1, x_2 \geq 0,$$
$$\max z = x_1 + x_2.$$

Show the extreme point of the convex set of solutions which corresponds to each iteration of the simplex method.

2–8. Solve Problem 2–7 by the revised simplex method.

2–9. Solve the dual of Problem 2–7 by the simplex method and thus obtain the optimal solution to Problem 2–7.

2–10. Solve the dual of Problem 2–7 by the revised simplex method and thus obtain the optimal solution to Problem 2–7.

2–11. Show that the set $X = \{\mathbf{x} \mid |\mathbf{x} - \mathbf{a}| = \epsilon\}$ is closed.

2–12. Give a graphical interpretation of a supporting hyperplane.

2–13. Find the characteristic values and a set of orthonormal characteristic vectors for the matrix

$$\mathbf{A} = \begin{bmatrix} 3 & 2 \\ 2 & 1 \end{bmatrix}.$$

2–14. Sketch the following quadratic forms in E^3 and also the level surfaces in E^2:

(a) $z = 3x_1 + 4x_2^2$ (b) $z = x_1x_2$

(c) $z = 4x_1^2 - x_2^2$ (d) $z = x_1^2 + 3x_1x_2 + 4x_2^2$

2–15. Determine a transformation of variables which diagonalizes the following quadratic form and illustrate it geometrically:

$$z = 2x_1^2 - 3x_1x_2 + x_2^2$$

2–16. Compute both first partial derivatives of the following functions:

(a) $z = 3x_1x_2^2 + 4e^{x_1x_2}$ (b) $z = x_1^{x_2} + \ln x_1x_2$

2–17. Determine the Hessian matrix for each of the functions given in Problem 2–16.

2–18. Determine the equation for the plane tangent to the surface

$$z = 4x_1^2 - 5x_1x_2 + 6x_2^2 + 8x_1 + 2x_2.$$

2–19. In the definition of a directional derivative, show that if $|\mathbf{r}| \neq 1$, then the proper definition is

$$D_{\mathbf{r}}f(\mathbf{x}_0) = \lim_{h \to 0} \frac{f(\mathbf{x}_0 + h\mathbf{r}) - f(\mathbf{x}_0)}{h|\mathbf{r}|}.$$

2–20. Consider the equation $g(x_1, x_2) = 0$. Assume that $\mathbf{x}_0 = [x_1^0, x_2^0]$ satisfies this equation. What conditions must be satisfied if it is possible, in a neighborhood of $\mathbf{x}_0$, to solve explicitly for one variable in terms of the other. Illustrate this geometrically. [*Hint:* The curve $g(x_1, x_2) = 0$, if it exists, is the intersection of the surface $z = g(x_1, x_2)$ with the x_1x_2-plane.]

2–21. Is it possible to solve $x_1^2 + x_2^2 = 0$ explicitly for x_1 or x_2 in a neighborhood of the origin? Illustrate geometrically. Are the conditions of the implicit function theorem satisfied at the origin?

2–22. Is it possible to solve $x_1x_2 = 0$ explicitly for x_1 or x_2 in a neighborhood of the origin? Illustrate geometrically. Are the conditions of the implicit function theorem satisfied at the origin?

2–23. Is it possible to solve $(x_1 - x_2)^2 = 0$ explicitly for x_1 or x_2 in a neighborhood of the origin? Illustrate geometrically. Are the conditions of the implicit function theorem satisfied in a neighborhood of the origin?

CHAPTER 3

CLASSICAL OPTIMIZATION METHODS AND PROPERTIES OF CONVEX FUNCTIONS

Something hidden—go and find it;
Go and look behind the Ranges.
Something lost behind the Ranges;
Lost and waiting for you. Go!

Rudyard Kipling

3–1 Introduction. In this chapter we shall study the classical techniques for applying the calculus to the solution of certain types of optimization problems. These techniques were originally formulated to solve problems referred to in Chapter 1 as classical optimization problems. As noted there, the classical results are of use mainly in theoretical analyses, and are not, in general, well suited for numerical computations. In certain, especially simple, situations, however, it is possible to use the classical theory to solve analytically for an optimal solution in terms of the various parameters appearing in the problem. In such cases the classical approach provides a very convenient way of solving the problem.

3–2 Maxima and minima in the absence of constraints. In studying the classical theory of maxima and minima we must recognize clearly the difference between absolute maxima and minima and relative maxima and minima.

Absolute Maximum: *The function $f(\mathbf{x})$ defined over a closed set X in E^n is said to take on its absolute maximum over X at the point $\mathbf{x}^*$ if $f(\mathbf{x}) \leq f(\mathbf{x}^*)$ for every point $\mathbf{x} \in X$.*

The absolute maximum of $f(\mathbf{x})$ is also often referred to as the global maximum. If the closed set X is strictly bounded, then the absolute maximum of $f(\mathbf{x})$ over X will actually be taken on at one or more points in X, if one assumes that $f(\mathbf{x})$ is continuous over the set X. This result is known as the theorem of Weierstrass. If X is not strictly bounded, then the absolute maximum may not be taken on at any point $\mathbf{x}$ with $|\mathbf{x}|$ finite, but may instead be the limiting value of $f(\mathbf{x})$ as $|\mathbf{x}| \to \infty$ in some specific way.

Strong Relative Maximum: *Let $f(\mathbf{x})$ be defined at all points in some δ-neighborhood of $\mathbf{x}_0$ in E^n. The function $f(\mathbf{x})$ is said to have a strong relative maximum at $\mathbf{x}_0$ if there exists an ϵ, $0 < \epsilon < \delta$, such that for all $\mathbf{x}$, $0 < |\mathbf{x} - \mathbf{x}_0| < \epsilon$, $f(\mathbf{x}) < f(\mathbf{x}_0)$.*

Intuitively, a function has a strong relative maximum at $\mathbf{x}_0$ if there exists an ϵ-neighborhood of $\mathbf{x}_0$ (perhaps with ϵ being very small) such that for all $\mathbf{x}$ in this ϵ-neighborhood different from $\mathbf{x}_0$, $f(\mathbf{x})$ is strictly less than $f(\mathbf{x}_0)$.

WEAK RELATIVE MAXIMUM: *Let $f(\mathbf{x})$ be defined at all points in some δ-neighborhood of $\mathbf{x}_0$ in E^n. The function $f(\mathbf{x})$ is said to have a weak relative maximum at $\mathbf{x}_0$ if it does not have a strong relative maximum at $\mathbf{x}_0$, but there exists an ϵ, $0 < \epsilon < \delta$, such that $f(\mathbf{x}) \leq f(\mathbf{x}_0)$ for all $\mathbf{x}$ in the ϵ-neighborhood of $\mathbf{x}_0$.*

Weak relative maxima are sometimes referred to as improper relative maxima. Frequently we shall not need to distinguish between strong and weak relative maxima. In such situations we shall simply refer to a relative maximum (which may be either strong or weak). Relative maxima are often referred to as local maxima.

The definitions of absolute minimum, strong relative minimum, and weak relative minimum are obtained from the corresponding definitions of maxima, by reversing the directions of the inequality signs in $f(\mathbf{x}) \leq f(\mathbf{x}^*)$, or $f(\mathbf{x}) < f(\mathbf{x}_0)$, or $f(\mathbf{x}) \leq f(\mathbf{x}_0)$. Note that if $f(\mathbf{x})$ has an absolute maximum at $\mathbf{x}^*$ or a strong (or weak) relative maximum at $\mathbf{x}_0$, then $-f(\mathbf{x})$ has an absolute minimum at $\mathbf{x}^*$ or a strong (or weak) relative minimum at $\mathbf{x}_0$.

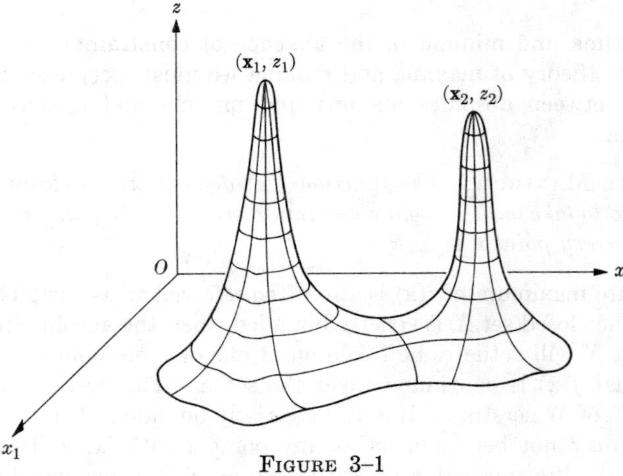

FIGURE 3–1

In Fig. 3–1, $f(\mathbf{x}) = f(x_1, x_2)$ has strong relative maxima at the points $\mathbf{x}_1$, $\mathbf{x}_2$. In Fig. 3–2, any point on the lines representing the crests of the waves yields a weak relative maximum, and any point on a line representing a trough yields a weak relative minimum.

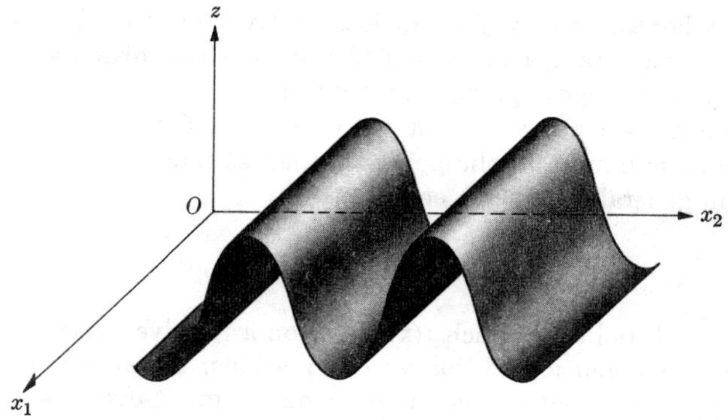

FIGURE 3–2

The classical approach to the theory of maxima and minima does not provide a direct way of obtaining the absolute maximum or minimum of a function. Instead, it only provides a means for determining the relative maxima and minima. To do this it is necessary to make use of the partial derivatives of f. Thus we shall assume that $f \in C^1$ over all of E^n or over any part of E^n which is of interest to us.

If $f(\mathbf{x})$ has a relative maximum at $\mathbf{x}_0$, then there exists an $\epsilon > 0$ such that $f(\mathbf{x}) \leq f(\mathbf{x}_0)$ for all $\mathbf{x}$ in the ϵ-neighborhood of $\mathbf{x}_0$. Consider points in this ϵ-neighborhood of $\mathbf{x}_0$ of the form $\mathbf{x} = \mathbf{x}_0 + h\mathbf{e}_j$, $0 < |h| < \epsilon$. Then

$$f(\mathbf{x}_0 + h\mathbf{e}_j) - f(\mathbf{x}_0) \leq 0, \qquad j = 1, \ldots, n,$$

for all h, $0 < |h| < \epsilon$, or

$$\frac{f(\mathbf{x}_0 + h\mathbf{e}_j) - f(\mathbf{x}_0)}{h} \leq 0, \quad h > 0; \quad \frac{f(\mathbf{x}_0 + h\mathbf{e}_j) - f(\mathbf{x}_0)}{h} \geq 0, \quad h < 0. \tag{3–1}$$

On taking the limits as $h \to 0$, we conclude from the inequality for $h > 0$ that $\partial f(\mathbf{x}_0)/\partial x_j \leq 0$, and from the one for $h < 0$ that $\partial f(\mathbf{x}_0)/\partial x_j \geq 0$. Thus

$$\frac{\partial f(\mathbf{x}_0)}{\partial x_j} = 0, \qquad j = 1, \ldots, n. \tag{3–2}$$

Note that even if $f(\mathbf{x})$ has a strong relative maximum at $\mathbf{x}_0$ so that the strict inequalities apply in (3–1), we must, in the limit as $h \to 0$, allow for the possibility of equality, so that (3–2) will hold if $f(\mathbf{x})$ takes on either a strong or weak relative maximum at $\mathbf{x}_0$. Similar arguments show that (3–2) holds if $f(\mathbf{x})$ takes on a relative minimum at $\mathbf{x}_0$. Equation (3–2) says that at a point $\mathbf{x}_0$ where $f(\mathbf{x})$ takes on a relative maximum or minimum, all n partial derivatives of f must vanish. This is equivalent to saying that

(a) the gradient vector of f at $\mathbf{x}_0$ is a null vector, that is, $\nabla f(\mathbf{x}_0) = \mathbf{0}$, (b) that the plane tangent to $z = f(\mathbf{x})$ at $\mathbf{x}_0$ has the form $z = z_0 = f(\mathbf{x}_0)$ (intuitively, the tangent plane is horizontal).

We have proved above that if $f \in C^1$, and if $f(\mathbf{x})$ takes on a relative maximum or minimum at the point $\mathbf{x}_0$, then $\mathbf{x}_0$ must be a solution to the set of n (in general nonlinear) equations

$$\frac{\partial f(\mathbf{x})}{\partial x_j} = 0, \qquad j = 1, \ldots, n. \tag{3-3}$$

Note that each point at which $f(\mathbf{x})$ takes on a relative maximum or minimum must be a solution to this set of equations. However, $f(\mathbf{x})$ does not necessarily have a relative maximum or minimum at every point which is a solution to (3–3). The reader will recall that for a function of a single variable, a solution to $df/dx = 0$ may yield a point of inflection where f has neither a relative maximum or a minimum. Similarly, $\partial f/\partial x_1 = \partial f/\partial x_2 = 0$ at a saddle point of a function of two variables; however, f has neither a relative maximum nor minimum at a saddle point. The solutions to (3–3) are called the stationary points of f. The points at which f takes on its relative maxima and minima are stationary points of f, but it is not necessarily true that f takes on a relative maximum or minimum at every stationary point.

If we know that $f(\mathbf{x})$ takes on its absolute maximum (minimum) at a point $\mathbf{x}^*$ such that $|\mathbf{x}^*|$ is finite, then the absolute maximum (minimum) of f over all of E^n must be taken on at a relative maximum (minimum). This follows since if $f(\mathbf{x})$ takes on its absolute maximum at $\mathbf{x}^*$, then $f(\mathbf{x}) \leq f(\mathbf{x}^*)$ for all $\mathbf{x}$, and hence for any $\epsilon > 0$, $f(\mathbf{x}) \leq f(\mathbf{x}^*)$ for all $\mathbf{x}$ in an ϵ-neighborhood of $\mathbf{x}^*$. This implies that $f(\mathbf{x})$ has a relative maximum at $\mathbf{x}^*$. Consequently, in such a case, the point (or points) $\mathbf{x}^*$ at which $f(\mathbf{x})$ takes on its absolute maximum must be solutions to (3–3). If we knew all the solutions to (3–3), it would only be necessary to compute $f(\mathbf{x})$ for each solution and pick the largest of these values to obtain the absolute maximum of $f(\mathbf{x})$ over E^n. We would thus determine the point (or points) where f takes on its absolute maximum, and would also determine the absolute maximum of $f(\mathbf{x})$.

Unfortunately, it can be very difficult to determine numerically any solution to a set of equations such as (3–3), especially if there are many variables. If the solution is not unique, the task of finding all solutions is, of course, even more difficult. No general numerical procedures exist for generating all solutions to a set of equations such as (3–3). In fact, even if it is known that there is a unique solution, it may be exceptionally difficult to obtain it. An iterative procedure which can sometimes be used to find a numerical solution to (3–3) is called Newton's method. To use Newton's method we must assume that $f \in C^2$. Suppose that we have an initial estimate $\mathbf{x}_1$ of a solution to (3-3). If $\hat{\mathbf{x}}$ is actually a solution, then we know by Taylor's theorem that

$$\frac{\partial f(\hat{\mathbf{x}})}{\partial x_j} = 0 = \frac{\partial f(\mathbf{x}_1)}{\partial x_j} + \nabla \frac{\partial}{\partial x_j} f[\theta\hat{\mathbf{x}} + (1 - \theta)\mathbf{x}_1](\hat{\mathbf{x}} - \mathbf{x}_1), \qquad j = 1, \ldots, n.$$

Consider instead the set of equations

$$0 = \frac{\partial f(\mathbf{x}_1)}{\partial x_j} + \nabla \frac{\partial f(\mathbf{x}_1)}{\partial x_j} (\mathbf{x} - \mathbf{x}_1), \qquad j = 1, \ldots, n,$$

or

$$(\mathbf{x} - \mathbf{x}_1)'\mathbf{H}_f(\mathbf{x}_1) = -\nabla f(\mathbf{x}_1). \tag{3-4}$$

This is a set of n simultaneous linear equations in n unknowns x_j, which has a unique solution if $\mathbf{H}_f(\mathbf{x}_1)$ is nonsingular. Imagine that we find the solution $\mathbf{x}$, call it $\mathbf{x}_2$, and then use $\mathbf{x}_2$ as our estimate of $\hat{\mathbf{x}}$ and repeat the process. At stage n, $\mathbf{x}_{n+1} = \mathbf{x}_n + \mathbf{y}_n$ where $\mathbf{y}_n$ is a solution to $\mathbf{y}_n'\mathbf{H}_f(\mathbf{x}_n) = -\nabla f(\mathbf{x}_n)$. Unfortunately, one cannot guarantee in general that this iterative scheme will converge to a solution to (3-3), even if it is known that there is only one solution.

Suppose now that instead of trying to find the absolute maximum of $f(\mathbf{x})$ over all of E^n, we are interested in finding the absolute maximum of $f(\mathbf{x})$ over the non-negative orthant. In this case, even if it is true that the absolute maximum of $f(\mathbf{x})$ is taken on at a point $\mathbf{x}^*$ such that $|\mathbf{x}^*|$ is finite, it is not necessarily true that f will take on its absolute maximum at one of the solutions to (3-3). The reason is that the absolute maximum may occur on the boundaries of the non-negative orthant where one or more $x_j = 0$. To find the absolute maximum we must now proceed as follows: First find all the solutions to (3-3) lying in the non-negative orthant. Next consider the n functions f_j of $n - 1$ variables, f_j being obtained from $f(\mathbf{x})$ by setting $x_j = 0$. For each f_j find the solutions to $\partial f_j/\partial x_i = 0$, $i \neq j$, lying in the non-negative orthant of E^{n-1}. When interpreted as n-component vectors with $x_j = 0$ these solutions lie on the boundary of the non-negative orthant in E^n. After this, consider the $n(n-1)/2$ functions f_{ij} of $n - 2$ variables, f_{ij} being obtained from f by setting $x_i = x_j = 0$. For each f_{ij} find the solution to $\partial f_{ij}/\partial x_k = 0$, $k \neq i$ or j, lying in the non-negative orthant of E^{n-2}. This procedure is continued by considering all functions with three of the variables set to zero, four of the variables set to zero, etc., until all the variables are zero. Evaluate $f(\mathbf{x})$ at each of the points obtained above. If the absolute maximum of $f(\mathbf{x})$ is taken on at an $\mathbf{x}$ with a finite magnitude, then the absolute maximum of $f(\mathbf{x})$ will be the largest of the values thus computed. It should be clear from this discussion that when the closed set over which the absolute maximum of $f(\mathbf{x})$ is being determined is not all of E^n so that it is necessary to consider the possibility that the maximum may occur on the boundaries of the set, the task of determining the absolute maximum of $f(\mathbf{x})$ is, in general, greatly complicated.

Sufficient conditions have been devised which, if satisfied, will guarantee that a given solution to (3–3) is either a strong relative maximum or minimum. The reader will be asked to develop these conditions in the problems. They are mainly of theoretical interest. When $f(\mathbf{x})$ involves many variables, a tremendous number of numerical computations are required to test whether or not a solution to (3–3) yields a relative maximum or minimum of $f(\mathbf{x})$. These conditions have the additional disadvantage that they provide no information at all about whether a given solution to (3–3) yields the absolute maximum or minimum of $f(\mathbf{x})$.

3–3 An example. We shall now present a type of problem to which the classical techniques discussed in the previous section are applicable. This example illustrates a feature common to many such problems, namely that the actual cost or profit for any given values of the variables will not be deterministic, but will instead depend on the value(s) taken on by one or more stochastic parameters associated with the system. The procedure typically used in this case is to maximize the expected profit or minimize the expected cost over the relevant time interval. In situations in which the same conditions will be repeated over and over and the expected profit or cost can be interpreted as the long-run average profit or cost, it seems quite logical to maximize the expected profit or minimize the expected cost. However, this same criterion will be used even when the given set of circumstances will be encountered only once and will never be repeated again, so that it is not possible to interpret the expected value as a long-run average. In this instance, it is more difficult to justify the use of expected values. However, justification is provided by the modern theory of utility introduced by von Neumann and Morgenstern [7]. We shall not attempt to discuss this subject, but merely point out that if the decision maker behaves in such a way that a certain set of axioms is satisfied, then there exists a numerical utility function having the property that if he selects the action which maximizes his expected utility, then this will be the optimal action for him to take. This will be equivalent to maximizing expected profits or minimizing expected costs if the utility can be measured in monetary units.

Let us now turn to the example. Consider a machined part which is produced on a particular lathe in a machine shop. The diameters of the parts turned out will not always be precisely the same, but will vary somewhat from one piece to another due to a variety of causes. The diameter x of any particular piece can be considered to be a random variable. The mean μ of this random variable can be varied by appropriately modifying the lathe setting. It will be assumed, however, that the standard deviation σ is a constant independent of the lathe setting, i.e., of the mean μ. The density function for x will be written $f(x; \mu)$ so that the probability that x lies between x and $x + dx$ is $f(x; \mu)\, dx$. In order to pass inspection, the diameter x must lie in the interval $x_1 \le x \le x_2$. If $x < x_1$, the piece must be scrapped. If $x > x_2$, the piece can be reworked. The shop under consideration does not rework pieces. Instead, it sells pieces with $x > x_2$ to another shop at a price of p_1 each for rework. Each piece which passes inspection is sold at a price of $p > p_1$. The cost of raw materials, labor, and machine time for each piece which enters production is k. It is desired to determine the value of μ which maximizes the expected weekly profit.

If W pieces are machined per week, the expected number which must be scrapped is

$$W \int_0^{x_1} f(x; \mu)\, dx,$$

where the integral is simply the probability that the diameter of any piece will be less than x_1. Similarly, the expected number which will be sold for rework is

$$W \int_{x_2}^{x_m} f(x; \mu)\, dx,$$

where x_m is the maximum diameter which any piece can have. Thus the expected weekly profit P is

$$\begin{aligned} P(\mu) &= pW\left[1 - \int_0^{x_1} f(x; \mu)\, dx - \int_{x_2}^{x_m} f(x; \mu)\, dx\right] \\ &\qquad\qquad + p_1 W \int_{x_2}^{x_m} f(x; \mu)\, dx - Wk \\ &= (p - k)W - W\left[p \int_0^{x_1} f(x; \mu)\, dx + (p - p_1) \int_{x_2}^{x_m} f(x; \mu)\, dx\right]. \end{aligned} \tag{3–5}$$

It is clear that the absolute maximum of $P(\mu)$ will not occur at the boundaries where $\mu = 0$ or x_m. Thus the value of μ when P takes on its maximum must be a solution to

$$\frac{dP}{d\mu} = 0 = -W\left[p \int_0^{x_1} \frac{\partial}{\partial \mu} f(x; \mu)\, dx + (p - p_1) \int_{x_2}^{x_m} \frac{\partial}{\partial \mu} f(x; \mu)\, dx\right]. \tag{3–6}$$

Let us now restrict our attention to the case where x is normally distributed. Then

$$f(x;\mu) = \frac{1}{\sigma\sqrt{2\pi}}\,e^{-(x-\mu)^2/2\sigma^2}; \qquad \frac{\partial f}{\partial \mu} = \frac{1}{\sigma^2\sqrt{2\pi}}\left(\frac{x-\mu}{\sigma}\right)e^{-(x-\mu)^2/2\sigma^2}. \tag{3-7}$$

If we write

$$v = \frac{1}{2}\left(\frac{x-\mu}{\sigma}\right)^2, \qquad v_1 = \frac{1}{2}\left(\frac{x_1-\mu}{\sigma}\right)^2, \qquad v_2 = \frac{1}{2}\left(\frac{x_2-\mu}{\sigma}\right)^2,$$

and if we assume that the areas under the normal curve to the left of $x = 0$ and to the right of $x = x_m$ are negligible so that the lower limit of the first integral in (3–6) may be replaced by $-\infty$ and the upper limit x on the second integral in (3–6) may be replaced by ∞, we have

$$\int_0^{x_1} \frac{\partial}{\partial \mu} f(x;\mu)\,dx = \frac{1}{\sigma\sqrt{2\pi}}\int_\infty^{v_1} e^{-v}\,dv = -\frac{1}{\sigma\sqrt{2\pi}}\,e^{-(x_1-\mu)^2/2\sigma^2},$$

$$\int_{x_2}^{x_m} \frac{\partial}{\partial \mu} f(x;\mu)\,dx = \frac{1}{\sigma\sqrt{2\pi}}\int_{v_2}^{\infty} e^{-v}\,dv = \frac{1}{\sigma\sqrt{2\pi}}\,e^{-(x_2-\mu)^2/2\sigma^2}.$$

Thus the condition (3–6) becomes

$$pe^{-(x_1-\mu)^2/2\sigma^2} = (p - p_1)e^{-(x_2-\mu)^2/2\sigma^2}$$

or

$$2\sigma^2 \ln\left(\frac{p}{p-p_1}\right) = (x_1-\mu)^2 - (x_2-\mu)^2.$$

Hence the unique solution is

$$\mu = \frac{x_1+x_2}{2} + \frac{\sigma^2}{x_2-x_1}\ln\left(\frac{p}{p-p_1}\right). \tag{3-8}$$

Since the solution is unique, this value of μ must yield the absolute maximum of the expected weekly profit.

3–4 Constrained maxima and minima; Lagrange multipliers. We shall now consider the classical approach to solving problems of the form referred to as classical optimization problems. We are seeking the point or points $\mathbf{x}^*$ which yield the absolute maximum or minimum of $z = f(\mathbf{x})$ over E^n for those $\mathbf{x}$ which satisfy $g_i(\mathbf{x}) = b_i$, $i = 1, \ldots, m$, $m < n$. We shall assume that $f \in C^1$ and $g_i \in C^1$, $i = 1, \ldots, m$, everywhere. Denote by Y the set of points $\mathbf{x}$ satisfying $g_i(\mathbf{x}) = b_i$, $i = 1, \ldots, m$. As in Section 3–2 it is convenient to begin by defining absolute and relative maxima.

Absolute Maximum: *The function* $f(\mathbf{x})$ *is said to take on its absolute maximum over the closed set* X *in* E^n *for those* $\mathbf{x}$ *satisfying* $g_i(\mathbf{x}) = b_i$, $i = 1, \ldots, m$, *at the point* $\mathbf{x}^* \in X \cap Y$ *if for all* $\mathbf{x} \in X \cap Y$, $f(\mathbf{x}) \leq f(\mathbf{x}^*)$.

Strong Relative Maximum: *The function* $f(\mathbf{x})$ *is said to take on a strong relative maximum at the point* $\mathbf{x}_0$ *for those* $\mathbf{x}$ *satisfying* $g_i(\mathbf{x}) = b_i$, $i = 1, \ldots, m$, *if* $\mathbf{x}_0 \in Y$ *and there exists an* $\epsilon > 0$ *such that for every* $\mathbf{x} \neq \mathbf{x}_0$ *in an* ϵ*-neighborhood of* $\mathbf{x}_0$ *for which* $\mathbf{x} \in Y$, $f(\mathbf{x}) < f(\mathbf{x}_0)$.

Weak Relative Maximum: *The function* $f(\mathbf{x})$ *is said to take on a weak relative maximum at the point* $\mathbf{x}_0$ *for those* $\mathbf{x}$ *satisfying* $g_i(\mathbf{x}) = b_i$, $i = 1, \ldots, m$, *if it does not have a strong relative maximum at* $\mathbf{x}_0$, *but* $\mathbf{x}_0 \in Y$ *and there exists an* $\epsilon > 0$ *such that for every point* $\mathbf{x} \in Y$ *in an* ϵ*-neighborhood of* $\mathbf{x}_0$, $f(\mathbf{x}) \leq f(\mathbf{x}_0)$.

When it is unnecessary to distinguish between strong and weak relative maxima we shall simply refer to relative maxima. The modifications necessary to define absolute minima and strong and weak relative minima are obvious. We shall sometimes refer to the maxima and minima just defined as constrained maxima and minima, whereas those defined in Section 3–2 will be called unconstrained maxima and minima.

The classical approach to solving problems of the form (1–12) provides a set of equations (necessary conditions) which must be satisfied by a point $\mathbf{x}_0$ at which $f(\mathbf{x})$ takes on a relative maximum or minimum for those points $\mathbf{x}$ satisfying $g_i(\mathbf{x}) = b_i$, $i = 1, \ldots, m$. The classical approach does not provide a means for obtaining directly the point or points where f takes on its absolute maximum (or minimum) for $\mathbf{x} \in Y$. However, if we know that the absolute maximum (or minimum) is taken on at a point $\mathbf{x}^*$ for which $|\mathbf{x}^*|$ is finite, then $\mathbf{x}^*$ must also yield a relative maximum (minimum). Hence, when $f \in C^1$ and $g_i \in C^1$, $i = 1, \ldots, m$, $\mathbf{x}^*$ must be a solution to the equations referred to above. In such cases, if all solutions to this set of equations can be found, it is only necessary to evaluate f at each of these points to determine the absolute maximum (minimum) and the point or points at which it is taken on.

We shall now derive the most useful, but not the most general, form of the necessary conditions referred to in the above paragraph. It will be instructive to begin by studying the case in which there are only two variables and a single constraint. In other words, we wish to find the necessary conditions which $\mathbf{x}_0 = [x_1^0, x_2^0]$ must satisfy if $z = f(x_1, x_2)$ takes on a relative maximum or minimum at $\mathbf{x}_0$ subject to $g(x_1, x_2) = b$. Recall that we are assuming that $f, g \in C^1$. Suppose now that either $\partial g/\partial x_1$ or $\partial g/\partial x_2$ does not vanish at $\mathbf{x}_0$. To be specific, suppose that $\partial g(\mathbf{x}_0)/\partial x_2 \neq 0$. Then by the implicit function theorem, there exists an ϵ-neighborhood of x_1^0 such that we can solve $g(x_1, x_2) - b = 0$ explicitly for x_2 to obtain

$x_2 = \phi(x_1)$. Any point $[x_1, \phi(x_1)]$ is then in Y. Thus we can eliminate x_2 in $f(x_1, x_2)$ to obtain

$$z = h(x_1) = f[x_1, \phi(x_1)] \tag{3-9}$$

for $|x_1 - x_1^0| < \epsilon$. However, if f takes on a relative maximum at $\mathbf{x}_0$ for $\mathbf{x}$ satisfying $g(\mathbf{x}) = b$, it must be true that there exists an ϵ_0, $0 < \epsilon_0 < \epsilon$, such that for all x_1 in this ϵ_0-neighborhood $h(x_1) \leq h(x_1^0)$. Hence the function $h(x_1)$ has an unconstrained relative maximum at x_1^0. Similarly, if f takes on a relative minimum at $\mathbf{x}_0$ for $\mathbf{x}$ satisfying $g(\mathbf{x}) = b$, $h(x_1)$ has an unconstrained relative minimum at x_1^0. By the implicit function theorem, $\phi(x_1)$ is differentiable in the ϵ-neighborhood of x_1^0, and so by the theorem on compound functions, $h(x_1)$ must be differentiable in the neighborhood of x_1^0. It then follows that, since $h(x_1)$ has an unconstrained relative maximum or minimum at $\mathbf{x}_0$, $dh(x_1^0)/dx_1 = 0$. Now by the rule for differentiating compound functions, we have

$$\frac{dh}{dx_1} = \frac{\partial f}{\partial x_1} + \frac{\partial f}{\partial x_2}\frac{d\phi}{dx_1} = \frac{\partial f}{\partial x_1} - \frac{\partial f}{\partial x_2}\frac{\partial g/\partial x_1}{\partial g/\partial x_2},$$

since by the implicit function theorem

$$\frac{d\phi}{dx_1} = -\frac{\partial g/\partial x_1}{\partial g/\partial x_2}.$$

Hence it must be true that

$$\frac{\partial f(\mathbf{x}_0)}{\partial x_1} - \frac{\partial f(\mathbf{x}_0)}{\partial x_2}\frac{\partial g(\mathbf{x}_0)/\partial x_1}{\partial g(\mathbf{x}_0)/\partial x_2} = 0.$$

Let

$$\lambda = \frac{\partial f(\mathbf{x}_0)/\partial x_2}{\partial g(\mathbf{x}_0)/\partial x_2}. \tag{3-10}$$

Consequently, it is necessary that the point $\mathbf{x}_0$ satisfy the equations

$$\frac{\partial f(\mathbf{x}_0)}{\partial x_1} - \lambda\frac{\partial g(\mathbf{x}_0)}{\partial x_1} = 0; \quad \frac{\partial f(\mathbf{x}_0)}{\partial x_2} - \lambda\frac{\partial g(\mathbf{x}_0)}{\partial x_2} = 0; \quad g(\mathbf{x}_0) = b. \tag{3-11}$$

Here we have three equations which $\mathbf{x}_0$ must satisfy if $f(\mathbf{x})$ takes on a relative maximum or minimum for $\mathbf{x}$ satisfying $g(\mathbf{x}) = b$, provided that both partial derivatives of g do not vanish at $\mathbf{x}_0$. Equation (3-11) represents a set of three equations in three variables x_1^0, x_2^0, and λ. It is not necessarily true that f will take on a relative maximum or minimum for $\mathbf{x}$ satisfying $g(\mathbf{x}) = b$ at every solution to (3-11). However, if we assume that both derivatives of g do not vanish at any point where f takes on a relative maximum or minimum for $\mathbf{x} \in Y$, then every point at which

$f(\mathbf{x})$ does take on a relative maximum or minimum for $\mathbf{x}$ satisifying $g(\mathbf{x}) = b$ will be a solution to these equations, so that by finding all solutions to (3–11) we determine all points at which $f(\mathbf{x})$ takes on a relative maximum or minimum for $\mathbf{x}$ satisfying $g(\mathbf{x}) = b$.

The necessary conditions (3–11) can be conveniently obtained as follows. Form the function

$$F(\mathbf{x}, \lambda) = f(\mathbf{x}) + \lambda[b - g(\mathbf{x})] \tag{3–12}$$

and set to zero the partial derivatives of $F(\mathbf{x}, \lambda)$ with respect to x_1, x_2, and λ. In taking the partial derivatives, all variables are treated as being independent. Thus

$$\frac{\partial F}{\partial x_j} = \frac{\partial f}{\partial x_j} - \lambda \frac{\partial g}{\partial x_j} = 0, \quad j = 1, 2; \qquad \frac{\partial F}{\partial \lambda} = b - g(\mathbf{x}) = 0. \tag{3–13}$$

The function $F(\mathbf{x}, \lambda)$ is called the Lagrangian function, and λ is called a Lagrange multiplier.

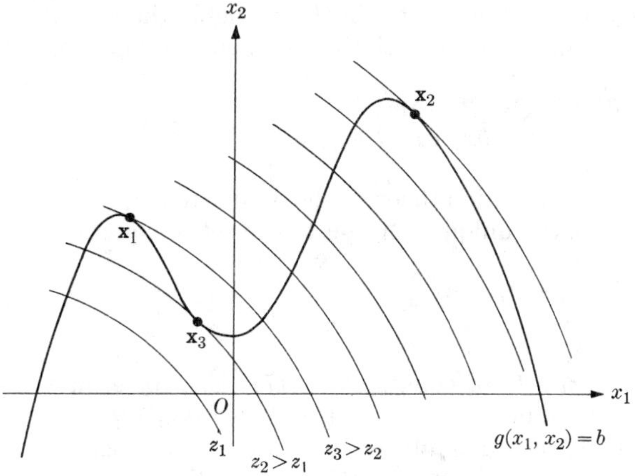

FIGURE 3–3

We can easily interpret geometrically a problem involving two variables and one constraint. All we need to do is plot $g(x_1, x_2) = b$ and the level curves for $z = f(x_1, x_2)$ in the x_1x_2-plane. Suppose that we wish to maximize $f(x_1, x_2)$. The geometric representation of the problem might be that shown in Fig. 3–3. The function $f(x_1, x_2)$ takes on a strong relative maximum at the points $\mathbf{x}_1$ and $\mathbf{x}_2$ and a strong relative minimum at $\mathbf{x}_3$ for those $\mathbf{x}$ satisifying $g(\mathbf{x}) = b$. The absolute maximum of $f(\mathbf{x})$ for $\mathbf{x}$ satisfying $g(\mathbf{x}) = b$ is taken on at $\mathbf{x}_2$. Each of the points $\mathbf{x}_1$, $\mathbf{x}_2$, and $\mathbf{x}_3$ would be solutions to (3–13).

Let us now turn to general case where there are n variables and $m < n$ constraints. Assume that $f(\mathbf{x})$ takes on a relative maximum or minimum for $\mathbf{x} \in Y$ at $\mathbf{x}_0$. Assume also that $r(\mathbf{G}) = m$ at $\mathbf{x}_0$, where $\mathbf{G} = \|\partial g_i/\partial x_j\|$. In particular, to simplify the notation, assume that $J_{\mathbf{x}_0}(1, \ldots, m)$ is nonsingular. Then by the implicit function theorem, there is an ϵ-neighborhood of $\hat{\mathbf{x}}_0 = [x^0_{m+1}, \ldots, x^0_n]$ such that for $\hat{\mathbf{x}}$ in this ϵ-neighborhood, we can solve explicitly for $x_1, \ldots, x_m$:

$$x_i = \phi_i(\hat{\mathbf{x}}), \qquad i = 1, \ldots, m.$$

Then the function

$$h(\hat{\mathbf{x}}) = f[\phi_1(\hat{\mathbf{x}}), \ldots, \phi_m(\hat{\mathbf{x}}), \hat{\mathbf{x}}] \tag{3–14}$$

has an unconstrained relative maximum or minimum at $\mathbf{x}_0$, and hence

$$\frac{\partial h(\hat{\mathbf{x}}_0)}{\partial x_j} = 0, \qquad j = m+1, \ldots, n, \tag{3–15}$$

since $h(\hat{\mathbf{x}})$ must be differentiable in the ϵ-neighborhood of $\hat{\mathbf{x}}_0$.

Now by the rule for differentiating compound functions,

$$\frac{\partial h}{\partial x_j} = \sum_{i=1}^{m} \frac{\partial f}{\partial x_i}\frac{\partial \phi_i}{\partial x_j} + \frac{\partial f}{\partial x_j}, \qquad j = m+1, \ldots, n. \tag{3–16}$$

From the implicit function theorem the derivatives $\partial\phi_i/\partial x_j$, $i = 1, \ldots, m$, for a given j are the unique solution to the set of equations

$$\sum_{k=1}^{m} \frac{\partial g_i}{\partial x_k}\frac{\partial \phi_k}{\partial x_j} = -\frac{\partial g_i}{\partial x_j}, \qquad i = 1, \ldots, m. \tag{3–17}$$

We have $n - m$ sets of equations (3–17)—one for each j. Rather than try to solve the sets of equations (3–17) for $\partial\phi_i/\partial x_j$ and substitute into (3–16), we shall proceed as follows. Consider the numbers λ_i, $i = 1, \ldots, m$, which are the unique solution to the set of m linear equations

$$\sum_{i=1}^{m} \lambda_i \frac{\partial g_i(\mathbf{x}_0)}{\partial x_k} = \frac{\partial f(\mathbf{x}_0)}{\partial x_k}, \qquad k = 1, \ldots, m. \tag{3–18}$$

There is a unique solution since the matrix of the coefficients is $J_{\mathbf{x}_0}(1, \ldots, m)$, which we have assumed to be nonsingular.

Now multiply equation i in (3–17) by λ_i and sum over i. This yields for each j, $j = m+1, \ldots, n$,

$$\sum_{k=1}^{m}\left(\sum_{i=1}^{m} \lambda_i \frac{\partial g_i}{\partial x_k}\right)\frac{\partial \phi_k}{\partial x_j} + \sum_{i=1}^{m} \lambda_i \frac{\partial g_i}{\partial x_j} = 0. \tag{3–19}$$

From (3–15) and (3–16) it must be true that

$$\sum_{k=1}^{m} \frac{\partial f(\mathbf{x}_0)}{\partial x_k} \frac{\partial \phi_k(\hat{\mathbf{x}}_0)}{\partial x_j} + \frac{\partial f(\mathbf{x}_0)}{\partial x_j} = 0, \qquad j = m+1, \ldots, n. \tag{3–20}$$

Next evaluate (3–19) at $\mathbf{x}_0$ and subtract it from (3–20) to yield

$$\sum_{k=1}^{m} \left[\frac{\partial f(\mathbf{x}_0)}{\partial x_k} - \sum_{i=1}^{m} \lambda_i \frac{\partial g_i(\mathbf{x}_0)}{\partial x_k}\right] \frac{\partial \phi_k(\hat{\mathbf{x}}_0)}{\partial x_j} + \frac{\partial f(\mathbf{x}_0)}{\partial x_j} - \sum_{i=1}^{m} \lambda_i \frac{\partial g_i(\mathbf{x}_0)}{\partial x_j} = 0,$$
$$j = m+1, \ldots, n. \tag{3–21}$$

However, by (3–18) it follows that

$$\frac{\partial f(\mathbf{x}_0)}{\partial x_j} - \sum_{i=1}^{m} \lambda_i \frac{\partial g_i(\mathbf{x}_0)}{\partial x_j} = 0, \qquad j = m+1, \ldots, n. \tag{3–22}$$

Combining these equations with (3–18) and the constraints, we conclude that it is necessary that the point $\mathbf{x}_0$ at which $f(\mathbf{x})$ takes on a relative maximum or minimum for $\mathbf{x} \in Y$ satisfy the following set of $m + n$ equations:

$$\begin{aligned} \frac{\partial f(\mathbf{x}_0)}{\partial x_j} - \sum_{i=1}^{m} \lambda_i \frac{\partial g_i(\mathbf{x}_0)}{\partial x_j} &= 0, \qquad j = 1, \ldots, n; \\ g_i(\mathbf{x}_0) &= b_i, \qquad i = 1, \ldots, m. \end{aligned} \tag{3–23}$$

The λ_i are uniquely determined for any such $\mathbf{x}_0$. It is not necessarily true that every $\mathbf{x}_0$ which is a solution to (3–23) will be a point at which $f(\mathbf{x})$ takes on a relative maximum or minimum for $\mathbf{x} \in Y$. However, every point $\mathbf{x}_0$ at which $f(\mathbf{x})$ does take on a relative maximum or minimum for $\mathbf{x} \in Y$ must be a solution to (3–23) provided that $\mathbf{G}(\mathbf{x}_0)$ has rank m.

The necessary conditions (3–23) can be conveniently obtained as follows. Form the function

$$F(\mathbf{x}, \boldsymbol{\lambda}) = f(\mathbf{x}) + \sum_{i=1}^{m} \lambda_i[b_i - g_i(\mathbf{x})] \tag{3–24}$$

and then set to zero the partial derivatives of $F(\mathbf{x}, \boldsymbol{\lambda})$ with respect to each of the $m + n$ variables x_j, $j = 1, \ldots, n$, and λ_i, $i = 1, \ldots, m$. In taking the partial derivatives, all variables are treated as being independent. Thus

$$\frac{\partial F}{\partial x_j} = \frac{\partial f}{\partial x_j} - \sum_{i=1}^{m} \lambda_i \frac{\partial g_i}{\partial x_j} = 0, \qquad j = 1, \ldots, n; \tag{3–25}$$

$$\frac{\partial F}{\partial \lambda_i} = b_i - g_i(\mathbf{x}) = 0, \qquad i = 1, \ldots, m. \tag{3–26}$$

The function $F(\mathbf{x}, \boldsymbol{\lambda})$ defined by (3–24) is called the Lagrangian function, and the λ_i are called Lagrange multipliers. For any solution $\mathbf{x}_0$ to (3–25) and (3–26) the Lagrange multipliers are uniquely determined if $r(\mathbf{G}) = m$ at $\mathbf{x}_0$.

The technique of determining the necessary conditions by forming the function F and setting its derivatives to zero is called the Lagrange multiplier technique. Its great advantage from a practical point of view is that it makes it unnecessary to solve explicitly for some of the variables in terms of the others or to take account of the fact that the variables are not all independent. Just as with the necessary conditions obtained in Section 3–2, there do not exist any computational algorithms for obtaining numerically all solutions to Eqs. (3–25) and (3–26). These conditions are most useful in cases where there is only one solution, and this solution can be obtained analytically or with relatively simple numerical techniques.

We have shown that if $f(\mathbf{x})$ takes on a relative maximum or minimum at $\mathbf{x}_0$ for $\mathbf{x} \in Y$, then $\mathbf{x}_0$ must satisfy (3–25) and (3–26) if $r(\mathbf{G}) = m$ at $\mathbf{x}_0$. It does not necessarily follow that $\mathbf{x}_0$ must satisfy (3–25) and (3–26) if $r(\mathbf{G}) \neq m$ at $\mathbf{x}_0$. We shall turn our attention to the more general necessary conditions which allow for the possibility that $r(\mathbf{G}) \neq m$ at $\mathbf{x}_0$ in the next section.

3–5 The general case. As in the previous section we shall be assuming that $f \in C^1$ and $g_i \in C^1$, $i = 1, \ldots, m$. Consider the $(m + 1) \times n$ matrix

$$\mathbf{G}_f = \begin{bmatrix} \mathbf{G} \\ \nabla f \end{bmatrix} = \begin{bmatrix} \dfrac{\partial g_1}{\partial x_1} \cdots \dfrac{\partial g_1}{\partial x_n} \\ \vdots \qquad \vdots \\ \dfrac{\partial g_m}{\partial x_1} \cdots \dfrac{\partial g_m}{\partial x_n} \\ \dfrac{\partial f}{\partial x_1} \cdots \dfrac{\partial f}{\partial x_n} \end{bmatrix}. \tag{3–27}$$

The maximum possible rank of $\mathbf{G}_f$ is $m + 1$. To begin, we shall show that *if $r(\mathbf{G}_f)$ at $\mathbf{x}_0$ is $m + 1$, then $f(\mathbf{x})$ does not take on a relative maximum or minimum at $\mathbf{x}_0$ for $\mathbf{x} \in Y$.*

To prove this statement, assume that $r(\mathbf{G}_f) = m + 1$ at $\mathbf{x}_0$. To be specific assume that the submatrix of order $m + 1$ formed from the first $m + 1$ columns of $\mathbf{G}_f$ is nonsingular at $\mathbf{x}_0$. Then the implicit function theorem assures us that for the $m + 1$ equations

$$f(\mathbf{x}) - z = 0; \qquad g_i(\mathbf{x}) = b_i, \quad i = 1, \ldots, m, \tag{3–28}$$

in $n + 1$ variables $x_1, \ldots, x_n$ and z, there exists an ϵ-neighborhood

($\epsilon > 0$) of $[x^0_{m+2}, \ldots, x^0_n, z_0]$, $z_0 = f(\mathbf{x}_0)$, in which we can solve (3–28) explicitly for $x_1, \ldots, x_{m+1}$ to yield

$$x_i = \phi_i(x_{m+2}, \ldots, x_n, z), \qquad i = 1, \ldots, m+1. \tag{3–29}$$

It is important to note that z is one of the variables which can be assigned arbitrarily in the functions ϕ_i. Consequently, if we set $x_{m+2} = x^0_{m+2}, \ldots, x_n = x^0_n$, then for all z, $|z - z_0| < \epsilon$, there exist points $\mathbf{x} \in Y$, such that $z = f(\mathbf{x})$. Since the functions ϕ_i are continuous, it follows that if we select any δ-neighborhood ($\delta > 0$) of $\mathbf{x}_0$ in E^n, there exist points $\mathbf{x} \in Y$ in this δ-neighborhood such that $x_{m+2} = x^0_{m+2}, \ldots, x_n = x^0_n$, with the property that for some of these points, $f(\mathbf{x}) > z_0$ while for others, $f(\mathbf{x}) < z_0$. Consequently, $f(\mathbf{x})$ cannot take on a relative maximum or minimum at $\mathbf{x}_0$ for $\mathbf{x} \in Y$. This proves what we wanted to show.

From what we have just demonstrated, it follows that if $f(\mathbf{x})$ takes on a relative maximum or minimum at $\mathbf{x}_0$ for $\mathbf{x} \in Y$, then $r(\mathbf{G}_f) < m + 1$ at $\mathbf{x}_0$. Let $\mathbf{x}_0$ be a point where $f(\mathbf{x})$ takes on a relative maximum or minimum for $\mathbf{x} \in Y$, and consider the set of n homogeneous linear equations in $m + 1$ unknowns λ_i,

$$\lambda_0 \frac{\partial f(\mathbf{x}_0)}{\partial x_j} - \lambda_1 \frac{\partial g_1(\mathbf{x}_0)}{\partial x_j} - \cdots - \lambda_m \frac{\partial g_m(\mathbf{x}_0)}{\partial x_j} = 0, \qquad j = 1, \ldots, n. \tag{3–30}$$

Since it must be true that $r(\mathbf{G}_f) < m + 1$ at $\mathbf{x}_0$, there exist nontrivial solutions to (3–30). We shall now study the various cases which can arise.

First suppose that $r(\mathbf{G}) = m$ at $\mathbf{x}_0$. Then we can select any m equations containing a nonsingular submatrix of order m whose elements are in $\mathbf{G}$, and solve uniquely for $\lambda_1, \ldots, \lambda_m$ in terms of λ_0. The value of λ_0 can be assigned arbitrarily. It cannot be zero, however, if we are to obtain a nontrivial solution. In this case, it is convenient to set $\lambda_0 = 1$. The other λ_i will then be uniquely determined. Next suppose that $r(\mathbf{G}_f) = m$ at $\mathbf{x}_0$, but $r(\mathbf{G}) = m - 1$. Select m equations from (3–30) the matrix of whose coefficients contains a nonsingular matrix of order m. It is clear from this set of equations that there does not exist any solution which does not have $\lambda_0 = 0$, for if λ_0 is set to any number other than zero, we obtain a set of equations for the remaining λ_i for which the rank of the augmented matrix is greater than the rank of the matrix of the coefficients. However, if $\lambda_0 = 0$, there exist λ_i, $i = 1, \ldots, m$, not all zero which satisfy (3–30). In this case the λ_i, $i = 1, \ldots, m$, are not uniquely determined, but instead, the solutions span a one-dimensional subspace of E^m.

Let us now move on to a case where at $\mathbf{x}_0$, $r(\mathbf{G}_f) = r(\mathbf{G}) = r < m$. Select r equations from (3–30) such that the matrix of the coefficients contains a nonsingular submatrix of order r whose elements are in $\mathbf{G}$. Then we can solve for r of the variables in terms of λ_0 and $m - r$ of the other λ_i. In this case, λ_0 can be assigned arbitrarily, and it is convenient to set $\lambda_0 = 1$. Given that $\lambda_0 = 1$, the other λ_i, $i = 1, \ldots, m$, will not be unique, but rather, $m - r$ of the λ_i can be assigned arbitrary values. The remaining case is that where at $\mathbf{x}_0$, $r(\mathbf{G}_f) = r < m$ and $r(\mathbf{G}_f) > r(\mathbf{G})$. In this case, select r equations from (3–30) the matrix of whose coefficients contains a submatrix of order r. As before, there do not exist any solutions which do not have $\lambda_0 = 0$. If we set $\lambda_0 = 0$, there do exist λ_i, $i = 1, \ldots, m$, not all zero which satisfy (3–30). In fact the set of λ_i, $i = 1, \ldots, m$, satisfying (3–30) spans a subspace of E^m of dimension $m - r + 1$.

The above discussion has shown that if $f(\mathbf{x})$ takes on a relative maximum or minimum at $\mathbf{x}_0$ for $\mathbf{x} \in Y$, it is necessary that $\mathbf{x}_0$ satisfy the set of equations

$$\lambda_0 \frac{\partial f(\mathbf{x}_0)}{\partial x_j} - \sum_{i=1}^{m} \lambda_i \frac{\partial g_i(\mathbf{x}_0)}{\partial x_j} = 0, \qquad j = 1, \ldots, n, \tag{3–31}$$

for at least one set of λ_i, $i = 0, 1, \ldots, m$, with not all $\lambda_i = 0$, as well as the set of equations

$$g_i(\mathbf{x}_0) = b_i, \qquad i = 1, \ldots, m. \tag{3–32}$$

These necessary conditions can be obtained by setting to zero the partial derivatives with respect to the x_j and λ_i $(i \neq 0)$ of the Lagrangian function

$$F(\mathbf{x}, \boldsymbol{\lambda}) = \lambda_0 f(\mathbf{x}) + \sum_{i=1}^{m} \lambda_i[b_i - g_i(\mathbf{x})].$$

We have shown that without loss of generality we can take λ_0 to be either 1 or 0 in (3–31). If $r(\mathbf{G}_f) = r(\mathbf{G})$ at $\mathbf{x}_0$, then we set $\lambda_0 = 1$. If $r(\mathbf{G}_f) > r(\mathbf{G})$, it is necessary that $\lambda_0 = 0$ in order that there exist λ_i not all zero satisfying (3–31). When $r(\mathbf{G}_f) > r(\mathbf{G})$, the λ_i, $i = 1, \ldots, m$, are not uniquely determined. If $r(\mathbf{G}_f) = r(\mathbf{G}) = m$ at $\mathbf{x}_0$, the λ_i are uniquely determined, and if $r(\mathbf{G}_f) = r(\mathbf{G}) < m$, the λ_i are not uniquely determined. This completes the determination of the necessary conditions in the general case. Most textbooks treat only the case where $\lambda_0 = 1$. However, [2] does contain a good discussion of the generalization presented in this section.

Sufficient conditions exist which, if satisfied, guarantee that a given solution to (3–31) and (3–32) will be a point at which $f(\mathbf{x})$ takes on a strong relative maximum or minimum for $\mathbf{x} \in Y$. The reader is asked to develop one form of these conditions in the problems. As in the unconstrained case, they are mainly of theoretical interest. Nonetheless they are of fundamental importance in certain theoretical developments in economics, for example.

3–6 Treatment of non-negative variables and inequality constraints. At the expense of greatly increased computational effort, it is possible to generalize the Lagrange multiplier technique to cases where the variables are restricted to be non-negative and/or some of the constraints involve inequalities. Let us begin by studying the problem of finding the global maximum or minimum of $z = f(\mathbf{x})$ for $\mathbf{x} \geq \mathbf{0}$ satisfying $g_i(\mathbf{x}) = b_i$, $i = 1, \ldots, m$, $m < n$. We shall continue to assume that $f \in C^1$ and $g_i \in C^1$, $i = 1, \ldots, m$. Now if the global optimum of $f(\mathbf{x})$ over the non-negative orthant is taken on at a point $\mathbf{x}^*$ with $|\mathbf{x}^*|$ finite, it must occur either at an interior point $\mathbf{x}^*$ where each component of $\mathbf{x}^*$ is positive, or at a point $\mathbf{x}^*$ on the boundaries, where one or more components of $\mathbf{x}^*$ will be zero. If $\mathbf{x}^*$ occurs at an interior point of the non-negative orthant, it must be a solution to Eqs. (3–31) and (3–32). Thus the first step is to determine all solutions to (3–31) and (3–32) lying inside the non-negative orthant and to evaluate z for each of these. Next the boundaries of the non-negative orthant must be examined. To do this we first consider the cases where only one of the variables is zero, i.e., we set one of the variables to zero and consider the resulting problem in $n - 1$ variables and m constraints. We determine the conditions (3–31) and (3–32) for this problem and find all solutions lying inside the non-negative orthant of E^{n-1}. Then z is evaluated for each of these solutions. Note that, in general, each variable can be set equal to zero, and hence we must solve n of these problems involving $n - 1$ variables and m constraints. Next we set two variables equal to zero and consider the resulting problem in $n - 2$ variables and m constraints. We do this for all $n!/2!(n - 2)!$ combinations of two variables set to zero. Then we examine the problems obtained by setting three variables to zero, etc. We cannot, in general, arbitrarily set more than $n - m$ of the variables to zero if the constraints are to be satisfied. When $n - m$ of the variables are set to zero, the constraints determine (often uniquely) the values of the remaining m variables. Thus at the last stage we evaluate z at each of the points at which $n - m$ of the variables are equal to zero. The absolute maximum of z is then the largest of all the z-values obtained above, and the absolute minimum of z is the smallest. It is quite clear from the foregoing that non-negative variables may greatly increase the computational work. If there were very many variables, it would be out of the question to carry out the necessary computations. Obviously, if not all the variables are required to be non-negative, we need to check the boundaries only for those that must be non-negative.

We can easily interpret geometrically the above procedure for the case of two variables and one constraint. Suppose that the problem had the structure shown in Fig. 3–3. The only point inside the non-negative orthant which is a solution to Eqs. (3–31) and (3–32) is $\mathbf{x}_2$. Next the boundaries are checked. When one variable is set equal to zero, the other is uniquely determined, and we obtain the points at which the curve $g(\mathbf{x}) = b$ crosses the x_1- and x_2-axes. The absolute maximum of $f(\mathbf{x})$ over the non-negative orthant occurs at $\mathbf{x}_2$, and the absolute minimum occurs on the boundary where $x_1 = 0$ at the point at which $g(\mathbf{x}) = b$ crosses the x_2-axis.

Let us now turn to the case where the variables are unrestricted, but one or more of the constraints are inequalities rather than equations. Let us number the constraints so that the first u, $u \geq 0$, are of the form $g_i(\mathbf{x}) \leq b_i$, constraints $u + 1, \ldots, v$ are of the form $g_i(\mathbf{x}) \geq b_i$, and the remaining constraints $i = v + 1, \ldots, m$ hold as strict equalities, that is, $g_i(\mathbf{x}) = b_i$. We can convert constraint i, $i = 1, \ldots, u$, to an equation by adding a slack variable x_{si}, thus obtaining $g_i(\mathbf{x}) + x_{si} = b_i$. Note that although the components of $\mathbf{x}$ are unrestricted, it must be true that $x_{si} \geq 0$ for any $\mathbf{x}$ satisfying $g_i(\mathbf{x}) \leq b_i$. Similarly, constraint i, $i = u + 1, \ldots, v$, can be converted to an equation by adding a surplus variable x_{si} thus yielding $g_i(\mathbf{x}) - x_{si} = b_i$. Note also that although the components of $\mathbf{x}$ are unrestricted, it must be true that $x_{si} \geq 0$ for any $\mathbf{x}$ satisfying $g_i(\mathbf{x}) \geq b_i$. There is a one-to-one correspondence between the set of points satisfying the original constraints and the set of points with non-negative slack and surplus variables satisfying the new set of equality constraints. Thus the original problem is equivalent to

$$
\begin{aligned}
&g_i(\mathbf{x}) + x_{si} = b_i, && i = 1, \ldots, u, \\
&g_i(\mathbf{x}) - x_{si} = b_i, && i = u + 1, \ldots, v, \\
&g_i(\mathbf{x}) = b_i, && i = v + 1, \ldots, m, \\
&x_{si} \geq 0, && i = 1, \ldots, v, \\
&\max \text{ or } \min z = f(\mathbf{x}).
\end{aligned}
\tag{3-33}
$$

We have now reduced the problem to a type studied at the beginning of this section. To determine the global optimum of f, we must consider both the interior of the non-negative orthant of E^v where each $x_{si} > 0$, and the boundaries where one or more $x_{si} = 0$. Note first that if we consider the case where each $x_{si} > 0$, the Lagrangian is

$$
\begin{aligned}
F(\mathbf{x}, \mathbf{x}_s, \boldsymbol{\lambda}) = \lambda_0 f(\mathbf{x}) &+ \sum_{i=1}^{u} \lambda_i[b_i - x_{si} - g_i(\mathbf{x})] \\
&+ \sum_{i=u+1}^{v} \lambda_i[b_i + x_{si} - g_i(\mathbf{x})] + \sum_{i=v+1}^{m} \lambda_i[b_i - g_i(\mathbf{x})].
\end{aligned}
\tag{3-34}
$$

Equation (3-31) requires that the partial derivative of F with respect to each variable including each x_{si} must be zero. On taking the derivative of F with respect to x_{si}, we obtain

$$\frac{\partial F}{\partial x_{si}} = -\lambda_i = 0, \qquad i = 1, \ldots, u;$$

$$\frac{\partial F}{\partial x_{si}} = \lambda_i = 0, \qquad i = u + 1, \ldots, v.$$

We conclude therefore that if $x_{si} > 0$, $i = 1, \ldots, v$, then $\lambda_i = 0$, $i = 1, \ldots, v$, and the problem becomes equivalent to one in which we ignore the inequality constraints. In other words, if the inequality constraints are inactive at the point where $f(\mathbf{x})$ takes on its optimal value, then we can ignore these constraints in finding the point where $f(\mathbf{x})$ takes on its optimum. This agrees with our physical intuition. When we move to the boundaries and set some given $x_{si} = 0$, we make constraint i active and allow λ_i to be different from zero.

To find the global optimum of $f(\mathbf{x})$ for $\mathbf{x}$ satisfying the constraints, we can then proceed as follows. First find all solutions to Eqs. (3–31) and (3–32) for the case where the inequality constraints are ignored, and compute the value of z for each such solution. Next repeat the procedure including just one of the inequality constraints and treating it as being active. This is done for the inclusion of each constraint i, $i = 1, \ldots, v$. Next repeat the procedure including two inequality constraints and treating both as active. This is done for all possible combinations of two constraints which can be included. The procedure is continued until all constraints are treated as active. The optimum value of z is the largest or smallest of all the z-values so obtained.

An additional observation will show us that it is not always necessary to carry out all the above computations. At each stage we can determine whether or not we have an optimal solution. We can do this for the following reason. Let z_m^* be the global maximum of $z = f(\mathbf{x})$ subject to the m constraints $g_i(\mathbf{x})\ \{\leq, =, \geq\}\ b_i$, $i = 1, \ldots, m$. Suppose that we now add another constraint $g_{m+1}(\mathbf{x})\ \{\leq, =, \geq\}\ b_{m+1}$ and let z_{m+1}^* be the global maximum of $z = f(\mathbf{x})$ subject to the $m + 1$ constraints (m of which were the constraints for the original problem). Then it is clear that $z_{m+1}^* \leq z_m^*$, since if $\mathbf{x}_{m+1}^*$ is the point such that $z_{m+1}^* = f(\mathbf{x}_{m+1}^*)$, then $\mathbf{x}_{m+1}^*$ satisfies the $m + 1$ constraints and hence the m constraints of the original problem. Therefore $\mathbf{x}_{m+1}^*$ is an allowable solution to the original problem, and since z_m^* is the global maximum for that problem, it must be true that $z_{m+1}^* \leq z_m^*$.

Using the result just proved, one can modify the computational procedure outlined above as follows. First compute the global optimum, ignoring the inequality constraints. If the point (or points) so obtained also satisfy the inequality constraints, then we have the global optimum to the problem which includes the inequality constraints. If one or more of the inequality constraints are not satisfied, select one of the inequality constraints (not necessarily one that was not satisfied at the first stage), treat it as active, and repeat the process. If the point (or points) yielding the global optimum to this problem satisfies the inequality constraints not included, then we have the global optimum to the problem which includes all the inequality constraints. If not, we continue the process until we have tried all combinations of including just one of the inequality constraints. If the optimum is not attained at this stage, we are sure that at least two of the inequality constraints will be active. We then proceed to include two constraints, etc., until the global optimum is found. If the components of $\mathbf{x}$ are required to be non-negative and there are some inequality constraints, we follow the procedure just outlined except that at each stage of determining the global optimum for the constraints which are active, we must also examine the boundaries at which one or more components of $\mathbf{x}$ are zero. Obviously, the computational effort required to handle a large number of inequality constraints by this procedure could be tremendous.

It is interesting to observe that the above computational technique has shown that if $\mathbf{x}^*$ is a point at which $f(\mathbf{x})$ takes on its global optimum subject to the constraints, x_{si}^* are the values of the slack and surplus variables corresponding to $\mathbf{x}^*$, and $\boldsymbol{\lambda}^* = [\lambda_1^*, \ldots, \lambda_m^*]$ contains the Lagrange multipliers corresponding to $\mathbf{x}^*$, then either $x_{si}^* = 0$ or $\lambda_i^* = 0$, $i = 1, \ldots, v$, that is, $\lambda_i^* x_{si}^* = 0$.

3–7 Interpretation of Lagrange multipliers. Let us return to the problem of finding the global optimum of $z = f(\mathbf{x})$ subject to the m constraints $g_i(\mathbf{x}) = b_i$, $i = 1, \ldots, m$. Assume that $\mathbf{x}^*$ is a point at which f takes on its global optimum, and assume that $r(\mathbf{G}) = m$ at $\mathbf{x}^*$ so that without loss of generality we can set $\lambda_0 = 1$. Let $\boldsymbol{\lambda}^* = [\lambda_1^*, \ldots, \lambda_m^*]$ be a vector containing a set of Lagrange multipliers corresponding to $\mathbf{x}^*$. Now, in general, the x_j^* and λ_i^* will depend on the particular values of the b_i which appear in the problem. Let us suppose that each x_j^* and λ_i^* is a continuous, differentiable function of $\mathbf{b} = [b_1, \ldots, b_m]$ in some ϵ-neighborhood of $\mathbf{b}_0$. Problem 3–15 asks the reader to supply sufficient conditions which guarantee the existence of these functions.

We shall now compute the partial derivatives of $z^* = f(\mathbf{x}^*)$, the global optimum, with respect to the b_i at points $\mathbf{b}$ lying in the ϵ-neighborhood of $\mathbf{b}_0$. Note that by the chain rule,

$$\frac{\partial z^*}{\partial b_i} = \sum_{j=1}^{n} \frac{\partial f}{\partial x_j^*} \frac{\partial x_j^*}{\partial b_i}. \tag{3–35}$$

However, from $g_k(\mathbf{x}^*) = b_k$ we have

$$\sum_{j=1}^{n} \frac{\partial g_k}{\partial x_j^*} \frac{\partial x_j^*}{\partial b_i} = \delta_{ik}$$

or

$$\delta_{ik} - \sum_{j=1}^{n} \frac{\partial g_k}{\partial x_j^*} \frac{\partial x_j^*}{\partial b_i} = 0, \qquad i, k = 1, \ldots, m, \tag{3-36}$$

where δ_{ik} is the Kronecker delta. Now multiply (3-36) by λ_k^*, sum over k, and add to (3-35). This yields

$$\frac{\partial z^*}{\partial b_i} = \sum_{k=1}^{m} \lambda_k^* \, \delta_{ik} + \sum_{j=1}^{n} \left[\frac{\partial f}{\partial x_j^*} - \sum_{k=1}^{m} \lambda_k^* \frac{\partial g_k}{\partial x_j^*} \right] \frac{\partial x_j^*}{\partial b_i}. \tag{3-37}$$

Then since $\mathbf{x}^*$ and $\boldsymbol{\lambda}^*$ must satisfy (3-23), we conclude that

$$\frac{\partial z^*}{\partial b_i} = \lambda_i^*. \tag{3-38}$$

The partial derivative of the global optimum with respect to b_i is simply equal to the Lagrange multiplier λ_i^* evaluated at $\mathbf{b}$. Not infrequently, z will be a profit or cost, and b_i will be the number of physical units of some resource. In this case, the physical dimensions of λ_i^* are dollars per unit of resource i, and λ_i^* can be interpreted as a price or value per unit of resource i. The Lagrange multipliers are sometimes called shadow prices or imputed values. Roughly speaking, λ_i^* tells us how much the maximum profit or the minimum cost will be changed if the quantity of resource i available is increased by one unit. The physical interpretation of Lagrange multipliers provided here can be extended to the case of inequality constraints and to problems in which the variables are required to be nonnegative. We ask the reader to do this in Problems 3-16 and 3-17.

3-8 Interpretation of the Lagrangian function; duality. Assume that $f(\mathbf{x})$ has a relative maximum at $\mathbf{x}_0$ for $\mathbf{x}$ satisfying $g_i(\mathbf{x}) = b_i$, $i = 1, \ldots, m$, such that $r(\mathbf{G}) = m$ at $\mathbf{x}_0$. Let $\boldsymbol{\lambda}_0 = [\lambda_1^0, \ldots, \lambda_m^0]$ be a vector containing a set of Lagrange multipliers corresponding to $\mathbf{x}_0$. In physical problems it frequently turns out that the Lagrangian function $F(\mathbf{x}, \boldsymbol{\lambda}_0)$ has an unconstrained relative maximum at $\mathbf{x}_0$, that is, $F(\mathbf{x}, \boldsymbol{\lambda}_0) \leq F(\mathbf{x}_0, \boldsymbol{\lambda}_0)$ for *all* $\mathbf{x}$ in some ϵ-neighborhood of $\mathbf{x}_0$. Let us now suppose that there exists a δ-neighborhood of $\boldsymbol{\lambda}_0$ in E^m such that for any $\boldsymbol{\lambda}$ in this δ-neighborhood, $F(\mathbf{x}, \boldsymbol{\lambda})$ has an unconstrained relative maximum with respect to $\mathbf{x}$ at a point which satisfies

$$\frac{\partial F}{\partial x_j} = 0 = \frac{\partial f}{\partial x_j} - \sum_{i=1}^{m} \lambda_i \frac{\partial g_i}{\partial x_j}, \quad j = 1, \ldots, n. \tag{3-39}$$

This will often be true for real-life problems.

Imagine that Eqs. (3–39) have a unique solution for every $\boldsymbol{\lambda}$ in the δ-neighborhood of $\boldsymbol{\lambda}_0$, and that maximizing point $\hat{\mathbf{x}}$ can be written $\hat{\mathbf{x}}(\boldsymbol{\lambda})$. We ask the reader in Problem 3–18 to provide the conditions which guarantee that this can be done. Then in the δ-neighborhood of $\boldsymbol{\lambda}_0$ we can write

$$\max_{\mathbf{x}} F(\mathbf{x}, \boldsymbol{\lambda}) = F(\hat{\mathbf{x}}, \boldsymbol{\lambda}) = h(\boldsymbol{\lambda}), \tag{3-40}$$

i.e., the maximum with respect to $\mathbf{x}$ will be a function of $\boldsymbol{\lambda}$ which we have denoted by $h(\boldsymbol{\lambda})$. Note that

$$h(\boldsymbol{\lambda}_0) = F(\mathbf{x}_0, \boldsymbol{\lambda}_0) = f(\mathbf{x}_0).$$

It is interesting to examine whether or not $h(\boldsymbol{\lambda})$ has a relative maximum or minimum at $\boldsymbol{\lambda}_0$. Consider $F(\mathbf{x}, \boldsymbol{\lambda})$ for a fixed $\boldsymbol{\lambda}$. Note that for $\mathbf{x}$ satisfying $g_i(\mathbf{x}) = b_i$, $i = 1, \ldots, m$,

$$F(\mathbf{x}, \boldsymbol{\lambda}) = f(\mathbf{x}).$$

Hence

$$\max_{\mathbf{x}} F(\mathbf{x}, \boldsymbol{\lambda}) = \max_{\mathbf{x}} f(\mathbf{x}) = f(\mathbf{x}_0) = h(\boldsymbol{\lambda}_0), \quad \mathbf{x} \in Y. \tag{3-41}$$

Since in (3–41) we have restricted the range of variation of $\mathbf{x}$ because we require that $\mathbf{x} \in Y$, it follows that

$$h(\boldsymbol{\lambda}) \geq h(\boldsymbol{\lambda}_0),$$

and hence $h(\boldsymbol{\lambda})$ has a relative minimum at $\boldsymbol{\lambda}_0$. Since $h(\boldsymbol{\lambda}) = F(\mathbf{x}, \boldsymbol{\lambda})$ when $\mathbf{x}$ and $\boldsymbol{\lambda}$ are related by (3–39), it follows that $F(\mathbf{x}, \boldsymbol{\lambda})$ has a relative minimum at $\boldsymbol{\lambda}_0$ with respect to $\boldsymbol{\lambda}$ subject to the constraints (3–39) which determine $\mathbf{x}$ for each $\boldsymbol{\lambda}$. The problem of minimizing $F(\mathbf{x}, \boldsymbol{\lambda})$ with respect to $\boldsymbol{\lambda}$ subject to the constraints (3–39) is called a dual of the problem which seeks to maximize $f(\mathbf{x})$ subject to $g_i(\mathbf{x}) = b_i$, $i = 1, \ldots, m$. These dual problems have the property that in a neighborhood of $\mathbf{x}_0$,

$$\min_{\boldsymbol{\lambda}} F(\mathbf{x}, \boldsymbol{\lambda}) = \max_{\mathbf{x}} f(\mathbf{x}) = f(\mathbf{x}_0) = h(\boldsymbol{\lambda}_0) \tag{3-42}$$

subject to the appropriate constraints.

Recall that by (3–40), $\max_{\mathbf{x}} F(\mathbf{x}, \boldsymbol{\lambda}) = h(\boldsymbol{\lambda})$ and $\min_{\boldsymbol{\lambda}} h(\boldsymbol{\lambda}) = h(\boldsymbol{\lambda}_0)$; hence we can write

$$f(\mathbf{x}_0) = \min_{\boldsymbol{\lambda}} \max_{\mathbf{x}} F(\mathbf{x}, \boldsymbol{\lambda}), \tag{3-43}$$

and $f(\mathbf{x}_0)$ is a solution to a min-max problem. This can be stated in a different form. Consider a neighborhood of $[\mathbf{x}_0, \boldsymbol{\lambda}_0]$ in E^{n+m}. Then by our previous assumption that $F(\mathbf{x}, \boldsymbol{\lambda})$ has a relative maximum with respect to $\mathbf{x}$ for any $\boldsymbol{\lambda}$ in a δ-neighborhood of $\boldsymbol{\lambda}_0$, it must be true that

$$F(\mathbf{x}, \boldsymbol{\lambda}_0) \leq F(\mathbf{x}_0, \boldsymbol{\lambda}_0) = f(\mathbf{x}_0).$$

Note also that $F(\mathbf{x}_0, \boldsymbol{\lambda}) = f(\mathbf{x}_0)$ since $\mathbf{x}_0 \in Y$. Thus, $F(\mathbf{x}_0, \boldsymbol{\lambda}_0) = F(\mathbf{x}_0, \boldsymbol{\lambda})$. Therefore we can write

$$F(\mathbf{x}, \boldsymbol{\lambda}_0) \leq F(\mathbf{x}_0, \boldsymbol{\lambda}_0) = F(\mathbf{x}_0, \boldsymbol{\lambda}). \tag{3–44}$$

A function $F(\mathbf{x}, \boldsymbol{\lambda})$ is said to have a saddle point at the point $[\mathbf{x}_0, \boldsymbol{\lambda}_0]$, if there exists an $\epsilon > 0$ such that for all $\mathbf{x}$, $|\mathbf{x} - \mathbf{x}_0| < \epsilon$, and all $|\boldsymbol{\lambda} - \boldsymbol{\lambda}_0| < \epsilon$,

$$F(\mathbf{x}, \boldsymbol{\lambda}_0) \leq F(\mathbf{x}_0, \boldsymbol{\lambda}_0) \leq F(\mathbf{x}_0, \boldsymbol{\lambda}).$$

We have just proved that if all the assumptions made above hold, then the Lagrangian function has a saddle point at $[\mathbf{x}_0, \boldsymbol{\lambda}_0]$, which, however, is a degenerate form of a saddle point, since the strict equality holds on the right of (3–44). The topics presented in this section will be elaborated in greater detail and generalized in Chapter 6. The material in the section is covered in Courant and Hilbert [3], pp. 231–233.

3–9 Examples. We shall now present three examples. Two of these will illustrate the types of problems which can be solved by the use of Lagrange multipliers. The third will illustrate why the Lagrange multiplier technique is of no assistance in solving linear programming problems.

1. The buyer for the women's sportwear department of a large department store may spend \$3000 on three different types of high-style dresses to be sold during the coming season. These dresses must be ordered at the start of the season, and there will be no opportunity for a reorder. Dress 1 costs \$35.00 and retails for \$66.00. Dress 2 costs \$20.00 and retails for \$37.00. Dress 3 costs \$50.00 and retails for \$105.00. Any dresses remaining unsold at the end of the season will be sold at 20 percent below cost. The buyer believes that there is a goodwill loss for each dress demanded that is not in stock. He estimates these goodwill losses to be \$70.00 for dress 1, \$40.00 for dress 2, and \$220.00 for dress 3. He thinks that the demand for each dress will be normally distributed, with the mean being 30 for dress 1, 60 for dress 2, and 15 for dress 3, and the standard deviations being 8, 12, and 3 for dresses 1, 2, and 3, respectively. How many of each dress style should he buy in order to maximize the expected profit obtained from all three dresses?

In solving the problem, we shall treat all variables as continuous. Let x_j be the number of dress j procured. If the demand for dress j is v_j, then the revenue received will be

$$\begin{aligned} &p_j v_j \quad \text{if} \quad v_j \leq x_j, \\ &p_j x_j \quad \text{if} \quad v_j \geq x_j, \end{aligned}$$

where p_j is the selling price. The goodwill loss for dress j will be

$$\begin{aligned} &0 \quad \text{if} \quad v_j \leq x_j, \\ &\pi_j(v_j - x_j) \quad \text{if} \quad v_j \geq x_j, \end{aligned}$$

where π_j is the good will loss for each demand which cannot be met. The revenue gain from sale at a reduced price of any dress remaining at the end of the season will be

$$\begin{aligned} &0.80c_j(x_j - v_j) \quad \text{if} \quad v_j \leq x_j, \\ &0 \quad \text{if} \quad v_j \geq x_j, \end{aligned}$$

where c_j is the cost of dress j. The expected profit received from dress j will then be the expected revenue minus the cost minus the expected goodwill loss plus the expected revenue from the sale of leftovers at reduced prices.

Denote by $n(v; \mu, \sigma)$ the normal distribution with mean μ and standard deviation σ. We shall assume that there are no interactions between the demands for the three different types of dresses, i.e., a customer will not buy a different type if the store is out of stock on one type. Thus the v_j are independent random variables. Then the expected profit P_j from dress j is

$$\begin{aligned} P_j = {} & p_j x_j \int_{x_j}^{\infty} n(v_j; \mu_j, \sigma_j)\, dv_j + p_j \int_{-\infty}^{x_j} v_j n(v_j; \mu_j, \sigma_j)\, dv_j \\ & - c_j x_j - \pi_j \int_{x_j}^{\infty} (v_j - x_j) n(v_j; \mu_j, \sigma_j)\, dv_j \\ & + 0.80c_j \int_{-\infty}^{x_j} (x_j - v_j) n(v_j; \mu_j, \sigma_j)\, dv_j. \end{aligned}$$

In the above equation we have assumed that the area under the normal curve to the left of $v_j = 0$ is negligible and hence we have used in the appropriate place a lower limit on the integrals of $-\infty$ rathern than zero. We can rearrange the equation for P_j as follows:

$$\begin{aligned} P_j = \mu_j(p_j - 0.80c_j) - 0.20c_j x_j - (p_j + \pi_j - 0.80c_j) \\ \times \int_{x_j}^{\infty} (v_j - x_j) n(v_j; \mu_j, \sigma_j)\, dv_j. \end{aligned}$$

To perform this transformation of P_j we have used

$$\int_{-\infty}^{x_j} v_j n(v_j; \mu_j, \sigma_j)\, dv_j = \mu_j - \int_{x_j}^{\infty} v_j n(v_j; \mu_j, \sigma_j)\, dv_j$$

and

$$\int_{-\infty}^{x_j} (x_j - v_j) n(v_j; \mu_j, \sigma_j)\, dv_j = x_j - \mu_j + \int_{x_j}^{\infty} (v_j - x_j) n(v_j; \mu_j, \sigma_j)\, dv_j.$$

The expected profit P obtained from the sale of the three dresses is then the sum of the three P_j:

$$\begin{aligned} P = 1140 - 7x_1 - 108 \int_{x_1}^{\infty} (v_1 - x_1) n(v_1; 30, 8)\, dv_1 + 1260 - 4x_2 \\ - 61 \int_{x_2}^{\infty} (v_2 - x_2) n(v_2; 60, 12)\, dv_2 + 975 - 10x_3 \\ - 285 \int_{x_3}^{\infty} (v_3 - x_3) n(v_3; 15, 3)\, dv_3. \end{aligned} \tag{3–45}$$

We wish to determine non-negative values of x_1, x_2, and x_3 which minimize P subject to the constraint

$$35x_1 + 20x_2 + 50x_3 \leq 3000. \tag{3–46}$$

In general, it is not necessarily true that it will be optimal for the buyer to spend the entire sum available.

To begin we shall find the absolute maximum of P, ignoring the constraint. Clearly, this will occur at a point where $|\mathbf{x}|$ is finite, and each x_j is positive. Hence the optimizing point must satisfy $\partial P/\partial x_j = 0$, $j = 1, 2, 3$. To evaluate these derivatives, let us first note that

$$\begin{aligned} \frac{d}{dx_j}\left[\int_{x_j}^{\infty} (v_j - x_j) n(v_j; \mu_j, \sigma_j)\, dv_j\right] \\ = \frac{d}{dx_j}\left[\int_{x_j}^{\infty} v_j n(v_j; \mu_j, \sigma_j)\, dv_j\right] - \frac{d}{dx_j}\left[x_j \int_{x_j}^{\infty} n(v_j; \mu_j, \sigma_j)\, dv_j\right] \\ = -x_j n(x_j; \mu_j, \sigma_j) - \int_{x_j}^{\infty} n(v_j; \mu_j, \sigma_j)\, dv_j + x_j n(x_j; \mu_j, \sigma_j) \\ = -\int_{x_j}^{\infty} n(v_j; \mu_j, \sigma_j)\, dv_j = -\Phi\left(\frac{x_j - \mu_j}{\sigma_j}\right), \end{aligned}$$

where

$$\Phi(t) = \frac{1}{\sqrt{2\pi}} \int_t^{\infty} e^{-\tau^2/2}\, d\tau;$$

$\Phi(t)$ [or a function from which $\Phi(t)$ may easily be determined] is listed in tables of the normal distribution. We have:

$$\frac{\partial P}{\partial x_1} = 0 = -7 + 108\Phi\left(\frac{x_1 - 30}{8}\right) \quad \text{or} \quad \Phi\left(\frac{x_1 - 30}{8}\right) = \frac{7}{108} = 0.0648,$$

$$\frac{\partial P}{\partial x_2} = 0 = -4 + 61\Phi\left(\frac{x_2 - 60}{12}\right) \quad \text{or} \quad \Phi\left(\frac{x_2 - 60}{12}\right) = \frac{4}{61} = 0.0656,$$

$$\frac{\partial P}{\partial x_3} = 0 = -10 + 285\Phi\left(\frac{x_3 - 15}{3}\right) \quad \text{or} \quad \Phi\left(\frac{x_3 - 15}{3}\right) = \frac{10}{285} = 0.0351.$$

From the tables, we then find that the unique solution to the above equations is

$$\frac{x_1 - 30}{8} = 1.515, \qquad \text{so} \qquad x_1 = 30 + 8(1.515) = 42.1 \approx 42;$$

$$\frac{x_2 - 60}{12} = 1.51, \qquad \text{so} \qquad x_2 = 60 + 12(1.51) = 78.1 \approx 78;$$

$$\frac{x_3 - 15}{3} = 1.81, \qquad \text{so} \qquad x_3 = 15 + 3(1.81) = 20.4 \approx 20.$$

If these x_j-values were used, the total sum spent would be $35(42) + 20(78) + 50(20) = \$4030$, which would exceed the amount of \$3000 the buyer has available. Thus the constraint will be active.

If we let $g(\mathbf{x}) = 35x_1 + 20x_2 + 50x_3$, it is clear that $r(\mathbf{G}) = 1$ at any $\mathbf{x} \neq \mathbf{0}$, and hence we can, without loss of generality, set $\lambda_0 = 1$. The Lagrangian function is then

$$F(\mathbf{x}, \lambda) = \sum_{j=1}^{3} P_j + \lambda[3000 - 35x_1 - 20x_2 - 50x_3].$$

If each component of the optimal $\mathbf{x}$ is positive, then $\mathbf{x}$ must satisfy

$$\frac{\partial F}{\partial x_1} = 0 = -(7 + 35\lambda) + 108\Phi\left(\frac{x_1 - 30}{8}\right),$$

or

$$\Phi\left(\frac{x_1 - 30}{8}\right) = \frac{7 + 35\lambda}{108},$$

$$\frac{\partial F}{\partial x_2} = 0 = -(4 + 20\lambda) + 61\Phi\left(\frac{x_2 - 60}{12}\right),$$

or

$$\Phi\left(\frac{x_2 - 60}{12}\right) = \frac{4 + 20\lambda}{61},$$

$$\frac{\partial F}{\partial x_3} = 0 = -(10 + 50\lambda) + 285\Phi\left(\frac{x_3 - 15}{3}\right),$$

or

$$\Phi\left(\frac{x_3 - 15}{3}\right) = \frac{10 + 50\lambda}{285}.$$

We must find the solutions to these three equations and $g(\mathbf{x}) = 3000$. A convenient method of solution is to select a $\lambda > 0$, determine the unique x_j-values from the above equations, and compute $g(\mathbf{x})$. If $g(\mathbf{x}) = 3000$, we have a solution. If $g(\mathbf{x}) > 3000$, we select a larger value of λ and repeat the computations. If $g(\mathbf{x}) < 3000$, we select a smaller value of λ and repeat the computations. There will be a unique solution to the necessary conditions since, for a given λ, the x_j are uniquely determined, and since the x_j-values decrease monotonically as λ is increased, so that there will be only one λ for which $g(\mathbf{x}) = 3000$. The results of the iterative computations beginning with $\lambda = 0.50$ are given in Table 3–1. By interpolation, one can quickly obtain the appropriate value of λ.

TABLE 3–1

COMPUTATIONS FOR EXAMPLE

λ	x_1	x_2	x_3	$g(\mathbf{x})$
0.50	36	69	18.5	3565
1.00	32	63.2	17.4	3254
1.50	29	58.3	16.6	3011
1.52	28.8	58.0	16.55	2996

Since it is obvious that the buyer should purchase a positive number of each of the three dress types, we need not check the boundaries where one or more $x_j = 0$. The optimal solution that the buyer would use might then be $x_1^* = 29$, $x_2^* = 58$, and $x_3^* = 17$ or 16, depending on whether he preferred to be slightly under or slightly over the given budget restriction. These solutions were obtained simply by rounding off to the nearest integers. It should be pointed out that any solution obtained in this way is not necessarily the optimal solution to the problem in which the x_j must be integers. For practical purposes, the above procedure is often quite adequate, however. In Chapter 10, we shall show how to solve the problem exactly when the x_j are required to be integers.

2. Recall that $D_{\mathbf{r}}f(\mathbf{x}_0)$, the derivative of $z = f(\mathbf{x})$ in the direction $\mathbf{r}$ evaluated at $\mathbf{x}_0$, gives the rate of change of z in the direction $\mathbf{r}$ at $\mathbf{x}_0$. For $f \in C^1$, we showed in Section 2–10 that when $|\mathbf{r}| = 1$, then

$$D_{\mathbf{r}}f(\mathbf{x}_0) = \sum_{j=1}^{n} \frac{\partial f(\mathbf{x}_0)}{\partial x_j}\, r_j. \tag{3–47}$$

Let us now determine the direction $\mathbf{r}$ such that the rate of change of z

at $\mathbf{x}_0$ is a maximum. This means that we wish to maximize

$$\sum_{j=1}^{n} \frac{\partial f(\mathbf{x}_0)}{\partial x_j} r_j$$

with respect to the r_j subject to the constraint $|\mathbf{r}| = 1$ or

$$g(\mathbf{r}) = \sum_{j=1}^{n} r_j^2 = 1. \tag{3–48}$$

Note that $\partial g/\partial r_j = 2r_j$. Hence $r(\mathbf{G}) = 1$ at any point satisfying $|\mathbf{r}| = 1$, and consequently, without loss of generality, we can set $\lambda_0 = 1$ in (3–31). It is clear from the constraint that the optimal $\mathbf{r}$, that is $\mathbf{r}^*$, must have $|\mathbf{r}^*| = 1$, and therefore the magnitude is finite. Thus, if we form the Lagrangian

$$F(\mathbf{r}, \lambda) = \sum_{j=1}^{n} \left[\frac{\partial f(\mathbf{x}_0)}{\partial x_j} r_j - \lambda r_j^2\right] + \lambda, \tag{3–49}$$

then $\mathbf{r}^*$ must be a solution to the equations

$$\frac{\partial F}{\partial r_j} = \frac{\partial f(\mathbf{x}_0)}{\partial x_j} - 2\lambda r_j = 0, \quad j = 1, \ldots, n; \qquad \frac{\partial F}{\partial \lambda} = 1 - \sum_{j=1}^{n} r_j^2 = 0.$$

Hence

$$r_j = \frac{1}{2\lambda} \frac{\partial f(\mathbf{x}_0)}{\partial x_j},$$

and from the constraint,

$$\lambda^2 = \tfrac{1}{4}|\nabla f(\mathbf{x}_0)|^2 \qquad \text{or} \qquad \lambda = \pm\tfrac{1}{2}|\nabla f(\mathbf{x}_0)|.$$

There are then two solutions:

$$\mathbf{r}' = \pm \frac{\nabla f(\mathbf{x}_0)}{|\nabla f(\mathbf{x}_0)|}. \tag{3–50}$$

One of these gives the direction for the maximum rate of increase in z, and the other gives the direction of the maximum rate of decrease in z. To determine which is which, it is only necessary to substitute (3–50) into (3–47). On taking the plus sign, we find that

$$D_{\mathbf{r}} f(\mathbf{x}_0) = |\nabla f(\mathbf{x}_0)| \geq 0, \tag{3–51}$$

so that z is nondecreasing. Hence the plus sign yields the direction of the maximum rate of increase in z, and the minus sign yields the direction of the maximum rate of decrease in z. Thus we have proved the important result that to move in the direction of the maximum rate of increase in z, we move the direction of the gradient vector, and to move in the direction of the maximum rate of decrease in z, we move in a direction opposite to that of the gradient vector. Note from (3–47) that

$$D_{\mathbf{r}}f(\mathbf{x}_0) = \nabla f(\mathbf{x}_0)\mathbf{r} = |\nabla f(\mathbf{x}_0)| \cos\theta,$$

where θ is the angle between $\mathbf{r}$ and $\nabla f(\mathbf{x}_0)$. Thus all we have been doing is finding the value of θ which maximizes $\cos\theta$. Clearly, this is $\theta = 0$, so that $\mathbf{r}$ "points" in the same direction as $\nabla f(\mathbf{x}_0)$.

3. As a final example, we shall show why the Lagrange multiplier technique is of no assistance in solving linear programming problems. Suppose that we wish to solve the problem

$$\mathbf{Ax} = \mathbf{b}, \qquad \mathbf{x} \geq \mathbf{0}, \qquad \max z = \mathbf{cx}.$$

Assume that $\mathbf{A}$ is $m \times n$ and $r(\mathbf{A}) = m$. Note that the constraints and the objective function are differentiable everywhere. Thus the Lagrange multiplier technique can be employed here. We shall follow the procedure suggested in Section 3–6 and begin by trying to determine any relative maxima inside the non-negative orthant where all n of the variables are positive. Then we shall investigate the boundaries where one or more $x_j = 0$.

For points in the interior of the non-negative orthant $r(\mathbf{G}) = m$ everywhere since $\mathbf{G} = \mathbf{A}$. Thus we set $\lambda_0 = 1$ and the appropriate Lagrangian function is

$$F(\mathbf{x}, \boldsymbol{\lambda}) = \sum_{j=1}^{n} c_j x_j + \sum_{i=1}^{m} \lambda_i \left[b_i - \sum_{j=1}^{n} a_{ij}x_j\right].$$

Any optimizing point in the interior of the non-negative orthant must satisfy the equations

$$\begin{aligned} \frac{\partial F}{\partial x_j} &= 0 = c_j - \sum_{i=1}^{m} \lambda_i a_{ij}, \qquad j = 1, \ldots, n, \\ \frac{\partial F}{\partial \lambda_i} &= 0 = b_i - \sum_{j=1}^{n} a_{ij}x_j, \qquad i = 1, \ldots, m, \end{aligned} \tag{3–52}$$

or in matrix form,

$$\mathbf{A}'\boldsymbol{\lambda} = \mathbf{c}', \qquad \mathbf{Ax} = \mathbf{b}.$$

At first glance, it would appear that any feasible solution could be made to satisfy the necessary conditions (3–52). This is not true, however. Let us examine the system of n equations in m unknowns, $\mathbf{A}'\boldsymbol{\lambda} = \mathbf{c}'$. It turns out that, in general, this system of equations is inconsistent, that is, $r(\mathbf{A}', \mathbf{c}') = m + 1$, so that in reality no point in the interior of the non-negative orthant can satisfy the necessary conditions, and hence no such point can yield a relative maximum. This can be seen more clearly if we note that

$$\mathbf{G}_f = \begin{bmatrix} \mathbf{A} \\ \mathbf{c} \end{bmatrix},$$

so that if $r(\mathbf{A}', \mathbf{c}') = m + 1$, then $r(\mathbf{G}_f) = m + 1$ at all points in the interior of the non-negative orthant, and from the results of Section 3–5 we know that no such points can yield a relative maximum or minimum of z. In the event that $r(\mathbf{A}', \mathbf{c}') = m$, $\mathbf{A}'\boldsymbol{\lambda} = \mathbf{c}'$ has a unique solution, z is a constant over the set of feasible solutions, and every feasible solution is optimal. The statements made in the previous sentence are to be proved in Problem 3–64.

In the usual case where $r(\mathbf{G}_f) = m + 1$, we next move to the boundaries of the non-negative orthant and first set one variable, say x_1, to zero. We obtain for the resulting problem a new set of necessary conditions $\mathbf{A}_1'\boldsymbol{\lambda} = \mathbf{c}'$, and $\mathbf{A}_1\mathbf{x}_1 = \mathbf{b}_1$, where $\mathbf{A}_1$, $\mathbf{c}_1$ and $\mathbf{x}_1$ differ from $\mathbf{A}$, $\mathbf{c}$, and $\mathbf{x}$ only in that the first column of each of the latter has been deleted. Typically, it is again true that $r(\mathbf{A}_1', \mathbf{c}_1') = m + 1$, and we conclude that there are no stationary points with only $x_1 = 0$. In the event that $r(\mathbf{A}_1', \mathbf{c}_1') = r(\mathbf{A}_1') = m$, the system $\mathbf{A}_1'\boldsymbol{\lambda} = \mathbf{c}_1'$ has a unique solution, z is a constant for every feasible solution with $x_1 = 0$, and every feasible solution with $x_1 = 0$ is a stationary value which will be either the maximum or the minimum of the objective function. When $x_1 = 0$, it is also possible that $r(\mathbf{A}_1') = m - 1$, and if there is a feasible solution, one constraint is redundant. On eliminating the redundant constraint, one can immediately see that if $r(\mathbf{A}_1', \mathbf{c}_1') = m$, there are no stationary points with only $x_1 = 0$. On the other hand, if $r(\mathbf{A}_1', \mathbf{c}_1') = m - 1$, all feasible solutions with $x_1 = 0$ are stationary points, and these will yield either the maximum or minimum of the objective function. The statements made in the last two sentences are to be developed in more detail in Problem 3–64. We have at this point concluded either that there are no stationary points having only $x_1 = 0$, or that every feasible solution with $x_1 = 0$ yields either the maximum or the minimum of the objective function. In the event that no stationary point has been found, we allow x_1 to be different from zero and set $x_2 = 0$. The analysis is repeated. This is continued as needed until every case has been considered in which just a single variable is set to zero. In the typical case, where no stationary points exist with just a single variable set to zero, we move on and set two variables equal to zero. In the absence of alternative optima, this process will continue until we set $n - m$ variables to zero. Then the remaining m variables are uniquely determined if the matrix of the coefficients is nonsingular, i.e., we are at an extreme point. Thus the Lagrange multiplier technique shows that in general an optimal solution to a linear programming problem will not (unless there are alternative optima) have more than m positive variables, i.e., it shows that in general an optimal solution will occur at an extreme point of the convex set of feasible solutions. However, in practice, the technique is not of any assistance in solving linear programming problems, because it provides no way of determining which extreme point is optimal. The method also points up the existence of alternative optima if there are any, but does not provide a convenient computation procedure in this case either. When the Lagrange multiplier approach is used, the possibility of an unbounded solution is left unanswered.

3–10 Convex and concave functions. In the remainder of the text, we shall frequently restrict our attention to functions which are known as convex or concave functions.

CONVEX FUNCTION: *The function $f(\mathbf{x})$ is said to be convex over a convex set X in E^n if for any two points $\mathbf{x}_1$ and $\mathbf{x}_2$ in X and for all λ, $0 \leq \lambda \leq 1$,*

$$f[\lambda\mathbf{x}_2 + (1 - \lambda)\mathbf{x}_1] \leq \lambda f(\mathbf{x}_2) + (1 - \lambda)f(\mathbf{x}_1). \tag{3–53}$$

Frequently, the convex set X of real interest to us will be all of E^n or the non-negative orthant.

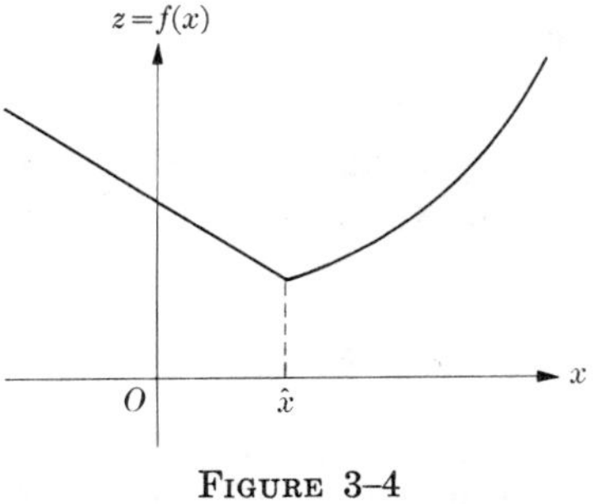

FIGURE 3–4

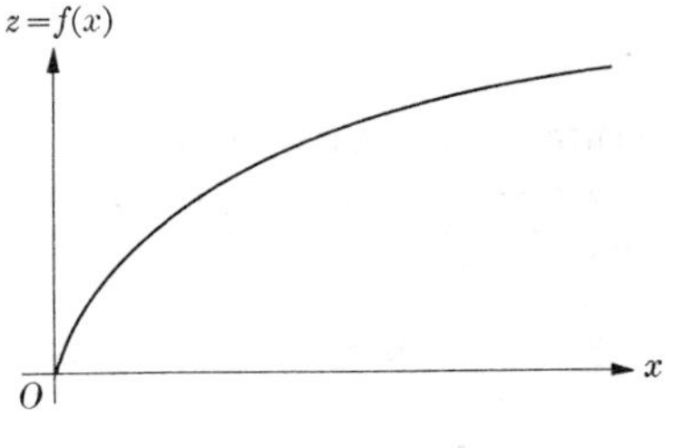

FIGURE 3–5

CONCAVE FUNCTION: *The function $f(\mathbf{x})$ is said to be concave over a convex set X in E^n if for any two points $\mathbf{x}_1$ and $\mathbf{x}_2$ in X and for all λ, $0 \leq \lambda \leq 1$,*

$$f[\lambda\mathbf{x}_2 + (1 - \lambda)\mathbf{x}_1] \geq \lambda f(\mathbf{x}_2) + (1 - \lambda)f(\mathbf{x}_1). \tag{3–54}$$

Observe that if $f(\mathbf{x})$ is convex, then $-f(\mathbf{x})$ is concave, and vice versa.

Intuitively, the hypersurface $z = f(\mathbf{x})$ is convex if the line segment joining any two points $[\mathbf{x}_1, z_1]$, $[\mathbf{x}_2, z_2]$ on the surface lies on or above the surface. A convex function of a single variable is illustrated in Fig. 3–4. Similarly, a hypersurface $z = f(\mathbf{x})$ is concave if the line segment joining any two points on the surface lies on or below the surface. The function of a single variable (Fig. 3–5) is concave for $x \geq 0$. The function shown in

Fig. 3–6 is neither convex nor concave since the line segment from $[x_1, f(x_1)]$ to $[x_3, f(x_3)]$ lies above $f(x)$ between x_1 and x_2 and below $f(x)$ between x_2 and x_3. Note, however, that the function is convex over the interval $0 \leq x \leq x_4$ and concave over the interval $x \geq x_4$. A typical convex function of two variables represented as a surface in E^3 has the shape of a bowl, whereas a concave function has the shape of an inverted bowl. It might be observed that we define convexity and concavity only with respect to convex sets in E^n, since the definition assumes that if $\mathbf{x}_1$ and $\mathbf{x}_2$ are in the set, then so is $\lambda\mathbf{x}_2 + (1 - \lambda)\mathbf{x}_1$ for all λ, $0 \leq \lambda \leq 1$. This will be true only if the set is convex.

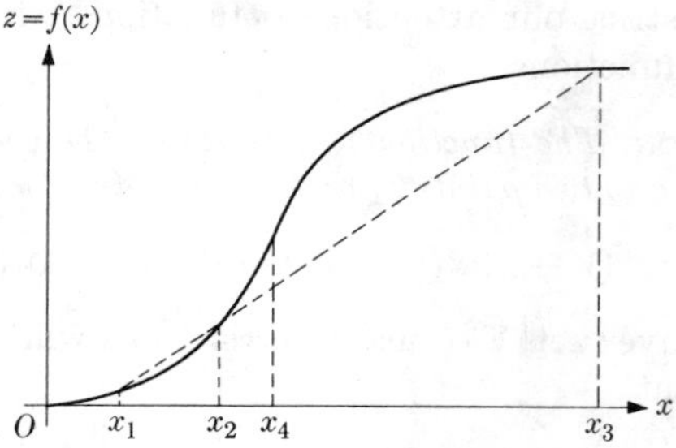

FIGURE 3–6

STRICTLY CONVEX FUNCTION: *A function $f(\mathbf{x})$ is said to be strictly convex over a convex set X in E^n if for any two points $\mathbf{x}_1$ and $\mathbf{x}_2$, $\mathbf{x}_1 \neq \mathbf{x}_2$, in X and all λ, $0 < \lambda < 1$,*

$$f[\lambda\mathbf{x}_2 + (1 - \lambda)\mathbf{x}_1] < \lambda f(\mathbf{x}_2) + (1 - \lambda)f(\mathbf{x}_1). \tag{3–55}$$

Note that the strict inequality holds in (3–55). *A function $f(\mathbf{x})$ is strictly concave over X if $-f(\mathbf{x})$ is strictly convex.* Intuitively, a function $z = f(\mathbf{x})$ is strictly convex if the line segment joining any two points on the surface lies above the surface for all $\mathbf{x} = \lambda\mathbf{x}_2 + (1 - \lambda)\mathbf{x}_1$, $0 < \lambda < 1$. The function in Fig. 3–4 is strictly convex for $x \geq \hat{x}$, but is not strictly convex for $x < \hat{x}$.

A linear function $z = \mathbf{cx}$ is a convex (and concave) function over all of E^n since for any two points $\mathbf{x}_1$ and $\mathbf{x}_2$ and any λ,

$$\mathbf{c}[\lambda\mathbf{x}_2 + (1 - \lambda)\mathbf{x}_1] = \lambda\mathbf{cx}_2 + (1 - \lambda)\mathbf{cx}_1.$$

However, a linear function is neither strictly convex nor strictly concave. *A positive semidefinite quadratic form $z = \mathbf{x}'\mathbf{Ax}$ is a convex function over all of E^n.* To prove this consider any two points $\mathbf{x}_1$ and $\mathbf{x}_2$ and any λ,

$0 \le \lambda \le 1$. Then if $\hat{\mathbf{x}} = \lambda\mathbf{x}_2 + (1 - \lambda)\mathbf{x}_1$, we have

$$\begin{aligned}\hat{\mathbf{x}}'\mathbf{A}\hat{\mathbf{x}} &= [\lambda\mathbf{x}_2 + (1 - \lambda)\mathbf{x}_1]'\mathbf{A}[\lambda\mathbf{x}_2 + (1 - \lambda)\mathbf{x}_1] \\ &= [\mathbf{x}_1 + \lambda(\mathbf{x}_2 - \mathbf{x}_1)]'\mathbf{A}[\mathbf{x}_1 + \lambda(\mathbf{x}_2 - \mathbf{x}_1)] \\ &= \mathbf{x}_1'\mathbf{A}\mathbf{x}_1 + 2\lambda(\mathbf{x}_2 - \mathbf{x}_1)'\mathbf{A}\mathbf{x}_1 + \lambda^2(\mathbf{x}_2 - \mathbf{x}_1)'\mathbf{A}(\mathbf{x}_2 - \mathbf{x}_1). \qquad (3\text{–}56)\end{aligned}$$

However, since by assumption $\mathbf{x}'\mathbf{A}\mathbf{x} \ge 0$ for all $\mathbf{x}$, then for $0 \le \lambda \le 1$, $\lambda\mathbf{x}'\mathbf{A}\mathbf{x} \ge \lambda^2\mathbf{x}'\mathbf{A}\mathbf{x}$. Using this result in (3–56), we can write

$$\hat{\mathbf{x}}'\mathbf{A}\hat{\mathbf{x}} \le \mathbf{x}_1'\mathbf{A}\mathbf{x}_1 + 2\lambda(\mathbf{x}_2 - \mathbf{x}_1)'\mathbf{A}\mathbf{x}_1 + \lambda(\mathbf{x}_2 - \mathbf{x}_1)'\mathbf{A}(\mathbf{x}_2 - \mathbf{x}_1) \qquad (3\text{–}57)$$

or

$$\begin{aligned}\hat{\mathbf{x}}'\mathbf{A}\hat{\mathbf{x}} &\le \mathbf{x}_1'\mathbf{A}\mathbf{x}_1 + \lambda(\mathbf{x}_2 - \mathbf{x}_1)'\mathbf{A}\mathbf{x}_1 + \lambda(\mathbf{x}_2 - \mathbf{x}_1)'\mathbf{A}\mathbf{x}_2 \\ &\le \lambda\mathbf{x}_2'\mathbf{A}\mathbf{x}_2 + (1 - \lambda)\mathbf{x}_1'\mathbf{A}\mathbf{x}_1, \qquad (3\text{–}58)\end{aligned}$$

which is what we wished to show. It immediately follows that *a negative semidefinite quadratic form is a concave function over all of* E^n. The same argument shows that *a positive definite quadratic form is a strictly convex function over all of* E^n since in this case,

$$\lambda(\mathbf{x}_2 - \mathbf{x}_1)'\mathbf{A}(\mathbf{x}_2 - \mathbf{x}_1) > \lambda^2(\mathbf{x}_2 - \mathbf{x}_1)'\mathbf{A}(\mathbf{x}_2 - \mathbf{x}_1) \qquad (3\text{–}59)$$

when $0 < \lambda < 1$ and $\mathbf{x}_2 \ne \mathbf{x}_1$. Hence the $\le$ sign in (3–57) can be replaced by a $<$ sign. Similarly, *a negative definite quadratic form is a strictly concave function over all of* E^n.

Suppose that the functions $f_j(\mathbf{x})$, $j = 1, \ldots, k$, *are convex over some convex set* X *in* E^n. *Then the function*

$$f(\mathbf{x}) = \sum_{j=1}^{k} f_j(\mathbf{x}) \qquad (3\text{–}60)$$

is also convex over X. To prove this it is only necessary to note that for any points $\mathbf{x}_1$, $\mathbf{x}_2$ in X and any λ, $0 \le \lambda \le 1$,

$$\begin{aligned}&f[\lambda\mathbf{x}_2 + (1 - \lambda)\mathbf{x}_1] \\ &\quad = \sum_{j=1}^{k} f_j[\lambda\mathbf{x}_2 + (1 - \lambda)\mathbf{x}_1] \le \sum_{j=1}^{k} [\lambda f_j(\mathbf{x}_2) + (1 - \lambda)f_j(\mathbf{x}_1)] \\ &\quad = \lambda \sum_{j=1}^{k} f_j(\mathbf{x}_2) + (1 - \lambda) \sum_{j=1}^{k} f_j(\mathbf{x}_1) = \lambda f(\mathbf{x}_2) + (1 - \lambda)f(\mathbf{x}_1).\end{aligned}$$

Thus the sum of convex functions is a convex function. Of course, it is also true that *the sum of concave functions is a concave function.*

In the definition of convexity and concavity, we did not require that $f(\mathbf{x})$ be either continuous or differentiable. It can be proved that if $f(\mathbf{x})$ is convex or concave over X and is bounded, then $f(\mathbf{x})$ is continuous at every interior point of X; $f(\mathbf{x})$ may be discontinuous on the boundaries of X, however. A special case of the proof can be found in [4]. It is not necessarily true that a convex or concave function $f(\mathbf{x})$ must be differentiable everywhere. For example, the derivative of the convex function shown in Fig. 3–4 does not exist at $x = \hat{x}$. If $f(\mathbf{x}) \in C^1$ over the interior of the convex set X and if f is convex over X, then we can obtain a new and sometimes useful result. By assumption, (3–53) holds for all λ, $0 < \lambda \leq 1$; so

$$\frac{f[\mathbf{x}_1 + \lambda(\mathbf{x}_2 - \mathbf{x}_1)] - f(\mathbf{x}_1)}{\lambda} \leq f(\mathbf{x}_2) - f(\mathbf{x}_1). \tag{3–61}$$

On expanding $f[\mathbf{x}_1 + \lambda(\mathbf{x}_2 - \mathbf{x}_1)]$ by Taylor's theorem we have

$$f[\mathbf{x}_1 + \lambda(\mathbf{x}_2 - \mathbf{x}_1)] = f(\mathbf{x}_1) + \lambda\nabla f[\mathbf{x}_1 + \lambda\theta(\mathbf{x}_2 - \mathbf{x}_1)](\mathbf{x}_2 - \mathbf{x}_1), \quad 0 \leq \theta \leq 1, \tag{3–62}$$

so that (3–61) becomes

$$\nabla f[\mathbf{x}_1 + \lambda\theta(\mathbf{x}_2 - \mathbf{x}_1)](\mathbf{x}_2 - \mathbf{x}_1) \leq f(\mathbf{x}_2) - f(\mathbf{x}_1). \tag{3–63}$$

In particular, on taking the limit as $\lambda \to 0$, we obtain

$$\nabla f(\mathbf{x}_1)(\mathbf{x}_2 - \mathbf{x}_1) \leq f(\mathbf{x}_2) - f(\mathbf{x}_1) \tag{3–64}$$

for all interior points $\mathbf{x}_1$ of X and all points $\mathbf{x}_2 \in X$. Similarly, if $f \in C^1$ and is concave over X, then the equivalent of (3–64) becomes

$$\nabla f(\mathbf{x}_1)(\mathbf{x}_2 - \mathbf{x}_1) \geq f(\mathbf{x}_2) - f(\mathbf{x}_1). \tag{3–65}$$

When f is a function of a single variable only, (3–64) can be written

$$f'(x_1) \leq \frac{f(x_2) - f(x_1)}{x_2 - x_1}, \qquad x_1 < x_2. \tag{3–66}$$

Intuitively, this says that the slope of $f(x)$ at x_1 is less than, or equal to, the slope of the secant through the points $[x_1, f(x_1)]$ and $[x_2, f(x_2)]$ when f is convex. This is obvious geometrically, as is shown in Fig. 3–7.

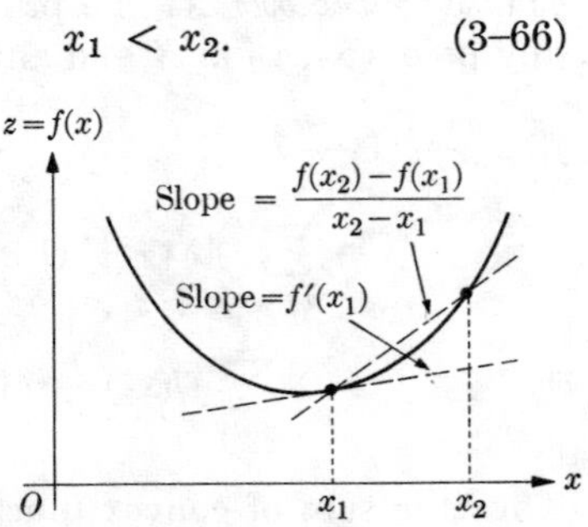

FIGURE 3–7

If $f(\mathbf{x})$ is a convex function over the non-negative orthant of E^n, then, if the set of points V satisfying $f(\mathbf{x}) \leq b$, $\mathbf{x} \geq \mathbf{0}$, *is not empty, V is a convex set.* To prove this we show that if $\mathbf{x}_1$ and $\mathbf{x}_2$ are in V, so is $\hat{\mathbf{x}} = \lambda\mathbf{x}_2 + (1 - \lambda)\mathbf{x}_1$ for any λ, $0 \leq \lambda \leq 1$. (If there is only one point in the set, the result follows automatically.) It is clear that $\hat{\mathbf{x}} \geq \mathbf{0}$. It remains to show that $f(\hat{\mathbf{x}}) \leq b$. This follows from the convexity of $f(\mathbf{x})$. We have

$$f(\hat{\mathbf{x}}) = f[\lambda\mathbf{x}_2 + (1 - \lambda)\mathbf{x}_1] \leq \lambda f(\mathbf{x}_2) + (1 - \lambda)f(\mathbf{x}_1).$$

Also $f(\mathbf{x}_1) \leq b$ and $f(\mathbf{x}_2) \leq b$. Furthermore, $\lambda f(\mathbf{x}_2) \leq \lambda b$ and $(1 - \lambda)f(\mathbf{x}_1) \leq (1 - \lambda)b$ since $0 \leq \lambda \leq 1$. Consequently

$$\lambda f(\mathbf{x}_2) + (1 - \lambda)f(\mathbf{x}_1) \leq \lambda b + (1 - \lambda)b = b \qquad \text{and} \qquad f(\hat{\mathbf{x}}) \leq b,$$

which is what we needed to prove. It should be observed that the set of points satisfying $f(\mathbf{x}) = b$, $\mathbf{x} \geq \mathbf{0}$, is not in general convex. The above method of proof also shows that *if $f(\mathbf{x})$ is a concave function over the non-negative orthant of E^n, then if the set of points V satisfying $f(\mathbf{x}) \geq b$, $\mathbf{x} \geq \mathbf{0}$, is not empty, V is a convex set.* Consequently, since the intersection of convex sets is convex, *if the set of points W satisfying*

$$f_i(\mathbf{x}) \{\leq, \geq\} b_i, \qquad i = 1, \ldots, m; \qquad \mathbf{x} \geq \mathbf{0},$$

is not empty, then W is convex when $f_i(\mathbf{x})$ is a convex function over the non-negative orthant of E^n if a $\leq$ sign holds for the ith relation and $f_i(\mathbf{x})$ is a concave function over the non-negative orthant of E^n if a $\geq$ sign holds for the ith relation.

Let $f(\mathbf{x})$ be a convex function over the non-negative orthant of E^n. Also assume that $f(\mathbf{x}) \in C^1$. Then a tangent hyperplane to the $(n - 1)$-dimensional surface described by $f(\mathbf{x}) = b$ at a point $\mathbf{x}_0 \geq \mathbf{0}$ satisfying $f(\mathbf{x}_0) = b$ is a supporting hyperplane to the convex set $K = \{\mathbf{x} | f(\mathbf{x}) \leq b, \mathbf{x} \geq \mathbf{0}\}$ at $\mathbf{x}_0$. To prove this recall that the equation of the tangent hyperplane at $\mathbf{x}_0$ is $\nabla f(\mathbf{x}_0)\mathbf{x} = \nabla f(\mathbf{x}_0)\mathbf{x}_0$. We wish to prove that if $\mathbf{w}$ is any point in K, then $\nabla f(\mathbf{x}_0)\mathbf{w} \leq \nabla f(\mathbf{x}_0)\mathbf{x}_0$. This follows immediately from the convexity of $f(\mathbf{x})$ when we apply (3–64) with $\mathbf{w} = \mathbf{x}_2$, $\mathbf{x}_0 = \mathbf{x}_1$, and note that $f(\mathbf{w}) \leq b$, $f(\mathbf{x}_0) = b$, since we obtain

$$\nabla f(\mathbf{x}_0)(\mathbf{w} - \mathbf{x}_0) \leq 0,$$

which is what we desired to show. *Similarly, if $f(\mathbf{x})$ is concave over the non-negative orthant and $f(\mathbf{x}) \in C^1$, then a tangent hyperplane to the surface $f(\mathbf{x}) = b$ at a point $\mathbf{x}_0 \geq \mathbf{0}$ satisfying $f(\mathbf{x}_0) = b$ is a supporting hyperplane to the convex set $K = \{\mathbf{x} | f(\mathbf{x}) \geq b, \mathbf{x} \geq \mathbf{0}\}$ at $\mathbf{x}_0$.*

3–11 Examples. 1. $f_1(x_1) = 3x_1^2$ is a positive definite quadratic form (in a single variable), and hence is a convex function over all of E^1. Similarly, $f_2(x_2) = 4x_2^2$ is a convex function over all of E^1. Note that

$f_1(x_1)$, as well as $f_2(x_2)$, can be considered functions of $\mathbf{x} = [x_1, x_2]$, where $f_1(x_1)$ depends only on the first component of $\mathbf{x}$ and $f_2(x_2)$ depends only on the second component of $\mathbf{x}$. Thus $f_1(x_1)$ and $f_2(x_2)$ are convex functions over E^2. Hence $f(\mathbf{x}) = 3x_1^2 + 4x_2^2$ is also a convex function over E^2.

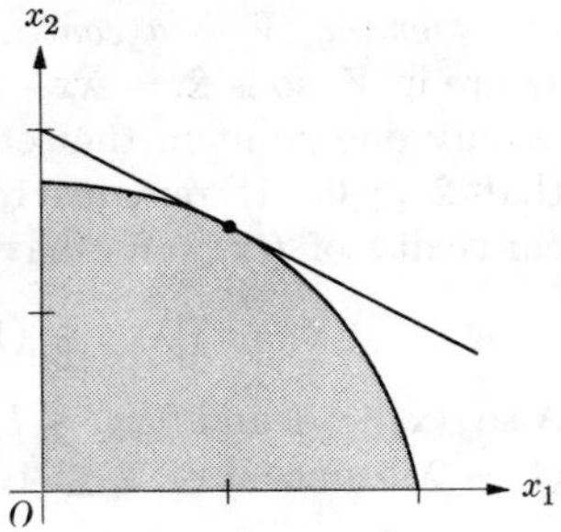

FIGURE 3–8

2. Since $f(\mathbf{x}) = 3x_1^2 + 4x_2^2$ is a convex function, the set

$$X = \{\mathbf{x}|f(\mathbf{x}) \leq 12, \mathbf{x} \geq \mathbf{0}\}$$

should be convex. The set is indeed convex (see Fig. 3–8). The point $[1, \frac{3}{2}]$ is on the curve $3x_1^2 + 4x_2^2 = 12$. At this point,

$$\nabla f = (6x_1, 8x_2) = (6, 12),$$

so that the equation of the tangent line (hyperplane) at this point is $6(x_1 - 1) + 12(x_2 - \frac{3}{2}) = 0$. This line is shown in Fig. 3–8. It will be noted that it is indeed a supporting line (hyperplane) to the convex set.

3. The function

$$f_1(x) = \begin{cases} 0, & x \leq \alpha, \\ a(x - \alpha), \quad a > 0, & x \geq \alpha \end{cases}$$

shown in Fig. 3–9 is a convex function. To prove this, consider $f[\lambda x_2 + (1 - \lambda)x_1]$. There are three cases to consider:

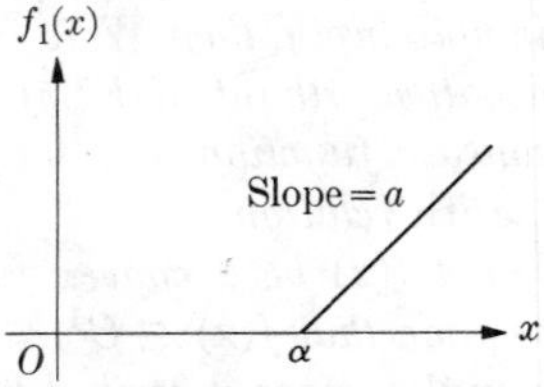

FIGURE 3–9

(a) $x_1, x_2 \leq \alpha$. Then

$$f_1[\lambda x_2 + (1 - \lambda)x_1] = \lambda f_1(x_2) + (1 - \lambda)f_1(x_1) = 0.$$

Hence $f_1(x)$ is convex for $x \leq \alpha$.

(b) $x_1, x_2 \geq \alpha$. Then

$$\begin{aligned} f_1[\lambda x_2 + (1 - \lambda)x_1] &= a\lambda(x_2 - \alpha) + a(1 - \lambda)(x_1 - \alpha) \\ &= \lambda f_1(x_2) + (1 - \lambda)f_1(x_1). \end{aligned}$$

Hence $f_1(x)$ is convex for $x \geq \alpha$.

(c) $x_2 \leq \alpha, x_1 > \alpha$. Then

$$f_1[\lambda x_2 + (1 - \lambda)x_1]$$

$$= \begin{cases} a[\lambda x_2 + (1 - \lambda)x_1 - \alpha] = a\lambda(x_2 - \alpha) + a(1 - \lambda)(x_1 - \alpha), \\ \qquad\qquad \lambda x_2 + (1 - \lambda)x_1 > \alpha, \\ 0, \; \lambda x_2 + (1 - \lambda)x_1 \leq \alpha, \end{cases}$$

and

$$\lambda f_1(x_2) + (1 - \lambda) f_1(x_1) = a(1 - \lambda)(x_1 - \alpha).$$

Hence, either when $\hat{x} = \lambda x_2 + (1 - \lambda)x_1 > \alpha$, or when $\hat{x} \leq \alpha$,

$$f_1(\hat{x}) \leq \lambda f_1(x_2) + (1 - \lambda) f_1(x_1)$$

since $x_2 - \alpha \leq 0$. Thus $f_1(x)$ is convex for all x. Similarly, the function

$$f_2(x) = \begin{cases} b(x - \alpha), & b < 0, \quad x \leq \alpha, \\ 0, & \quad\quad\quad\; x \geq \alpha \end{cases}$$

is convex for all x.

4. The function

$$f(x) = \begin{cases} a(x - \alpha), & a > 0, \quad x \geq \alpha, \\ b(x - \alpha), & b < 0, \quad x \leq \alpha \end{cases}$$

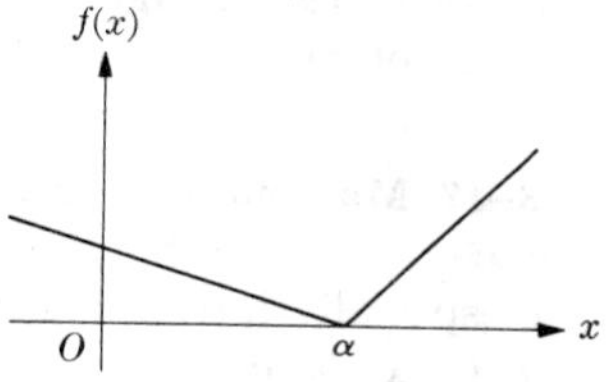

FIGURE 3–10

is a convex function for all x since $f(x)$ is the sum of two functions $f_1(x)$ and $f_2(x)$ which were shown to be convex (see above). A plot of $f(x)$ is given in Fig. 3–10.

5. Assume that $f(x)$ is continuous and $f(x) \geq 0$, $-\infty < x < \infty$. Then the function

$$\psi(x) = \int_x^\infty (y - x) f(y)\, dy$$

is a convex function, provided that the integral converges. To prove this, let $\hat{x} = \lambda x_2 + (1 - \lambda)x_1$, $0 \leq \lambda \leq 1$, and to be specific assume that $x_2 > x_1$. Then

$$\begin{aligned} \psi(\hat{x}) &= \int_{\hat{x}}^\infty [y - \lambda x_2 - (1 - \lambda)x_1] f(y)\, dy \\ &= \lambda \int_{\hat{x}}^\infty (y - x_2) f(y)\, dy + (1 - \lambda) \int_{\hat{x}}^\infty (y - x_1) f(y)\, dy \\ &= \lambda \int_{x_2}^\infty (y - x_2) f(y)\, dy + \lambda \int_{\hat{x}}^{x_2} (y - x_2) f(y)\, dy \\ &\quad + (1 - \lambda) \int_{x_1}^\infty (y - x_1) f(y)\, dy - (1 - \lambda) \int_{x_1}^{\hat{x}} (y - x_1) f(y)\, dy. \end{aligned}$$

However, since $f(y) \geq 0$ and $y - x_1 \geq 0$ for y lying between x_1 and $\hat{x}$, and $y - x_2 \leq 0$ for y lying between $\hat{x}$ and x_2, we conclude that

$$\int_{\hat{x}}^{x_2} (y - x_2) f(y)\, dy \leq 0 \qquad \text{and} \qquad \int_{x_1}^{\hat{x}} (y - x_1) f(y)\, dy \geq 0.$$

Thus it follows immediately from the expression for $\psi(\hat{x})$ that

$$\psi(\hat{x}) \leq \lambda\psi(x_2) + (1 - \lambda)\psi(x_1).$$

Therefore $\psi(x)$ is convex. Furthermore, if $f(x) > 0$ everywhere, the above argument shows that $\psi(x)$ is strictly convex. This result demonstrates that the P_j in Example 1 of Section 3–9 are strictly concave. Hence P is strictly concave, and the Lagrangian function is strictly concave, since $g(x)$ is convex. Why is the Lagrangian *strictly* concave?

3–12 Maxima and minima of convex and concave functions. We now come to the results which illustrate why convex and concave functions are especially interesting in the theory of nonlinear programming.

Let $f(\mathbf{x})$ be a convex function over the closed convex set X in E^n. Then any relative minimum of $f(\mathbf{x})$ in X is also the absolute (global) minimum of $f(\mathbf{x})$ over X. We shall prove this by contradiction. Assume that f takes on a relative minimum at $\mathbf{x}_0 \in X$, whereas the absolute minimum over X is taken on at $\mathbf{x}^*$, and that $f(\mathbf{x}_0) > f(\mathbf{x}^*)$. Since $f(\mathbf{x})$ is convex, then for all λ, $0 \leq \lambda \leq 1$,

$$f[\lambda\mathbf{x}^* + (1 - \lambda)\mathbf{x}_0] \leq \lambda f(\mathbf{x}^*) + (1 - \lambda)f(\mathbf{x}_0).$$

However, since $f(\mathbf{x}^*) < f(\mathbf{x}_0)$, it must be true that for all λ, $0 < \lambda < 1$,

$$f[\lambda\mathbf{x}^* + (1 - \lambda)\mathbf{x}_0] < \lambda f(\mathbf{x}_0) + (1 - \lambda)f(\mathbf{x}_0) = f(\mathbf{x}_0). \qquad (3\text{–}67)$$

But consider any ϵ-neighborhood of $\mathbf{x}_0$, with $\epsilon < |\mathbf{x}^* - \mathbf{x}_0|$. If $0 < \lambda < \epsilon/|\mathbf{x}^* - \mathbf{x}_0|$, then $\mathbf{x} = \lambda\mathbf{x}^* + (1 - \lambda)\mathbf{x}_0$ is in the ϵ-neighborhood of $\mathbf{x}_0$ and $f(\mathbf{x}) < f(\mathbf{x}_0)$. This contradicts the fact that $f(\mathbf{x})$ takes on a relative minimum at $\mathbf{x}_0$. Thus we have shown that any relative minimum of $f(\mathbf{x})$ is also the global minimum. In the above proof we have implicitly assumed that the absolute minimum was taken on at a point $\mathbf{x}^*$ such that $|\mathbf{x}^*|$ was finite. The proof can be generalized to the case where the absolute minimum is taken on in the limit as $|\mathbf{x}| \to \infty$ in some specified way, when the set X is not strictly bounded. We ask the reader to make this generalization in Problem 3–19.

We shall next show that the set of points in X at which $f(\mathbf{x})$ takes on its global minimum is a convex set. If the global minimum is taken on at just a single point, the result follows immediately. Suppose then that the global minimum is taken on at two different points $\mathbf{x}_1$ and $\mathbf{x}_2$. We shall now show that the absolute minimum must be taken on at every point $\mathbf{x} = \lambda\mathbf{x}_2 + (1 - \lambda)\mathbf{x}_1$, $0 \leq \lambda \leq 1$. This follows immediately from the convexity of $f(\mathbf{x})$ and the fact that $f(\mathbf{x}_1) = f(\mathbf{x}_2)$ is the global minimum of

$f(\mathbf{x})$, since by the convexity property

$$f(\mathbf{x}) = f[\lambda \mathbf{x}_2 + (1 - \lambda)\mathbf{x}_1] \leq \lambda f(\mathbf{x}_2) + (1 - \lambda)f(\mathbf{x}_1) = f(\mathbf{x}_2). \quad (3\text{–}68)$$

Inasmuch as $f(\mathbf{x})$ cannot be less than $f(\mathbf{x}_2)$, we must have $f(\mathbf{x}) = f(\mathbf{x}_2) = f(\mathbf{x}_1)$. Thus the set of points for which $f(\mathbf{x})$ takes on its global minimum is convex. This result leads to two additional ones: First, *if the absolute minimum is taken on at two different points, it is taken on at an infinite number of points.* Secondly, *there cannot be two (or more) points at which $f(\mathbf{x})$ takes on a strong relative minimum* (also the global minimum), since every point on the line segment joining these two points would have to yield the same value of $f(\mathbf{x})$, contradicting the fact that these points yield strong relative minima of $f(\mathbf{x})$. *If $f(\mathbf{x})$ is strictly convex, then it is clear that the absolute minimum of $f(\mathbf{x})$ over a convex set X is assumed at a unique point,* i.e., there cannot exist two different points of X where the global minimum of $f(\mathbf{x})$ is taken on. This follows from the observation that if the absolute minimum were taken on at two distinct points, the point halfway between them would have to yield a smaller value of $f(\mathbf{x})$; this leads to a contradiction.

Assume that $f(\mathbf{x})$ is convex over a convex set X in E^n, and moreover, $f \in C^1$ at all points in X. Let $\mathbf{x}_0$ be a point such that $\partial f(\mathbf{x}_0)/\partial x_j = 0$, $j = 1, \ldots, n$, that is $\nabla f(\mathbf{x}_0) = \mathbf{0}$. Then $f(\mathbf{x})$ has a relative minimum at $\mathbf{x}_0$, and in addition takes on its global minimum over X at $\mathbf{x}_0$. To see this, consider any point $\mathbf{x}$ in X. From (3–64), on setting $\mathbf{x}_0 = \mathbf{x}_1$ and $\mathbf{x} = \mathbf{x}_2$, we conclude that $f(\mathbf{x}) \geq f(\mathbf{x}_0)$, which is what we wished to show. Thus *$f(\mathbf{x})$ must assume its global minimum over X at every point in X which satisfies $\nabla f(\mathbf{x}) = \mathbf{0}$.*

Let us now imagine that we are trying to determine the global *maximum* (rather than the minimum) of the convex function $f(\mathbf{x})$ over the closed convex set X which is bounded from below. We shall prove the following: *Let X be a closed convex set which is bounded from below. If the absolute maximum of the convex function $f(\mathbf{x})$ over X is finite, the absolute maximum of $f(\mathbf{x})$ will be taken on at one or more extreme points of X.* To begin the proof, first note that $f(\mathbf{x})$ cannot have a strong relative maximum at an interior point $\mathbf{x}_0$ of X, for suppose that $f(\mathbf{x})$ has a strong relative maximum at $\mathbf{x}_0$. Since $\mathbf{x}_0$ is an interior point, there exists an ϵ-neighborhood of $\mathbf{x}_0$ which contains only points in X. Let $\mathbf{x}_1$ be any such point in this ϵ-neighborhood different from $\mathbf{x}_0$. The point $\mathbf{x}_2 = 2\mathbf{x}_0 - \mathbf{x}_1$ is also in the ϵ-neighborhood, and $\mathbf{x}_0 = (\mathbf{x}_1 + \mathbf{x}_2)/2$. But by the convexity property (with $\lambda = \frac{1}{2}$),

$$f(\mathbf{x}_0) \leq \tfrac{1}{2}f(\mathbf{x}_1) + \tfrac{1}{2}f(\mathbf{x}_2),$$

which implies that $f(\mathbf{x}_0) = f(\mathbf{x}_1) = f(\mathbf{x}_2)$ or either $f(\mathbf{x}_1)$ or $f(\mathbf{x}_2)$ is greater than $f(\mathbf{x}_0)$. This is true for every $\mathbf{x}_1 \neq \mathbf{x}_0$ in the ϵ-neighborhood, which contradicts the fact that $f(\mathbf{x})$ assumes a strong relative maximum at $\mathbf{x}_0$. Thus it follows that if the global maximum is taken on at an interior point $\mathbf{x}_0$ of X, it is taken on at every point in any ϵ-neighborhood of $\mathbf{x}_0$ which contains only points of X. From this we can then show that the absolute maximum is taken on at every point in X, and hence $z = f(\mathbf{x}) =$ constant over X. To prove that if the global maximum is taken on at an interior point $\mathbf{x}_0$ it is taken on at every point in X, consider any other point $\hat{\mathbf{x}}$ in X. If $\hat{\mathbf{x}}$ is in an ϵ-neighborhood of $\mathbf{x}_0$ containing only points of X, it follows from the above argument that the global maximum is also taken on at $\hat{\mathbf{x}}$. Now suppose $\hat{\mathbf{x}}$ is not in such an ϵ-neighborhood. Select any $\epsilon_0 > 0$ such that all $\mathbf{x}$ in ϵ_0-neighborhood of $\mathbf{x}_0$ lie in X. Then consider the line segment joining $\hat{\mathbf{x}}$ and $\mathbf{x}_0$. The point

$$\mathbf{x}_1 = \mathbf{x}_0 + 0.9\epsilon_0 \frac{\hat{\mathbf{x}} - \mathbf{x}_0}{|\hat{\mathbf{x}} - \mathbf{x}_0|} \tag{3-69}$$

is in the ϵ-neighborhood of $\mathbf{x}_0$ and hence is also a point where $f(\mathbf{x})$ assumes its global maximum. Let us examine an ϵ_0-neighborhood about $\mathbf{x}_1$. All points

$$\mathbf{x} = \mathbf{x}_1 + \lambda\epsilon_0 \frac{\hat{\mathbf{x}} - \mathbf{x}_0}{|\mathbf{x} - \mathbf{x}_0|}, \qquad 0 \leq \lambda < 1, \tag{3-70}$$

are points where $f(\mathbf{x})$ takes on its global maximum since

$$\mathbf{x}_1 = \frac{1}{2}\mathbf{x} + \frac{1}{2}\left(\mathbf{x}_1 - \lambda\epsilon_0 \frac{\hat{\mathbf{x}} - \mathbf{x}_0}{|\hat{\mathbf{x}} - \mathbf{x}_0|}\right).$$

If $\hat{\mathbf{x}}$ cannot be written in the form (3–70), consider the point $\mathbf{x}_2$ given by (3–70) when $\lambda = 0.9$ and consider an ϵ_0-neighborhood about this point. This procedure is repeated until, in a finite number of steps, we conclude that the global maximum is taken on at $\hat{\mathbf{x}}$ also. Note that all ϵ_0-neighborhoods after the first can contain points not in X. Thus the global maximum is taken on at all points in X and $z = c$. The procedure just used is illustrated in Fig. 3–11. Therefore, since X is bounded from below, it has at least one extreme point, and hence the theorem is true in this case.

Now suppose that the global maximum is taken on at a boundary point $\mathbf{x}_0$ of X, but not at any interior point of X. If $\mathbf{x}_0$ is an extreme point, we have satisfied the theorem. If $\mathbf{x}_0$ is not an extreme point, consider the intersection of X with a supporting hyperplane H at $\mathbf{x}_0$. This intersection will be a closed convex set, call it T, and will contain at least one extreme point of X if X is bounded from below. Note that T lies in the $(n-1)$-dimensional space H. Let us then study T as a set in a space of dimension $n - 1$. If $\mathbf{x}_0$ is an interior point of T with respect to this space of dimension $n - 1$, the above arguments show that the global maximum of $f(\mathbf{x})$ must be taken on at every point in T and hence at an extreme point of X. If $\mathbf{x}_0$ is on the boundary of T, consider the set T_1, which is the intersection of a supporting hyperplane to T at $\mathbf{x}_0$ with T. The set

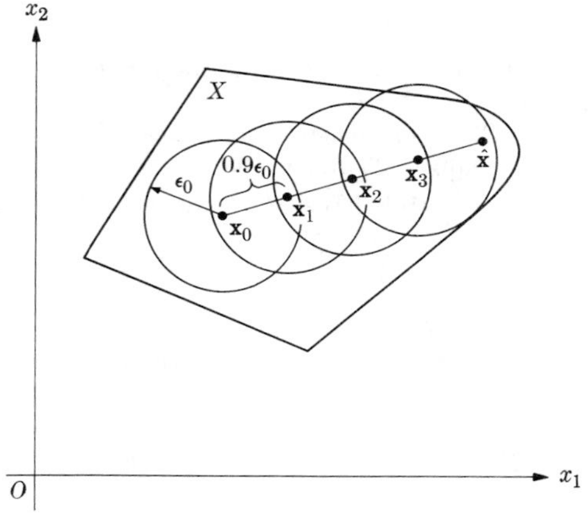

FIGURE 3-11

T_1 then lies in a space of dimension $n - 2$. The above arguments are now repeated with T_1. This process must terminate in no more than $n - 1$ stages, because T_{n-1} will lie in a space of dimension 0, and will be the single point $\mathbf{x}_0$ which must then be an extreme point of X (why?). This completes the proof of the theorem. If X is a convex polyhedron, the proof of the theorem is much easier and is left for Problem 3-34. Although we have shown that the global maximum of $f(\mathbf{x})$ will be taken on at one or more extreme points, there also exists the possibility for relative maxima different from the global maximum to occur at extreme points. (Such a case is illustrated in Fig. 1-4.) Hence, when devising computational schemes, one might find it difficult to exploit the fact that the global maximum occurs at an extreme point, since the familiar "adjacent extreme point procedures" typical of the simplex method will not necessarily yield the global maximum.

The results for concave functions analogous to those proved for the convex functions discussed above are as follows: *Let $f(\mathbf{x})$ be a concave function over the closed convex set X in E^n. Then any relative maximum of $f(\mathbf{x})$ in X is also the global maximum of $f(\mathbf{x})$ over X. Furthermore, the set of points in X at which $f(\mathbf{x})$ assumes its global maximum is a convex set. Hence, if the global maximum is taken on at two different points, it is taken on at an infinite number of points. In addition, there cannot be two or more distinct strong relative maxima. If $f(\mathbf{x})$ is strictly concave, then the point in X at which the global maximum is assumed is unique. If $f(\mathbf{x})$ is concave over a convex set X and if $f(\mathbf{x}) \in C^1$, then if $\nabla f(\mathbf{x}) = \mathbf{0}$ at $\mathbf{x}_0$, $f(\mathbf{x})$ takes on its global maximum over X at $\mathbf{x}_0$. When X is closed and bounded from below, and the global minimum of the concave function $f(\mathbf{x})$ is finite, then the global minimim of $f(\mathbf{x})$ will be taken on at one or more extreme points of X.*

References

1. Allen, R. G. D., *Mathematical Analysis for Economists.* New York: St. Martin's Press, 1938.

2. Carathéodory, C., *Variatonsrechnung und Partielle Differentialgleichungen erster Ordung.* Leipzig: Teubner, 1935.

3. Courant, R., and D. Hilbert, *Methods of Mathematical Physics,* Vol. 1. New York: Interscience Publishers, 1953.

4. Courant, R., *Differential and Integral Calculus,* Vol. 2. New York: Interscience, 1936.

5. Hancock, H., *Theory of Maxima and Minima.* New York: Dover, 1960.

6. Samuelson, P., *Foundations of Economic Analysis.* Cambridge: Harvard University Press, 1947.

7. Von Neumann, J., and O. Morgenstern, *Theory of Games and Economic Behavior.* Princeton, N. J.: Princeton University Press, 1953.

Problems

3–1. Certain crystals such as sodium chloride (NaCl) are composed of ions arranged in an orderly way to form a lattice. In NaCl, each Na^+ or Cl^- ion is surrounded by six nearest neighbors of opposite charge and twelve next nearest neighbors of the same charge. There are two sets of forces which oppose each other: the Coulomb attraction which varies inversely as the square of the interionic distance, and a repulsive force which varies as the $(n + 1)$-power of the interionic distance, $n \geq 2$. After summing over all ions, we may write the potential energy of the crystal as

$$U = \frac{c_1}{R^n} - \frac{c_2}{R},$$

where c_1, c_2 are constants such that $c_1, c_2 > 0$, and R is the nearest-neighbor separation in the crystal. Given that nature tends to minimize the potential energy, find R_0, the equilibrium value of R, and the equilibrium potential energy. Find the amount of energy required to dissociate the crystal, i.e., to yield $R = \infty$.

3–2. A manufacturer must supply customers with D units per year of one of his products. This article is not turned out continuously but in several discrete production runs during the course of a year. He would like to determine the number of units to be made in each run (we assume that the same number will be produced in each run) in order to minimize costs. The total setup cost for each run is c_1 (this is independent of the number of units produced during the run), and c_2 is the cost of holding one unit in inventory for a year. Assume that the cost of storing a unit for any length of time is proportional to the time for which it is kept in stock. Suppose that the customer's demand rate over time is constant. Show that if it is not permissible to run out of inventory, and the time required to produce the units is ignored, then the optimal number of units to be made in a run is

$$Q^* = \sqrt{2Dc_1/c_2}.$$

Consider all variables to be continuous.

3–3. For the situation described in Problem 3–2, repeat the computation under the assumption that it is permissible to run out of inventory. The cost of having one unit out of stock one year is c_3. Assume that the unfilled orders on hand are filled immediately when a production run is completed. [*Hint:* The function to be optimized will now involve two variables, the order quantity and the maximum number of backorders that are incurred.]

3–4. Given that a monopolist produces q units in a given time period, he can sell them all if he sets the selling price to be $p = \phi(q)$ or less. He has no reason to charge less, and hence will have $p = \phi(q)$. If $c(q)$ is the total cost of producing q units, then determine the quantity to be manufactured in order to maximize the total profit π for the time period. Solve for dc/dq and provide an economic interpretation of the result. In particular, explain the $q\,dp/dq$-term. What happens in the case of pure competition, where a given manufacturer can sell all he produces at the fixed market price?

3–5. A monopolist produces jointly two goods in quantities x_1 and x_2 in a given time period. The total cost function is

$$c(x_1, x_2) = x_1 + 2x_2 + 1300.$$

The demand curves are

$$x_1 = 600p_2 - 400p_1, \quad x_2 = 1800 - 100p_1 - 300p_2.$$

Find the quantities to be produced and the corresponding prices that will ensure a maximum profit.

3–6. The value of some physical variable y depends on n other physical variables $x_1, \ldots, x_n$. Imagine that a set of m observations has been made. Each set of observations $[x_{i1}, \ldots, x_{in}, y_i]$ represents a point in E^{n+1}. It is desired to find the hyperplane

$$\hat{y} = \sum_{j=1}^{n} a_j x_j + b$$

which comes closest to passing through the m points in E^{n+1}. By "closest" we mean that if $\hat{y}_i = \sum a_j x_{ij} + b$, then the $a_j, j = 1, \ldots, n$, and b are to be determined in such a way that

$$\sum_{i=1}^{m} \epsilon_i^2 = \sum (y_i - \hat{y}_i)^2$$

is a minimum. This is the classical least-squares problem. Find the equations which determine the optimal a_j and b. [*Hint:* If we write $\boldsymbol{\epsilon} = [\epsilon_1, \ldots, \epsilon_m]$, $\mathbf{a} = [a_1, \ldots, a_n, b]$, $\mathbf{X} = \|x_{ij}\|$, $\mathbf{X}_1 = (\mathbf{X}, \mathbf{1})$, where $\mathbf{1} = [1, \ldots, 1]$, $\mathbf{y} = [y_1, \ldots, y_m]$, then $\boldsymbol{\epsilon} = \mathbf{y} - \mathbf{X}_1\mathbf{a}$ and $\sum \epsilon_j^2 = \boldsymbol{\epsilon}'\boldsymbol{\epsilon}$.] Prove that the resulting necessary conditions always have at least one solution.

3–7. Assume that we are given the function $f(\mathbf{x})$, $\mathbf{x} \in E^n$, and we suspect that $\mathbf{x}_0$ is a relative maximum of $f(\mathbf{x})$. We would like to test this conjecture numerically. Is there any straightforward way of doing this? Is it sufficient to evaluate $f(\mathbf{x}_0 \pm \epsilon\mathbf{e}_j)$, $j = 1, \ldots, n$, with ϵ very small?

3–8. Consider a function of n variables in which the variables are defined only at the points $x_j = k_j \Delta x_j$, $k_j = 0, 1, 2, \ldots, j = 1, \ldots, n$. Show that $f(\mathbf{x}_0)$ is a relative maximum of $f(\mathbf{x})$ if $f(\mathbf{x}_0)$ is greater than $f(\mathbf{x})$ at all neighboring points, neighboring points being all points for which the jth coordinate, $j = 1, \ldots, n$, does not differ from x_j^0 by more than Δx_j, that is, points for which the jth coordinate can be x_j^0 or $x_j^0 \pm \Delta x_j$. Show that in E^n there are $3^n - 1$ neighboring points. Note that even the task of checking neighboring points when n is large can be an almost impossible undertaking.

3–9. Find the shortest distance from the point (1, 0) to the parabola $y^2 = 4x$ by (a) eliminating the variable y; (b) the Lagrange multiplier technique. Note that procedure (a) does not give the correct answer, whereas (b) does. Explain why this is so.

3–10. Derive a formula for the shortest distance d from the point $\mathbf{x}_0 \in E^n$ to the hyperplane $z = \mathbf{c}\mathbf{x}$. Assume that $|\mathbf{c}| = 1$. Show that $d^2 = (z - \mathbf{c}\mathbf{x}_0)^2$.

3–11. Consider the quadratic form $f(\mathbf{x}) = x_1x_2$. Find the maxima and minima of this quadratic form on the unit circle $x_1^2 + x_2^2 = 1$. Illustrate geometrically. Which points correspond to maxima and which to minima?

3–12. Assume that the absolute maximum $\mathbf{x}^*$ of $f(\mathbf{x})$ over the non-negative orthant occurs on the boundary and that $x_j^* = 0$. Show that if $f \in C^1$, then $\partial f(\mathbf{x}^*)/\partial x_j \leq 0$.

3–13. A company produces a single good using n factors of production in quantities $x_1, \ldots, x_n$. The production function (which relates the quantity produced to the quantities of the factors used) is

$$q = f(x_1, \ldots, x_n),$$

and the total cost of production is

$$C = \sum_{j=1}^{n} p_j x_j + K,$$

where p_j is the unit price of x_j and is assumed to be constant. Determine how much of each factor of production one should use to make a quantity q of the good while at the same time minimizing the cost. When can we obtain demand functions $x_j = \phi_j(p_1, \ldots, p_n, q)$?

3–14. Assume that we wish to maximize $f(\mathbf{x})$ subject to $g_i(\mathbf{x}) = b_i$, $i = 1, \ldots, m$. Suppose that $f(\mathbf{x})$ has a relative maximum at $\mathbf{x}_0$ subject to the constraints, and that $r(\mathbf{G}) = m$ at $\mathbf{x}_0$. If $\partial f/\partial x_j = 0$, $j = 1, \ldots, n$, at $\mathbf{x}_0$, then what are the values of the Lagrange multipliers? What is the physical interpretation of such a situation?

3–15. Provide the sufficient condition that each x_j and λ_i in Section 3–7 is a continuous differentiable function of $\mathbf{b}$ in some ϵ-neighborhood of $\mathbf{b}_0$.

3–16. Consider the problem of maximizing $z = f(\mathbf{x})$ subject to the constraints $g_i(\mathbf{x}) \leq b_i$, $i = 1, \ldots, k$; $g_i(\mathbf{x}) = b_i$, $i = k + 1, \ldots, m$. Let $f(\mathbf{x})$ assume its absolute maximum at $\mathbf{x}^*$ for $\mathbf{x}$ satisfying the constraints. Show that if constraint

i is inactive at $\mathbf{x}^*$, then $\partial z^*/\partial b_i = 0$. What is the physical interpretation of this situation? In economics, resource i would be called a free good. Why? Show that if constraint i, $i = 1, \ldots, k$, is active at $\mathbf{x}^*$, as well as in a neighborhood of the value of b_i under consideration, then $\partial z^*/\partial b_i$ can be computed as was done in Section 3–7. Now suppose that constraint i, $i = 1, \ldots, k$, is active at $\mathbf{x}^*$, but any increase in b_i will make it inactive. Show that in this case, $\partial z^*/\partial b_i$ must be interpreted as a one-sided derivative. Illustrate geometrically.

3–17. What changes need to be made in the material presented in Section 3–7 and developed in Problem 3–16 if the variables are required to be non-negative?

3–18. Provide the conditions which guarantee that Eqs. (3–39) can be solved uniquely for $\mathbf{x}$ in terms of $\boldsymbol{\lambda}$ in a neighborhood of $\boldsymbol{\lambda}_0$.

3–19. Generalize the proof given in Section 3–12, that any relative minimum of a convex function must also be a global minimum, to the case where it is assumed that the global minimum is taken on as $|\mathbf{x}| \to \infty$. [*Hint:* If $f(\mathbf{x}_0)$ is not the global minimum, then for sufficiently large $|\mathbf{x}|$, there exists an $\mathbf{x}$ such that $f(\mathbf{x}) < f(\mathbf{x}_0)$.

3–20. Prove that the function $1/x$ is strictly convex for $x > 0$ and strictly concave for $x < 0$.

3–21. Assume that $f_1(\mathbf{x})$ and $f_2(\mathbf{x})$ are convex functions. Show that, in general, $f_1(\mathbf{x})f_2(\mathbf{x})$ is not a convex function. Do this by providing a counter-example. Are there any special conditions under which $f_1(\mathbf{x})f_2(\mathbf{x})$ will be convex?

3–22. Let $\mathbf{x}^*$ be a point such that $z = f(\mathbf{x})$ assumes its absolute minimum at $\mathbf{x}^*$ for $\mathbf{x}$ satisfying the constraints $g_i(\mathbf{x}) = b_i$, $i = 1, \ldots, m$. Assume that $r(\mathbf{G}) = m$ at $\mathbf{x}^*$. Assume also that we define the Lagrangian function as

$$F(\mathbf{x}, \boldsymbol{\lambda}) = f(\mathbf{x}) + \sum_{i=1}^{m} \lambda_i[g_i(\mathbf{x}) - b_i].$$

Show that $\partial z^*/\partial b_i = -\lambda_i$.

3–23. Consider the problem of finding the absolute minimum of $z = f(\mathbf{x})$ subject to m linear constraints $\mathbf{Ax} = \mathbf{b}$ with $r(\mathbf{A}) = m$. Assume that $f(\mathbf{x})$ is a convex function. Show that the Lagrangian function $F(\mathbf{x}, \boldsymbol{\lambda})$ is also convex, and that $F(\mathbf{x}, \boldsymbol{\lambda})$ assumes a relative and global minimum for fixed $\boldsymbol{\lambda}$ at any point satisfying $\partial F/\partial x_j = 0$, $j = 1, \ldots, n$. Show also that $f(\mathbf{x})$ takes on its global minimum for points satisfying the constraints at any point satisfying the constraints, and $\partial F/\partial x_j = 0$, $j = 1, \ldots, n$. Thus conclude that $F(\mathbf{x}, \boldsymbol{\lambda})$ takes on a relative minimum with respect to $\mathbf{x}$ at the point where $f(\mathbf{x})$ assumes its global minimum for points satisfying the constraints.

3–24. A bakery must decide how much of a given type of cake should be purchased each day. The cost of a cake is c dollars, and it retails for p dollars. Any cakes not sold at the end of the day will be placed on a special counter to be sold at 10% below cost on the following day. All cakes placed on this counter will be sold. If a customer wants a cake that is not in stock, there is a goodwill loss of π dollars. From past experience it has been established that the density function for the demand is $f(x)$. Find the equation which determines the optimal number of cakes to order. Solve the problem for the special case where $p =$ \$2.50, $c =$ \$1.10, $\pi =$ \$0.50, and $f(x)$ is a normal distribution with a mean of 25 and a standard deviation of 7.

3–25. Consider a time series $f(t) = g(t) + \epsilon(t)$ which consists of a signal plus noise, $g(t)$ being the signal and $\epsilon(t)$ being the noise. Suppose that the function $f(t)$ is defined only at times $t = n\,\Delta t$, $n = 0, \pm 1, \pm 2, \ldots$ We shall write $f(n\,\Delta t) = f_n$. Assume that we wish to estimate the actual signal g_n, using a linear combination of the values $f_n, f_{n-1}, \ldots, f_{n-m}$, that is, if $\hat{g}_n$ is our estimate of g_n, then

$$\hat{g}_n = \sum_{i=0}^{m} \alpha_i f_{n-i}.$$

The α_i are to be determined by minimizing the average square of the deviation between g_n and $\hat{g}_n$, i.e., by minimizing

$$\lim_{N\to\infty} \frac{1}{2N+1} \sum_{n=-N}^{N} \left[g_n - \sum_{i=0}^{m} \alpha_i f_{n-i} \right]^2.$$

Assume that g_n and ϵ_n are random variables. Determine the equations which yield the optimal values of the α_i. What statistical properties of g_n and ϵ_n must be known?

3–26. Discuss the problem of finding the maximum and minimum values of the quadratic form $z = \mathbf{x}'\mathbf{A}\mathbf{x}$ lying on the unit hypersphere $|\mathbf{x}| = 1$. Determine the equations whose solutions contain the points at which z takes on its maximum and minimum values. Generalize the discussion to find the points at which $z = \mathbf{x}'\mathbf{A}\mathbf{x}$ assumes its maximum and minimum values for $|\mathbf{x}| = 1$ when, in addition, the $\mathbf{x}$ must satisfy $\mathbf{D}\mathbf{x} = \mathbf{0}$, $\mathbf{D}$ being an $m \times n$ matrix, $m < n$, and $r(\mathbf{D}) = m$.

3–27. Consider again the second part of Problem 3–26. The maximum value z^* of z will clearly depend on $\mathbf{D}$. Let us vary the elements of $\mathbf{D}$ so that z^* takes on its minimum value, call it $\hat{z}$. Then $\hat{z} = \min_{\mathbf{D}} \max_{\mathbf{x}} z$. Now number the eigenvalues λ_j of $\mathbf{A}$ in order of decreasing value so that $\lambda_1 \geq \lambda_2 \geq \cdots \geq \lambda_n$. Then prove that $\hat{z} \geq \lambda_{m+1}$. *Hint:* Introduce a nonsingular orthogonal transformation $\mathbf{x} = \mathbf{R}\mathbf{y}$ such that $z = \sum \lambda_j y_j^2$. But $\hat{z} \geq z$ for any $\mathbf{y}$ satisfying $\mathbf{D}\mathbf{R}\mathbf{y} = \mathbf{F}\mathbf{y} = \mathbf{0}$. If we set $y_{m+2} = \cdots = y_n = 0$, $\mathbf{F}\mathbf{y} = \mathbf{0}$ becomes a set of m equations in $m + 1$ unknowns so that there are solutions with not all $y_j = 0$. Then

$$\hat{z} \geq \sum_{j=1}^{m+1} \lambda_j y_j^2.$$

3–28. Let $f(\mathbf{x})$ be a convex function over the convex set X, and let $\mathbf{x}_1, \ldots, \mathbf{x}_k$ be any k points in X. Then prove that for all $\mu_i \geq 0$, $\sum_i \mu_i = 1$,

$$f(\mathbf{x}) \leq \sum_{i=1}^{k} \mu_i f(\mathbf{x}_i), \qquad \text{where} \quad \mathbf{x} = \sum_{i=1}^{k} \mu_i \mathbf{x}_i.$$

What is the geometrical interpretation of this result? [*Hint:* Prove by induction, writing $\mathbf{x} = \mu_n \mathbf{x}_n + (1 - \mu_n)\hat{\mathbf{x}}_{n-1}$. What is $\hat{\mathbf{x}}_{n-1}$?]

3–29. A set of n functions $g_i(\mathbf{x})$, $i = 1, \ldots, n$, is said to be functionally dependent if there exists a compound function $F(g_1, \ldots, g_n)$ which vanishes identically for all $\mathbf{x}$. Show that if the $g_i(\mathbf{x})$ are functionally dependent, then the Jacobian matrix of these functions is singular for all $\mathbf{x}$. [*Hint:* Show that $\nabla F(\mathbf{x}) \equiv \mathbf{0}$.]

3–30. In economics, in the theory of consumer behavior, it is often assumed that each individual has a utility function $U(\mathbf{x})$, and that he makes consumption decisions in such a way that his utility function will be maximized subject to a budget constraint $\mathbf{px} \leq I$. Determine the equations which the optimal x_j must satisfy. Assume that $U(\mathbf{x}) \in C^1$. When is the solution to these equations unique? When can one solve for the demands x_j explicitly in terms of the prices p_j and I? Give an economic interpretation of the Lagrange multiplier. What is a dual of this problem?

3–31. A food processor cans an entire year's supply of a given vegetable immediately after the harvest, and then ships it to m regional warehouses for later distribution to retailers. When any warehouse i runs out of stock later in the season, a cost π_j is incurred. Let $f_j(x_j)$ be the density function for demand during the coming season at warehouse j. Determine how the cases of the vegetable should be allocated to the warehouses in order to minimize the expected stockout costs. Assume that there are R cases to be allocated. Solve the problem for a specific situation, i.e., assume that there are three warehouses and one million cases are to be allocated. The demands at each of the warehouses are normally distributed with the means being 200,000, 500,000, and 100,000, and the standard deviations are 50,000, 100,000, and 10,000, respectively. The stockout costs are \$10,000, \$4000, and \$600, respectively.

3–32. Determine the dimensions of the rectangle of maximum area whose diagonal has length b.

3–33. Using the material in Section 3–8, give the dual of the general linear programming problem presented in Example 3 of Section 3–9. What is an optimal solution to the dual if $\mathbf{x}_B^* = \mathbf{B}^{-1}\mathbf{b}$ is an optimal basic solution to the primal?

3–34. Let X be a convex polyhedron so that every point in X can be written as a convex combination of the extreme points of X. Use a simpler proof than that given in Section 3–12 to show that the absolute maximum of a convex function over x is taken on at an extreme point of X. [*Hint:* See Problem 3–28.]

3–35. Consider the situation described in Problem 3–2. However, assume that N different products are produced and inventoried, and that the warehouse capacity is limited to H square feet; let h_j be the number of square feet of warehouse space taken up by one unit of product j. Show how the optimal lot size for each product is determined in the presence of this constraint. Give an economic interpretation of the Lagrange multiplier. Suppose that, in addition, there is a constraint on the number of setups which can be made in a given time period. Show how to solve the problem when there are two constraints.

3–36. A consumer has a given income I and can buy three goods at prices p_1, p_2, p_3 per unit. His utility function is $x_1^a x_2^b x_3^c$, a, b, c being positive constants, where x_1, x_2, x_3 are the quantities of the three goods which he purchases. Find his demand for each good in terms of I, p_1, p_2, p_3. Refer to Problem 3–30 for more details.

3–37. Study the application of the Lagrange multiplier technique to the solution of the problem

$$x_1^2 + x_2^2 = 0, \qquad \max z = x_1 + x_2.$$

3–38. Prove in complete detail that the procedure outlined in Section 3–2 for finding the absolute maximum of $f(\mathbf{x})$ over the non-negative orthant does yield the absolute maximum if $|\mathbf{x}^*|$ is finite.

3–39. Use Newton's method to solve the equation $e^x - 2 = 0$.

3–40. Consider the example of Section 3–3. Assume that a good machined piece has a value of \$25.00, whereas it can be sold for rework at \$15.00. The cost of a piece is \$12.50. To pass specifications the diameter x of a finished part must lie in the interval $2.5000 \leq x \leq 2.5050$ in. Assume that the standard deviation of the random variable x is $\sigma = 0.0015$ in. What lathe setting for μ, the mean of x, maximizes the rate of profits? Given that 500 units per week are put into production, plot the expected weekly profit as a function of μ.

3–41. Prove that $\sum_i \alpha_i f_i(\mathbf{x})$ is convex when f_i is convex if $\alpha_i > 0$ and f_i is concave if $\alpha_i < 0$.

3–42. Prove that e^x is a convex function.

3–43. Let x_1 be a random variable representing the demand for an item in time t, and x_2 a random variable representing the demand in time $t + \tau$, $\tau > 0$. Let $f_1(x_1)$ and $f_2(x_2)$ be the density functions for x_1 and x_2, respectively. Let y be the quantity of the product on hand at time zero. Compute the expected number of demands that will occur between t and $t + \tau$ when the item is out of stock. Denote this function by $F(y)$. Is $F(y)$ a convex function?

3–44. Let

$$F(x, y) = \frac{1}{y} \int_x^\infty (u - x) f(u)\, du, \quad y > 0; \quad f(u) \geq 0, \quad -\infty < u < \infty.$$

Is $F(x, y)$ a convex function of x and y?

3–45. Prove that $|x|$ is a convex function of x.

3–46. Assume that $f(\mathbf{x}; \alpha)$ is convex over a convex set X for each α, $a \leq \alpha \leq b$. Prove that if $\phi(\alpha) \geq 0$, then

$$\int_a^b f(\mathbf{x}; \alpha)\phi(\alpha)\, d\alpha$$

is a convex function over X.

3–47. Find the shortest distance from the ellipse $2x_1^2 + 3x_2^2 = 12$ to the line $x_1 + x_2 = 6$.

3–48. Consider the function $f(\mathbf{x})$, $f \in C^2$, and let $\mathbf{x}_0$ be a point for which $\nabla f(\mathbf{x}_0) = \mathbf{0}$. Then show that $f(\mathbf{x})$ assumes a strong relative maximum at $\mathbf{x}_0$ if the quadratic form $\mathbf{h}'\mathbf{H}_f(\mathbf{x}_0)\mathbf{h}$ is negative definite, and that $f(\mathbf{x})$ takes on a strong relative minimum at $\mathbf{x}_0$ if $\mathbf{h}'\mathbf{H}_f(\mathbf{x}_0)\mathbf{h}$ is positive definite. [*Hint:* Expand $f(\mathbf{x})$ in a neighborhood of $\mathbf{x}_0$, using Taylor's theorem. Next use the fact that $\mathbf{h}'\mathbf{H}_f(\mathbf{x})\mathbf{h}$ is a continuous function of $\mathbf{x}$.]

3–49. Consider the function $f(\mathbf{x})$, $f \in C^2$, and let $\mathbf{x}_0$ be a point for which $\nabla f(\mathbf{x}_0) = \mathbf{0}$. Show that $f(\mathbf{x})$ takes on a strong relative maximum at $\mathbf{x}_0$ if

$$\frac{\partial^2 f(\mathbf{x}_0)}{\partial x_1^2} < 0, \quad \begin{vmatrix} \dfrac{\partial^2 f(\mathbf{x}_0)}{\partial x_1^2} & \dfrac{\partial^2 f(\mathbf{x}_0)}{\partial x_1 \partial x_2} \\ \dfrac{\partial^2 f(\mathbf{x}_0)}{\partial x_1 \partial x_2} & \dfrac{\partial^2 f(\mathbf{x}_0)}{\partial x_2^2} \end{vmatrix} > 0, \ldots, \quad |-\mathbf{H}_f(\mathbf{x}_0)| > 0,$$

and $f(\mathbf{x})$ takes on a strong relative minimum at $\mathbf{x}_0$ if

$$\frac{\partial^2 f(\mathbf{x}_0)}{\partial x_1^2} > 0, \quad \begin{vmatrix} \dfrac{\partial^2 f(\mathbf{x}_0)}{\partial x_1^2} & \dfrac{\partial^2 f(\mathbf{x}_0)}{\partial x_1 \partial x_2} \\ \dfrac{\partial^2 f(\mathbf{x}_0)}{\partial x_1 \partial x_2} & \dfrac{\partial^2 f(\mathbf{x}_0)}{\partial x_2^2} \end{vmatrix} > 0, \ldots, \quad |\mathbf{H}_f(\mathbf{x}_0)| > 0.$$

[*Hint:* Use the results of Problem 3–48 and {LA 7–12}.]

3–50. Let $\mathbf{x}_0$ be a point such that $g_i(\mathbf{x}_0) = b_i$, $i = 1, \ldots, m$, and such that there exist λ_i^0 which satisfy

$$\frac{\partial f(\mathbf{x}_0)}{\partial x_j} - \sum_{i=1}^{m} \lambda_i^0 \frac{\partial g_i(\mathbf{x}_0)}{\partial x_j} = 0, \qquad j = 1, \ldots, n.$$

Assume that $f \in C^2$ and $g_i \in C^2$, $i = 1, \ldots, m$. Let $F(\mathbf{x}, \boldsymbol{\lambda})$ be the Lagrangian function. Then prove that $f(\mathbf{x})$ takes on a strong relative maximum at $\mathbf{x}_0$ for $\mathbf{x} \in Y$ if the quadratic form $\mathbf{h}'\mathbf{H}_F(\mathbf{x}_0, \boldsymbol{\lambda}_0)\mathbf{h}$ is negative definite for $\mathbf{h}$ satisfying $\nabla g_i(\mathbf{x}_0)\mathbf{h} = 0$, $i = 1, \ldots, m$, and $f(\mathbf{x})$ assumes a strong relative minimum at $\mathbf{x}_0$ if $\mathbf{h}'\mathbf{H}_F(\mathbf{x}_0, \boldsymbol{\lambda}_0)\mathbf{h}$ is positive definite for $\mathbf{h}$ satisfying $\nabla g_i(\mathbf{x}_0)\mathbf{h} = 0$, $i = 1, \ldots, m$. By $\mathbf{H}_F$ we shall mean the Hessian matrix of F (not f) with respect to the x_j. [*Hint:* Expand F by Taylor's theorem in a neighborhood of $\mathbf{x}_0$, keeping $\boldsymbol{\lambda}_0$ fixed. Note that for $\mathbf{x} \in Y$, $F(\mathbf{x}, \boldsymbol{\lambda}_0) = f(\mathbf{x})$. Also expand $g_i(\mathbf{x})$ in a Taylor series about $\mathbf{x}_0$, and note to what expression this reduces for $\mathbf{x} \in Y$.] Next show that $\mathbf{h}'\mathbf{A}\mathbf{h}$ will be positive definite for $\mathbf{h}$ satisfying $\mathbf{D}\mathbf{h} = \mathbf{0}$ if the smallest root of

$$P(\lambda) = \begin{vmatrix} \mathbf{A} - \lambda\mathbf{I} & \mathbf{D}' \\ \mathbf{D} & \mathbf{0} \end{vmatrix} = 0.$$

is positive. Demonstrate that this follows from the fact that $\mathbf{h}'\mathbf{A}\mathbf{h}$ is positive definite for all **h** satisfying **Dh** = **0** if the minimum of **h'Ah** over the unit hypersphere for **h** satisfying **Dh** = **0** is positive. Now use the fact that the λ are continuous functions of the a_{ij} and d_{ij}.

3–51. Show by an example involving a function of a single variable that a function which is convex over a closed convex set may not be continuous on the boundaries of the set.

3–52. Show that the only function $g(\mathbf{x})$ such that the set of $\mathbf{x}$ satisfying $g(\mathbf{x}) = b$ is convex is $g(\mathbf{x}) = \mathbf{cx}$.

3–53. Prove directly that if $f_j(x_j)$, $j = 1, \ldots, n$, is a convex function of x_j, then

$$f(\mathbf{x}) = \sum_{j=1}^{n} f_j(x_j)$$

is a convex function of $\mathbf{x} = [x_1, \ldots, x_n]$.

3–54. Prove that if $f(x_j)$ is a convex function of the single variable x_j, then f can also be considered to be a convex function of $\mathbf{x} = [x_1, \ldots, x_n]$. Illustrate this geometrically with $f(x_1) = x_1^2$, considering f to be a function of $\mathbf{x} = [x_1, x_2]$.

3–55. Use the results of Problem 3–54 to prove the result in Problem 3–53.

3–56. Prove that if $f(\mathbf{x})$ is a convex function of $\mathbf{x}$ over E^n, then $f(\mathbf{x} + \mathbf{b})$ is a convex function of $\mathbf{x}$ for any $\mathbf{b}$.

3–57. Consider the linear programming problem $\mathbf{Ax} = \mathbf{b}, \mathbf{x} \geq \mathbf{0}$, max $z = \mathbf{cx}$. Note that for a fixed **A** and **c**, z^*, the maximum value of z, will be a function of **b**. Show that $z^*(\mathbf{b})$ is a concave function of **b**.

3–58. Prove that $f_1(x) = x^2$ is a convex function for $-\infty < x < \infty$, and as a result conclude that $f_2(x) = 3(x - 2)^2$ is also a convex function over the same interval. Plot both these functions and also $f_1(x) + f_2(x)$, and illustrate geometrically, for this particular case, that the sum of two convex functions is also a convex function.

3–59. Let $f(x)$ be a differentiable and convex function of x in some interval $a < x < b$. Given any two values of x in the interval, say x_1 and x_2, with $x_2 > x_1$, prove that $f'(x_2) \geq f'(x_1)$. Thus conclude that $f'(x)$ is a monotone nondecreasing function as x is increased. Give the corresponding result for concave functions. [*Hint:* Recall that Eq. (3–64) holds for *any* x_1 and x_2.]

3–60. Let $f(\mathbf{x})$ be a differentiable and convex function of $\mathbf{x}$ over some open convex set in E^n. Let $\mathbf{x}_1$ and $\mathbf{x}_2$ be any two points in X. Also, let $\mathbf{y}$ be any point on the line segment joining $\mathbf{x}_1$ and $\mathbf{x}_2$. For all such $\mathbf{y}$, prove that

$$\nabla f(\mathbf{y})(\mathbf{x}_2 - \mathbf{x}_1) \geq \nabla f(\mathbf{x}_1)(\mathbf{x}_2 - \mathbf{x}_1).$$

3–61. Consider the differentiable function $f(x)$ which has the property that for all x_1 and x_2 in the interval $a < x < b$,

$$f(x_2) \geq f(x_1) + f'(x_1)(x_2 - x_1).$$

Prove that $f(x)$ is a convex function over the interval $a < x < b$.

3–62. Consider the differentiable function $f(\mathbf{x})$ which has the property that for all points $\mathbf{x}_1$ and $\mathbf{x}_2$ in the open convex set X,

$$f(\mathbf{x}_2) \geq f(\mathbf{x}_1) + \nabla f(\mathbf{x}_1)(\mathbf{x}_2 - \mathbf{x}_1).$$

Prove that $f(\mathbf{x})$ is a convex function over X.

3–63. Assume that $f \in C^2$ over an open convex set X. Prove that $f(\mathbf{x})$ is convex over X if and only if the quadratic form $\mathbf{h}'\mathbf{H}_f(\mathbf{x})\mathbf{h}$ is positive semidefinite for each $\mathbf{x} \in X$. Under what conditions is $f(\mathbf{x})$ strictly convex?

3–64. For Example 3 of Section 3–9, show that if $r(\mathbf{A}', \mathbf{c}') = m$, then every feasible solution is optimal. Extend the analysis to include the case where k of the variables are set to zero. Be sure to consider that in this case one or more of the constraints may be redundant.

3–65. Show that the set of points satisfying $g(\mathbf{x}) \leq b$ or $g(\mathbf{x}) \geq b$ is a closed set.

3–66. One might assume that one could avoid the difficulties connected with the application of the Lagrange multiplier technique to linear programming problems by making a transformation of variables, such as $x_j = y_j^2$. Then no non-negativity restrictions are needed on the y_j. Show that this transformation can indeed be made, and that the Lagrange multiplier approach can be applied to the problem in which the variables are the y_j. Furthermore, show that even with this transformation, one encounters the same difficulty that was present when the variables x_j were used. Illustrate the procedure by studying the problem

$$x_1 + x_2 \leq 2, \qquad x_1, x_2 \geq 0, \qquad \max z = 2x_1 + 3x_2.$$

Give a graphical interpretation of this problem both in x_1x_2-space and y_1y_2-space. Show that the same problems are encountered for any transformation $x_j = f_j(y_j)$, where $x_j = 0$ at $y_j = y_j^0$ and $f_j(y_j)$ is symmetric about y_j^0. Why do we impose these special conditions on $f_j(y_j)$?

CHAPTER 4

APPROXIMATE METHODS FOR SOLVING PROBLEMS INVOLVING SEPARABLE FUNCTIONS

Although this may seem a paradox, all science is dominated by the idea of approximation.

Bertrand Russell

4–1 Introduction. In this chapter we shall concern ourselves with approximate techniques for solving nonlinear programming problems of the form

$$\sum_{j=1}^{n} g_{ij}(x_j)\{\leq, =, \geq\}b_i, \qquad i = 1, \ldots, m,$$

$$x_j \geq 0, \qquad j = 1, \ldots, n, \tag{4–1}$$

$$\max z = \sum_{j=1}^{n} f_j(x_j).$$

Note that we are assuming that all functions are separable, both in the constraints and the objective function. The basic approximation technique to be used will be that of replacing the functions $g_{ij}(x_j)$ and $f_j(x_j)$ by polygonal approximations, thereby reducing the problem to a form which can be solved by the simplex method. In general, we shall only be able to determine a local maximum for the approximating problem, and therefore an approximate local maximum for (4–1). It is only when the functions $g_{ij}(x_j), f_j(x_j)$ have the appropriate convexity or concavity properties which assure us that a local maximum is also a global maximum that we can find a global maximum for the approximating problem, and hence an approximate optimal solution to (4–1). To begin, we shall show how to construct the approximating problem, and how to determine a local maximum for this problem.

4–2 Determination of the approximating problem and a local maximum for it. Consider some arbitrary continuous function $h(x)$ of a single variable x which is defined for all x, $0 \leq x \leq \alpha$. We shall suppose that the value of x cannot be greater than α. The function $h(x)$ might look something like that shown in Fig. 4–1. Assume that we select $r + 1$ points x_k, where $x_0 = 0$, $x_1 < x_2 < \cdots < x_r = \alpha$ in the interval $0 \leq x \leq \alpha$. It need not be true that the x_k are equally spaced. Now for each x_k we

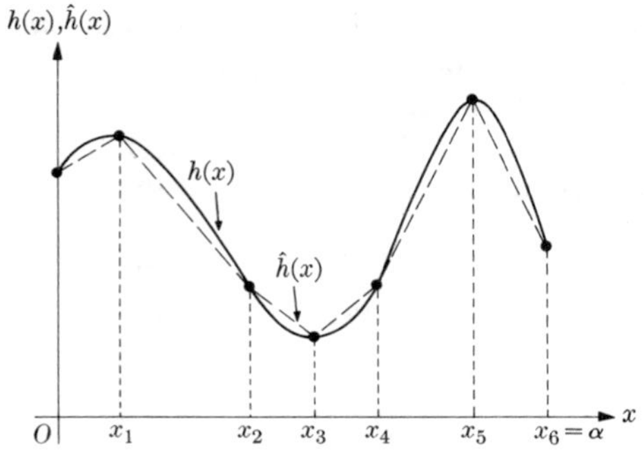

FIGURE 4–1

compute $h_k = h(x_k)$. Imagine that for each k we next connect the points (x_k, h_k) and (x_{k+1}, h_{k+1}) by a straight line. We thus obtain the dashed curve shown in Fig. 4–1, which is then an approximation to $h(x)$ in the interval $0 \leq x \leq \alpha$. The dashed curve or polygonal approximation to $h(x)$, will be denoted by $\hat{h}(x)$. The approximation can be made arbitrarily good by selecting the x_k properly and subdividing the interval $0 \leq x \leq \alpha$ finely enough.

Suppose then that for problem (4–1), we assume that all the f_j and g_{ij} are continuous. Now we subdivide the interval over which each variable x_j can range by a number of mesh points x_{kj} and, using the method just described, determine polygonal approximations $\hat{g}_{ij}(x_j), \hat{f}_j(x_j)$ to the functions $g_{ij}(x_j)$, $f_j(x_j)$, respectively. We then replace the given problem (4–1) by

$$\sum_{j=1}^{n} \hat{g}_{ij}(x_j)\{\leq, =, \geq\}b_i,$$

$$x_j \geq 0, \qquad j = 1, \ldots, n, \tag{4–2}$$

$$\max \hat{z} = \sum_{j=1}^{n} \hat{f}_j(x_j),$$

which we shall call an *approximating problem* for (4–1). We would now like to concentrate on determining a local maximum of the approximating problem (4–2). To do this, we must first show how one expresses analytically the polygonal functions $\hat{g}_{ij}(x_j)$ and $\hat{f}_j(x_j)$.

Let us return to Fig. 4–1. When x lies in the interval $x_k \leq x \leq x_{k+1}$, we are approximating $h(x)$ by $\hat{h}(x)$, where

$$\hat{h}(x) = h_k + \frac{h_{k+1} - h_k}{x_{k+1} - x_k}(x - x_k). \tag{4–3}$$

Note that any x in the interval $x_k \leq x \leq x_{k+1}$ can be written $x = \lambda x_{k+1} + (1 - \lambda)x_k$ for some λ, $0 \leq \lambda \leq 1$. Then $(x - x_k) = \lambda(x_{k+1} - x_k)$, so that (4–3) can be written $\hat{h}(x) = \lambda h_{k+1} + (1 - \lambda)h_k$. If we now write $\lambda = \lambda_{k+1}$, $(1 - \lambda) = \lambda_k$, it follows that when $x_k \leq x \leq x_{k+1}$, there exist a unique λ_k and λ_{k+1} such that

$$\begin{aligned} x &= \lambda_k x_k + \lambda_{k+1}x_{k+1}, \\ \hat{h}(x) &= \lambda_k h_k + \lambda_{k+1}h_{k+1}, \\ \lambda_k + \lambda_{k+1} &= 1, \qquad \lambda_k, \lambda_{k+1} \geq 0. \end{aligned} \tag{4–4}$$

Indeed, for any x, $0 \leq x \leq \alpha$, we can write

$$x = \sum_{k=0}^{r} \lambda_k x_k, \tag{4–5}$$

$$\hat{h}(x) = \sum_{k=0}^{r} \lambda_k h_k, \tag{4–6}$$

$$\sum_{k=0}^{r} \lambda_k = 1, \qquad \lambda_k \geq 0, \qquad k = 0, \ldots, r, \tag{4–7}$$

provided that we require in addition that no more than two of the λ_k shall be positive, and if two, say λ_k, λ_s, $s > k$, are positive, it must be true that $s = k + 1$; that is, they are adjacent λ's. With this restriction, the λ_k are uniquely determined, and for the x given by (4–5), $\hat{h}(x)$ determined by (4–6) will be on the dashed curve of Fig. 4–1, and is an analytic representation of $\hat{h}(x)$. By allowing no more than two λ_k to be positive, and then requiring that they be adjacent, we ensure that the points of (4–5) and (4–6) will be on the dashed curve. If these restrictions were not placed on the λ_k, it would not necessarily be true at all that the points would be on dashed curve.

We have now seen how any continuous function can be approximated by a broken line, and we have obtained the mathematical representations (4–5) through (4–7) for this line. Let us now return to the problem (4–2). Assume that we determined from physical considerations that the maximum value which the variable x_j can take on is α_j. We then subdivide the interval $0 \leq x_j \leq \alpha_j$ into r_j subintervals by the $r_j + 1$ points x_{kj}, $x_{0j} = 0$, $x_{r_j,j} = \alpha_j$. Then, for all the functions $\hat{f}_j(x_j)$, $\hat{g}_{ij}(x_j)$ we can write

$$\hat{f}_j(x_j) = \sum_{k=0}^{r_j} \lambda_{kj} f_{kj}, \qquad f_{kj} = f_j(x_k), \tag{4–8}$$

$$\hat{g}_{ij}(x_j) = \sum_{k=0}^{r_j} \lambda_{kj} g_{kij}, \qquad g_{kij} = g_{ij}(x_k), \qquad i = 1, \ldots, m, \tag{4–9}$$

where
$$x_j = \sum_{k=0}^{r_j} \lambda_{kj} x_{kj}, \tag{4-10}$$

$$\sum_{k=0}^{r_j} \lambda_{kj} = 1, \qquad \lambda_{kj} \geq 0, \qquad \text{all } k, j, \tag{4-11}$$

and for a given j, no more than two λ_{kj} are allowed to be positive and these must be adjacent. Note that in representing each of the functions $\hat{f}_j(x_j)$ and $\hat{g}_{ij}(x_j)$, we have used the same subdivision of the interval $0 \leq x_j \leq \alpha_j$. The x_{kj} should be chosen so that all the appropriate functions $f_j(x_j)$ and $g_{ij}(x_j)$ can be represented with sufficient accuracy.

We now use (4–8) and (4–9) to eliminate the functions $\hat{f}_j(x_j)$ and $\hat{g}_{ij}(x_j)$ in (4–2), to yield the following representation of the approximating problem in terms of the variables λ_{kj} rather than the variables x_j:

$$\sum_{j=1}^{n} \sum_{k=0}^{r_j} g_{kij} \lambda_{kj} \{\leq, =, \geq\} b_i, \qquad i = 1, \ldots, m, \tag{4-12}$$

$$\sum_{k=0}^{r_j} \lambda_{kj} = 1, \qquad j = 1, \ldots, n, \tag{4-13}$$

$$\lambda_{kj} \geq 0, \qquad \text{all } k, j,$$

$$\max \hat{z} = \sum_{j=1}^{n} \sum_{k=0}^{r_j} f_{kj} \lambda_{kj}. \tag{4-14}$$

This problem would be linear if it were not for the fact that for each j, we require that no more than two λ_{kj} be positive and then only if they are adjacent. We can determine a local maximum for the problem represented by (4–12) through (4–14) by applying the simplex method in the usual manner except that we restrict entry into the basis in such a way that we never allow more than two λ_{kj} to be positive for a given j. Furthermore, two λ_{kj} can be positive only if they are adjacent. Note that we did not include equations (4–10) explicitly as constraints in the above. Once the problem has been solved, (4–10) can be used to determine the appropriate values of the x_j.

After adding slack or surplus variables in (4–12), we can write (4–12) through (4–14) in the following abbreviated form

$$\mathbf{G}\boldsymbol{\lambda} = \mathbf{b}, \qquad \boldsymbol{\lambda} \geq \mathbf{0}, \qquad \max \hat{z} = \mathbf{f}\boldsymbol{\lambda}. \tag{4-15}$$

The matrix $\mathbf{G}$ contains $m + n$ rows and $\sum_j r_j + s + n$ columns (s being the number of slack or surplus variables added).

We shall next prove that when the simplex method with restricted basis entry (described above) is applied to (4–15), and the stage is reached where

$z_{kj} - f_{kj} \geq 0$ for every λ_{kj} that is allowed to enter the basis, then we have obtained a relative maximum of the approximating problem with respect to the x_j variables (not the λ_{kj}). In other words, if $\mathbf{x}_0$ is the value of $\mathbf{x}$ corresponding to the terminal basic solution $\boldsymbol{\lambda}_0$ for (4–15), $\mathbf{x}_0$ being obtained from $\boldsymbol{\lambda}_0$ by (4–10), there exists an $\epsilon > 0$ such that for all $\mathbf{x} \geq \mathbf{0}$, $|\mathbf{x} - \mathbf{x}_0| < \epsilon$, for which the $\boldsymbol{\lambda}$ determined by $\mathbf{x}$ satisfy the constraints of (4–15), it is true that $\mathbf{f}\boldsymbol{\lambda} \leq \mathbf{f}\boldsymbol{\lambda}_0$, that is, $\sum \hat{f}_j(x_j) \leq \sum \hat{f}_j(x_j^0)$, x_j^0 being the jth component of $\mathbf{x}_0$.

Consider then the state of affairs when the simplex method is applied to (4–15), using the restricted-entry procedure mentioned above, and the stage is reached where no additional iterations can be made. Let $\mathbf{B}$ be the final basis matrix, $\boldsymbol{\lambda}_B$ contain the basic variables, and $\boldsymbol{\lambda}_R$ contain the nonbasic variables. Then, if $\mathbf{R}$ contains the columns of $\mathbf{G}$ not in $\mathbf{B}$, *every* solution to $\mathbf{G}\boldsymbol{\lambda} = \mathbf{b}$ must satisfy the equation

$$\boldsymbol{\lambda}_B = \mathbf{B}^{-1}\mathbf{b} - \mathbf{B}^{-1}\mathbf{R}\boldsymbol{\lambda}_R. \tag{4–16}$$

For any solution to $\mathbf{G}\boldsymbol{\lambda} = \mathbf{b}$ we can then use (4–16) to eliminate the basic variables, and express $\hat{z}$ only in terms of the nonbasic variables. Thus, in general,

$$\begin{aligned}\hat{z} &= \mathbf{f}_B\boldsymbol{\lambda}_B + \mathbf{f}_R\boldsymbol{\lambda}_R = \mathbf{f}_B\mathbf{B}^{-1}\mathbf{b} + (\mathbf{f}_R - \mathbf{f}_B\mathbf{B}^{-1}\mathbf{R})\boldsymbol{\lambda}_R \\ &= \sum_v (f_{Rv} - z_{Rv})\lambda_{Rv} + \mathbf{f}_B\mathbf{B}^{-1}\mathbf{b}.\end{aligned} \tag{4–17}$$

For the terminal solution to (4–15) obtained by applying the simplex method with restricted basis entry, we have $\boldsymbol{\lambda}_R = \mathbf{0}$, $\boldsymbol{\lambda}_B = \mathbf{B}^{-1}\mathbf{b}$, $\hat{z} = \mathbf{f}_B\mathbf{B}^{-1}\mathbf{b}$. Let $\mathbf{x}_0$ be the value of $\mathbf{x}$ corresponding to this solution. We would like to show that $\mathbf{x}_0$ yields a relative maximum for the approximating problem. To do this we must show that there exists an $\epsilon > 0$ such that for all $\boldsymbol{\lambda} \geq \mathbf{0}$ satisfying the constraints of (4–15) for which $|\mathbf{x}(\boldsymbol{\lambda}) - \mathbf{x}_0| < \epsilon$, it is true that $\hat{z} \leq \mathbf{f}_B\mathbf{B}^{-1}\mathbf{b}$. In the notation of (4–12) through (4–14), the terminal solution $\boldsymbol{\lambda}_0 = [\mathbf{B}^{-1}\mathbf{b}, \mathbf{0}]$ to (4–15) will have the property that for each j one and only one of the following will hold: (a) λ_{kj} and $\lambda_{k+1,j}$ are positive; (b) precisely one λ_{kj} is positive. At least one λ_{kj} must be positive, since the λ_{kj} must sum over k to unity. Suppose for a particular j that (a) holds. Then x_j^0 lies between x_{kj} and $x_{k+1,j}$. For ϵ sufficiently small, the jth component of any $\mathbf{x}$ in an ϵ-neighborhood of $\mathbf{x}_0$ must lie between x_{kj} and $x_{k+1,j}$ so that λ_{kj} and $\lambda_{k+1,j}$ must remain positive, i.e., all other λ_{uj} must remain zero. When (b) holds for some j, $\lambda_{kj} = 1$ and $x_j^0 = x_{kj}$. Then for ϵ sufficiently small, if $\mathbf{x}$ is in an ϵ-neighborhood of $\mathbf{x}_0$, x_j cannot move as far to the left of x_{kj} as $x_{k-1,j}$ or as far to the right as $x_{k+1,j}$. Hence in any such ϵ-neighborhood, only $\lambda_{k-1,j}$ or $\lambda_{k+1,j}$ can become positive while all other λ_{uj} must remain zero. Furthermore, $\lambda_{k-1,j}$ can become positive only if $k \geq 1$. However, for each of these λ_{kj} which are allowed to become positive, the termination conditions for solving (4–15) guarantee that $z_{kj} - f_{kj} \geq 0$, and thus from (4–17), for any such $\mathbf{x}$, $\hat{z} \leq \mathbf{f}_B\mathbf{B}^{-1}\mathbf{b}$, so that we have indeed obtained a local maximum for the approximating problem.

We have developed a procedure for finding a relative maximum for the approximating problem. Since the restricted entry conditions can be coded for a computer, it is possible to modify a simplex code to solve (4–15) with restricted entry. At this point, it should be noted that a fairly small problem (4–1) can give rise to a rather large problem (4–15). It is important to observe, however, that if some particular variable x_j enters into the problem linearly, so that $g_{ij}(x_j) = a_{ij}x_j$, $i = 1, \ldots, m$, and $f_j(x_j) = c_jx_j$, then it is unnecessary to write x_j in terms of the λ_{kj}. We can simply use x_j as the variable. Since it will often be true that a sizable number of variables will enter the problem linearly, this observation may make it possible to reduce considerably the size of the approximating problem. In general, we obtain only a local maximum to the approximating problem, and there is often no way of knowing how close it is to the global maximum. In order to solve (4–15) with restricted entry, a Phase I of the simplex method will usually be required. It may even happen that a local maximum will be encountered in Phase I (which will be interpreted as meaning that there is no feasible solution), and hence we may not find a feasible solution to (4–15) even though it has one. Furthermore, in some cases, the approximating problem may have local maxima which do not at all approximate local maxima of (4–1), i.e., because of the approximations, extraneous local optima may be introduced. Indeed, in the general case, it is difficult to say whether the solutions to the approximating problems will converge to a local maximum of (4–1) as the subdivisions of the x_j intervals are made finer and finer.

It might be noted that, in general, we do not even have a guarantee that a point which yields a relative maximum for the approximating problem will be a feasible solution to (4–1). In practice, the fact that a solution obtained to (4–2) may not quite be a feasible solution to (4–1) does not cause any great problems. The reader will be asked to show in the problems that if the set of feasible solutions to (4–1) is convex, then any feasible solution to the approximating problem (4–2) will also be a feasible solution to (4–1), and there does not exist the possibility that the solution obtained to (4–2) will not be a feasible solution to (4–1).

In spite of the difficulties referred to in the above paragraph, the technique developed in this section for finding an approximate local maximum to (4–1) has proved a very useful tool. Several companies have developed computer codes which permit application of the simplex method with restricted basis entry to (4–15). The method has been found quite valuable because in many practical problems the constraints are nonlinear, and furthermore, they do not normally have the proper convexity or concavity properties which ensure that the set of feasible solutions is convex. Consequently, there can exist local optima even if the objective function is linear. It is interesting that for some classes of practical problems, in spite of a large number of local maxima, the value of the objective function at these local maxima appears to be quite close to the global optimum, and hence the fact that only a local optimum is obtained is not a serious drawback. We shall point out later by example, however, that it is easy to think of realistic problems with local optima for which the value of the objective function is far removed from the global optimum of the objective function. Therefore the method must be used with great care if the answers obtained from the approximating problem are to be used as though they were good approximations to the global optimum of the original problem.

We wish to note several other interesting observations based on the rather limited computational experience with the technique. First of all, even though the use of finer and finer subdivisions does not increase the number of constraints, it may increase considerably the number of iterations required, as well as the computational effort per iteration. The reason for the increase in the number of iterations is that if the x_j for the initial feasible solution happen to be far removed from their final values, it is often necessary to move from the initial interval for a given j to an adjacent interval, etc., until the final interval is reached. Each such change requires an iteration, and hence, when the number of intervals is increased, the number of iterations required also increases. In certain cases, however, it is possible to make large jumps in x_j. Problem 4–49 asks the reader to study the situations when this can occur.

To investigate whether or not a local maximum of the approximating problem really approximates a local maximum of (4–1), or to test the accuracy of the approximation method, a technique known as interval halfing has been used by at least one company. With this technique one solves a sequence of two or more problems, with the property that the interval spacing for problem $u + 1$ is one-half that for u. Unfortunately, with this technique, one cannot guarantee that the solution to problem u will be either a basic or a feasible solution to problem $u + 1$. Thus, in general, problem $u + 1$ is solved all over again starting with a Phase I. It has been observed that if interval halfing is used everywhere (not merely in the neighborhood of the solution to problem u), the solution for problem $u + 1$ may turn out to be a local optimum that is completely different from the one for problem u. Furthermore, the local optimum for problem $u + 1$ normally tends to yield a lower value of z than that for problem u. In other words, for certain types of problems at least, one reaches the neighborhood of a better local optimum by using a coarse, rather than a finer, subdivision.

The above observations suggest that, at least for some special classes of problems, it might be of advantage to solve the problem initially by means of fairly coarse subdivisions, and then re-solve it, using finer subdivisions only in the neighborhood of the solution to the original problem. This can be done quite easily. Equally helpful would be the ability to use one of the basic feasible solutions for the original problem as a basic feasible solution for the new problem, thus eliminating the need for a Phase I computation to be performed on the new problem. However, it does not appear to be easy to develop an efficient restart procedure. The reader is asked to examine the difficulties in Problem 4–50.

4–3 Example. To illustrate the use of the approximation technique introduced in the previous section, let us determine an approximate relative maximum for the following problem:

$$\begin{aligned} 2x_1^2 + 3x_2^2 &\leq 6, \\ x_1, x_2 &\geq 0, \\ z = 2x_1 - x_1^2 &+ x_2. \end{aligned} \tag{4–18}$$

Note that all functions appearing in (4–18) are separable, and in the notation of (4–1), $g_1(x_1) = 2x_1^2$, $g_2(x_2) = 3x_2^2$, $f_1(x_1) = 2x_1 - x_1^2$, $f_2(x_2) = x_2$. The set of feasible solutions is convex. Furthermore, f_1 and f_2 are concave. Hence from Section 3–12 any local maximum for (4–18) will be a global maximum. For this problem, then, the technique of the previous section will yield approximately the global optimum.

It is very easy to find the global optimum of (4–18) graphically (Fig. 4–2). The global optimum of z is taken on at the unique point $x_1^* = 0.7906$, $x_2^* = 1.258$. This point, as is seen from the figure, can be determined algebraically as the point where the constraint holds as a strict equality and where the slope of the constraint is equal to the slope of the objective function, i.e., the point is the solution to

$$2x_1^2 + 3x_2^2 = 6, \qquad \frac{2}{3}\frac{x_1}{x_2} = 2(1 - x_1). \tag{4–19}$$

The second equation of (4–19) yields $x_2 = x_1/3(1 - x_1)$, which when substituted into the first, gives

$$x_1^2\left[2 + \frac{1}{3}\frac{1}{(1 - x_1)^2}\right] = 6.$$

This can be solved very quickly by trial and error to give the value for

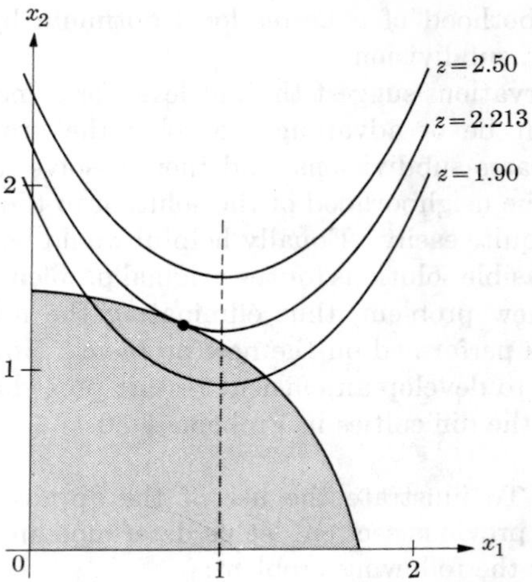

FIGURE 4–2

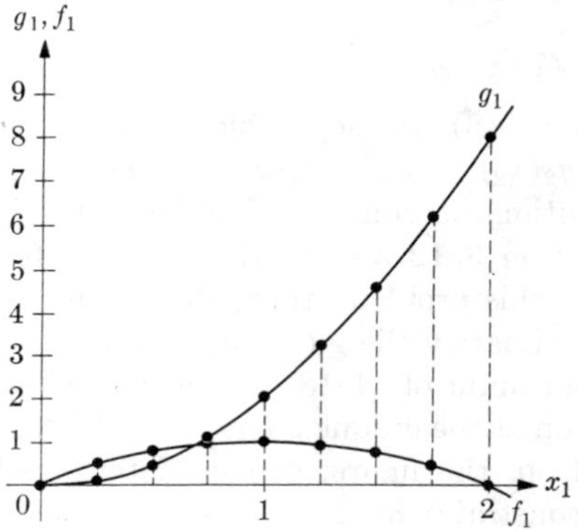

FIGURE 4–3

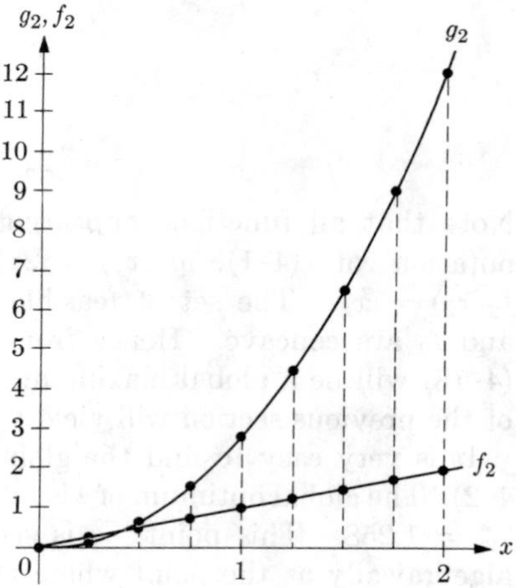

FIGURE 4–4

x_1 recorded above. The optimal value of z is $z^* = 2.213$. Having obtained the actual point at which z takes on its global maximum, we are able to determine how well the approximation method works.

Let us now set up an approximating problem. Observe that both x_1 and x_2 must be ≤ 2. Suppose that we take the x_{kj} to be equally spaced, the spacing being 0.25. Hence for each $j = 1, 2$, there will be nine λ_{kj}. The functions $g_1(x_1)$, $f_1(x_1)$ are plotted in Fig. 4–3, and $g_2(x_2)$, $f_2(x_2)$ are plotted in Fig. 4–4. The broken line approximations are not indicated, since they almost coincide with the curves and hence would be difficult to

TABLE 4-1

DATA FOR EXAMPLE

x_1 or x_2	g_1	f_1	g_2	f_2
0	0	0	0	0
0.25	0.1250	0.4375	0.1875	0.2500
0.50	0.5000	0.7500	0.7500	0.5000
0.75	1.1250	0.9375	1.6875	0.7500
1.00	2.0000	1.0000	3.0000	1.0000
1.25	3.1250	0.9375	4.6875	1.2500
1.50	4.5000	0.7500	6.7500	1.5000
1.75	6.1250	0.4375	9.1875	1.7500
2.00	8.0000	0	12.0000	2.0000

distinguish from the curves on figures of such small size. The values of the functions at the appropriate mesh points are given in Table 4-1. Since there are 19 variables, the approximating problem expressed by (4-12) through (4-14) becomes rather long when written out explicitly. In abbreviated form, it is

$$\sum_{j=1}^{2}\sum_{k=0}^{8} g_{kj}\lambda_{kj} + x_3 = 6,$$

$$\sum_{k=0}^{8} \lambda_{k1} = 1,$$

$$\sum_{k=0}^{8} \lambda_{k2} = 1, \tag{4-20}$$

$$\lambda_{k1} \geq 0, \qquad \lambda_{k2} \geq 0, \qquad \text{all } k, \qquad x_3 \geq 0,$$

$$\max \hat{z} = \sum_{j=1}^{2}\sum_{k=0}^{8} f_{kj}\lambda_{kj},$$

where the g_{kj} and f_{kj} are given in Table 4-1, and x_3 is a slack variable (it need not be expressed as a sum of λ's). We shall solve (4-20), using the revised simplex method. Note that $g_{01} = g_{02} = 0$. Thus we can immediately obtain an initial basic solution to (4-20) with the basis matrix being an identity matrix by using x_3, λ_{01}, λ_{02} as the initial basic variables. The price of each of these variables is zero, and hence $\mathbf{f}_B\mathbf{B}^{-1} = \mathbf{0}$ for this

TABLEAUX FOR SOLUTION OF EXAMPLE

TABLE 4–2. TABLEAU 1

Basic variables	$\boldsymbol{\beta}_1$	$\boldsymbol{\beta}_2$	$\boldsymbol{\beta}_3$	$\boldsymbol{\lambda}_B^{(1)}$	$\mathbf{y}_k^{(1)}$
$\hat{z}$	0	0	0	0	−1.2500
x_3	1	0	0	6	4.6875
λ_{01}	0	1	0	1	0
λ_{02}	0	0	1	1	(1)

TABLE 4–3. TABLEAU 2

$\hat{z}$	0	0	1.2500	1.2500	−0.9375
x_3	1	0	−4.6875	1.3125	1.1250
λ_{01}	0	1	0	1	(1)
λ_{52}	0	0	1	1	0

TABLE 4–4. TABLEAU 3

$\hat{z}$	0	0.9375	1.2500	2.1875	−0.2500
x_3	1	−1.1250	−4.6875	0.1875	(2.0625)
λ_{31}	0	1	0	1	0
λ_{52}	0	0	1	1	1

TABLE 4–5. TABLEAU 4

$\hat{z}$	0.1212	0.8013	0.6819	2.2102	
λ_{62}	0.4848	−0.5454	−2.2725	0.0909	
λ_{31}	0	1	0	1	
λ_{52}	−0.4848	0.5454	3.2724	0.9091	

basic solution. The initial tableau is given in Table 4–2. The vectors $\mathbf{g}_{kj}^{(1)}$ (having $-f_{kj}$ as the first component) which we shall need are:

$$\mathbf{g}_{01}^{(1)} = [0, 0, 1, 0]; \qquad \mathbf{g}_{02}^{(1)} = [0, 0, 0, 1];$$
$$\mathbf{g}_{11}^{(1)} = [-0.4375, 0.1250, 1, 0]; \qquad \mathbf{g}_{12}^{(1)} = [-0.2500, 0.1875, 0, 1];$$
$$\mathbf{g}_{21}^{(1)} = [-0.7500, 0.5000, 1, 0]; \qquad \mathbf{g}_{22}^{(1)} = [-0.5000, 0.7500, 0, 1];$$
$$\mathbf{g}_{31}^{(1)} = [-0.9375, 1.1250, 1, 0]; \qquad \mathbf{g}_{32}^{(1)} = [-0.7500, 1.6875, 0, 1];$$
$$\mathbf{g}_{41}^{(1)} = [-1, 2, 1, 0]; \qquad \mathbf{g}_{42}^{(1)} = [-1, 3, 0, 1];$$
$$\mathbf{g}_{51}^{(1)} = [-0.9375, 3.1250, 1, 0]; \qquad \mathbf{g}_{52}^{(1)} = [-1.2500, 4.6875, 0, 1];$$
$$\mathbf{g}_{61}^{(1)} = [-0.7500, 4.5000, 1, 0]; \qquad \mathbf{g}_{62}^{(1)} = [-1.5000, 6.7500, 0, 1];$$
$$\mathbf{g}_{71}^{(1)} = [-0.4375, 6.1250, 1, 0]; \qquad \mathbf{g}_{72}^{(1)} = [-1.7500, 9.1875, 0, 1];$$
$$\mathbf{g}_{81}^{(1)} = [0, 8, 1, 0]; \qquad \mathbf{g}_{82}^{(1)} = [-2, 12, 0, 1];$$
$$\mathbf{g}_{x_3}^{(1)} = [0, 1, 0, 0].$$

An examination of the first components of the vectors above shows that

$$\min (z_{kj} - f_{kj}) = z_{82} - f_{82} = -2.$$

Note that $\mathbf{g}_{02}^{(1)}$ is in the basis; thus $\mathbf{g}_{82}^{(1)}$ can enter only if $\mathbf{g}_{02}^{(1)}$ is removed. We see, however, that $\mathbf{g}_{x_3}^{(1)}$ must be removed. Hence $\mathbf{g}_{82}^{(1)}$ cannot enter the basis. Moving to the next smallest $z_{kj} - f_{kj}$, we obtain $z_{72} - f_{72}$. However, $\mathbf{g}_{72}^{(1)}$ cannot enter the basis either, because $\mathbf{g}_{x_3}^{(1)}$ would have to be removed. We then examine $\mathbf{g}_{62}^{(1)}$ and reach the same conclusion. However, when we get to $\mathbf{g}_{52}^{(1)}$, we see that the situation changes, and $\mathbf{g}_{02}^{(1)}$ must be removed. Thus $\mathbf{g}_{52}^{(1)}$ enters the basis and λ_{52} becomes positive. The new tableau is presented in Table 4–3. Note that

$$z_{k1} - f_{k1} = -f_{k1}, \qquad z_{k2} - f_{k2} = 1.25 - f_{k2}.$$

The most negative $z_{kj} - f_{kj}$ is $z_{41} - f_{41}$. However, $\mathbf{g}_{41}^{(1)}$ cannot enter the basis because x_3 would be driven to zero, yielding λ_{41} and λ_{01} both positive. The next most negative $z_{kj} - f_{kj}$ is $z_{31} - f_{31}$. Now λ_{01} will be driven to zero, and thus $\mathbf{g}_{31}^{(1)}$ can enter the basis. Thus at the next iteration, λ_{01} is driven to zero, and λ_{31} becomes unity. The new tableau is given in Table 4–4.

Only $z_{41} - f_{41}$, $z_{82} - f_{82}$, $z_{72} - f_{72}$, and $z_{62} - f_{62}$ are negative. Of these, only λ_{41} and λ_{62} are allowed to become positive; $z_{62} - f_{62} < z_{41} - f_{41}$, so that $\mathbf{g}_{62}^{(1)}$ enters the basis at the next iteration. Now x_3 is driven to zero. The new tableau is shown in Table 4–5. Now all $z_{kj} - f_{kj} \geq 0$. Therefore Table 4–5 contains an optimal basic solution for the approximating problem. It is

$$\lambda_{31} = 1, \qquad \lambda_{52} = 0.9091, \qquad \lambda_{62} = 0.0909, \qquad \hat{z} = 2.2102,$$

or

$$x_1 = \lambda_{31}x_{31} = 1(0.75) = 0.7500;$$

$$x_2 = \lambda_{52}x_{52} + \lambda_{62}x_{62} = (0.9091)(1.25) + (0.0909)(1.50)$$
$$= 1.1363 + 0.1363 = 1.2726.$$

We obtained previously the optimal solution $x_1^* = 0.7906$, $x_2^* = 1.258$, $z^* = 2.213$. It is seen that the approximating problem gives a solution which is quite close to the optimal solution. The approximation could be improved, of course, by making the initial subdivisions of the x_1- and x_2-intervals finer. Note that the value of $\hat{z}$ is much closer to z^* than are x_1, x_2 to x_1^* and x_2^*.

In Fig. 4–5 we have shown the convex set of feasible solutions for the approximating problem (4–2), as well as for the given problem. The sequence of solutions to (4–2) corresponding to each tableau obtained when the simplex method with restricted basis entry is applied to (4–20) is also shown, with the points being numbered to correspond to the tableaux. Note the unusual sequence of points. When solving (4–20) by means of the simplex method with restricted basis entry, we move, at each iteration, to an adjacent extreme point only in the **λ**-space, but it is by no means true that we move by adjacent extreme points in the **x**-space.

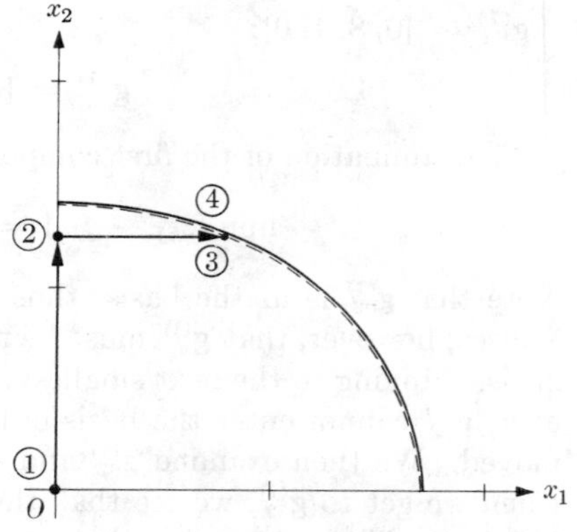

FIGURE 4–5

4–4 An alternative formulation. The approximating problem for (4–1) can be cast into a different form by the introduction of a new set of variables. In (4–8), (4–9), and (4–10), let

$$\Delta f_{kj} = f_{kj} - f_{k-1,j}; \qquad \Delta g_{kij} = g_{kij} - g_{k-1,ij};$$
$$\Delta x_{kj} = x_{kj} - x_{k-1,j}; \qquad k = 1, \ldots, r_j. \tag{4–21}$$

Then, if x_j lies in the interval $x_{k-1,j} \leq x_j \leq x_{kj}$, we can write

$$x_j = x_{k-1,j} + (\Delta x_{kj})\,\delta_{kj}, \tag{4–22}$$

where*

$$\delta_{kj} = \frac{x_j - x_{k-1,j}}{\Delta x_{kj}} \tag{4-23}$$

is uniquely determined by x_j. Furthermore, for x_j in the interval under consideration,

$$0 \le \delta_{kj} \le 1. \tag{4-24}$$

From (4-3), we see that if x_j is in the interval $x_{k-1,j} \le x_j \le x_{kj}$, then $\hat{g}_{ij}(x_j)$ and $\hat{f}_j(x_j)$, the polygonal approximations to $g_{ij}(x_j)$ and $f_j(x_j)$, respectively, can be written

$$\hat{g}_{ij}(x_j) = g_{k-1,ij} + (\Delta g_{kij})\, \delta_{kj}; \qquad \hat{f}_j(x_j) = f_{k-1,j} + (\Delta f_{kj})\, \delta_{kj}. \tag{4-25}$$

Suppose now that we impose the additional restriction that if $\delta_{kj} > 0$, then $\delta_{uj} = 1$, $u = 1, \ldots, k-1$. For the case being considered, we can therefore write

$$\begin{aligned} x_{k-1,j} &= \sum_{u=1}^{k-1} (\Delta x_{uj})\, \delta_{uj}; \\ g_{k-1,ij} &= \sum_{u=1}^{k-1} (\Delta g_{uij})\, \delta_{uj} + g_{0ij}; \\ f_{k-1,j} &= \sum_{u=1}^{k-1} (\Delta f_{uj})\, \delta_{uj} + f_{0j}. \end{aligned} \tag{4-26}$$

Furthermore, if $0 < \delta_{kj} < 1$, the above restriction implies that $\delta_{uj} = 0$, $u > k$. Consequently, if we require that when $\delta_{kj} > 0$, then $\delta_{uj} = 1$, $u = 1, \ldots, k-1$, we can write

$$\begin{aligned} x_j &= \sum_{k=1}^{r_j} (\Delta x_{kj})\, \delta_{kj}; \\ \hat{g}_{ij}(x_j) &= \sum_{k=1}^{r_j} (\Delta g_{kij})\, \delta_{kj} + g_{0ij}; \\ \hat{f}_j(x_j) &= \sum_{k=1}^{r_j} (\Delta f_{kj})\, \delta_{kj} + f_{0j}, \end{aligned} \tag{4-27}$$

and the δ_{kj} are uniquely determined when (4-24) holds. The approximating problem (4-2) can then be expressed in terms of the variables δ_{kj}, rather than the variables λ_{kj} used in Section 4-2. In terms of the δ_{kj}-

---

* Note that here the variables δ_{kj} are *not* to be interpreted as the Kronecker delta.

variables, the approximating problem becomes

$$\sum_{j=1}^{n}\sum_{k=1}^{r_j} (\Delta g_{kij})\, \delta_{kj}\{\leq, =, \geq\} b_i - \sum_{j=1}^{n} g_{0ij}, \qquad i = 1, \ldots, m,$$

$$0 \leq \delta_{kj} \leq 1, \qquad \text{all } k \text{ and } j, \tag{4–28}$$

$$\max \hat{z} = \sum_{j=1}^{n}\sum_{k=1}^{r_j} (\Delta f_{kj})\, \delta_{kj},$$

where we require in addition that if $\delta_{kj} > 0$, $\delta_{uj} = 1$, $u = 1, \ldots, k-1$. In the objective function, we have omitted the constant $\sum_{j=1}^{n} f_{0j}$. Problem (4–28) would be linear if it were not for the restrictions on the δ_{kj} just stated. We can solve this problem by using the simplex method with restricted basis entry just as was done in Section 4–3. We do not allow δ_{kj} to become positive unless $\delta_{uj} = 1$, $u = 1, \ldots, k-1$. When a stage is reached such that $z_{kj} - \Delta f_{kj} \geq 0$ for every δ_{kj} which is permitted to enter the basis, then the current basic solution yields a relative maximum of the approximating problem (4–28) (in terms of the x_j-variables, not the δ_{kj}). The proof is almost identical to that provided in Section 4–3. It will not be given here, but the reader is asked to provide it in Problem 4–13. In the future, we shall refer to (4–28) as the δ-form of the approximating problem, whereas (4–12) through (4–14) will be referred to as the λ-form of the approximating problem.

One may apply the simplex method to (4–28) without explicitly including the upper bounds as constraints, i.e., it is only necessary to work with basis matrices of order m. The special algorithm is described in {LP 11–7}. It is also possible to restrict the entry of the δ_{kj} into the basis, as required when this algorithm is employed. If one did not use such an algorithm, the size of the basis would be extremely large, even for very small problems (the order of the basis matrix would be $m + \sum_j r_j$), and the formulation in terms of the δ_{kj}-variables would be of little value.) It should be recalled though that if x_j enters the problem linearly, then x_j need not be expressed in terms of δ_{kj}-variables. This observation frequently helps to reduce considerably the size of the problem to be solved.

It is interesting to compare the λ-form of the approximating problem with the δ-form. This will be done for the case where each variable is assumed to enter the problem in a nonlinear fashion. The λ-form involves $n + \sum_j r_j$ variables (plus slack and surplus variables) and $m + n$ constraints. The final solution will involve no more than $n + m$ positive λ_{kj} (and for a given j, no more than two λ_{kj} can be positive). The δ-variable form involves $\sum_j r_j$ variables (plus slack and surplus variables) and m constraints. In addition, there are $\sum_j r_j$ upper-bound constraints which need not be included explicitly as constraints. The final solution to the

δ-variable problem will involve as many as $m + \sum_j r_j$ positive δ_{kj}. The δ-variable form has the advantage that one works with a smaller basis, but it has the disadvantage that it is necessary to use the special upper-bounds algorithm. Both the λ- and δ-forms require the use of restricted entry into the basis, the restrictions being somewhat different for the two cases. Both forms of the approximating problem have been coded for solution on high-speed digital computers. Problems have been run with both codes, and from the limited computational experience available, it appears that the δ-form definitely requires less computation time because of the smaller basis, even though the number of iterations may be slightly greater than for the λ-form. Experience has also suggested that, at least in some cases, either of the forms may require considerably more iterations than a strictly linear problem of equivalent size. For example, a λ-form problem with 120 constraints required roughly 1200 iterations before termination, whereas a strictly linear problem might be expected to be solved in 400 or less.

4–5 Transformations of variables to obtain separability. Although a problem may not originally have the form (4–1), defining a number of new variables frequently permits conversion of the original problem to form (4–1), where all functions are separable. We shall illustrate in this section some of the more useful procedures for doing this.

As a first simple example, imagine that the product $x_i x_j$ appears in one of the constraints or the objective function. To eliminate such a product and obtain a separable form, suppose that we define two new variables y_i, y_j by

$$y_i = \tfrac{1}{2}(x_i + x_j), \qquad y_j = \tfrac{1}{2}(x_i - x_j). \tag{4–29}$$

Then

$$x_i x_j = y_i^2 - y_j^2, \tag{4–30}$$

and we have a separable form in the new variables y_i, y_j. The procedure would then be as follows: Wherever $x_i x_j$ appeared in the original problem, we would replace it by $y_i^2 - y_j^2$. Furthermore, we would include the two additional constraints (4–29) in the problem. Note that since y_j involves the difference of x_i and x_j, y_j will be unrestricted in sign even if x_i, x_j are to be non-negative. This need not cause any problems in setting up the δ- or λ-forms of the approximating problems, since the λ_{kj} and δ_{kj} will always be non-negative. Problem 4–37 asks the reader to show how to handle unrestricted variables. If the ranges of variation of x_i, x_j were $0 \leq x_i \leq a_i$ and $0 \leq x_j \leq a_j$, respectively, the range over which y_j would have to be represented would be $-a_j \leq zy_j \leq a_i$. If the appearance of $x_i x_j$ were the only nonseparable feature in the original problem, we would, after the above transformations, have a problem of the form (4–1) and could then proceed to convert it to a λ- or δ-form of the approximating problem. Note that to obtain a separable form we had to enlarge the problem by including two additional constraints.

The product $x_i x_j$ can be separated in another way which can be generalized to handle problems involving the product of three or more variables, provided that all variables are positive. Let us introduce the new variable

$$y = x_i x_j. \tag{4-31}$$

Now take the natural logarithm (or logarithm to the base 10) of this expression to yield

$$\ln y = \ln x_i + \ln x_j. \tag{4-32}$$

Then wherever $x_i x_j$ appears in the problem, replace it by y. Next add (4–32) as an additional constraint on the problem. If the appearance of $x_i x_j$ is the only nonseparable part of the problem, it will be separable after introduction of the variable y and the additional constraint (4–32). The above procedure will work only if it is known that x_i and x_j must be positive. If either or both of the variables can be zero, then difficulties will be encountered with (4–32), since $\ln 0 = -\infty$, and one cannot represent (4–32) properly in either the λ- or δ-form.

It is straightforward, however, to modify the above approach to take care of non-negative variables x_i and x_j. Suppose that we introduce the new variables w_i and w_j,

$$w_i = x_i + \epsilon_i, \qquad w_j = x_j + \epsilon_j, \tag{4-33}$$

where ϵ_i and ϵ_j are arbitrary positive numbers. Then $w_i \geq \epsilon_i > 0$ and $w_j \geq \epsilon_j > 0$. Furthermore,

$$x_i x_j = (w_i - \epsilon_i)(w_j - \epsilon_j) = w_i w_j - \epsilon_i w_j - \epsilon_j w_i + \epsilon_i \epsilon_j. \tag{4-34}$$

Next we write

$$y = w_i w_j, \tag{4-35}$$

and

$$\ln y = \ln w_i + \ln w_j. \tag{4-36}$$

The procedure then is to replace $x_i x_j$ by

$$y - \epsilon_i w_j - \epsilon_j w_i + \epsilon_i \epsilon_j \tag{4-37}$$

wherever this product appears and introduce three new constraints, (4–33) and (4–36). Note that this procedure requires the introduction of three new variables and three additional constraints. This method can be generalized to separate the product of any number of variables. Problem

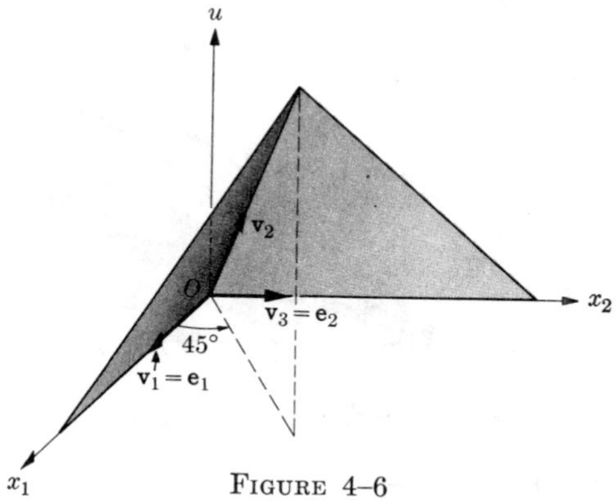

FIGURE 4-6

4-17 asks the reader to provide the transformations for the case of three variables. One can, in a less straightforward way, make the separation of $x_i x_j$, introducing only the additional constraint (4-32). Problem 4-21 deals with this point.

It is easy to separate expressions such as $e^{(ax_i^2 + bx_j)}$, where $x_i \geq 0$, $x_j \geq 0$, by writing

$$y = e^{(ax_i^2 + bx_j)}, \tag{4-38}$$

$$\ln y = ax_i^2 + bx_j. \tag{4-39}$$

Similarly, to separate $x_i^{x_j}$, $x_i > 0$, $x_j \geq 0$, we write

$$y = x_i^{x_j}, \tag{4-40}$$

$$w_j = x_j + \epsilon_j, \qquad \epsilon_j > 0, \tag{4-41}$$

$$v = w_j \ln x_i, \tag{4-42}$$

$$\ln y = v - \epsilon_j \ln x_i, \tag{4-43}$$

$$\ln v = \ln w_j + \ln \ln x_i. \tag{4-44}$$

Other tricks may be used to represent rather unusual functions within the framework being considered. Suppose that $x_1, x_2 \geq 0$, and

$$u = \min [x_1, x_2]; \tag{4-45}$$

that is,

$$u = \begin{cases} x_1, & x_2 \geq x_1, \\ x_2, & x_1 \geq x_2. \end{cases} \tag{4-46}$$

The function $u(x_1, x_2)$ is plotted in Fig. 4-6. Note that the surface consists of two planar parts. This function can be represented in separable form as

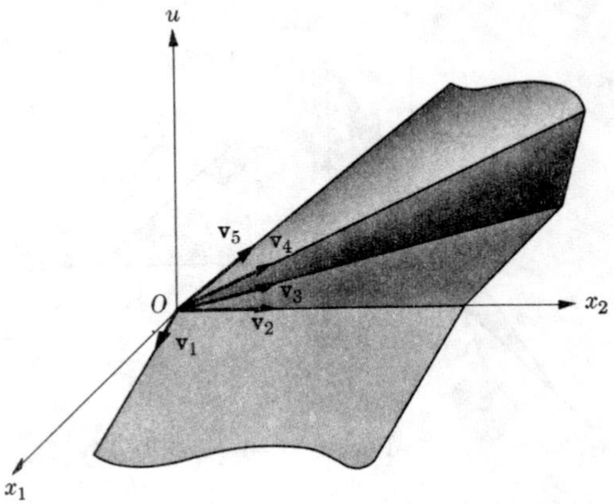

FIGURE 4–7

follows: Consider the three vectors $\mathbf{v}_1 = \mathbf{e}_1$, $\mathbf{v}_2 = [1, 1, 1]$, $\mathbf{v}_3 = \mathbf{e}_2$. When $x_1 \geq x_2$, then $u = x_2$, and the planar surface is simply the convex polyhedral cone generated by $\mathbf{v}_1$ and $\mathbf{v}_2$; i.e., any point $[x_1, x_2, u]$ on the surface can be written

$$[x_1, x_2, u] = \lambda_1\mathbf{v}_1 + \lambda_2\mathbf{v}_2, \qquad \lambda_1, \lambda_2 \geq 0. \tag{4-47}$$

Similarly, when $x_2 \geq x_1$, then $u = x_1$, and the planar surface is simply the convex polyhedral cone generated by $\mathbf{v}_2$ and $\mathbf{v}_3$; i.e., any point $[x_1, x_2, u]$ on the surface can be written

$$[x_1, x_2, u] = \lambda_2\mathbf{v}_2 + \lambda_3\mathbf{v}_3, \qquad \lambda_2, \lambda_3 \geq 0. \tag{4-48}$$

Consequently, any point $[x_1, x_2, u]$ on the surface can be written

$$[x_1, x_2, u] = \lambda_1\mathbf{v}_1 + \lambda_2\mathbf{v}_2 + \lambda_3\mathbf{v}_3, \qquad \lambda_1, \lambda_2, \lambda_3 \geq 0, \tag{4-49}$$

or

$$x_1 = \lambda_1 + \lambda_2, \qquad x_2 = \lambda_2 + \lambda_3, \qquad u = \lambda_2 \tag{4-50}$$

if we also stipulate that no more than two of the λ_i can be positive, and two can be positive only if they are adjacent. Note that here the λ_i do not have to sum to unity. In order to use this representation conveniently, we would have to solve the approximating problem, using the λ-form, since it is the one which uses the proper rules for restricting entry into the basis.

The procedure just discussed could be used to represent the surface consisting of several planar parts shown in Fig. 4–7. The vectors $\mathbf{v}_1$, $\mathbf{v}_2$, $\mathbf{v}_3$, $\mathbf{v}_4$, $\mathbf{v}_5$ would be drawn as shown, and then any point $[x_1, x_2, u]$ on the surface could be written

$$[x_1, x_2, u] = \lambda_1\mathbf{v}_1 + \lambda_2\mathbf{v}_2 + \lambda_3\mathbf{v}_3 + \lambda_4\mathbf{v}_4 + \lambda_5\mathbf{v}_5, \tag{4-51}$$

where all $\lambda_i \geq 0$, no more than two λ_i can be positive, and two can be positive only if they are adjacent.

The techniques for converting a problem to the separable form (4–1) illustrated in this section should be sufficient to indicate how such conversions can be made. There seem to be very few problems which arise in practice that one cannot convert to the form (4–1) by introducing a sufficient number of new variables and constraints. However, if many expressions have to be converted to a separable form, the size of the approximating problem can become very large, because of the number of new constraints which must be added to the original ones.

4–6 Cases where a local optimum is also a global optimum. We have shown in Section 3–12 that if the set of feasible solutions for a nonlinear programming problem is convex, and if the objective function is a concave function, then any relative maximum of the objective function over the convex set of feasible solutions is also a global maximum. When the problem has the form (4–1), the objective function will be concave if each $f_j(x_j)$ is concave. Furthermore, if there is a feasible solution, the set of feasible solutions will be convex if (a) $g_{ij}(x_j)$ is a concave function for each j when the ith constraint involves a $\geq$ sign, (b) $g_{ij}(x_j)$ is a convex function for each j if the ith constraint involves a $\leq$ sign, (c) $g_{ij}(x_j)$ is linear for each j, that is, $g_{ij}(x_j) = a_{ij}x_j$, when the ith constraint involves an $=$ sign.

By the manner in which the polygonal approximations are introduced, it is clear that if f_j, g_{ij} are convex (concave) functions, then $\hat{f}_j$, $\hat{g}_{ij}$ are also convex (concave) functions. Consequently, if the functions f_j, g_{ij} have the proper convexity-concavity properties so that any relative maximum of (4–1) is also a global maximum, then any local maximum of the approximating problem (4–2) is also a global maximum. Furthermore, in such cases, the set of points where the global maximum of the approximating problem is taken on is convex, so that there cannot be two or more isolated relative maxima for the approximating problem. When a local maximum is also a global maximum, the solution of the approximating problem will be an approximation to a point at which the given problem (4–1) assumes its global maximum. Furthermore, by making the subdivision of the x_j-intervals finer and finer, the sequence of optimal values for the objective function for the approximating problem will approach, in the limit, the optimal value of the objective function for (4–1) (see Problem 4–34). One cannot conclude that the sequence of solutions to the approximating problems will approach a unique limit unless it is known that (4–1) has a unique optimal solution. Note that if the objective function of (4–1) is strictly concave and the set of feasible solutions is convex so that the point at which the global maximum is taken on is unique, it is not necessarily true that the approximating problem will have a unique global maximum, since the objective function will not be strictly concave. However, as the subdivisions are made finer and finer, all points which yield an optimal solution of the approximating problem will approach the point yielding the global optimum of (4–1), and in the limit, the optimal solution to the approximating problem will be taken on at only a single point.

We shall now prove that *if the $f_j(x_j)$ are concave functions and if the $g_{ij}(x_j)$ have the proper convexity and concavity properties so that the set of feasible solutions is convex, then, if the approximating problem is solved strictly as a linear programming problem without the use of restricted basis entry, the solution so obtained will be an optimal solution to the approximating problem.* In other words, we obtain an optimal solution whether or not we use restricted basis entry. This is a rather surprising result at first glance. It is also an important result, because, as we shall show in the next section, it is possible to introduce a more efficient computational technique for solving the approximating problem when it is not necessary to use restricted basis entry. We shall give the proof for the δ-form of the approximating problem. The reader is asked to provide the corresponding proof for the λ-form of the approximating problem in the problems. To carry out the proof for the δ-form of the approximating problem, it is convenient to introduce a new set of variables $\psi_{kj} = \delta_{kj}\,\Delta x_{kj}$, so that the problem can be written

$$\sum_j \sum_k \left(\frac{\Delta g_{kij}}{\Delta x_{kj}}\right) \psi_{kj} \{\le, =, \ge\} b_i - \sum_j g_{0ij}, \qquad i = 1, \ldots, m,$$

$$0 \le \psi_{kj} \le \Delta x_{kj}, \qquad \text{all } k, j, \tag{4–52}$$

$$\max \hat{z} = \sum_j \sum_k \left(\frac{\Delta f_{kj}}{\Delta x_{kj}}\right) \psi_{kj}.$$

Note that in terms of the variables ψ_{kj},

$$x_j = \sum_k \psi_{kj}, \qquad j = 1, \ldots, n. \tag{4–53}$$

We shall carry out the proof by contradiction. Assume that (4–52) has been solved strictly as a linear programming problem without the use of restricted basis entry. We shall show that the assumption that there does not exist an optimal solution to this linear programming problem having the property that if $\psi_{kj} > 0$, then $\psi_{uj} = \Delta x_{uj}$, $u = 1, \ldots, k-1$, leads to a contradiction. To see this assume that we have solved (4–52) as a linear programming problem and that the optimal solution so obtained has the property that for a particular j, $\psi_{rj} > 0$, but $\psi_{vj} < \Delta x_{vj}$, where $v < r$. We shall show that without changing the values of any of the x_j,

$x_j = \sum_k \psi_{kj}$, we can obtain either a new set of feasible ψ_{kj} which yield an improved value of the objective function or a new set of feasible ψ_{kj} yielding the same value of the objective function; in either case, the new set of ψ_{kj} will have the property that $\psi_{uj} = \Delta x_{uj}$, $u = 1, \ldots, k-1$ if $\psi_{kj} > 0$. Either of these alternatives will contradict our original assumption. We simply decrease ψ_{rj} and simultaneously increase ψ_{vj} by the same amount until either $\psi_{rj} = 0$ or $\psi_{vj} = \Delta x_{vj}$. This does not change the value of any x_j. Let ρ be the amount by which ψ_{rj} is decreased and ψ_{vj} is increased. The value of the objective function is changed by an amount

$$\left(\frac{\Delta f_{vj}}{\Delta x_{vj}} - \frac{\Delta f_{rj}}{\Delta x_{rj}}\right) \rho, \tag{4-54}$$

and the left-hand side of constraint i is changed by

$$\left(\frac{\Delta g_{vij}}{\Delta x_{vj}} - \frac{\Delta g_{rij}}{\Delta x_{rj}}\right) \rho. \tag{4-55}$$

Now since $f_j(x_j)$ is a concave function, $\hat{f}_j(x_j)$ is also a concave function. Therefore

$$\frac{\Delta f_{vj}}{\Delta x_{vj}} \geq \frac{\Delta f_{rj}}{\Delta x_{rj}},$$

and hence the objective function has either been increased or remains unchanged in value. For constraints having a $\leq$ sign, each $g_{ij}(x_j)$, and therefore each $\hat{g}_{ij}(x_j)$ will be a convex function. For convex functions, however,

$$\frac{\Delta g_{vij}}{\Delta x_{vj}} - \frac{\Delta g_{rij}}{\Delta x_{rj}} \leq 0.$$

Thus, since the original set of ψ_{kj} satisfied all the constraints, the new set of ψ_{kj} will clearly satisfy those constraints having a $\leq$ sign, since the left-hand side remains unchanged or decreases algebraically. Similarly, for constraints having a $\geq$ sign, each $\hat{g}_{ij}(x_j)$ will be a concave function. For such functions,

$$\frac{\Delta g_{vij}}{\Delta x_{vj}} - \frac{\Delta g_{rij}}{\Delta x_{rj}} \geq 0,$$

and hence the new set of ψ_{kj} will satisfy constraints having a $\geq$ sign. Finally, for constraints that are equations, the $\hat{g}_{ij}(x_j)$ are linear,

$$\frac{\Delta g_{vij}}{\Delta x_{vj}} - \frac{\Delta g_{rij}}{\Delta x_{rj}} = 0,$$

and the new set of ψ_{kj} also satisfies these constraints. We conclude that the new set of ψ_{kj} satisfies $0 \leq \psi_{kj} \leq \Delta x_{kj}$ and all the remaining constraints. Thus they represent a feasible solution for which the objective function has either been increased or remains unchanged in value. By continuing this process, if necessary, we can either obtain an improved feasible solution or an alternative optimum having $\psi_{uj} = \Delta x_{uj}$, $u = 1, \ldots, k-1$ if $\psi_{kj} > 0$, with the values of the x_j remaining unchanged. Both of these contradict our original hypothesis. Thus, by solving (4–52) strictly as a linear programming problem, the set of x_j computed from the optimal solution so obtained yields an optimal solution to the approximating problem. Note that it is conceivable that the solution obtained to (4–52), solving (4–52) as a linear programming problem, may not have $\psi_{uj} = \Delta x_{uj}$, $u = 1, \ldots, k-1$ if $\psi_{kj} > 0$. Nonetheless, it follows from the preceding argument that the x_j determined from the set of ψ_{uj} yield an optimal solution to the approximating problem.

When an optimal solution to the approximating problem can be obtained by solving it as a strict linear programming problem, the decomposition principle {LP 11–10} can be usefully employed to simplify the computational procedure. We explain how this is done for the δ-form of the approximating problem in the next section. The reader is asked to obtain the corresponding results for the λ-form in Problem 4–57.

The use of polygonal approximations to obtain approximate solutions to problems with separable functions was initially restricted to problems of the form (4–52) in which only the objective function was nonlinear and concave. Charnes and Lemke [4] were the first to study this problem. They used a formulation roughly similar, but slightly different from, the λ-form of the approximating problem. Shortly thereafter Dantzig [5] introduced the δ-form essentially as it is used here. Later, he supplied more details [6]. Much more recently, C. Miller [14] generalized the results to nonlinear constraints where only a local maximum might be obtained. In his work at Standard Oil Company of California, Miller used both the λ- and δ-forms of the approximating problems.

4–7 Use of the decomposition principle to treat upper bounds. One method for treating upper bounds without explicitly including them as constraints is given in {LP 11–7}. A seemingly much more efficient method can be obtained by applying the decomposition principle {LP 11–10} to the problem. However, one need not be familiar with the decomposition principle to understand the arguments given below, since all the results follow directly and in a simple way.

Consider a linear programming problem of the form

$$\begin{gathered} \mathbf{A}_1\mathbf{x}_1 + \mathbf{A}_2\mathbf{x}_2 = \mathbf{b}, \\ \mathbf{I}\mathbf{x}_1 \leq \mathbf{h}, \qquad \mathbf{x}_1, \mathbf{x}_2 \geq \mathbf{0}, \\ \max z = \mathbf{c}_1\mathbf{x}_1 + \mathbf{c}_2\mathbf{x}_2. \end{gathered} \tag{4–56}$$

Here we have a situation in which there are upper bounds on the variables appearing in $\mathbf{x}_1$, whereas there are no upper bounds placed on the variables appearing in $\mathbf{x}_2$. Assume that $\mathbf{A}_1$ is $m \times n_1$ and $\mathbf{A}_2$ is $m \times n_2$. Denote by J_2 the set of subscripts j for which $j = n_1 + 1, \ldots, n_1 + n_2$.

The set of points satisfying $\mathbf{I}\mathbf{x}_1 \leq \mathbf{h}, \mathbf{x}_1 \geq \mathbf{0}$, is a closed, strictly bounded convex set X with a finite number of extreme points. In fact, there are precisely 2^{n_1} extreme points, and it is easy to write down the general form for any such extreme point $\mathbf{x}_{v1}^*$:

$$\mathbf{x}_{v1}^* = [h_1\delta_1, \ldots, h_n\delta_n], \tag{4–57}$$

where $\delta_j = 1$ or 0. All extreme points are generated by assigning all combinations of the values 0 or 1 to the δ_j. We ask the reader to prove in Problem 4–22 that the extreme points have this form. Since X is a closed, strictly bounded convex set with a finite number of extreme points, we know that every point in the set can be written as a convex combination of the extreme points, i.e., if $\mathbf{x}_1 \in X$, then there exist ρ_v (not necessarily unique) such that

$$\mathbf{x}_1 = \sum_{v=1}^{2^{n_1}} \rho_v \mathbf{x}_{v1}^*; \qquad \rho_v \geq 0, \quad \text{all } v; \qquad \sum_v \rho_v = 1. \tag{4–58}$$

Furthermore, any set of $\rho_v \geq 0$ with $\sum \rho_v = 1$ is such that $\mathbf{x}_1$ computed from (4–58) is in X. Consequently, the original problem is equivalent to one in which we omit the upper-bound constraints and introduce the variables ρ_v, i.e., it is equivalent to the problem

$$\begin{aligned} \sum_v (\mathbf{A}_1\mathbf{x}_{v1}^*)\rho_v + \mathbf{A}_2\mathbf{x}_2 &= \mathbf{b}, \\ \sum_v \rho_v &= 1, \\ \rho_v \geq 0, \quad \text{all } v; \quad \mathbf{x}_2 &\geq \mathbf{0}, \\ \max z = \sum_v (\mathbf{c}_1\mathbf{x}_{v1}^*)\rho_v &+ \mathbf{c}_2\mathbf{x}_2. \end{aligned} \tag{4–59}$$

This follows, since any feasible solution to (4–59) is such that the unique $\mathbf{x}_1$ computed from (4–58) and $\mathbf{x}_2$ yield a feasible solution to (4–56) (including the upper bound constraints) with the same value of the objective function, and, conversely, any feasible solution to (4–56) is such that $\mathbf{x}_1$ determines a set of ρ_v (not necessarily unique) such that the ρ_v and $\mathbf{x}_2$ are a feasible solution to (4–59) with the same value of the objective function. Thus we can concentrate our attention on solving (4–59). An optimal solution to (4–59) will give us an optimal solution to (4–56) when (4–58) is used.

We have seen that it is straightforward to write down the extreme points $\mathbf{x}_{v1}^*$, and thus we could compute the quantities $\mathbf{A}_1\mathbf{x}_{v1}^*$ and $\mathbf{c}_1\mathbf{x}_{v1}^*$ and solve the problem (4–59) directly. However, there may be a very large number of extreme points, and it can be extremely tedious to obtain them all and compute the quantities $\mathbf{A}_1\mathbf{x}_{v1}^*$, $\mathbf{c}_1\mathbf{x}_{v1}^*$. This is especially true in view of the fact that most of the ρ_v may always remain zero, and the corresponding $\mathbf{A}_1\mathbf{x}_{v1}^*$, $\mathbf{c}_1\mathbf{x}_{v1}^*$ will never be needed. We shall now show that it is unnecessary to go through this procedure. Instead, it is possible to generate the extreme points as needed in the solution of the problem. Write

$$\mathbf{d}_v = \mathbf{A}_1\mathbf{x}_{v1}^*, \qquad e_v = \mathbf{c}_1\mathbf{x}_{v1}^*. \tag{4–60}$$

Imagine that we have a basic feasible solution to (4–59), and let $\mathbf{B}$ be the basis matrix of order $m + 1$ and $\mathbf{c}_B$ contain the prices of the variables in the basis. Let

$$\boldsymbol{\sigma} = [\boldsymbol{\sigma}_1, \sigma_{m+1}] = \mathbf{c}_B\mathbf{B}^{-1}. \tag{4–61}$$

It is convenient to partition $\boldsymbol{\sigma}$ as shown to separate out the last component.

Imagine now that we wish to determine the variable to become basic at the next iteration. For all $j \in J_2$ not in the basic set, we compute

$$z_j - c_j = \boldsymbol{\sigma}_1\mathbf{a}_j - c_j, \tag{4–62}$$

where $\mathbf{a}_j$ refers to the appropriate column of $\mathbf{A}_2$. Now for ρ_v

$$z_v - e_v = \boldsymbol{\sigma}_1\mathbf{d}_v + \sigma_{m+1} - e_v = (\boldsymbol{\sigma}_1\mathbf{A}_1 - \mathbf{c}_1)\mathbf{x}_{v1}^* + \sigma_{m+1}. \tag{4–63}$$

If we have not tabulated the $\mathbf{x}_{v1}^*$, we cannot compute (4–63) directly. Note, however, that we do not need all $z_v - e_v$ and $\mathbf{x}_{v1}^*$. We need only that $\mathbf{x}_{v1}^*$ which corresponds to the smallest $z_v - e_v$. In other words, all we need is the $\mathbf{x}_{v1}^*$ which minimizes $(\boldsymbol{\sigma}_1\mathbf{A}_1 - \mathbf{c}_1)\mathbf{x}_{v1}^*$. We can, however, make the interesting observation that this extreme point will be generated automatically if we solve the linear programming problem

$$\mathbf{Ix} \le \mathbf{h}, \qquad \mathbf{x} \ge \mathbf{0}, \qquad \min Z = (\boldsymbol{\sigma}_1\mathbf{A}_1 - \mathbf{c}_1)\mathbf{x}, \tag{4–64}$$

since an optimal solution will be an extreme point of X. The next thing to note is that no computational effort is required to solve (4–64), since it decomposes into n_1 linear programming problems

$$0 \le x_j \le h_j, \qquad \min Z_j = (\boldsymbol{\sigma}_1\mathbf{A}_1 - \mathbf{c}_1)_j x_j, \qquad j = 1, \ldots, n_1. \tag{4–65}$$

The solution to the jth problem is

$$x_j^* = \begin{cases} 0 & \text{if} \quad (\boldsymbol{\sigma}_1\mathbf{A}_1 - \mathbf{c}_1)_j > 0, \\ h_j & \text{if} \quad (\boldsymbol{\sigma}_1\mathbf{A}_1 - \mathbf{c}_1)_j < 0, \end{cases} \tag{4–66}$$

and when $(\boldsymbol{\sigma}_1\mathbf{A}_1 - \mathbf{c}_1)_j = 0$, any x_j in the interval $0 \leq x_j \leq h_j$ is optimal. Then we can use either 0 or h_j in generating the extreme point.

Denote by $\mathbf{x}_{t1}^*$ the extreme point obtained by solving (4-64). Then

$$\min (z_v - e_v) = z_t - e_t = (\boldsymbol{\sigma}_1\mathbf{A}_1 - \mathbf{c}_1)\mathbf{x}_{t1}^* + \sigma_{m+1}. \tag{4-67}$$

Next we compute

$$\min \{z_t - e_t, \min (z_j - c_j), j \in J_2\}. \tag{4-68}$$

If this number is non-negative, the current basic feasible solution is optimal. If the number is negative, the vector (or any one of the vectors) corresponding to the $z_t - e_t$ or $z_j - c_j$ which yield this number enters the basis at the next iteration.

If the variable to enter the basis is an x_j, $j \in J_2$, we compute $\mathbf{y}_j = \mathbf{B}^{-1}[\mathbf{a}_j, 0]$, and determine the variable to leave the basis in the usual way. If ρ_t is to enter the basis, we first compute $\mathbf{d}_t = \mathbf{A}_1\mathbf{x}_{v1}^*$, thus generating the vector needed. Then we compute $\mathbf{y}_t = \mathbf{B}^{-1}[\mathbf{d}_t, 1]$, and determine the variable to leave the basis in the usual way. We then make a transformation to obtain the tableau. This yields a new $\boldsymbol{\sigma}$ which determines a new set of prices to be used in (4-64). The above procedure is repeated to determine whether the new solution is optimal, or, if not, what variable enters the basis at the next step.

The algorithm just described has the great advantage over the technique presented in {LP 11-7} that a large number of variables can reach their upper bounds in a single iteration, whereas with the method of {LP 11-7} one iteration is needed for each variable which reaches its upper bound. Trials on small sample problems suggest that the present technique can reduce the computational effort by as much as fifty percent. Unfortunately, the present method cannot be conveniently used in cases where restricted entry into the basis must be used to guarantee that $\delta_{uj} = 1$, $u = 1, \ldots, k - 1$, if $\delta_{kj} > 0$, since one no longer deals directly with the variables δ_{kj}. It is useful, however, for the case studied in the previous section where restricted entry is not needed.

4-8 Example. We shall now illustrate by an example how an approximate global maximum of a problem with linear constraints and a concave separable objective function is determined by making use of the δ-form of the approximating problem and the theory discussed in the last two sections. Consider the problem

$$\begin{aligned} 2x_1 + 3x_2 &\leq 6, \\ 2x_1 + x_2 &\leq 4, \\ x_1, x_2 &\geq 0, \\ \max z = 2x_1 - x_1^2 + x_2&. \end{aligned} \tag{4-69}$$

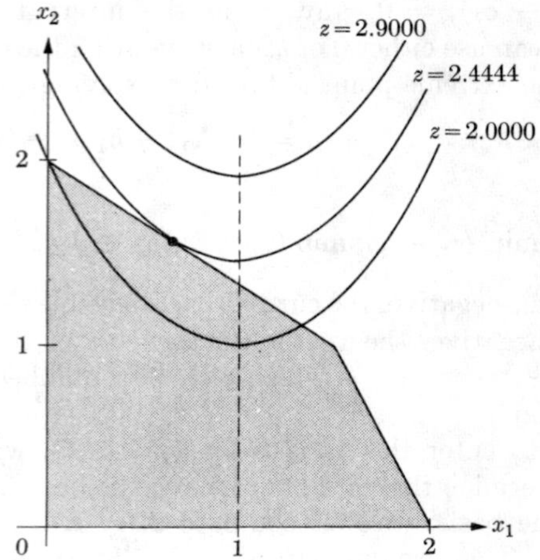

FIGURE 4-8

Note that the objective function for this problem is precisely the same as that for the example considered in Section 4-3. Now, however, the constraints are linear.

This problem can be easily solved graphically and the situation is illustrated in Fig. 4-8. It is immediately clear that the unique optimal solution occurs at the point where $2x_1 + 3x_2 = 6$ and the slope of the objective function is $-\frac{2}{3}$:

$$2(x_1 - 1) = -\tfrac{2}{3}.$$

Solving these two equations simultaneously we find that $x_1^* = \frac{2}{3}$, $x_2^* = \frac{14}{9} = 1.5555$. On substitution of these values into the objective function, we obtain $z^* = 2.4444$.

The objective function can be written $z = f_1(x_1) + f_2(x_2)$, where $f_1(x_1) = 2x_1 - x_1^2$ and $f_2(x_2) = x_2$. Since f_2 is already linear, we need not introduce any polygonal approximation, i.e., it is unnecessary to write x_2 in terms of δ-variables. Note that x_1 can never be larger than 2. Imagine that the interval $0 \le x_1 \le 2$ is subdivided as in Section 4-3 so that $\Delta x_{k1} = 0.25$. Then, $x_1 = 0.25 \sum_k \delta_k$, and using Table 4-1 to obtain the Δf_{k1}, we see that the approximating problem becomes

$$0.50 \sum_{k=1}^{8} \delta_k + 3x_2 + x_3 = 6, \qquad 0.50 \sum_{k=1}^{8} \delta_k + x_2 + x_4 = 4, \tag{4-70}$$

$$0 \le \delta_k \le 1, \qquad k = 1, \ldots, 8; \qquad x_2, x_3, x_4 \ge 0,$$

$$\max \hat{z} = 0.4375\,\delta_1 + 0.3125\,\delta_2 + 0.1875\,\delta_3 + 0.0625\,\delta_4 - 0.0625\,\delta_5 \\ -0.1875\,\delta_6 - 0.3125\,\delta_7 - 0.4375\,\delta_8 + x_2.$$

As has been noted previously, we can solve this as a strictly linear programming problem. It will follow automatically that $\delta_k = 0$ unless $\delta_u = 1$, $u = 1, \ldots, k-1$. The upper bounds will be handled by means of the decomposition technique, as discussed in the preceding section.

For the present problem, the matrix $\mathbf{A}_1$ of the previous section is a 2×8 matrix each of whose elements has the value 0.50. Furthermore

$$\mathbf{c}_1 = (0.4375, 0.3125, 0.1875, 0.0625, \\ -0.0625, -0.1875, -0.3125, -0.4375), \qquad (4\text{–}71)$$

and any extreme point $\boldsymbol{\delta}_v^*$ of the convex set $0 \le \delta_k \le 1$, $k = 1, \ldots, 8$, will have only 0 or 1 as the value of each of its components.

Any $\boldsymbol{\delta} \ge \mathbf{0}$ satisfying the upper-bound constraints can be written $\boldsymbol{\delta} = \sum_v \boldsymbol{\delta}_v^* \rho_v$, where $\sum_v \rho_v = 1$ and $\rho_v \ge 0$ for all v. On introducing the ρ_v, we obtain a problem of the form (4–59) having three constraints. Note that $\boldsymbol{\delta}_1^* = \mathbf{0}$ is an extreme point solution to the upper-bound constraints, and for this solution, $\mathbf{d}_1 = \mathbf{A}_1\boldsymbol{\delta}_1^* = \mathbf{0}$, $e_1 = \mathbf{c}_1\boldsymbol{\delta}_1^* = 0$. Thus, if we set $\rho_1 = 1$, $x_3 = 6$, $x_4 = 4$, we obtain an initial basic feasible solution with the basis matrix $\mathbf{B}$ being $\mathbf{I}_3$. No Phase I is needed. The initial revised simplex tableau is presented in Table 4–6. For this basic solution, $\boldsymbol{\sigma}_B = \mathbf{0}$ so that

$$\min (z_v - e_v) = \min - \mathbf{c}_1\boldsymbol{\delta} = -\max \mathbf{c}_1\boldsymbol{\delta}.$$

The extreme point of the convex set generated by the upper bound constraints which maximizes $\mathbf{c}_1\boldsymbol{\delta}$ is found by setting $\delta_k = 1$ if $c_{k1} > 0$ and $\delta_k = 0$ if $c_{k1} < 0$. Thus, from (4–71), the extreme point, call it $\boldsymbol{\delta}_2^*$, is

$$\boldsymbol{\delta}_2^* = [1, 1, 1, 1, 0, 0, 0, 0],$$

and

$$\min (z_v - e_v) = -0.4375 - 0.3125 - 0.1875 - 0.0625 = -1.$$

The only other variable not in the basis is x_2, and for this variable, $z_2 - c_2 = -c_2 = -1$. Therefore, we have a tie for the variable to enter the basis. We can allow x_2 or ρ_2 to become positive. We shall arbitrarily select ρ_2 to become positive. Then $\mathbf{d}_2 = \mathbf{A}_1\boldsymbol{\delta}_2^* = [2, 2]$, $e_2 = \mathbf{c}_1\boldsymbol{\delta}_2^* = 1$. The $\mathbf{y}_k^{(1)}$-column for Tableau 1 is now computed and is shown in Table 4–6. It is seen that ρ_1 is driven to zero when ρ_2 becomes positive. The new tableau is given in Table 4–7.

Now $\boldsymbol{\sigma}_1 = \mathbf{0}$, but $\sigma_3 = 1$; so

$$\min (z_v - e_v) = \min [-\mathbf{c}_1\boldsymbol{\delta} + \sigma_3] = (-\max \mathbf{c}_1\boldsymbol{\delta}) + \sigma_3 = 0,$$

since from the above, $\max \mathbf{c}_1\boldsymbol{\delta} = 1$ and $\sigma_3 = 1$. Thus no ρ_v not in the basis should become positive. The only other variable not in the basis is

TABLEAUX FOR SOLUTION OF EXAMPLE

TABLE 4–6. TABLEAU 1

Basic variables	$\boldsymbol{\beta}_1$	$\boldsymbol{\beta}_2$	$\boldsymbol{\beta}_3$	$\mathbf{x}_B^{(1)}$	$\mathbf{y}_k^{(1)}$
$\hat{z}$	0	0	0	0	−1
x_3	1	0	0	6	2
x_4	0	1	0	4	2
ρ_1	0	0	1	1	1

TABLE 4–7. TABLEAU 2

$\hat{z}$	0	0	1	1	−1
x_3	1	0	−2	4	3
x_4	0	1	−2	2	1
ρ_2	0	0	1	1	0

TABLE 4–8. TABLEAU 3

$\hat{z}$	0.3333	0	0.3333	2.3333	−0.1041
x_2	0.3333	0	−0.6667	1.3333	−0.1667
x_4	−0.3333	1	−1.3333	0.6667	−0.3333
ρ_2	0	0	1	1	1

TABLE 4–9. TABLEAU 4

$\hat{z}$	0.3333	0	0.4374	2.4374	
x_2	0.3333	0	−0.5000	1.5000	
x_4	−0.3333	1	−1	1	
ρ_3	0	0	1	1	

x_2. We see that $z_2 - c_2 = -1$. Thus x_2 should become positive at the next iteration. The $\mathbf{y}_k^{(1)}$-column for Tableau 2 is now computed, and is shown in Table 4-7. It is seen that x_3 is driven to zero when x_2 enters the basis. The new tableau is presented in Table 4-8.

At this stage, $\boldsymbol{\sigma}_1 = (0.3333, 0), \sigma_3 = 0.3333$,

$$\boldsymbol{\sigma}_1\mathbf{A}_1 = (\tfrac{1}{6}, \tfrac{1}{6}, \tfrac{1}{6}, \tfrac{1}{6}, \tfrac{1}{6}, \tfrac{1}{6}, \tfrac{1}{6}, \tfrac{1}{6}),$$

and

$$\boldsymbol{\sigma}_1\mathbf{A}_1 - \mathbf{c}_1 = (-0.2708, -0.1458, -0.0208, 0.1042, 0.2292, 0.3542, 0.4792, 0.6042).$$

The $\boldsymbol{\delta}$, call it $\boldsymbol{\delta}_3^*$, which minimizes $(\boldsymbol{\sigma}_1\mathbf{A}_1 - \mathbf{c}_1)\boldsymbol{\delta}$ is

$$\boldsymbol{\delta}_3^* = [1, 1, 1, 0, 0, 0, 0, 0].$$

Thus

$$\begin{aligned}\min (z_v - e_v) &= (\boldsymbol{\sigma}_1\mathbf{A}_1 - \mathbf{c}_1)\boldsymbol{\delta}_3^* + \sigma_3 \\ &= -0.2708 - 0.1458 - 0.0208 + 0.3333 = -0.1041.\end{aligned}$$

The only variable not in the basis beside the ρ_v's is x_3; x_3 will not enter the basis since it was removed at the previous iteration. Thus ρ_3 becomes positive at the next step. We quickly determine that $\mathbf{d}_3 = [1.50, 1.50]$. The $\mathbf{y}_k^{(1)}$-column of Tableau 3 can then be determined and is shown in Table 4-8. We see that ρ_2 is driven to zero. The new tableau is given in Table 4-9.

For the new tableau, we see that $\boldsymbol{\sigma}_1 = (0.3333, 0)$, which is the same as for the previous iteration, and $\sigma_3 = 0.4374$. We then know that the $\boldsymbol{\delta}$ which minimizes $(\boldsymbol{\sigma}_1\mathbf{A}_1 - \mathbf{c}_1)\boldsymbol{\delta}$ is $\boldsymbol{\delta}_3^*$, and

$$\min (z_v - e_v) = (\boldsymbol{\sigma}_1\mathbf{A}_1 - \mathbf{c}_1)\boldsymbol{\delta}_3^* + \sigma_3 = -0.4374 + 0.4374 = 0,$$

so that $z_v - e_v \geq 0$ for every ρ_v not in the basis. The only other variable not in the basis is x_3, and we note that $z_3 - x_3 = z_3 = 0.3333$. Hence an optimal solution to the approximating problem has been found. It is $x_2 = 1.5000$, $x_4 = 1$, $\rho_3 = 1$ (that is, $x_1 = 0.7500$), $\hat{z} = 2.4374$. We found previously that the optimal solution to the actual problem is $x_1^* = 0.6667$, $x_2^* = 1.5555$, $z^* = 2.4444$. Thus we see that the optimal solution obtained to the approximating problem is a reasonably good approximation to the optimal solution to the actual problem, the value of the objective function being obtained more accurately than the values of the variables themselves.

The reader should trace out on Fig. 4-8 the sequence of solutions represented by Tables 4-6 through 4-9.

It will be noted that we could have saved one iteration if at the first step we had inserted x_2 rather than ρ_2, since ρ_2 was later removed. For this simple problem, we could have looked ahead, knowing the optimal solution to the actual problem, and seen that x_2 was the proper one to insert at the first step. In general, however, it is not possible to do this.

4–9 Hartley's method for maximizing a linear function over a convex set when the constraints are separable. Consider a nonlinear programming problem of the following sort:

$$\sum_{j=1}^{n} g_{ij}(x_j)\{\leq, =, \geq\}b_i, \qquad i = 1, \ldots, m,$$

$$x_j \geq 0, \qquad j = 1, \ldots, n, \tag{4–72}$$

$$\max z = \sum_{j=1}^{n} c_j x_j,$$

where $g_{ij}(x_j)$ is convex for all j if a $\leq$ sign holds for constraint i, $g_{ij}(x_j) = a_{ij}x_j$ if an $=$ sign holds for constraint i, and $g_{ij}(x_j)$ is concave for all j if a $\geq$ sign holds for constraint i. Then, if there is a feasible solution, the set of feasible solutions is convex, and, since the objective function is linear, any local maximum will be a global maximum.

An approximate global maximum for this problem could be found by use of either the λ- or δ-forms of the approximating problem introduced in Section 4–2. Hartley [10] has suggested what is essentially a dual approach to finding an approximate global maximum of the problem. Let us proceed as in Section 4–2 and replace the $g_{ij}(x_j)$ by their polygonal approximations $\hat{g}_{ij}(x_j)$. Then from (4–3) we can write

$$\hat{g}_{ij} = g_{kij} + s_{kij}(x_j - x_{kj}), \qquad x_{kj} \leq x_j \leq x_{k+1,j},$$

where

$$s_{kij} = \frac{g_{k+1,ij} - g_{kij}}{x_{k+1,j} - x_{kj}}. \tag{4–73}$$

Then when the x_j lie in the intervals

$$x_{k_j,j} \leq x_j \leq x_{k_j+1,j}, \qquad j = 1, \ldots, n, \tag{4–74}$$

the function $\hat{g}_i(\mathbf{x}) = \sum_j \hat{g}_{ij}(x_j)$ is given by

$$\hat{g}_i(\mathbf{x}) = \sum_{j=1}^{n} (g_{k_j,ij} - s_{k_j,ij}x_{k_j,j}) + \sum_{j=1}^{n} s_{k_j,ij}x_j. \tag{4–75}$$

Consider now a constraint of (4–72) having the form $g_i(\mathbf{x}) \leq b_i$. By assumption, $g_i(\mathbf{x})$ must be a convex function of $\mathbf{x}$. However, it must also be true that $\hat{g}_i(\mathbf{x})$ is a convex function of $\mathbf{x}$. Let us now examine the surface $\hat{g}_i(\mathbf{x}) - x_{n+1} = 0$ in E^{n+1}. For every $\mathbf{x}$ in E^n for which $\hat{g}_i(\mathbf{x})$ is defined, there will be a point $[\mathbf{x}, x_{n+1}]$ satisfying $\hat{g}_i(\mathbf{x}) - x_{n+1} = 0$. Furthermore, the set of points in E^{n+1} satisfying $\hat{g}_i(\mathbf{x}) - x_{n+1} \leq 0$ must be a convex set, since $\hat{g}_i(\mathbf{x}) - x_{n+1}$ is a convex function of $[\mathbf{x}, x_{n+1}]$. For any $\mathbf{x}$ with the x_j in the intervals (4-74), the surface $\hat{g}_i(\mathbf{x}) - x_{n+1} = 0$ is represented by

$$\sum_{j=1}^{n} s_{k_j,ij}x_j - x_{n+1} = -\sum_{j=1}^{n} (g_{k_j,ij} - s_{k_j,ij}x_{k_j,j}), \tag{4-76}$$

since $\hat{g}_i(\mathbf{x})$ is represented by (4-75). Consequently, (4-76) is also a plane tangent to $\hat{g}_i(\mathbf{x}) - x_{n+1} = 0$ for any $\mathbf{x}$ having its components x_j in the intervals (4-74). However, we know that any plane tangent to $\hat{g}_i(\mathbf{x}) - x_{n+1} = 0$ is a supporting hyperplane to the convex set $\hat{g}_i(\mathbf{x}) - x_{n+1} \leq 0$, and any $[\mathbf{x}, x_{n+1}]$ in this convex set must satisfy

$$\sum_{j=1}^{n} s_{k_j,ij}x_j - x_{n+1} \leq -\sum_{j=1}^{n} (g_{k_j,ij} - s_{k_j,ij}x_{k_j,j}).$$

In particular, any $\mathbf{x}$ satisfying $\hat{g}_i(\mathbf{x}) \leq b_i$ must satisfy

$$\sum_{j=1}^{n} s_{k_j,ij}x_j \leq b_i - \sum_{j=1}^{n} (g_{k_j,ij} - s_{k_j,ij}x_{k_j,j}).$$

Applying the same arguments to constraints of the form $\hat{g}_i(\mathbf{x}) \geq b_i$ or linear equations, we conclude that if X is the convex set of feasible solutions to the approximating problem, then any $\mathbf{x} \in X$ must satisfy the set of all constraints,

$$\sum_{j=1}^{n} s_{k_j,ij}x_j\{\leq, =, \geq\}b_i - \sum_{j=1}^{n} (g_{k_j,ij} - s_{k_j,ij}x_{k_j,j}), \tag{4-77}$$

where the sign $\leq$ or $=$ or $\geq$ which applies is that corresponding to the ith constraint of (4-72).

There are only a finite number of constraints (4-77) of the type just described. If the interval over which x_j can range is subdivided into r_j intervals, there will be $R = \prod_{j=1}^{n} r_j$ such constraints, where $\prod$ means the product, since x_1 can be in any of the r_1 possible subintervals, x_2 in any of the r_2 possible subintervals, etc. They can be generated from the general form (4-77) by assigning all possible combinations of values to the

$$s_{k_j,ij} \quad \text{and} \quad g_{k_j,ij}.$$

Every point in X must satisfy the R constraints (4-77). Furthermore, there is no point which satisfies the constraints (4-77) and $\mathbf{x} \geq \mathbf{0}$ which is not in X. To see this, suppose that $\mathbf{y}$ satisfied the R constraints (4–77) and $\mathbf{y} \geq \mathbf{0}$, but was not in X. Let $\mathbf{w}$ be the point in X closest to $\mathbf{y}$. Then there is at least one supporting hyperplane to X at $\mathbf{w}$ of the form (4–77) such that $\mathbf{y}$ lies in one open half-space produced by this hyperplane while X lies in the other closed half-space (see {LA 6–6}). But this is a contradiction, since it implies that we did not originally have all the hyperplanes of the form (4–77). Thus X is the intersection of the R hyperplanes (4–77), and $\mathbf{x} \geq \mathbf{0}$. Therefore the approximating problem for (4–72) is equivalent to a linear programming problem with R constraints (4–77) and the objective function of (4–72). Here we have a problem in n variables, and more than n constraints (usually a very large number of constraints). The procedure for solving this problem, then, is to solve the dual which will have $R + n$ variables and n constraints. The solution will yield an approximate global optimum for (4–72) just as would be the case if either the λ- or δ-forms of the approximating problems were solved.

It might be worthwhile to compare the size of the dual problem discussed above with the size of the λ- or δ-forms of the approximating problem. The λ-form would have as many as $\sum r_j + n + s$ variables, s being the number of slack and surplus variables, and $m + n$ constraints so that it would have m more constraints but fewer variables than the dual problem. The δ-form would have as many as $\sum r_j + s$ variables and m constraints plus the upper-bound constraints. It would appear that if the form of the problem was solved treating the upper bounds by means of the decomposition principle, then the computational effort would be considerably reduced over that required for the solution of the dual. Furthermore, Hartley's approach cannot be used unless the functions have the proper convexity and concavity properties and the objective function is linear. However, the latter restriction is not important (see Problem 4–24). Thus it would appear that Hartley's approach has little to offer computationally, but it does illustrate another approach to the problem. It might also be noted that the simple idea of representing the convex set of feasible solutions approximately by the intersection of hyperplanes was suggested (probably many times) previous to Hartley's use of the idea, for example, in [9].

4–10 The fixed-charge problem. Consider a nonlinear programming problem of the form

$$\begin{aligned} \mathbf{Ax} &= \mathbf{b}, \\ \mathbf{x} &\geq \mathbf{0}, \\ \min z &= \sum_{j=1}^{n} f_j(x_j), \end{aligned} \tag{4–78}$$

where

$$f_j(x_j) = c_j x_j + A_j \delta_j, \qquad A_j > 0, \tag{4–79}$$

and

$$\delta_j = \begin{cases} 0 & \text{if} \quad x_j = 0, \\ 1 & \text{if} \quad x_j > 0. \end{cases} \tag{4–80}$$

A typical function $f_j(x_j)$ will then look like that shown in Fig. 4–9. The numbers A_j are called *fixed charges*, since A_j is incurred only if $x_j > 0$. In practice, such costs are encountered, for example, in transportation where a fixed charge is incurred regardless of the quantity shipped (provided that a positive quantity is shipped), or in the building of production facilities where a plant under construction must have a certain minimum size. If it were not for the fixed charges, (4–78) would be a linear programming problem. Problems of the form (4–78) are often referred to as fixed-charge problems.

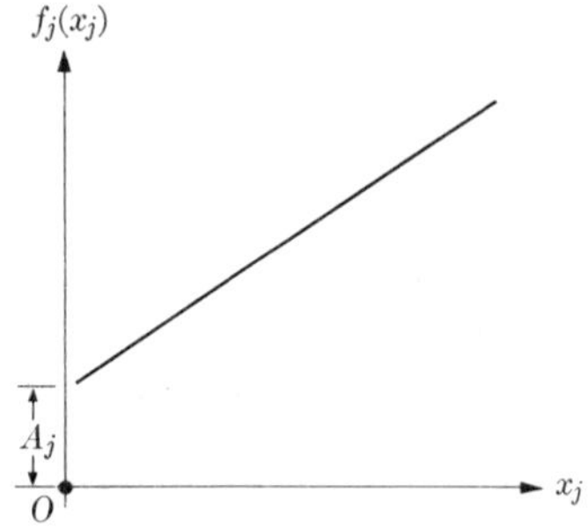

FIGURE 4–9

It is clear from Fig. 4–9 that the functions $f_j(x_j)$ are concave for $x_j \geq 0$; the analytic proof is to be provided in Problem 4–35. Note that the objective function is being minimized in (4–78). Thus from Section 3–12 we know that an optimal solution to (4–78) will occur at an extreme point of the convex set of feasible solutions. Unfortunately, however, there can be local optima different from the global optimum. Indeed, if there is a fixed charge associated with each variable, then every extreme point of the convex set of feasible solutions yields a local optimum, the reason being that if one moves away a bit from any extreme point while remaining in the convex set of feasible solutions, more of the variables will have to be positive. This means that more of the fixed charges will be incurred. However, if one stays close enough to the extreme point, any reduction in variable costs cannot outweigh the increase in fixed costs, and hence the extreme point yields a local optimum. As would be expected, the existence of local optima complicates the task of solving fixed-charge linear programming problems. It will be shown in Chapter 8 that this type of problem can be formulated as a mixed integer-continuous variable linear programming problem. Unfortunately, as we shall see in Chapter 8, although algorithms exist for solving such integer programming problems, they do not seem to provide the computational efficiency that would be required to solve these problems in a reasonable amount of time, even on the largest computers available.

The approximate methods introduced in this chapter can be used to determine a local optimum for a fixed-charge problem. However, as we can see from the preceding paragraph, they will not necessarily yield any better results than merely solving the linear programming problem obtained by omitting the fixed charges, since the solution to this latter problem will also yield a local optimum for the fixed-charge problem. We shall, though, illustrate how the λ-form of the approximating problem can be used to find a local optimum for the fixed-charge problem. As usual, we begin by finding the largest value α_j which x_j can assume. Then we write

$$\hat{f}_j(x_j) = A_j\lambda_{1j} + (A_j + c_j\alpha_j)\lambda_{2j}, \tag{4-81}$$

$$x_j = \lambda_{2j}\alpha_j, \tag{4-82}$$

$$\lambda_{0j} + \lambda_{1j} + \lambda_{2j} = 1, \tag{4-83}$$

where no more than two λ_{kj} can be positive for a given j, and these can be positive only if they are adjacent. Note that when $x_j = 0$, i.e., $\lambda_{2j} = 0$, the value of $\hat{f}_j(x_j)$ is not determined. Instead, (4–81) and (4–83) reduce to

$$\hat{f}_j(0) = \lambda_{1j}A_j, \qquad \lambda_{0j} + \lambda_{1j} = 1,$$

so that by properly choosing λ_{0j}, $\hat{f}_j(0)$ can have any value between 0 and A_j. Geometrically, then, we are representing $\hat{f}_j(0)$ by a vertical line, and $\hat{f}_j(0)$ is multivalued. The approximating problem then becomes

$$\sum_{j=1}^{n} a_{ij}\alpha_j\lambda_{2j} = b_i, \qquad i = 1, \ldots, m,$$

$$\lambda_{0j} + \lambda_{1j} + \lambda_{2j} = 1, \qquad j = 1, \ldots, n,$$

$$\lambda_{kj} \geq 0, \qquad \text{all } k, j, \tag{4-84}$$

$$\min z = \sum_{j=1}^{n} [A_j\lambda_{1j} + (A_j + c_j\alpha_j)\lambda_{2j}].$$

In Problem 4–36 the reader is asked to show that when this problem is solved using restricted basis entry, then the solution has the property that if $\lambda_{2j} = 0$, then $\lambda_{0j} = 1$, that is, $\hat{f}_j(0) = 0$, so that $\hat{f}_j(0)$ never has a value different from zero. Thus the solution obtained to (4–84) yields a local optimum for the fixed-charge problem (not an approximate local optimum).

One of the first papers to deal with the fixed-charge problem was that of Hirsh and Dantzig [11]. In this article they made the simple observation (see above) that an optimal solution must occur at an extreme point of the convex set of feasible solutions. They made another rather obvious observation, namely, that if all fixed charges A_j are equal, and if there is no degeneracy, then a point $\mathbf{x}$ which yields an optimal solution to the linear programming problem obtained by ignoring the fixed charges also yields an optimal solution to the fixed-charge problem. This statement requires the nondegeneracy assumption, of course, because it might be that a degenerate basic solution in which less than m fixed charges are incurred would be optimal, and this might not be the solution obtained to the linear programming problem. Little has really appeared in the intervening years to add to the theoretical or computational aspects of the problem except the integer programming formulation which will be considered later.

Some effort has been concentrated on finding approximate solutions to fixed-charge transportation problems. Two papers dealing with this subject are those of Balinski [1], and Kuhn and Baumol [13]. We shall briefly consider Balinski's approach to the problem. The paper of Kuhn and Baumol will not be discussed, since the authors were mainly concerned with the development of very simple means for getting approximate solutions requiring very little computation.

A fixed-charge transportation problem has the form

$$\sum_{j=1}^{n} x_{ij} = a_i, \quad a_i > 0, \qquad i = 1, \ldots, m,$$

$$\sum_{i=1}^{m} x_{ij} = b_j, \quad b_j > 0, \qquad j = 1, \ldots, n,$$

$$x_{ij} \geq 0, \qquad \text{all } i, j, \tag{4-85}$$

$$\min z = \sum_{i,j} c_{ij}x_{ij} + \sum_{i,j} A_{ij}\,\delta_{ij},$$

where $\delta_{ij} = 0$ if $x_{ij} = 0$ and $\delta_{ij} = 1$ if $x_{ij} > 0$. Typical transportation problems encountered in practice will have many destinations (n large) and relatively few origins (m small). Since an optimal solution to (4-85) occurs at an extreme point of the convex set of feasible solutions, an optimal solution need have no more than $n + m - 1$ positive x_{ij} (only $n + m - 1$ constraints are independent). Now, if n is large with respect to m, then an optimal solution will have the property that there will be only very few cases where the demand at a given destination can be supplied by more than one origin, so that the amount shipped to destination j if shipped from origin i will frequently be min $(b_j, a_i) = m_{ij}$. Balinski's approximation method for solving the fixed-charge problem thus involves nothing more than replacing the fixed-charge problem by a standard transportation problem with the same origin availabilities, destination requirements, and unit transportation costs:

$$d_{ij} = c_{ij} + \frac{A_{ij}}{m_{ij}}, \tag{4-86}$$

that is, he solves a transportation problem with the same constraints as (4–85) and the objective function $z = \sum d_{ij}x_{ij}$. The transportation problem solved is

$$\begin{aligned} \sum_{j=1}^{n} x_{ij} &= a_i, \qquad i = 1, \ldots, m, \\ \sum_{i=1}^{m} x_{ij} &= b_j, \qquad j = 1, \ldots, n, \\ x_{ij} &\geq 0, \qquad \text{all } i, j, \\ \min \hat{z} &= \sum_{i,j} d_{ij}x_{ij}. \end{aligned} \tag{4-87}$$

He uses the optimal solution obtained for this problem as the approximate solution to the fixed-charge transportation problem. This is allowable, of course, since the set of x_{ij} obtained by solving problem (4–87) is a feasible solution to the fixed-charge problem because both problems have the same set of constraints.

If z^* is the minimum value of the objective function for the fixed-charge problem, and if z_+ is the value of the objective function in (4–85) obtained *by using the x_{ij} obtained from the approximating problem*, i.e., from solving (4–87), then it is clear that $z^* \leq z_+$. Suppose now that we solve (4–85), treating the δ_{ij} as variables and including constraints $0 \leq \delta_{ij} \leq 1$, and $0 \leq x_{ij} \leq m_{ij}\delta_{ij}$ without requiring that the δ_{ij} be integers. Let z_- be the minimum value of the objective function for this problem. Then $z_- \leq z^*$, since the optimal solution to (4–85) is a feasible solution to the problem for which the δ_{ij} are not required to be integers, but is not necessarily an optimal solution to problem (4–87). In this way we can obtain bounds on z^*.

Now it happens to be easy to obtain z_-, since an optimal solution to the problem where the δ_{ij} do need to be integers has the property that $x_{ij} = m_{ij}\delta_{ij}$. To prove this, note that if in an optimal solution $\delta_{ij} = 0$, then $x_{ij} = 0$ and $x_{ij} = m_{ij}\delta_{ij}$. Suppose next that $\delta_{ij} > 0$. However, if $x_{ij} < m_{ij}\delta_{ij}$, one could reduce δ_{ij} until $x_{ij} = m_{ij}\delta_{ij}$ while maintaining a feasible solution, thus decreasing the value of the objective function. This contradicts the fact that we had an optimal solution. Hence we must obtain the same optimal solution when using the constraints $x_{ij} = m_{ij}\delta_{ij}$, rather than $x_{ij} \leq m_{ij}\delta_{ij}$. But the constraints $x_{ij} = m_{ij}\delta_{ij}$ can be used to eliminate the δ_{ij} in the problem. The constraints $0 \leq \delta_{ij} \leq 1$ become redundant and need not be included, since they take the form $0 \leq x_{ij} \leq m_{ij}$ which will always be satisfied. In the objective function, $A_{ij}\delta_{ij}$ becomes $A_{ij}x_{ij}/m_{ij}$. The resulting problem to be solved is then nothing but (4–87), that is, $z_- = \min \hat{z}$. Consequently, by solving (4–87), we obtain z_- directly, and z_+ is obtained by using an optimal solution from (4–87) in the objective function of (4–85), so that when (4–87) is solved, we find an approximate solution to the fixed-charge problem and bounds on z^*. While the approximation technique is no doubt quite good in some cases, it is equally true that it has failed in others. Hence, it cannot always be relied on to give a satisfactory answer. Of course, if z_- and z_+ are very close together, then the answer should be satisfactory.

We have noted in this section that the technique of Section 4–2 can be used to obtain a local optimum of a fixed-charge linear programming problem. The method can, of course, be applied to fixed-charge transportation problems. Unfortunately, however, it does not seem easy, in general, to apply special algorithms which take account of the special structure of transportation problems. One situation is the exception: when the costs are convex functions, it is possible to make use of the special structure to gain computational efficiency. This case will be discussed in Section 4–12.

4–11 Example involving a fixed-charge problem. We shall show by an example that the methods of this chapter are generally of little assistance in solving fixed-charge problems. Consider the following situation. A manufacturer makes in lots a certain item which he in turn supplies to another producer. The manufacturer has a contract with the other producer to supply the following quantities of the part in each of the next seven months: 90, 125, 140, 100, 45, 60, 130. Note that the number of parts to be supplied varies from one month to the next. The manufacturer must deliver the parts in the month specified. However, he need not manufacture them during that month. He can, if desired, produce several months supply in advance and inventory the parts until needed. There is an inventory-carrying cost of $2.00 per unit per month. Imagine, for simplicity, that this cost is based on the inventory on hand at the end of the month. The cost of the setup for one production run is $300. Setups are considered only at the beginning of a month. The time required to carry out a production run will be ignored, so that if a production run is made at the beginning of month j, the units produced are available to meet the demand in month j. We wish to determine when setups should be made and how many units should be produced in each of the production runs, given that the combined setup and inventory-carrying charges are to be minimized. Assume that no units are on hand at the beginning of the first month, and it is desired not to have any on hand at the end of the seventh month.

To formulate the problem mathematically, let $x_j \geq 0$ be the number of units produced in month j, $y_j \geq 0$ the number of units in inventory at the end of month $j - 1$ (beginning of month j), and d_j the demand in month j. Then by a material balance, it must be true that

$$\begin{aligned} x_1 - y_2 &= d_1 = 90, \\ y_j + x_j - y_{j+1} &= d_j, \quad j = 2, \ldots 6, \\ y_7 + x_7 &= d_7 = 130. \end{aligned} \tag{4-88}$$

These represent the constraints on the problem. We wish to minimize

$$z = 300 \sum_{j=1}^{7} \delta_j + 2 \sum_{j=2}^{7} y_j.$$

Here we have a fixed-charge linear programming problem with seven constraints (4–88). We can find a local minimum of this problem, using the method introduced in the previous section.

Note that the largest value that any x_j can have is the sum of the demands for the seven months, i.e., 690. In fact, x_j cannot be greater than the sum of the demands from month j onward, but it will suffice to use 690 as the upper limit to the value for all x_j. Then, on using the method introduced in the previous section, we write

$$x_j = 690\lambda_{2j},$$

so that (4–88) becomes

$$\begin{aligned} &690\lambda_{21} - y_2 = 90; \qquad y_j + 690\lambda_{2j} - y_{j+1} = d_j, \\ &j = 2, \ldots, 6; \qquad y_7 + 690\lambda_{27} = 130. \\ &\lambda_{0j} + \lambda_{1j} + \lambda_{2j} = 1, \qquad j = 1, \ldots, 7. \end{aligned} \tag{4-89}$$

Next

$$f_j(x_j) = 300\delta_j = 300(\lambda_{1j} + \lambda_{2j}),$$

so that the objective function becomes

$$z = 300 \sum_{j=1}^{7} (\lambda_{1j} + \lambda_{2j}) + 2 \sum_{j=2}^{7} y_j. \tag{4-90}$$

We must require that for a given j, no more than two λ_{kj} be positive, and then only if they are adjacent. In terms of the λ_{kj}, we have a problem with fourteen constraints. This is much too large to be solved by hand.

It was solved on the IBM 7090, using a modified simplex code which had provisions for the needed restricted entry into the basis.

Before discussing the results computed in this way, we might point out that the problem can easily be solved by dynamic programming. (The method used will be presented in Chapter 10.) It turns out that the absolute minimum of $z = 1770$ and the unique optimal set of x_j is

$$x_1^* = 215, \quad x_2^* = 0, \quad x_3^* = 240, \quad x_4^* = 0,$$
$$x_5^* = 105, \quad x_6^* = 0, \quad x_7^* = 130.$$

Consider now the results obtained by determining a local optimum of the λ-problem by IBM 7090 code. On solving the problem directly, one obtained the following solution:

$$z = 2100, \quad x_1 = 90, \quad x_2 = 125, \quad x_3 = 140,$$
$$x_4 = 100, \quad x_5 = 45, \quad x_6 = 60, \quad x_7 = 130,$$

so that there is a setup each month. This is indeed a local minimum, but the z-value so obtained is quite a bit higher than the global minimum. In the basic solution, only y_7 appeared in the basis and it was at a zero level. The computer code was flexible enough to be capable of specifying that a certain set of vectors must enter the basis first. The problem was then rerun with the requirement that the y_j must enter the basis first. A different local minimum was obtained in this case, namely:

$$z = 2180, \quad x_1 = 90, \quad x_2 = 365, \quad x_3 = x_4 = 0,$$
$$x_5 = 45, \quad x_6 = 60, \quad x_7 = 130.$$

This has a higher value of z than the previous solution. From the optimal solution displayed above, it is seen that it is optimal not to have any setup in the second month. The problem was then rerun, forcing $\lambda_{02} = 1$ so that $x_2 = 0$, and a third local minimum was obtained in this manner, namely:

$$z = 2050, \quad x_1 = 215, \quad x_2 = 0, \quad x_3 = 140,$$
$$x_4 = 100, \quad x_5 = 45, \quad x_6 = 60, \quad x_7 = 130,$$

which is still not the global minimum.

Here we have a good example of a rather simple problem in which there are many local minima, with the values of the objective function for them being rather far from that of the global minimum. Furthermore, the technique for determining a local minimum did not yield in any direct way the global minimum.

4–12 Transportation problems with separable convex objective functions. Consider the transportation problem

$$\sum_{j=1}^{n} x_{ij} = a_i, \qquad a_i > 0, \qquad i = 1, \ldots, m,$$

$$\sum_{i=1}^{m} x_{ij} = b_j, \qquad b_j > 0, \qquad j = 1, \ldots, n, \tag{4–91}$$

$$x_{ij} \geq 0, \qquad \text{all } i, j,$$

$$\min z = \sum_{i,j} f_{ij}(x_{ij}),$$

where all $f_{ij}(x_{ij})$ are convex functions. We then know that any local optimum is also a global optimum. An approximate global optimum could then be found by means of the δ-form of the approximating problem and the technique described in Section 4–7 for handling upper bounds. However, difficulties can be encountered with this approach for the following reason: Typically, transportation problems will have a relatively small number of origins, say, from 2 to 50, and a rather large number of destinations, say 1000, or 2000, or more. The procedure suggested above would then lead to a problem involving $m + n + 1$ constraints (not counting the upper bounds). It is impossible at the present time to handle problems involving several thousand constraints. Even if it were, the process would be exceptionally time consuming. It is interesting to observe, however, that by applying the decomposition principle in a slightly different way, we can obtain a problem involving only $m + 1$ constraints. Such a problem can easily be handled, and moreover, the computational method appears to be quite efficient.

Rather than using the variables δ_{kij}, we shall find it convenient to work with

$$\psi_{kij} = (\Delta x_{kij})\, \delta_{kij}, \tag{4–92}$$

so that the upper-bound constraints on the ψ_{kij} become

$$0 \leq \psi_{kij} \leq \Delta x_{kij}. \tag{4–93}$$

Then

$$x_{ij} = \sum_{k} \psi_{kij}, \tag{4–94}$$

where, if $\psi_{kij} > 0$, $\psi_{uij} = \Delta x_{uij}$, $u = 1, \ldots, k - 1$. In terms of these variables, $\hat{f}_{ij}(x_{ij})$, the polygonal approximation to $f_{ij}(x_{ij})$, can be written

$$\hat{f}_{ij}(x_j) = \sum_{k} \alpha_{kij}\psi_{kij} + f_{ij}(0), \tag{4–95}$$

where $\alpha_{kij} = \Delta f_{kij}/\Delta x_{kij}$.

The approximating problem can then be written

$$\sum_{j=1}^{n} \sum_{k=1}^{r_{ij}} \psi_{kij} = a_i, \qquad i = 1, \ldots, m,$$

$$\sum_{i=1}^{m} \sum_{k=1}^{r_{ij}} \psi_{kij} = b_j, \qquad j = 1, \ldots, n, \tag{4-96}$$

$$0 \leq \psi_{kij} \leq \Delta x_{kij}, \qquad \text{all } k, i, j,$$

$$\min \hat{z} = \sum_{i,j,k} \alpha_{kij} \psi_{kij}.$$

We remember that (4-96) can be solved as a strict linear programming problem without the use of restricted basis entry, and the optimal solution so obtained will yield an approximate optimal solution to (4-91).

The total number of variables in problem (4-96) is

$$\sum_{i,j} r_{ij}.$$

Denote by $\boldsymbol{\psi}$ a row vector containing these variables. The set of $\boldsymbol{\psi}$ satisfying

$$\sum_{i=1}^{m} \sum_{k=1}^{r_{ij}} \psi_{kij} = b_j, \qquad j = 1, \ldots, n, \tag{4-97}$$

$$0 \leq \psi_{kij} \leq \Delta x_{kij}, \qquad \text{all } k, i, j,$$

is a closed convex set with a finite number of extreme points. Denote the extreme points by $\boldsymbol{\psi}_v^*$. Then any solution to (4-97) can be written as a convex combination of the extreme points:

$$\boldsymbol{\psi} = \sum_v \rho_v \boldsymbol{\psi}_v^*; \qquad \rho_v \geq 0, \qquad \text{all } v, \qquad \sum_v \rho_v = 1.$$

Thus we can replace (4-96) by the equivalent problem involving only $m + 1$ constraints:

$$\sum_v \left(\sum_{k,j} \psi_{kijv}^* \right) \rho_v = a_i, \qquad i = 1, \ldots, m,$$

$$\sum_v \rho_v = 1, \qquad \rho_v \geq 0, \qquad \text{all } v, \tag{4-98}$$

$$\max \hat{z} = \sum_v \left(\sum_{k,i,j} \alpha_{kij} \psi_{kijv}^* \right) \rho_v,$$

where the ψ_{kijv}^* are the components of $\boldsymbol{\psi}_v^*$.

Denote by $\mathbf{d}_v$ an m-component vector whose i-component is $\sum_{k,j} \psi^*_{kijv}$. Also write

$$e_v = \sum_{k,i,j} \alpha_{kij}\psi^*_{kijv}.$$

Imagine that we have a basic feasible solution to (4–98), and denote the basis matrix of order $m + 1$ by $\mathbf{B}$. Let $\mathbf{e}_B$ contain the e_v corresponding to the ρ_v in the basis. Write

$$\boldsymbol{\sigma} = (\sigma_1, \sigma_2, \ldots, \sigma_{m+1}) = \mathbf{e}_B\mathbf{B}^{-1}. \tag{4–99}$$

Then

$$z_v - e_v = \boldsymbol{\sigma}[\mathbf{d}_v, 1] - e_v = \sum_{k,i,j} (\sigma_i - \alpha_{kij})\psi^*_{kijv} + \sigma_{m+1}. \tag{4–100}$$

Just as in Section 4–7, we do not need to know the ψ^*_v and $\mathbf{d}_v$ at the outset. They can be generated. To determine whether the current solution is optimal or, if not, what vector enters the basis at the next iteration, we must compute max $(z_v - e_v)$. If max $(z_v - e_v) \leq 0$, the current solution is optimal. Otherwise more iterations are required. Note that as in Section 4–7,

$$\max\,(z_v - e_v) = \max Z + \sigma_{m+1}, \tag{4–101}$$

where max Z is found by solving the linear programming problem

$$\begin{gathered} \sum_{i=1}^{m}\sum_{k=1}^{r_{ij}} \psi_{kij} = b_j, \quad j = 1, \ldots, n, \\ 0 \leq \psi_{kij} \leq \Delta x_{kij}, \quad \text{all } k, i, j, \\ \max Z = \sum_{k,i,j} (\sigma_i - \alpha_{kij})\psi_{kij}. \end{gathered} \tag{4–102}$$

However, this problem immediately decomposes into n subproblems, one for each j:

$$\begin{gathered} \sum_{i=1}^{m}\sum_{k=1}^{r_{ij}} \psi_{kij} = b_j, \\ 0 \leq \psi_{kij} \leq \Delta x_{kij}, \quad \text{all } k, i, \\ \max Z_j = \sum_{k,i} (\sigma_i - \alpha_{kij})\psi_{kij}. \end{gathered} \tag{4–103}$$

No simplex iterations are required to solve each of the subproblems (4–103). They may be solved by inspection. We look for the largest price among the $\sigma_i - \alpha_{kij}$, and then set the corresponding variable equal to the minimum of b_j and its upper bound. If the value of the variable is b_j, we set all the remaining variables to zero, and the resulting feasible solution is optimal. If the value of the variable is its upper bound, we denote by b_j' the number obtained by subtracting this upper bound from b_j. Among the variables not at their upper bounds (there is only one at its upper bound at this stage), we look for the one with the largest value $\sigma_i - \alpha_{kij}$. We then set the value of this variable equal to the minimum of b_j' and its upper bound. If the minimum is b_j', we set all other variables not at their upper bound to zero, and the resulting feasible solution is optimal. Otherwise, we repeat the above process. By successively allocating as much of the total requirement b_j as possible to the variable with the largest value of $\sigma_i - \alpha_{kij}$ we obtain an optimal solution. Each of the n problems (4–103) is solved in this way. Then

$$\max Z = \sum_j \max Z_j.$$

On combining the components of the optimal solution obtained for each of the problems (4–103), we obtain an optimal solution ψ_u^* to (4–102). We next compute the m-component vector $\mathbf{d}_u$ whose ith component is $\sum_{j,k} \psi_{kiju}$. The vector to enter the basis in (4–98) at the next iteration is $[\mathbf{d}_u, 1]$. After the vector to be removed is determined and the tableau for (4–98) is transformed, we obtain a new $\boldsymbol{\sigma}$ and the process is repeated.

The great advantage of the method just suggested is that although there are necessarily many variables if the initial problem has many destinations, it is usually possible to work with a small number of constraints. Very little computational effort is required to generate the vectors to enter the basis, since no simplex iterations are needed to solve the subproblems. In [2], Beale has suggested a different method for solving transportation problems with convex, separable costs. His algorithm does not use the simplex method. No computational experience is available with either of the algorithms on large problems, and hence it is not possible to make any definite statements regarding the relative efficiency of the two. We shall not discuss Beale's algorithm here. It seems to be seldom, if ever, true that actual transportation costs are convex (unless they are linear), and thus the material in the present section might not seem to be of practical value. However, practical problems with convex separable objective functions can arise in other ways, for example, as will be seen in the next chapter, in studying stochastic programming problems.

References

1. Balinski, M. L., "Fixed Cost Transportation Problems," *Naval Research Logistics Quarterly*, **8**, 1961, pp. 41–54.

2. Beale, E. M. L., "An Algorithm for Solving the Transportation Problem when the Shipping Cost over each Route is Convex," *Naval Research Logistics Quarterly*, **6**, 1959, pp. 43–56.

3. Charnes, A., and W. W. Cooper, *Management Models and Industrial Applications of Linear Programming*, Vols. I, II. New York: Wiley, 1961.

4. Charnes, A., and C. Lemke, "Minimization of Nonlinear Separable Convex Functionals," *Naval Research Logistics Quarterly*, **1**, 1954, pp. 301–312.

5. Dantzig, G. B., "Recent Advances in Linear Programming," *Management Science*, **2**, 1956, pp. 131–144.

6. Dantzig, G. B., "On the Status of Multistage Linear Programming Problems," *Management Science*, **6**, 1959, pp. 53–72.

7. Dantzig, G. B., S. Johnson, and W. White, "A Linear Programming Approach to the Chemical Equilibrium Problem," *Management Science*, **5**, 1958, pp. 38–43. This paper provides an example from the field of chemistry where the techniques discussed in this chapter can usefully be applied.

8. Griffith, R. E., and R. A. Stewart, "A Nonlinear Programming Technique for the Optimization of Continuous Processing Systems," *Management Science*, **7**, 1961, pp. 379–392. See Problem 4–52 for a discussion of this work.

9. Hadley, G., "How Practical is Nonlinear Programming?" *Product Engineering*, **31**, April 18, 1960, pp. 78–80.

10. Hartley, H. O., "Nonlinear Programming by the Simplex Method," *Econometrica*, **29**, 1961, pp. 223–237.

11. Hirsch, W. M., and G. B. Dantzig, "The Fixed Charge Problem," *RM-1383*, The *RAND* Corp., 1954.

12. Kelley, J. E., "The Cutting-Plane Method for Solving Convex Programs," *Journal of the Society for Industrial and Applied Mathematics*, **8**, 1960, pp. 703–712. This paper discusses a method for minimizing a linear form over a convex set. The iterative technique for solving the problem may require an infinite number of steps for convergence. Each iteration requires the solution of a linear programming problem. The method does not seem to have any advantages over the techniques for solving such a problem discussed in this chapter.

13. Kuhn, H., and W. Baumol, "An Approximative Algorithm for the Fixed Charge Transportation Problem," *Naval Research Logistics Quarterly*, **9**, 1962, pp. 1–15.

14. Miller, C., "The Simplex Method for Local Separable Programming," in *Recent Advances in Mathematical Programming*, R. Graves and P. Wolfe, editors. New York: McGraw-Hill, 1963.

15. Vajda, S., *Mathematical Programming*. Reading, Mass.: Addison-Wesley, 1961.

16. Wolfe, P., *Computational Techniques for Nonlinear Programs*. Princeton University Conference on Linear Programming, March 13–15, 1957.

17. Wolfe, P., editor, "*The RAND Symposium on Mathematical Programming*," *R-351*, The *RAND* Corp., 1960.

Problems

4–1. Use the λ-form of the approximating problem to find an approximate optimal solution to the following problem:

$$4x_1^2 + x_2^2 \le 16, \qquad x_1, x_2 \ge 0, \qquad \max z = 3x_1 + 2x_2.$$

Solve the problem graphically.

4–2. Using the λ-form of the approximating problem, find an approximate local maximum to the following problem:

$$4x_1^2 + x_2^2 \le 16, \qquad x_1, x_2 \ge 0, \qquad \max z = x_1x_2.$$

Solve the problem graphically. Can one guarantee that the computational method will yield an approximate global optimum in this case?

4–3. Using the λ-form of the approximating problem, find an approximate optimal solution to the following problem:

$$x_1^2 + x_2^2 \le 6, \qquad x_1, x_2 \ge 0, \qquad \min z = (x_1 - 5)^2 + (x_2 - 8)^2.$$

Solve the problem graphically.

4–4. Using the λ-form of the approximating problem, find an approximate optimal solution to the following problem:

$$x_1 + x_2 \le 2, \qquad x_1, x_2 \ge 0, \qquad \min z = 4(x_1 - 1)^2 + 16(x_2 - 5)^2.$$

Solve the problem graphically.

4–5. Solve Problem 4–4, using the δ-form of the approximating problem and the technique developed in Section 4–7 to treat the upper bounds.

4–6. Using the δ-form of the approximating problem, determine an approximate optimal solution to the following problem:

$$3x_1 + 2x_2 \le 6, \qquad x_1, x_2 \ge 0, \qquad \max z = 8x_1 + 10x_2 - x_1^2 - x_2^2.$$

4–7. Use the δ-form of the approximating problem to determine an approximate optimal solution to the following problem:

$$\begin{aligned} x_1 + 4x_2 &\le 4, \\ x_1 + x_2 &\le 2, \\ x_1, x_2 &\ge 0, \\ \max z &= 2x_1 + 3x_2 - 2x_2^2. \end{aligned}$$

4–8. Using the δ-form of the approximating problem, find an approximate local optimum for the following problem:

$$3x_1 + 2x_2 \le 6, \qquad x_1, x_2 \ge 0, \qquad \max z = x_1^2 + x_2^2.$$

Is the local optimum of the approximate problem close to the global optimum of the given problem?

4–9. Using the δ-form of the approximating problem, determine an approximate optimal solution to the following problem:

$$x_1 + 3x_2 \geq 5,$$
$$2x_2 + 0.5x_1 \geq 2,$$
$$x_1, x_2 \geq 0,$$
$$\min z = 4x_1^2 + 3x_2^2.$$

4–10. Using the δ-form of the approximating problem, try to determine an approximate optimal solution to the following problem:

$$x_1 - x_2 \geq 0,$$
$$-x_1 + 2x_2 \leq 2,$$
$$x_1, x_2 \geq 0,$$
$$\max z = 2x_1 + 3x_2 - x_1^2.$$

4–11. Determine an approximate solution to the example of Section 4–3, using the δ-form of the approximating problem. Treat the upper bounds by means of the algorithm discussed in {LP 11–7}.

4–12. Why can't the decomposition principle be applied directly to the λ-form of the approximating problem to handle the constraints of the form $\sum \lambda_{kj} = 1$?

4–13. Prove directly that when no more simplex iterations can be made by means of the restricted basis entry for the δ-form of the approximating problem, then the current solution yields a local optimum of the approximating problem.

4–14. Show how one converts the δ-form of the approximating problem to the λ-form and vice versa, i.e., show that there is a one-to-one correspondence between the feasible solutions to the δ- and λ-forms of the approximating problem, and that the value of the objective function is the same for corresponding solutions.

Hint:

$$\begin{aligned} x_j &= \sum_k \Delta x_{kj}\delta_{kj} = \sum_k (x_{kj} - x_{k-1,j})\delta_{kj} \\ &= x_{1j}\delta_{1j} + (x_{2j} - x_{1j})\delta_{1j} + \cdots + (x_{r_j,j} - x_{r_j-1,j})\delta_{r_j,j} \\ &= x_{1j}(\delta_{1j} - \delta_{2j}) + x_{2j}(\delta_{2j} - \delta_{3j}) + \cdots + \delta_{r_j,j}x_{r_j,j}. \end{aligned}$$

Can we write

$$\lambda_{kj} = \delta_{kj} - \delta_{k+1,j}, \qquad k = 1, \ldots, r_j - 1; \qquad \lambda_{r_j,j} = \delta_{r_j,j}?$$

4–15. Make a transformation of variables to convert the following problem to a separable form. Determine an approximate local maximum, using the λ-form of the approximating problem. Illustrate graphically.

$$x_1^2 x_2 \leq 16,$$
$$x_1, x_2 \geq 0,$$
$$\max z = 3e^{x_1} + x_2.$$

4–16. Make a transformation of variables to convert the following problem to a separable form. Write down the λ-form of the approximating problem, but do not attempt to solve it.

$$\begin{aligned} x_1 \sin x_2 + x_3^2 \ln x_4 &\geq 17, \\ 4e^{x_1 x_3} + \sin [x_2 \cos x_4] &\geq 8, \\ x_1, x_2, x_3, x_4 &\geq 0, \\ \max z = 2x_1 + x_2^2 &+ \ln x_3 x_4. \end{aligned}$$

4–17. Show how by a transformation of variables that

$$x_1^a x_2^b x_3^c, \qquad a, b, c > 0, \qquad x_1, x_2, x_3 \geq 0$$

can be written in separable form.

4–18. Re-solve the example of Section 4–3, using half of the interval spacing used there. Compare the results. Solve the problem again, changing the interval spacing only in the neighborhood of the optimal solution.

4–19. Re-solve the example of Section 4–8, using half of the interval spacing used there. Change the interval spacing only in the neighborhood of the optimal solution, however. Compare the results.

4–20. For the example solved in Section 4–3, show that the basic solution with $\lambda_{52} = 1$, that is, $x_2 = 1.25$, and λ_{31}, λ_{41} determined by the constraint yields a set of x_j-values which are closer to the optimal values for the actual problem, but gives a value of the objective function for the approximating problem which is smaller than that for the solution obtained.

4–21. To avoid introducing new variables $u_j = x_j + \epsilon_j$ when separating terms such as $x_i x_j$ one can proceed as follows: For a typical variable x_j, select a

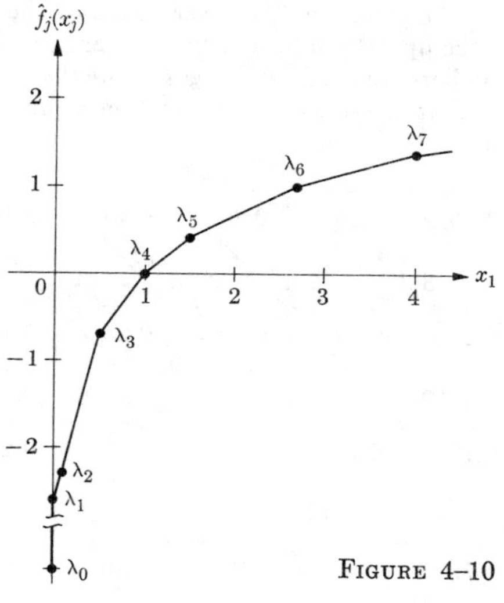

FIGURE 4–10

value $x_{cj} > 0$ such that it is unnecessary to distinguish between 0 and x_{cj}. Then $\hat{f}_j(x_j)$, the function used to approximate ln x, is written

$$\hat{f}_j(x_j) = L_{0j}\lambda_0 + L_{1j}\lambda_1 + L_{2j}\lambda_2 + \cdots + L_{rj}\lambda_r,$$
$$x_j = x_{cj}\lambda_2 + x_{3j}\lambda_3 + \cdots + x_{rj}\lambda_r,$$
$$\sum_{k=0}^{r} \lambda_{kj} = 1,$$

where, as usual, no more than two λ_{kj} can be positive, and two can be positive only if they are adjacent. The function $\hat{f}_j(x_j)$ is then being represented as shown in Fig. 4–10. The vertical line is needed to ensure that in an equation such as $y = ax_1^2x_2^3$, all variables can be equal to zero when the logarithm of this expression is taken.

Explain in more detail why such a vertical line is needed. Construct a numerical example to illustrate the problem.

4–22. Prove that the extreme points of $\mathbf{Ix} \leq \mathbf{h}$, $\mathbf{x} \geq \mathbf{0}$, have the form given in Eq. (4–57).

4–23. Use the method of Section 4–9 to find an approximate optimal solution to

$$2x_1^2 + 3x_2^2 \leq 6, \qquad x_1, x_2 \geq 0, \qquad \max z = x_1 + x_2.$$

4–24. Consider the problem of maximizing a concave function $f(\mathbf{x})$ over a convex set. Show that one can convert this problem to that of maximizing a linear function over a convex set, by introducing the additional constraint $f(\mathbf{x}) - y \geq 0$ and then maximizing the variable y.

4–25. Use the results of Problem 4–24 to find an approximate optimal solution to the example of Section 4–3 by means of the method described in Section 4–9.

4–26. Find an approximate solution to the fixed-charge transportation problem described below. Also, determine the lower bound on the true optimum. In the following tableau the upper numbers in the cells are the unit transportation costs and the lower numbers are the fixed charges. Note that the sum of the origin availabilities is greater than the sum of the destination requirements so that there is slack in the system.

0.25 / 10	0.35 / 5	0.15 / 12	0.20 / 7	0.40 / 13	0.16 / 18	300
0.45 / 8	0.25 / 12	0.30 / 7	0.50 / 6	0.25 / 10	0.30 / 14	200
0.27 / 15	0.16 / 18	0.10 / 14	0.30 / 10	0.15 / 11	0.25 / 12	200
50	75	50	100	80	100	

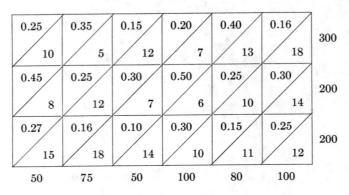

4–27. Prove that by proper choice of the fixed charges, any extreme point of the convex set of feasible solutions for a fixed-charge problem can be made optimal, regardless of what the prices of the variables are.

4–28. Let $f(x_1, x_2)$ be a homogeneous function of degree one, so that $f(\lambda x_1, \lambda x_2) = \lambda f(x_1, x_2)$. Then

$$f(x_1, x_2) = x_1 f\left(1, \frac{x_2}{x_1}\right), \qquad x_1 \neq 0.$$

How can this relation be usefully applied to separate homogeneous functions of degree one? Apply the method to $(x_1 x_2)^{1/2}$ and compare the number of equations needed with that required if one makes the substitution $y = x_1 x_2$. Assume in the above that $x_1 > 0$.

4–29. Is it possible to determine an initial basic feasible solution to Eq. (4–98) without using a Phase I computation?

4–30. Generalize the technique developed in Section 4–12 to include the case where there are upper bounds on the variables x_{ij}.

4–31. Assume that the set X of feasible solutions to Eq. (4–1) is convex. Then show that every point in the convex set of feasible solutions for the approximating problem, Eq. (4–2), is in X.

4–32. Assume that the objective function in Eq. (4–1) is concave. Show that if $z(\mathbf{x})$ is the value of the objective function in Eq. (4–1) for any $\mathbf{x}$, and $z_1(\mathbf{x})$ is the value of the objective function to the approximating problem Eq. (4–2) for the same $\mathbf{x}$, it follows that $z_1(\mathbf{x}) \leq z(\mathbf{x})$. Then, using the results of Problem 4–31, show that when in Eq. (4–1) the set of feasible solutions is convex and the objective function is concave, then the optimal value of the objective function for Eq. (4–2) is never greater than the optimal value of the objective function for Eq. (4–1).

4–33. Prove that for the computational technique described in Section 4–9, there exists a sequence of problems p_u with finer and finer subdivisions such that the sequence z_u of optimal values of the objective functions for those problems converges to z^*, the optimal value of the objective function for the given problem. Thus prove that if the optimal solution to the given problem is unique, the sequence of solutions to p_u must converge to this solution. [*Hint:* Make the subdivisions such that the mesh points for p_u include all the mesh points for p_{u-1}, so that any basic feasible solution to the dual of p_{u-1} is also a basic feasible solution to the dual of p_u. Hence $z_{u-1} \leq z_u$. This sequence must approach a limiting value if the given problem has a finite maximum.] Show that the limit is z^*.

4–34. Answer Problem 4–33 for the computational method of Section 4–2 when the set of feasible solutions is convex, and the objective function is concave.

4–35. Prove that the functions $f_j(x_j)$ defined by Eqs. (4–79) and (4–80) are concave for $x_j \geq 0$.

4–36. Show that the solution to Eq. (4–84) has the property that if $\lambda_{2j} = 0$, then $\lambda_{0j} = 1$. Thus show that the solution to Eq. (4–84) yields a relative minimum for the fixed-charge problem of Eq. (4–78).

4-37. Show that if the variable x_j is unrestricted in sign, but upper and lower bounds are known for x_j, it is just as easy to use the δ- or λ-forms of the approximating problem as it is when x_j is restricted to be non-negative. Thus one can handle unrestricted variables x_j without an attempt to convert them to non-negative variables. [*Hint:* For the δ-form of the approximating problem, it is convenient to introduce the change of variable $x_j = y_j - \beta_j$, where $-\beta_j$ is the lower bound on x_j. Why?]

4-38. Prove that if the f_j, g_{ij} are convex (concave) functions, then the $\hat{f}_j$, $\hat{g}_{ij}$ are also convex (concave) functions.

4-39. Show that if the $f_j(x_j)$ are concave functions and the $g_{ij}(x_j)$ have the proper convexity and concavity relations so that the set of feasible solutions is convex, then, if one solves the λ-form of the approximating problem as a strict linear programming problem, the set of x_j so obtained will be an optimal solution to the approximating problem.

4-40. Illustrate the results of Problem 4-39 by solving Eq. (4-20) without restricted basis entry.

4-41. Solve Problem 4-1, using the method of Section 4-7 and the theory of Problem 4-39.

4-42. On Fig. 4-2, sketch the bounding hyperplanes for the constraints of Eq. (4-77) corresponding to (x_1, x_2) in the intervals $0.25 \leq x_1 \leq 0.50$, $0.25 \leq x_2 \leq 0.50$, and in the intervals $1.0 \leq x_1 \leq 1.25$, $0.50 \leq x_2 \leq 0.75$.

4-43. When the δ- or λ-form of the approximating problem is used, what will happen if the optimal x_j is greater than α_j, our initial estimate of the largest possible value of x_j?

4-44. In using either the δ- or λ-forms of the approximating problem, it is possible to allow x_j to range in the interval $-\infty < x_j < \infty$. This can be done by representing $f_j(x_j)$, as discussed in this chapter, in the interval $-\beta_j \leq x_j \leq \alpha_j$, and by $f_j(x_j) = \gamma_j\lambda_j + f_j(\alpha_j)$, $\lambda_j \geq 0$, for $x_j > \alpha_j$ and $f_j(x_j) = -\rho_j\lambda_j' + f_j(-\beta_j)$, $\lambda_j' \geq 0$ for $x_j < -\beta_j$. There are no other restrictions on λ_j and λ_j'. Thus f_j is being represented by straight lines outside the interval $-\beta_j \leq x_j \leq \alpha_j$. Illustrate this graphically. It is clear that the representation of f_j will not be accurate if x_j gets far outside the interval $-\beta_j \leq x_j \leq \alpha_j$. Discuss why this procedure might nonetheless be useful sometimes. Also discuss how this procedure can be incorporated in both the λ- and δ-forms of the approximating problem.

4-45. Consider the following type of nonlinear programming problem:

$$\mathbf{Ax} = \mathbf{b},$$

$$\mathbf{x} \geq \mathbf{0},$$

$$\max z = \frac{\mathbf{cx} + c_0}{\mathbf{dx} + d_0},$$

where it will be assumed that $\mathbf{dx} + d_0 > 0$ for all $\mathbf{x} \geq \mathbf{0}$ that are of interest. Note that the constraints are linear, and the objective function is the quotient of two linear forms. Show that by a transformation of variables, this problem can be converted into a linear programming problem. [*Hint:* Let $v = \mathbf{dx} + d_0 > 0$.] Write $y_j = x_j/v \geq 0$, $j = 1, \ldots, n$, and $y_0 = 1/v > 0$ so that the constraints then become $\sum \mathbf{a}_j y_j - \mathbf{b} y_0 = 0$, $\sum d_j y_j - d_0 y_0 = 1$, max $z = \sum c_j y_j + c_0 y_0$. This latter problem is linear. Consider an optimal solution to it obtained by requiring that $\mathbf{y} \geq \mathbf{0}$, $y_0 \geq 0$. Show that if $y_0 \neq 0$, we can obtain from the linear problem an optimal solution to the original problem. What happens if $y_0 = 0$? Show that when $y_0 > 0$, there is a correspondence between every feasible solution to the given problem and the linear programming problem in the variables y_j.

4–46. Suppose that we solve either the λ- or δ-form of the approximating problem and obtain a local optimum with z_0 being the value of the objective function. Why will it not necessarily be of any value to add the constraint (for the λ-form)

$$\sum_{k,j} f_{kj}\lambda_{kj} \geq z_0 + \epsilon, \qquad \epsilon > 0,$$

in an effort to try to find a solution with a larger value of z? [*Hint:* There can be local optima in Phase I.]

4–47. Suppose that we are using the δ-form of the approximating problem to solve some problem in which x_j is unrestricted in sign. What difficulties might be encountered if we represented x_j as

$$x_j = \sum_k \Delta x_{kj}\, \delta_{kj} - \sum_k \Delta x_{-kj}\, \delta_{-kj}, \qquad \Delta x_{kj}, \Delta x_{-kj} > 0?$$

Show, however, that if the constraint set is convex and the objective function to be maximized is concave, then in the final solution both δ_{kj} and $\delta_{-k'j}$ will never be positive.

4–48. We have noted that when the set of feasible solutions is convex and the $f_j(x_j)$ are concave functions, then one can solve either the λ- or the δ-forms of the approximating problems as strict linear programming problems and thereby obtain an optimal solution to the approximating problem. Could we obtain useful information concerning the extent to which a local optimum may deviate from the global optimum if, in addition to solving the approximating problem with restricted entry, we also solved it as a strict linear programming problem in those cases where the set of feasible solutions is not convex and/or the $f_j(x_j)$ are not concave functions?

4–49. When the λ-form of the approximating problem is used, under what conditions is it possible to make a large jump in x_j rather than simply move from one interval to an adjacent interval? Show that one would never expect the λ-form of the problem to require more iterations than the δ-form does if the standard upper-bounds algorithm is used to treat the upper bounds (not the special algorithm based on the decomposition principle). [*Hint:* Review the example of Section 4–3.]

4–50. Suppose that we have solved either the δ- or λ-form of the approximating problem, and we would now like to improve the accuracy of the approximation by using finer subdivisions. Note that the current solution may not be a basic or feasible solution to the new problem. List the cases that can occur. Assume that finer subdivisions are being used only in a neighborhood of the current solution. Suggest how one might select the region where finer subdivisions are to be used. Suggest some ways by which one might get started on solving the new problem without the use of a Phase I, such as, for example, keeping a record of the basic solution obtained at each iteration when solving the original problem and then using one of these. Discuss the difficulties associated with each method suggested.

4–51. Suppose that we have solved either the δ- or λ-forms of the approximating problem, and all $z_j - c_j \geq 0$, not merely those corresponding to the variables which are allowed to become positive. Show that in this case we have obtained a global optimum for the approximating problem.

4–52. In reference 8, Griffith and Stewart suggest a procedure for determining a local optimum for nonlinear programming problems even for those cases where the constraints and the objective function are not separable. Consider the problem

$$g_i(\mathbf{x}) \leq b_i, \qquad i = 1, \ldots, m; \qquad \mathbf{x} \geq \mathbf{0}; \qquad \max z = f(\mathbf{x}).$$

Assume that we have a feasible solution $\mathbf{x}_0$. Then replace $g_i(\mathbf{x})$ by $g_i(\mathbf{x}_0) + \nabla g_i(\mathbf{x}_0)(\mathbf{x} - \mathbf{x}_0)$ and $f(\mathbf{x})$ by $f(\mathbf{x}_0) + \nabla f(\mathbf{x}_0)(\mathbf{x} - \mathbf{x}_0)$ to obtain the approximating problem

$$\nabla g_i(\mathbf{x}_0)(\mathbf{x} - \mathbf{x}_0) \leq b_i - g_i(\mathbf{x}_0), \qquad i = 1, \ldots, m,$$
$$\mathbf{x} \geq \mathbf{0}$$
$$\max z = \nabla f(\mathbf{x}_0)(\mathbf{x} - \mathbf{x}_0).$$

One can introduce a new set of unrestricted variables

$$\boldsymbol{\mu} = \mathbf{x} - \mathbf{x}_0.$$

Then μ_j is the change in x_j. One next places some upper bounds on the magnitudes of the μ_j and solves the resulting linear programming problem. This yields a new $\mathbf{x}$, call it $\mathbf{x}_1$. The entire procedure is now repeated. Develop an algorithmic procedure based on this method. Note that the procedure does not guarantee that the entire sequence of $\mathbf{x}_k$ obtained will be feasible solutions. Show that this does not necessarily lead to any difficulties, and one can proceed in the same way as if the solution were feasible, the only difference being that the right-hand side will be negative for one or more constraints. No proof can be given that the procedure will always converge to a local optimum, since it does not always converge. However, it has been found useful for solving certain types of practical problems. How might one decide what the upper bounds on the magnitudes of the μ_j should be? Should they be changed from one iteration to another? If the upper bound on the magnitudes of μ_j is B_j, then Griffith and Stewart suggest that the following constraint be included:

$$p_j\mu_j' + q_j\mu_j'' \leq B_j, \qquad \mu_j' \geq 0, \qquad \mu_j'' \geq 0,$$

where

$$p_j = \max\left(1, \frac{B_j}{U_j - x_j^0}\right), \qquad q_j = \max\left(1, \frac{B_j}{x_j^0 - L_j}\right), \text{ respectively,}$$

and U_j and L_j are any upper and lower bound which may have been imposed on x_j. Explain the reasoning for this. Can an upper-bounds algorithm be used here? Compare the size of the problem Griffith and Stewart must solve at each iteration with the λ- or δ-forms of the approximating problem discussed in this chapter. Which procedure is more efficient?

4–53. Solve the example of Section 4–3, using the method discussed in Problem 4–52. Illustrate each iteration geometrically.

4–54. Solve the example of Section 4–8, using the method discussed in Problem 4–52. Illustrate each iteration geometrically.

4–55. Solve Problem 4–1, using the method discussed in Problem 4–52. Illustrate each iteration geometrically.

4–56. Write out explicitly the λ- and δ-forms of the approximating problems for the case where the last $n - r$ variables enter the problem in a linear fashion. How does one handle these variables which enter linearly in applying the simplex algorithm to solve the approximating problem?

4–57. Suppose that the functions $g_{ij}(x_j)$ and $f_j(x_j)$ in Eq. (4–1) have the proper convexity and concavity properties so that any local optimum is also a global optimum. Then the global optimum for the approximating problem can be found by solving it strictly as a linear programming problem. Show how the decomposition principle can be applied in this case to the λ-form of the approximating problem to simplify the computational procedure, just as it was in Section 4–7 to the δ-form of the approximating problem.

CHAPTER 5

STOCHASTIC PROGRAMMING

If a man will begin with certainties he will end with doubts, but if he will be content to begin with doubts he shall end in certainties.

Francis Bacon, *Advancement of Learning*

5-1 Introduction. The variables in a programming problem are frequently referred to as the control variables, or policy variables, or decision variables. They are the real-world physical variables which the decision maker is free to specify arbitrarily (within the limits imposed by the constraints). The decision maker's problem is to determine the values of the control variables which optimize some specified objective function. The purpose of solving the programming problem is to determine an optimal set of control variables. The optimal values of the control variables will be functions of the various parameters which appear in the programming problem (i.e., the availabilities of resources, cost coefficients, and technological coefficients, such as the time to make one unit of a given product on a given machine type). When the value of one or more of the parameters is changed, it will in general be true that the optimal values of some or all of the control variables will change somewhat. The standard techniques for solving such problems, which are based on the simplex algorithm, provide an optimal solution only for one specified set of values of the parameters. Using these methods, one cannot obtain explicit expressions for a set of optimal values of the control variables as functions of all the parameters. Indeed, a detailed sensitivity analysis to determine how the optimal values of the control variables change as various parameters are changed (singly or in different combinations) could require considerable computational effort.

In many cases of practical importance, it turns out that some of the parameters appearing in the problem must be treated as random variables rather than as deterministic ones. Two of the examples presented in Chapter 3 illustrated programming problems where some of the parameters had to be treated as random variables. It was also pointed out in Chapter 3 that if the decision maker's behavior satisfies a certain set of axioms, then there exists a utility function defined over the possible outcomes with the property that he should proceed by selecting the action which maximizes his expected utility. Consequently, when some of the parameters in a programming problem are random variables, the standard procedure which is followed is to optimize the expected value of the objective function. Usually, the objective function will be either a profit or a cost. The justification for maximizing the expected profit or minimizing the expected cost lies in the assumption that the decision maker has the appropriate sort of utility function, and that it can be represented for any outcome with sufficient accuracy by either the appropriate profit or the negative of the cost for that outcome. In this chapter, we shall always assume that when some parameters appearing in a programming problem are random variables, one should determine a set of optimal values of the control variables by optimizing the expected value of the objective function.

Procedures for cases where it cannot be assumed that the decision maker has a utility function of the type needed and/or where the probability distributions for the random variables are not known are much less clear-cut and also more controversial. These will not be discussed here.

In studying programming problems in which some of the parameters can be random variables, it is convenient to subdivide the problems into two major classes. The first will include those problems which involve the making of two or more decisions at different points in time, and which have the property that the later decision(s) may be influenced not only by the previous decisions, but also by some stochastic parameters whose values will actually have been observed before later decisions are made. These will be referred to as sequential decision problems. The other class of problems is then what might be called nonsequential decision problems. For such problems, one can imagine that there is only one decision to be made, or if the problem is imagined to consist of several decisions, it is not true that parameters which must be considered to be random variables before the first decision is made will occur, be observed, and perhaps have an influence on later decisions. From a practical point of view, it would seem to be true that the most important problems are sequential decision problems. Unfortunately, we shall also see that the solution of these sequential decision problems is in general vastly more complicated than that of nonsequential problems.

We shall refer to programming problems in which some of the parameters are random variables as stochastic programming problems. These are almost always nonlinear, since some of the costs will depend on the values that are actually taken on by the random variables, and these costs are nonlinear in the control variables. Therefore, when the expected value is taken over the random variables, the objective function becomes a nonlinear function of the control variables. In this chapter, we shall study some of the various types of stochastic programming problems that can arise and examine the difficulties involved in their solution.

5-2 Nonsequential stochastic programming problems with random variables appearing only in the requirements. A simple example of such a problem is provided by the first example of Section 3-9. Recall that the buyer is attempting to allocate his funds among three different types of dresses so as to maximize the store's expected profit on the three styles. The problem reduces to maximizing (3-45) subject to the constraint (3-46). The objective function is nonlinear because the revenue received on each dress j and the goodwill loss are nonlinear functions of the control variable x_j. However, the objective function is indeed concave and separable (from example 5 of Section 3-11), and hence an approximate global optimum for this problem could be found by the methods of the previous chapter. We ask the reader to do this in Problem 5-1. For the problem under consideration, the parameters (requirements) that are the random variables are the demands for the dresses. At the time the buyer decides how many of each kind of dress to buy, he does not know what the demand for each dress will be. For any given distribution of funds among the dresses, i.e., for any given set of values for the control variables, the ultimate profit received by the store will depend strongly on the values of the random variables which represent the demand for the dresses. For specified values of the demands and the x_j, it is simple to obtain an expression for the profit. When we average this result over all possible values taken on by the demands, using the probability density function for the demands as a weighting function in obtaining the average, we get the expected profit for the given set of x_j. The buyer's problem is then to determine the set of x_j which maximize this expected profit.

It is interesting to compare the above problem with the one the buyer would have to solve if he knew ahead of time what the demand for each type of dress would be. In such a case, there would be no parameters which were random variables. Suppose that the demand for dress j is to be v_j. Then write $x_j = v_j + w_j$, where w_j is an unrestricted variable which indicates the amount by which the quantity procured differs from the actual demand v_j. Next write $w_j = u_j - y_j$, where $u_j, y_j \geq 0$. The constraint in terms of the u_j, y_j then becomes

$$35u_1 - 35y_1 + 20u_2 - 20y_2 + 50u_3 - 50y_3 \leq 3000 - 35v_1 - 20v_2 - 50v_3, \qquad (5\text{-}1)$$

and the profit would be

$$P = 31v_1 - 31y_1 - 7u_1 + 17v_2 - 17y_2 - 4u_2 + 55v_3 - 55y_3 - 10u_3 - 70y_1 - 40y_2 - 220y_3. \qquad (5\text{-}2)$$

This is a very simple linear programming problem. It is clear that the buyer would never buy dresses in excess of the demand. However, he may have to buy a smaller quantity, since he might not have sufficient funds to purchase enough stock to meet all the demands. To avoid solving the nonlinear programming problem (3–45), (3–46), the buyer might be tempted not to consider the demands to be random variables, but instead use their mean values, and then solve the linear programming problem (5–1) and (5–2), using the x_j obtained from this solution in the real world, where the demands are actually random variables. Such a procedure for trying to determine approximately the optimal x_j by ignoring the randomness inherent in the problem may be a very poor procedure to follow, since the x_j so obtained may not even be close to their optimal values. This will be discussed in more detail in a later section.

In practice, the simple type of problem just discussed occurs rather frequently in a variety of guises. It might be helpful to illustrate one other situation which leads to the same type of problem. Consider a nuclear submarine about to go on patrol. A certain amount of space is available for stocking spare parts for the submarine itself and for the missiles it carries. Let b be the volume available. There are n different spare parts which are to be stocked. The volume of one unit of part j is a_j. For each spare part of type j demanded and not in stock a cost π_j is incurred. The probability that v_j units of spare part j will be demanded during the patrol will be denoted by $p_j(v_j)$. It is desired to determine the number x_j of spare parts to stock which will minimize the expected stockout costs while not exceeding the available volume. It is immediately clear that the optimal x_j are solutions to the following programming problem:

$$
\begin{aligned}
&\sum_{j=1}^{n} a_j x_j \leq b, \\
&x_j \geq 0, \qquad j = 1, \ldots, n, \\
&\min z = \pi_1 \sum_{v_1=x_1+1}^{\infty} (v_1 - x_1) p_1(v_1) \\
&\qquad + \cdots + \pi_n \sum_{v_n=x_n+1}^{\infty} (v_n - x_n) p_n(v_n),
\end{aligned}
\tag{5-3}
$$

where we require in addition that all x_j be integers. One cannot, in general, ignore the integer requirements here, since the x_j will normally be small whole numbers. We shall see in Chapter 10 that this problem with its integer requirements can be solved by means of dynamic programming. It should be recognized that the formulation just given may, in certain cases, not be sufficiently good because the actual shape of the parts, rather than merely their unit volumes, will influence the number that can be stocked.

Let us now consider a slightly different type of stochastic programming problem where random variables appear only in the requirements. This problem has been discussed in some detail by Dantzig [5]. Imagine that we have a uniform product available in n warehouses. The quantity available in warehouse i is a_i. During the coming period the product will be demanded at each of n retail outlets. However, the demand at any one outlet cannot be determined precisely ahead of time. The demands at the outlets must be considered to be random variables. It will be assumed that the demands can be treated as continuous random variables and the probability density for the demand v_j for the product at outlet j will be written $\phi_j(v_j)$. The v_j will be treated as independent random variables, i.e., it will be imagined that the demand at one outlet has no influence on the demands at the other outlets. Let c_{ij} be the cost of shipping one unit from warehouse i to outlet j. The shipping cost will be taken to be proportional to the number of units shipped. Denote by y_j the total number of units shipped to outlet j. Then, if $y_j < v_j$, there is a goodwill loss of $\pi_j(v_j - y_j)$. This is equivalent to saying that for each unit demanded in excess of the number of units shipped there is a goodwill loss of π_j. Assume that if $y_j > v_j$, there is a cost $k_j(y_j - v_j)$. This may be interpreted as implying that if the number of units shipped is greater than the demand, they must be sold at a loss (it may be too expensive to ship them back to the warehouses again). It is desired to determine how much each warehouse should ship to each outlet j in order to minimize the sum of the transportation costs and the expected costs of overage and underage.

The expected cost of underage at outlet j is

$$\pi_j \int_{y_j}^{\infty} (v_j - y_j)\phi_j(v_j)\, dv_j, \tag{5–4}$$

and the expected cost of overage is

$$k_j \int_0^{y_j} (y_j - v_j)\phi_j(v_j)\, dv_j = k_j(y_j - \mu_j) + k_j \int_{y_j}^{\infty} (v_j - y_j)\phi_j(v_j)\, dv_j, \tag{5–5}$$

where μ_j is the expected demand at outlet j. The expected cost of overage and underage is then

$$\sum_{j=1}^{n} k_j(y_j - \mu_j) + \sum_{j=1}^{n} (k_j + \pi_j) \int_{y_j}^{\infty} (v_j - y_j)\phi_j(v_j)\, dv_j, \tag{5–6}$$

which is a convex separable function of the y_j. The problem which it is desired to solve thus becomes

$$\sum_{j=1}^{n} x_{ij} \leq a_i, \qquad i = 1, \ldots, m,$$

$$\sum_{i=1}^{m} x_{ij} - y_j = 0, \qquad j = 1, \ldots, n, \tag{5–7}$$

$$x_{ij} \geq 0, \quad \text{all } i, j; \qquad y_j \geq 0, \qquad j = 1, \ldots, n,$$

$$\min z = \sum_{i,j} c_{ij}x_{ij} + \sum_j k_j y_j + \sum_j (k_j + \pi_j) \int_{y_j}^{\infty} (v_j - y_j)\phi_j(v_j)\, dv_j.$$

It is unnecessary to include $-\sum k_j\mu_j$ in the objective function, since this is just a constant. It can be added in after the problem is solved. If desired, one can eliminate the second set of n constraints which define the y_j in terms of the x_{ij}, by using these constraints to eliminate the y_j in the objective function. However, if this were done, the objective function would no longer be separable. Thus (5–7) is the preferred form.

An approximate optimal solution to this problem could be obtained by applying directly the methods of Chapter 4. However, the structure of this problem is sufficiently close to that of a transportation problem that the simplified scheme of Section 4–12 should be applicable in a slightly modified form. Write

$$f_j(y_j) = k_j y_j + (k_j + \pi_j) \int_{y_j}^{\infty} (v_j - y_j)\phi_j(v_j)\, dv_j \tag{5–8}$$

and

$$y_j = \sum_k \psi_{kj}; \qquad \hat{f}_j(y_j) = \sum_k \alpha_{kj}\psi_{kj} + f_j(0), \tag{5–9}$$

where

$$0 \leq \psi_{kj} \leq \Delta y_{kj}. \tag{5–10}$$

Then the problem becomes

$$\sum_{j=1}^{n} x_{ij} \leq a_i, \qquad i = 1, \ldots, m,$$

$$\sum_{i=1}^{m} x_{ij} - \sum_k \psi_{kj} = 0, \qquad j = 1, \ldots, n, \tag{5–11}$$

$$0 \leq \psi_{kj} \leq \Delta y_{kj}, \quad \text{all } k, j; \qquad x_{ij} \geq 0, \quad \text{all } i, j;$$

$$\min z = \sum_{i,j} c_{ij}x_{ij} + \sum_{k,j} \alpha_{kj}\psi_{kj}.$$

Denote by $[\mathbf{x}_v^*, \psi_v^*]$ an extreme point of the convex set of solutions to

$$\sum_{i=1}^{m} x_{ij} - \sum_{k} \psi_{kj} = 0, \qquad j = 1, \ldots, n,$$
$$0 \le \psi_{kj} \le \Delta y_{kj}, \quad \text{all } k, j; \qquad x_{ij} \ge 0, \quad \text{all } i, j. \tag{5–12}$$

Then any feasible solution $[\mathbf{x}, \psi]$ to (5–12) can be written as a convex combination of the extreme points

$$[\mathbf{x}, \psi] = \sum \rho_v[\mathbf{x}_v^*, \psi_v^*], \qquad \rho_v \ge 0, \qquad \sum \rho_v = 1, \tag{5–13}$$

and problem (5–11) is equivalent to

$$\sum \mathbf{d}_v \rho_v \le \mathbf{a}, \qquad \sum \rho_v = 1, \qquad \rho_v \ge 0, \qquad \min z = \sum h_v \rho_v, \tag{5–14}$$

where

$$h_v = \sum_{i,j} c_{ij} x_{ijv}^* + \sum_{k,j} \alpha_{kj} \psi_{kjv}^*, \tag{5–15}$$

and

$$\mathbf{d}_v = \mathbf{A}_1 \mathbf{x}_v^* + \mathbf{A}_2 \psi_{v}^*, \qquad \mathbf{A}_2 = \mathbf{0},$$

and $\mathbf{A}_1$ is such that the ith component of $\mathbf{d}_v$ is $\sum_j x_{ijv}^*$. One now proceeds just as in Section 4–12 and gets n subproblems to solve, whose form for a fixed j is

$$\sum_{i=1}^{m} x_{ij} - \sum_{k} \psi_{kj} = 0;$$
$$0 \le \psi_{kj} \le \Delta y_{kj}, \quad \text{all } k; \qquad x_{ij} \ge 0, \quad \text{all } i; \tag{5–16}$$
$$\max Z_j = \sum_{i} (\sigma_i - c_{ij}) x_{ij} - \sum_{k} \alpha_{kj} \psi_{kj}.$$

These problems can also be solved without performing any simplex iterations. In Problem 5–2, we ask the reader to show how to do this.

If the demands at the outlets for the product to be shipped from the various warehouses had been deterministic with the value b_j at outlet j, there would have been no need for any overage or underage costs (if $\sum a_i > \sum b_j$), and the problem would have reduced to a standard transportation problem:

$$\sum_{j=1}^{n} x_{ij} \le a_i, \qquad i = 1, \ldots, m,$$
$$\sum_{i=1}^{m} x_{ij} = b_j, \qquad j = 1, \ldots, n,$$
$$x_{ij} \ge 0, \qquad \text{all } i, j, \tag{5–17}$$
$$\min z = \sum_{i,j} c_{ij} x_{ij}.$$

Treating the demands as random variables had the effect of removing the constraints $\sum_i x_{ij} = b_j$, since the total quantity to be shipped to each outlet also had to be determined, and thus made the problem seem less constrained. However, it only seems to be less constrained, since we could formulate the standard transportation problem in such a way that the quantity to be shipped to each outlet is not specified, but instead there exist overage and underage costs. Indeed this is a generalization of the standard transportation problem, since it has meaning for any $\sum a_i$ (it is not necessary that $\sum a_i \geq \sum b_j$, because the b_j are not specified). When formulated in this manner, there is a complete parallelism between the deterministic and stochastic problems. However, the stochastic problem is more difficult to solve since it is nonlinear, whereas the deterministic problem is linear.

The problem in which the demands are random variables has been interpreted by Beale [2] and by Dantzig [5] as one where some components of the requirements vector are random variables, i.e., the b_j, and thus a problem where there are random variables in the constraints. In other words, the constraints $\sum_i x_{ij} = b_j$ of (5–17) are assumed to hold in the modified form

$$\sum_{i=1}^{m} x_{ij} + \delta_j = v_j, \tag{5–18}$$

where δ_j is an unrestricted random variable defined so that (5–18) holds as a strict equality. In our previous notation, $\delta_j = v_j - y_j$, and when positive represents the underage, and negative the overage, then there is a cost associated with δ_j (the cost being different depending on whether $\delta_j > 0$ or $\delta_j < 0$). Although this interpretation is quite legitimate—it only seems to obscure the basic fact that treating the demands as random variables has the effect of making the total quantity which must be sent to each outlet also a variable to be determined. Furthermore, the constraints in the form (5–18) are never employed directly.

Another problem of some practical interest with a structure quite similar to the one just discussed has been considered by Ferguson and Dantzig [6]. This problem deals with allocating aircraft to routes. A complete and accurate formulation of the problem is quite difficult. However, consider the following simplified formulation: An airline has m different types of aircraft and n routes, and wants to allocate the planes to the routes for some future time period. A total of a_i planes of type i will be available. If a plane of type i is allocated to route j, it can carry a total d_{ij} of passengers during the time period (it is assumed that this includes trips in both directions). It is imagined that the demand will be the same in either direction, and if a passenger gets off at an intermediate stop, someone else takes his place. Unfortunately, the demand v_j on route j cannot be predicted with certainty, but must instead be considered to be a random variable with density $\phi_j(v_j)$. Let y_j be the total number of demands which can be handled on route j if x_{ij} planes of type i are allocated to route j. Thus

$$y_j = \sum_{i=1}^{m} d_{ij}x_{ij}, \qquad j = 1, \ldots, n. \tag{5-19}$$

Then, as above, there will be a goodwill loss π_j for each ticket demanded on route j which cannot be supplied, and in addition a cost k_j (the lost revenue) for each space demanded and not available. It is desired to find those x_{ij} which minimize the expected costs over the period, given that c_{ij} is the cost for the period of operating a plane of type i on route j. Mathematically, the problem reduces to the following nonlinear programming problem:

$$\begin{gathered} \sum_{j=1}^{n} x_{ij} \leq a_i, \qquad i = 1, \ldots, m, \\ \sum_{i=1}^{m} d_{ij}x_{ij} - y_j = 0, \qquad j = 1, \ldots, n, \\ x_{ij} \geq 0, \qquad \text{all } i, j; \qquad y_j \geq 0, \qquad j = 1, \ldots, n, \\ \min z = \sum_{i,j} c_{ij}x_{ij} + \sum_j (k_j + \pi_j) \int_{y_j}^{\infty} (v_j - y_j)\phi_j(v_j)\, dv_j. \end{gathered} \tag{5-20}$$

This problem can be solved in the same way as (5-7).

We shall give one final example of a stochastic programming problem where random variables appear only in the requirements. Food processors typically have to make their entire year's production of certain products during a very short period of time when the vegetables, say, are in season. Suppose that a food processor produces n different products using m resources (tomatoes, beans, etc.). Making one case of product j requires a_{ij} units of resource i. Assume that b_i units of resource i are available. The processor cannot predict precisely what the demand for each product will be. Instead the demand v_j for product j must be treated as a random variable with density $\phi_j(v_j)$. If the demand for product j during the year turns out to be greater than his supply, there is a goodwill loss of π_j for each case demanded which cannot be supplied. On the other hand, if too much of product j is produced, additional storage charges and taxes will be incurred which amount to k_j per case. Let p_j be the selling price per case of product j, and c_j the cost of production. The processor wishes to determine the quantity x_j of each product which he should make in order to maximize his expected profits for the coming year. Assume that before processing new stock he has in inventory y_j cases of product j. It is clear that the problem which must be solved is then

$$\sum_{j=1}^{n} a_{ij}x_j \leq b_i, \qquad i = 1, \ldots, m,$$

$$x_j \geq 0, \qquad j = 1, \ldots, n, \tag{5-21}$$

$$\max z = -\sum_j (k_j + c_j)x_j - \sum_j (p_j + \pi_j + k_j) \int_{y_j+x_j}^{\infty} (v_j - y_j - x_j)\phi_j(v_j)\, dv_j,$$

where the constants $\sum p_j\mu_j$ and $\sum k_j(\mu_j - y_j)$, μ_j being the expected demand for product j, are not included in the profit, since they can be added after the problem is solved. Here we have a nonlinear programming problem with linear constraints and a separable concave objective function. An approximate global optimum can be found by means of the techniques described in Chapter 4.

In this section we have presented several nonsequential stochastic programming problems in which random variables appeared only in the requirements. We have seen that their formulation caused no problems, and if the costs were of a simple form, they yielded problems with separable objective functions having the proper convexity or concavity properties such that the methods of Chapter 4 could be used to yield an approximate global optimum. Each of the problems considered would have been linear if the parameters had been deterministic rather than random variables. Allowing the parameters to become random variables changed the problems to ones with linear constraints but nonlinear objective functions. Hence the introduction of randomness into some of the parameters made it considerably more difficult to determine a set of optimal values of the control variables. If the problems had been nonlinear when all the parameters were treated as deterministic, the task of converting the problem to obtain the expected value of the objective function and account for the costs of overage and underage would have been just as straightforward as in the above cases. However, the possibility of determining a solution to the resulting problem would depend on whether or not the deterministic version could be solved.

5-3 Nonsequential stochastic programming problems with random variables appearing in the technological coefficients. We would now like to consider a class of stochastic programming problems which is different from those considered above. To illustrate how such problems can arise, let us consider a small shop which has a number of highly skilled employees who specialize in making small precision parts by hand. The shop's business consists principally of special-order jobs, and the majority of orders are defense department contracts. For the coming month, the shop is given the opportunity to produce as much as it wishes of each of n precision parts. The total quantity of each of the n parts to be procured by the military is quite large, and orders are placed with a number of contractors, since a single contractor could not possibly produce the entire order for any part in the time available. However, the procedure is that the shop must decide ahead of time how much it wants to produce of each of the parts and then guarantee to deliver the stated quantities at the end of the month. Factors which limit the number of each type of part which can be produced are: (1) workers' time available and (2) availability of raw materials. We shall assume that the craftsmen can be subdivided into groups, according to the type of part they can make. All members of a group do the same type of work. In general, several different parts can be made by the workers in a given group, but a given part can be made only by the workers in a single group.

Consider first the standard linear programming approach to the problem just considered. Let a_{ij} be the units of resource i required to make one part of type j, where i may refer to the time required by a worker or to the quantity of some raw material. Let b_i be the quantity of resource i available for the coming month. Denote by p_j the return per unit of part j after deducting the cost of raw materials. It will be assumed that workers' salaries, overhead, etc., are independent of the decisions to be made and hence need not be included. Let x_j be the number of units of part j that the shop will guarantee to deliver. Then an optimal set of x_j is found by solving the linear programming problem

$$\begin{aligned} \sum_{j=1}^{n} a_{ij}x_j \le b_i, &\qquad i = 1, \ldots, m, \\ x_j \ge 0, &\qquad j = 1, \ldots, n, \\ \max z = \sum_j p_j x_j. & \end{aligned} \tag{5–22}$$

In the real world, the time required by a workman to turn out a part of type j will vary somewhat from man to man, and from piece to piece for a given workman. It is therefore more realistic to treat this time as a random variable. Similarly, the quantity of a given raw material required to make a part of type j may not be absolutely constant, but may fluctuate from one piece to another. Thus this raw material usage per piece may also be more adequately described as a random variable. What we are saying is that the technological coefficients a_{ij} are really random variables. For many practical problems, the variance of these random variables is so small that for all practical purposes, they can be treated as deterministic. However, let us imagine that for the situation being studied, the effects due to randomness are considered to be important enough that they should be accounted for. When the a_{ij} are random variables, then for any given set of x_j, it may turn out that the total amount of resource i required is greater than b_i. For example, the workers may not be able to finish all the work scheduled in the time allowed.

In order to proceed, we must say what happens if the set of x_j scheduled requires more of resource i than is available. It might turn out that the parts are not finished on schedule, and the shop must get an extension of time which will involve a loss of goodwill. On the other hand, it may be possible to work overtime to meet the deadline. If more of some raw material is required than is available, it may be necessary to place an order to obtain some more, or again get an extension. In any event, there will be some cost associated with these emergency actions. We shall suppose here that if the actual amount of resource i exceeds by w_i the amount originally planned to be available for use, then a cost $\pi_i w_i$ is incurred.

Suppose that we wish to determine a set of x_j which maximize $\sum p_j x_j$ minus the expected shortage costs. Imagine now that for any set of the random variables a_{ij}, we define the random variables y_i by

$$y_i = \sum_{j=1}^{n} a_{ij}x_j, \qquad i = 1, \ldots, m. \tag{5–23}$$

Let us suppose that we know the density functions $\phi_{ij}(a_{ij})$ for the a_{ij}. Denote by μ_{ij} and σ_{ij}^2 the mean and variance of ϕ_{ij}. We would like to determine the density function for y_i. Before considering this, we must ask what can be said about the random variable $y_{ij} = a_{ij}x_j$. As written, $a_{ij}x_j$ no longer means x_j times a_{ij}, but rather the amount of resource i needed to make x_j units of part j. If we assume (and this would, in general, appear to be a good assumption) that the random variables denoting the amount of resource i to produce one unit of part j are independent for a given j, as well as for different j, so that, for example, the time required to turn out the piece currently in production will have no influence on how long it will take to make the next, then $\phi_{ij}^{(x_j)}(y_{ij})$, the density function for y_{ij}, is the x_j-fold convolution of $\phi_{ij}(a_{ij})$, and the mean $\hat{\mu}_{ij}$ of y_{ij} is $\hat{\mu}_{ij} = x_j\mu_{ij}$, whereas the variance $\hat{\sigma}_{ij}^2$ of y_{ij} is $\hat{\sigma}_{ij}^2 = x_j\sigma_{ij}^2$. Since the y_{ij} are assumed to be independent for different j, then y_i is the sum of n independent random variables. The density function $\phi_i(y_i)$ must be obtained as the convolution of the $\phi_{ij}^{(x_j)}(y_{ij})$ for fixed i. The expected value μ_i and variance σ_i^2 of y_i are then

$$\mu_i = \sum_j \mu_{ij}x_j; \qquad \sigma_i^2 = \sum_j \sigma_{ij}^2 x_j. \tag{5–24}$$

Whether or not it is an easy task to compute the $\phi_i(y_i)$ depends on the densities $\phi_{ij}(a_{ij})$.

Once the density functions $\phi_i(y_i)$ have been determined, the problem reduces to that of maximizing

$$z = \sum_j p_j x_j - \sum_i \pi_i \int_{b_i}^{\infty} (y_i - b_i)\phi_i(y_i)\, dy_i \tag{5-25}$$

subject only to the non-negativity restrictions $x_j \geq 0$. There are no longer any constraints (provided that all a_{ij} are treated as random variables). They have been digested into the cost terms involving the y_i. It should be noted that the x_j appear in the $\phi_i(y_i)$, since by (5–24) the mean and variance of $\phi_i(y_i)$ depend on the x_j. This makes it extremely difficult, in general, to maximize (5–25) subject to $x_j \geq 0$. The function z is not necessarily a concave function of the x_j, and it is not necessarily separable either. Given the current state of nonlinear programming there does not seem to be any general method for obtaining the global maximum of (5–25), although sometimes a local maximum can be found.

To clarify the above discussion a little it may be helpful to consider a specific example. Imagine that there are only two constraints. The first, $\sum a_{1j}x_j \leq b_1$ represents a raw-material availability constraint. We shall assume that the quantity of raw material needed to produce one unit of j is deterministic, so that the a_{1j} will not be treated as random variables. The raw-material constraint will then remain a constraint. The second constraint deals with worker time available. Assume that b_2 is the amount of time available under normal conditions. The time a_{2j} required by a worker to make one unit of part j will be assumed to be normally distributed with mean μ_{2j} and variance σ_{2j}^2. Then y_{2j} is the sum of x_j normally distributed random variables and hence is normally distributed with mean $\mu_{2j}x_j$ and variance $\sigma_{2j}^2 x_j$. Thus $y = \sum y_{2j}$ is also normally distributed with mean μ and variance σ^2, where

$$\mu = \sum_j \mu_{2j}x_j; \qquad \sigma^2 = \sum_j \sigma_{2j}^2 x_j. \tag{5-26}$$

Consequently, to determine an optimal set of x_j, one must solve the problem

$$\sum_j a_{1j}x_j \leq b_1,$$

$$x_j \geq 0, \qquad j = 1, \ldots, n, \tag{5-27}$$

$$\max z = \sum_j p_j x_j - \pi \int_{b_2}^{\infty} (y - b_2) n\left(y; \sum_j \mu_{2j}x_j, \sqrt{\sum_j \sigma_{2j}^2 x_j}\right) dy,$$

where $n(y; \mu, \sigma)$ is the normal density function with mean μ and standard deviation σ. There seems to be no straightforward method of determining the global optimum of z. However, Problem 5–10 asks the reader to show that it is possible to obtain a local optimum for this problem. Because of the central limit theorem, if the y_i can be looked on as the sum of a rather large number of random variables, then y_i will be approximately normally distributed, even if the $\phi_{ij}(a_{ij})$ are not.

In this section we have shown by our example how problems may arise in which some of the technological coefficients must be treated as random variables. We have seen that if the technological coefficients in what would be a constraint i in the deterministic case must be treated as random variables, then this constraint disappears, and the relationship between the x_j and the amount of resource i used is then employed as a means of determining the density function for y_i, the random variable representing the quantity of resource i used, from the density functions for the technological coefficients. In computing the expected cost incurred if more than the available resources are needed, we must then use the random variable y_i in the objective function. Thus, as in the previous section, it seems, at first glance, that making some of the parameters random variables makes the problem less constrained. This is true in a sense. However, one could, in the deterministic case, formulate a completely parallel problem in which there were no direct constraints, but only costs for using more than the available quantities of the resources. This problem can be formulated as a linear programming problem, but in doing so, it is convenient to introduce constraints to define new variables y_i representing the quantity of resource i used. We ask the reader to provide this formulation in Problem 5–3. When some of the technological coefficients are made random variables, the problem becomes nonlinear and assumes a form for which, at present, there do not exist any general techniques for finding an optimal solution.

5–4 Sequential decision stochastic programming problems. From a practical point of view, sequential stochastic programming problems are probably the most interesting ones. As we shall see, they also tend to be exceedingly difficult to solve. To illustrate what we mean by a *sequential decision stochastic programming problem,* consider the following type of inventory problem. Plans are being made to control the inventory of some single item over the coming n periods of time. Orders to replenish the inventory can be placed only at the beginning of each period. It is unnecessary, however, to place an order at the beginning of a period unless it is desirable to do so. For simplicity, it will be imagined that an order placed at the beginning of a period will arrive before the end of that period. The demand v_j for the product in period j will be treated as a continuous random variable with density function $\phi_j(v_j)$. The demands in different periods will be assumed to be independent random variables. However, the density function for the demand can change from one period to the next. This means, in particular, that the expected demand for a period can change from one period to the next. Any demands that may occur when the system is out of stock are back-ordered, and are filled when the next order arrives before that order is used to meet any other demands. The cost of procuring x_j units at the beginning of period j will be assumed to have the form

$$A_j\delta_j + C_jx_j, \qquad \text{where} \qquad \delta_j = \begin{cases} 0 & \text{if} \quad x_j = 0, \\ 1 & \text{if} \quad x_j > 0, \end{cases}$$

so that there is a fixed charge plus a term linear in the number of units ordered. There will, in addition, be costs of carrying inventory and stockout costs if demands occur when the system is out of stock. To eliminate the work involved in making an accurate computation of the carrying cost and stockout costs (as is done in [8], for example), we shall simply assume that the carrying cost for period j is k_jh_j, where $h_j \geq 0$ is the inventory on hand at the *end* of period j, and the stockout cost for period j is π_js_j, where $s_j \geq 0$ is the number of backorders at the end of period j.

Denote by y_1 the inventory on hand at the beginning of period 1. Then the inventory on hand at the end of period j if v_i is the demand and x_i is the quantity ordered in period i, $i \leq j$, is

$$h_j = y_1 + \sum_{i=1}^{j} x_i - \sum_{i=1}^{j} v_i \qquad \text{if} \quad h_j \geq 0, \tag{5-28}$$

and the number of backorders outstanding at the end of period j is

$$s_j = \sum_{i=1}^{j} v_i - \sum_{i=1}^{j} x_i - y_1 \qquad \text{if} \quad s_j > 0. \tag{5-29}$$

Note that if there is a carrying cost in period j, there will be no stockout cost, and vice versa. Let us then define the functions

$$F_j\left(y_1 + \sum_{i=1}^{j} x_i - \sum_{i=1}^{j} v_i\right) = \begin{cases} k_jh_j & \text{if} \quad h_j \geq 0, \\ \pi_j s_j & \text{if} \quad s_j > 0, \end{cases} \tag{5-30}$$

where h_j, s_j are given by (5-28) and (5-29), respectively. For a given set of x_j and a given set of random variables v_j, the cost of operating the inventory system for the n periods is

$$\sum_{j=1}^{n} \alpha_j[A_j\delta_j + C_jx_j] + \sum_{j=1}^{n} \alpha_jF_j\left(y_1 + \sum_{i=1}^{j} x_i - \sum_{i=1}^{j} v_i\right) \cdot \tag{5-31}$$

If the length of the time period for which planning is being done is long enough, then we should use the *discounted* cost rather than the cost. The α_j in (5–31) can then be interpreted as discounting factors. If no discounting is used, each $\alpha_j = 1$. The probability density for getting a specific set of v_j is

$$\prod_{j=1}^{n} \phi_j(v_j) = \phi_1(v_1) \cdots \phi_n(v_n). \tag{5–32}$$

Equation (5–32) follows since the demands in different periods were assumed to be independent random variables. For any given set of $x_j \geq 0$, the expected cost over the n periods is found by averaging over all possible values of $v_1, \ldots, v_n$ so that this (discounted) expected cost is

$$z = \int_0^\infty \cdots \int_0^\infty \left[\prod_{j=1}^{n} \phi_j(v_j)\right]\left\{\sum_{j=1}^{n} \alpha_j[A_j\delta_j + C_jx_j] + \sum_{j=1}^{n} \alpha_j F_j\left(y_1 + \sum_{i=1}^{j} x_i - \sum_{i=1}^{j} v_i\right)\right\} dv_1 \cdots dv_n. \tag{5–33}$$

In (5–33) we have the expected cost of operating the inventory system for n periods for any set of $x_j \geq 0$. We would like to find a set of x_j which minimizes the z of (5–33). It is at this point that we come to the crucial distinction between sequential decision problems and nonsequential problems. We are tempted to proceed as in the past and attempt to find a set of n numbers $x_j \geq 0$ which minimize z. We could indeed proceed in this manner. However, consider the actual physical nature of the problem. In practice, the decision on how much to order at the beginning of period 2 would not be made until the beginning of period 2, when it is known what the state of the system is at the beginning of period 2 (or at least more is known about the state of the system than was known at the beginning of period 1). To be specific, let us assume that at the beginning of period k, the decision maker knows what was ordered and what the actual demands were in periods 1 through $k - 1$. Clearly, a knowledge of the values assumed by the random variables v_j in periods 1 through k should have an influence on the decision maker's choice of x_k. Let us examine how this information will be useful. From (5–33) we see that the cost incurred in period k depends only on

$$y_k + x_k - v_k,$$

where

$$y_k = y_1 + \sum_{i=1}^{k-1} x_i - \sum_{i=1}^{k-1} v_i, \tag{5–34}$$

and y_k is known at the beginning of period k before x_k is decided on. The only randomness that will influence the cost in period k is due to v_k. Thus the value of all previous information, that is, $x_1, \ldots, x_{k-1}, v_1, \ldots, v_{k-1}$, can be summed up in the variable y_k. The variable y_k, called the net inventory, is the inventory on hand at the beginning of period k if $y_k \geq 0$ and is the negative of the backorders outstanding at the beginning of period k if $y_k < 0$.

Clearly, at the beginning of period k, when the decision is made on how much to order for period k, the optimal value of x_k will depend on y_k. If y_k is large so that there is a considerable amount of inventory on hand, it will be desirable to make x_k small, but if y_k is negative, it may be desirable to make x_k quite large. Therefore the optimal value of x_k is not a single number, but is a complete function $x_k^*(y_k)$ which gives the optimal order quantity once y_k is known.

Here we have come upon the feature which distinguishes sequential stochastic programming problems from the nonsequential variety. In sequential problems, at least one decision k will not be made until one or more of the random parameters of the system have actually been observed. To make the best possible decision, one must, when making decision k, use the observed values of the random parameters. This means that x_k^* will not be simply a number, but rather a function of one or more variables which are related to the random variables observed before decision k is made. None of the procedures we have discussed thus far would be capable of solving directly sequential decision problems, since they can provide no more than a set of numbers for the control variables. They are totally incapable of providing a set of functions such as $x_k^*(y_k)$ needed in the above example. Thus the task of solving sequential decision stochastic programming problems is normally of an order of difficulty completely different from that encountered in solving nonsequential stochastic programming problems. Interestingly enough, it will be shown in Chapter 11 that the inventory problem considered in this section can be formulated as a linear programming problem, provided that all the variables are treated as discrete. However, this does not, in general, lead to an efficient computational procedure, since the linear programming problem may easily have 1000 or more constraints.

We shall see in Chapter 10 that the inventory problem we have been studying can be solved by dynamic programming, and it will indeed be possible to compute the functions $x_k^*(y_k)$. However, the inventory example is only an exceptionally simple illustration of a sequential decision stochastic programming problem. It is by no means true that dynamic programming can be used to solve more complicated types of such problems. It is only for very special classes that this technique will yield a solution. We shall illustrate below the nature of more complicated types of sequential decision stochastic programming problems. Charnes and Cooper [3] have discussed what is essentially a special case of the inventory problem formulated above. They seemed to have overlooked the fact that the problem can be solved in a straightforward way by use of dynamic programming. Instead they proposed (but not in any detail) a very complicated approximate method of solving the problem which first involved the solution of a mixed integer-continuous variable linear programming problem followed by the solution of a classical optimization problem.

In solving sequential decision stochastic programming problems, one is normally interested only in the optimal initial decision. When it is time to make the second decision, things may have changed enough that it is desirable to revise the data used in the problem and solve it all over again. This will be done each time a decision is made. Thus in the inventory problem formulated above, only x_1^* would be of interest at the time the problem is solved. Note that the optimal value of the variable x_1^* is simply a number, not a function, since at the time x_1 is chosen, none of the random variables have been observed and therefore x_1^* is not a function of them. However, to compute x_1^*, one must usually determine the functions $x_j^*(y_j), j \geq 2$, so that the mere fact that these functions are not of interest does not remove the necessity of computing them.

In the above we have really considered two possible ways of determining a set of control variables x_j. The first was to assume that all x_j were to be determined without making use of any of the information available on the state of the system at the time when the decision was to be made, i.e., without using the observed values of the v_j. Thus one would simply determine a set of numbers which minimized (5–33). With this policy, $x_j^*, j \geq 2$, would be independent of y_j, the inventory on hand. We noted that it would be foolish to use this policy in practice, because one can make a better decision by noting the value of y_j before deciding how much to order. In other words, by allowing the $x_j^*, j \geq 2$, to be functions of y_j, we are able to reduce the expected cost (5–33) below that attainable in the case where the x_j are independent of the y_j. In the second case considered, all available information was used, i.e., it was assumed that y_j was known at the time the decision was made. In the real world, the latter situation might exist, but under other conditions, we might encounter a situation which lies between the two extremes discussed above. For example, the decision maker might not know y_j at the time x_j is being selected, but he might know $y_{j-1} + x_{j-1}$. This may happen because of a time lag in reporting the demand v_{j-1} for the previous period. One can solve the problem, allowing x_j to be a function of $y_{j-1} + x_{j-1}$, rather than y_j, although the task of solving it becomes a little more complicated. The above discussion serves to point out, however, that one can obtain different (and possibly widely different) solutions and optimal expected costs for a sequential decision problem depending on what information is assumed to be available to the decision maker at the time the decision is made. In order that the results obtained fit the practical situation under consideration, it is necessary to solve the problem allowing the x_j to be a function of precisely the information that is available to the decision maker when he makes decision j—and not to assume that he knows more or less than he really does.

In the above formulation of the inventory control problem, we assumed that the demands in different periods were independent random variables. This may not be true in practice. Instead, these demands may be correlated in some way, so that if the demand is high in one period, it may, for example, tend to be high in the next. In other words, the density function for the demand in different periods that should be used is a conditional density function $\phi_j(v_j|v_1, \ldots, v_{j-1})$ for the demand v_j, given the demands in the first $j - 1$ periods (or for whatever periods the decision maker knows what the demands have been). The introduction of these conditional densities can considerably complicate the solution of the problem.

In the inventory example which we have been considering, it is sometimes difficult to specify a numerical value for the stockout cost, or more generally, the precise nature of the stockout cost as a function of the number of backorders. To avoid the determination of a stockout cost, one might specify that the probability of running out of stock in period j be less than, or equal to, some specified number β_j, that is,

$$\int_{x_j+y_j}^{\infty} \phi_j(v_j)\, dv_j \leq \beta_j, \qquad j = 1, \ldots, n. \tag{5–35}$$

In this particular case, the nature of the density function $\phi_j(v_j)$ determines a number γ_j such that if $\rho_j \geq \gamma_j$, then

$$\int_{\rho_j}^{\infty} \phi_j(v_j)\, dv_j \leq \beta_j,$$

so that the constraints (5–35) are equivalent to

$$x_j + y_j \geq \gamma_j, \qquad j = 1, \ldots, n. \tag{5–36}$$

If we assume that the decision maker knows y_j at the time decision j is made, the problem reduces to minimizing

$$z = \int_0^{\infty} \cdots \int_0^{\infty} \left[\prod_{j=1}^{n} \phi_j(v_j)\right] \left\{\sum_{j=1}^{n} \alpha_j(A_j\delta_j + C_jx_j) + \sum_{j=1}^{n} \alpha_j G_j\left(y_1 + \sum_{i=1}^{j} x_i - \sum_{i=1}^{j} v_i\right)\right\} dv_1 \cdots dv_n \tag{5–37}$$

subject to $x_j \geq 0$ and the constraints (5-36), where

$$G_j\left(y_1 + \sum_{i=1}^{j} x_i - \sum_{i=1}^{j} v_i\right) = \begin{cases} k_j h_j & \text{if} \quad h_j \geq 0, \\ 0 & \text{if} \quad s_j > 0. \end{cases} \tag{5-38}$$

This is also a problem that can be solved in a straightforward way by dynamic programming.

It is generally true that constraints such as (5-35) which require that the probability of some event occurring be less than, or equal to, some number can be removed and included in the objective function by assigning a cost to the occurrence of the event. It is not always true that probability constraints such as (5-35) can be easily reduced to simple constraints such as (5-36), which can be applied directly in solving the problem (as will be seen in Chapter 10). However, it does always seem to be true that the probability constraints can be eliminated and replaced by a suitable cost term in the objective function. As a general rule, it would seem better to add a term to the expected cost, rather than introduce a constraint such as (5-35), which really imputes some minimum cost to the occurrence of the event. This can be determined by solving the problem for different assumed costs, and then finding the smallest cost for which a probability constraint such as (5-35) holds. It is a very good idea to know this imputed cost, because arbitrarily setting the value of β_j in (5-35) may yield a cost which is absurdly low or absurdly high.

In this section we have illustrated by a simple example the nature of sequential decision stochastic programming problems. We have seen that solving such problems is more difficult than solving deterministic or nonsequential stochastic programming problems. The additional difficulties arise because in sequential problems one should consider the fact that the decision maker can use to advantage the knowledge of the values of the random variables which have been observed before the current decision is made. The optimal policies now become functions of the random variables rather than merely numbers. None of the programming techniques thus far discussed is capable of directly generating such functions. We have already noted that the simple problem formulated here can be solved by dynamic programming, which, however, cannot be used to solve all sequential decision stochastic programming problems (as has also been noted). It should be mentioned in passing that there are certain very special classes of sequential decision stochastic programming problems which are relatively easy to solve. Typical of such problems are inventory problems in which the system is imagined to operate for all future time and the distribution of demand does not change with time. Problems of this sort have been discussed in detail by Hadley and Whitin [8]. More will be said about analyzing such problems in Chapters 10 and 11.

In the real world, most problems are sequential decision problems in some sense or other. Frequently, the random elements are important enough that they should also be considered to be stochastic programming problems. It is only with the assumption that future decisions have a negligible effect on the current decision that they can be treated as non-sequential problems.

We shall close this section by discussing in general terms a very complicated version of a sequential decision stochastic programming problem. Consider an integrated oil company with world-wide operations. Each year many investment decisions have to be made. For example, how much should be added to the capacity of existing refineries, should the construction of any new refineries be undertaken, and if so, where and of what size should they be; should construction of additional tanker capacity be initiated, and if so, how much; how much capital should be devoted to increasing crude production and where; how much should be assigned to exploration, to research, to advertising, to developing new markets, etc.? The important characteristic of decisions on large capital expenditures, such as the construction of a refinery, is that they influence the operation of the company for many years in the future. Furthermore, investment decisions must be made within the limits of the funds available, so that if it is company policy not to borrow funds, investments cannot be made faster than the funds are generated internally. There are, of course, various trade-offs in the investment possibilities, since by building a refinery in the Far East, less tanker capacity may be needed, or if more tankers are built, the refinery will not be needed; if a refinery is built in the Far East, it will then be desirable to increase or utilize crude production there, and so on. To make sound decisions today the company might need to use a ten-year or longer planning horizon. To be realistic, the demands for the many products produced and marketed in many areas would have to be treated as random variables whose mean was changing with time. If it is imagined that the investment considerations are made on a yearly basis, the problem becomes a sequential decision stochastic programming problem. Although only decisions pertaining to the current year are of interest, one must consider the long planning horizon and the decisions which can be made in future years. No numerical techniques exist today which could solve a problem of this magnitude. In fact, even if all the parameters were assumed to be deterministic, and enough approximations were made to convert the problem to a linear programming problem, the resulting problem would be much too large to be solved by the means available at present.

In this section, we have not attempted to formulate in any detail a sequential decision problem involving randomness in the technological coefficients. The petroleum company's problem discussed above in general terms might have such features, but we have not indicated how to handle them. The formulation of problems of this sort is much more complicated, and it is usually not possible to solve them numerically. We shall not attempt to study an example of this type of problem in any detail.

5-5 The expected cost of uncertainty. A quantity which is often of interest in dealing with stochastic programming problems (sequential or nonsequential) is what is called the *expected cost of uncertainty.* To provide a definition of this term we must first define what the *expected cost under certainty* is. Let us suppose that the problem to be solved contains a number of parameters which must be treated as random variables. Denote these by $\zeta_1, \ldots, \zeta_t$. Imagine now that we knew ahead of time what values nature was going to assign to these parameters. Then a set of optimal values of the control variables could be found by solving a deterministic programming problem. Denote by $z^*(\zeta_1, \ldots, \zeta_t)$ the optimal value of the objective function for a given set of the random variables. Suppose, however, that we encounter the same problem many times, but the frequency with which any parameter ζ_i lies in some interval is determined by its density function. Although the values of the random variables will change from one time we meet the problem to the next, we shall suppose that we always find out in advance what values the random variables will assume and solve the appropriate deterministic problem. Then, if we average the optimal value of the objective function over a very large number of times in which we encounter the problem, the average value will approach

$$z_c = \int \cdots \int z^*(\zeta_1, \ldots, \zeta_t)\phi(\zeta_1, \ldots, \zeta_t)\, d\zeta_1 \cdots d\zeta_t, \qquad (5\text{-}39)$$

where $\phi(\zeta_1, \ldots, \zeta_t)$ is the joint density function for the t random variables. The number z_c is called the expected cost under certainty. To compute z_c, we determine the optimal value of the objective function for every possible set of the random variables, assuming that the values of the random variables are known before the problem is solved, and then average this over all values of the random variables. The result is (for a problem which minimizes cost) the long-run average minimum cost under certainty.

If z^* is the optimal value of the objective function determined by minimizing the expected cost, then it is clear that $z^* \geq z_c$, since in computing z_c we assumed that the values of the random variables were known before the problem was solved. The number $z^* - z_c$ is called the expected cost of uncertainty. It tells by how much costs could be reduced on the average (in the long run) if all uncertainties in the parameters could be removed, i.e., it is the maximum amount one should be willing to pay for the ability to determine ahead of time the values of the random variables.

If the expected cost of uncertainty is high, it is very worthwhile to try to gain more information on the values which the random variables will take on. If it is small, it will not, on the average, be worthwhile to make a great effort to learn more about these values. In general, it is very difficult to compute z_c, because one must solve a number of deterministic problems, and then compute (5–39). Quite often, it is much easier to compute z^*. However, since both z_c and z^* may be difficult to compute, it is obvious that it will frequently be equally difficult to determine the expected cost of uncertainty.

5–6 Replacement of random parameters by their expected values. A method which has been employed frequently to find approximate solutions to stochastic programming problems is to replace all the random parameters by their expected values and solve the resulting deterministic programming problem. The values of the control variables so obtained are then those used in the real world situation. The expected cost of using the control variables obtained from solving the deterministic problem in the real situation where the parameters are actually random variables can be determined by evaluating the objective function (the expected cost) for these values of the control variables. Denote by z_d the expected cost, using the control variables found in solving the deterministic problem. Then clearly $z^* \leq z_d$, since these variables form a feasible but not necessarily optimal solution to the stochastic programming problem. What we would really like to know is $(z_d - z^*)/z^*$, that is, by what fraction of z^* can the expected costs be reduced when we use the control variables found by solving the stochastic programming problem rather than the deterministic approximation. The answer to this question can vary widely with circumstances, and it depends critically on the costs of errors and the nature of the distributions of the random variables. In some cases, $z_d - z^*$ is very small relative to z^*, and it is quite satisfactory to use the values of the control variables found by solving the deterministic problem. In other situations, $(z_d - z^*)/z^*$ is large, and the same approach gives very poor results. Both cases will be illustrated by very simple examples in the problems. Frequently, however, the physical nature of the problem itself indicates whether or not the control variables obtained by solving the deterministic problem will be accurate enough to use. It is also true that one will often know the direction in which they should be changed to come closer to an optimal solution to the stochastic programming problem.

It will be observed from what has been discussed above that z_c, z_d form bounds on z^*, since $z_c \leq z^* \leq z_d$. In principle, one might attempt to use these bounds by computing z_c and z_d, and if $z_d - z_c$ was small with respect to z_d (or z_c), one could conclude that it would be satisfactory to use the control variables obtained by solving the deterministic problem, but if

$z_d - z_c$ was large compared to z_d, it might be dangerous to do so. However, since z_c is usually quite difficult to compute, one can seldom proceed in this way. In practice, one can make probably as good a decision in many cases simply by qualitatively studying the problem as suggested above.

5–7 Distribution problems. Consider once again a stochastic programming problem with parameters $\zeta_1, \ldots, \zeta_t$ which are to be treated as random variables. If we knew ahead of time what values these random variables would assume, or conversely, if we waited until they had been observed and solved the problem *a posteriori*, we would have a deterministic programming problem to solve. Let $\mathbf{x}^*(\zeta_1, \ldots, \zeta_t)$, $z^*(\zeta_1, \ldots, \zeta_t)$ be an optimal solution and the optimal value of the objective function, respectively, for this deterministic programming problem for a specific set of values of the random variables. Thus $\mathbf{x}^*$ and z^* are functions of the random variables ζ_j, and $x_1^*, \ldots, x_n^*$, z^* can be interpreted as random variables as follows: *a priori*, before the ζ_j are observed, it is known that some $\mathbf{x}^*$, z^* from the above set will be discovered to be optimal *a posteriori*, after the ζ_j have been observed. *A priori* it is not known which $\mathbf{x}^*$, z^* will be optimal, but there is a long-run relative frequency that the x_j^* (and z^*) lie in specified intervals, i.e., there is a probability density function for $\mathbf{x}^*$.

The task of finding the density function for $\mathbf{x}^*$ or z^* described above is called a distribution problem. The computation of these density functions could be exceptionally difficult even if we could provide an explicit expression for $\mathbf{x}^*$, z^* in terms of $\zeta_1, \ldots, \zeta_t$. For most programming problems, this is not possible. Consequently, there do not seem to exist any techniques for computing these distributions, and the problem remains unsolved. From a practical point of view, these distribution problems are not nearly of so much interest as problems which seek to optimize the expected value of the objective function. The reason is, of course, that distribution problems take an *a posteriori* view of the problem and provide no information as to what is the optimal $\mathbf{x}^*$ that one should select before an observation is made.

References

1. Babbar, M. M., "Distributions of Solutions of a Set of Linear Equations (With an Application to Linear Programming)," *Journal of the American Statistical Association*, **50,** 1955, pp. 854–869.

2. Beale, E. M. L., "On Minimizing a Convex Function Subject to Linear Inequalities," *Journal of the Royal Statistical Society* (*B*), **17,** 1955, pp. 173–184.

3. Charnes, A., and W. W. Cooper, "Chance-Constrained Programming," *Management Science*, **6,** 1959, pp. 73–79.

4. Charnes, A., W. W. Cooper, and G. H. Symonds, "Cost Horizons and Certainty Equivalents: An Approach to Stochastic Programming of Heating Oil," *Management Science*, **4,** 1958.

5. Dantzig, G. B., "Linear Programming Under Uncertainty," *Management Science*, **1,** 1955, pp. 197–206.

6. Ferguson, A. R., and G. B. Dantzig, "The Allocation of Aircraft to Routes—An Example of Linear Programming Under Uncertain Demand," *Management Science*, **3,** 1956, pp. 45–73.

7. Freund, R. J., "The Introduction of Risk into a Programming Model," *Econometrica*, **24,** 1956, pp. 253–263.

8. Hadley, G., and T, M. Whitin, *Analysis of Inventory Systems.* Englewood Cliffs, N. J.: Prentice-Hall, 1963.

9. Hanson, M. A., "Errors and Stochastic Variations in Linear Programming," *Australian Journal of Statistics*, **2,** 1960, pp. 41–46.

10. Madansky, A., "Inequalities for Stochastic Linear Programming Problems," *Management Science*, **6,** 1960, pp. 197–204.

11. Manne, A. S., "Linear Programming and Sequential Decisions," *Management Science*, **6,** 1960, pp. 259–267.

12. Tinter, G., "Stochastic Linear Programming with Applications to Agricultural Economics," in *Second Symposium in Linear Programming*, 1955, pp. 197–228.

13. Vajda, S., "Inequalities in Stochastic Linear Programming," *Bulletin of the International Statistical Institute*, **36,** 1958, pp. 357–363.

14. Vajda, S., *Mathematical Programming.* Reading, Mass.: Addison-Wesley, 1961.

15. Wagner, H., "On the Distribution of Solutions in Linear Programming Problems," *Journal of the American Statistical Association*, **53,** 1958, pp. 161–163.

16. Wagner, H., "On the Optimality of Pure Strategies," *Management Science*, **6,** 1960, pp. 268–269.

Problems

5–1. Find an approximate optimal solution to the first example of Section 3–9 by the use of the methods of Chapter 4.

5–2. Show how to solve the problem of Eq. (5–16) without requiring any simplex iterations.

5–3. Formulate the deterministic problem (in which there are no constraints) corresponding to the stochastic one considered in Section 5–3.

5–4. Write out Eq. (5–33) explicitly in the case where there are only two periods.

5–5. A bakery shop must decide how much bread to purchase for a specific day of the week, say Tuesday. Past history for Tuesdays has shown that the demand can be considered to be normally distributed with mean 300 and standard deviation 50. A loaf of bread sells for \$0.25 and costs the store \$0.19. Any bread not sold at the end of the day is placed on a special counter and sold on Wednesday for \$0.15 per loaf. All bread on the counter can be sold at this price. Determine the number of loaves that should be bought so as to maximize the expected profit from the purchase. Determine the expected profit, the expected cost under certainty, the expected cost of uncertainty, and the expected profit if the expected demand is stocked. Use the above to determine z_c, z^*, and z_d discussed in Sections 5–5 and 5–6.

5–6. Re-solve Problem 5–5, making the assumption that the store also attaches a goodwill loss of \$0.50 to every loaf demanded when the store is out of stock.

5–7. Consider a stochastic programming problem in which randomness is present only in the cost functions appearing in the objective function. Show that to obtain the expected value of the objective function, each cost term should be replaced by its expected value. If the objective function is $\sum c_j x_j$, where the c_j are random variables which are independent of the x_j, what is the expected value of the objective function? Suppose that the density function for the c_j depended on the x_j. What would be the form for the expected value of the objective function?

5–8. Show that the problems of Eq. (5–11) can be converted into one of the forms of a capacitated transportation problem by introducing new variables $\Delta_{kj} = -\psi_{kj}$ and additional constraints of the form

$$\sum_j \Delta_{kj} \leq 0.$$

Note, however, that $\Delta_{kj} \leq 0$ and that the Δ_{kj} have lower bounds.

5–9. Consider the following production-scheduling problem. At the beginning of each month a firm schedules how much it will manufacture of the single item which it produces. In month j, it can produce a_j units on regular time, and an additional b_j units on overtime. The production cost of a unit on regular time is c_j and on overtime is d_j. The item can be inventoried, and there is in period j an inventory charge of f_j per unit in stock at the beginning of the period. The demand v_j in period j must be treated as a random variable with density function $\phi_j(v_j)$. All demands that occur when the system is out of stock are backordered. If backorders exist at the end of a month j, a cost π_j is incurred for each backorder. The initial inventory is y_0. Set up the problem of scheduling production over the coming 12 months so as to minimize expected costs. Discuss the problems involved in finding a solution.

5–10. Show that by introducing a sufficient number of new variables, it is possible to cast the problem of Eq. (5–27) into separable form. Note, however, that after doing this it would only be possible to obtain a local maximum. [*Hint:* Remove the variables from the density function by introducing the new random variable $t = (y - \mu)/\sigma$.]

5–11. Prove directly that for z^* and z_c defined in Section 5–5, $z^* - z_c \geq 0$. Do this by showing that both are the integral over all possible values of the random variables of a function times the density function. Subtract the two integrals and note the sign of the integrand.

5–12. Consider a stochastic programming problem in which there is randomness in the requirements and in the technological coefficients. Show how to formulate such problems, and discuss the difficulties involved in solving them. Is the problem made any more difficult if the random variables associated with the technological coefficients are not independent of those associated with the requirements?

CHAPTER 6

KUHN-TUCKER THEORY

To catch Dame Fortune's golden smile,
Assiduous wait upon her;
And gather gear to every wile
That's justified by honor.

Robert Burns, *Epistle to a Young Friend*

6–1 Introduction. In Chapter 3 we noted that the Lagrange multiplier technique could be generalized, at the expense of greatly increased computational effort, to handle problems involving inequality constraints and non-negative variables. This chapter will continue the examination of procedures for generalizing Lagrange multiplier techniques to inequality constraints and non-negative variables. The emphasis will not be on computational methods, but rather on generalizations of the theory. The impetus for these generalizations is contained in the material presented in Section 3–8, where we observed that under certain conditions, a point at which $f(\mathbf{x})$ takes on a relative maximum for points satisfying $g_i(\mathbf{x}) = b_i$, $i = 1, \ldots, m$, is a saddle point of the Lagrangian function $F(\mathbf{x}, \boldsymbol{\lambda})$. The material to be presented was originally developed by H. Kuhn and A. W. Tucker [7]. Although the theory to be discussed is not directly concerned with computational techniques, it has been of fundamental importance in developing a numerical procedure for solving quadratic programming problems, as we shall see in the next chapter.

6–2 Necessary and sufficient conditions for saddle points. Recall from Section 3–8 that a function $F(\mathbf{x}, \boldsymbol{\lambda})$, $\mathbf{x}$ being an n-component and $\boldsymbol{\lambda}$ an m-component vector, is said to have a saddle point at $[\mathbf{x}_0, \boldsymbol{\lambda}_0]$ if

$$F(\mathbf{x}, \boldsymbol{\lambda}_0) \le F(\mathbf{x}_0, \boldsymbol{\lambda}_0) \le F(\mathbf{x}_0, \boldsymbol{\lambda}) \tag{6–1}$$

holds for all $\mathbf{x}$ in an ϵ-neighborhood of $\mathbf{x}_0$, and all $\boldsymbol{\lambda}$ in an ϵ-neighborhood of $\boldsymbol{\lambda}_0$. If (6–1) holds for all $\mathbf{x}$ and $\boldsymbol{\lambda}$, then $F(\mathbf{x}, \boldsymbol{\lambda})$ is said to have a saddle point in the large or a global saddle point at $[\mathbf{x}_0, \boldsymbol{\lambda}_0]$.

In this chapter, we shall find it convenient to specialize the definition of a saddle point to cases where certain components of $\mathbf{x}$ and $\boldsymbol{\lambda}$ are restricted to be non-negative, others are to be nonpositive, and a third category is to be unrestricted in sign. Write $\mathbf{x} = [\mathbf{x}^{(1)}, \mathbf{x}^{(2)}, \mathbf{x}^{(3)}]$ and $\boldsymbol{\lambda} = [\boldsymbol{\lambda}^{(1)}, \boldsymbol{\lambda}^{(2)}, \boldsymbol{\lambda}^{(3)}]$. Assume that $\mathbf{x}^{(1)}$ has s components, $\mathbf{x}^{(2)}$ has $t - s$ components and $\mathbf{x}^{(3)}$ has $n - t$ components. Also assume that $\boldsymbol{\lambda}^{(1)}$ has u components, $\boldsymbol{\lambda}^{(2)}$ has $v - u$ components, and $\boldsymbol{\lambda}^{(3)}$ has $m - v$ components. Suppose we require that $\mathbf{x}^{(1)} \geq \mathbf{0}$, $\boldsymbol{\lambda}^{(1)} \geq \mathbf{0}$, and $\mathbf{x}^{(2)} \leq \mathbf{0}$, $\boldsymbol{\lambda}^{(2)} \leq \mathbf{0}$, while $\mathbf{x}^{(3)}$, $\boldsymbol{\lambda}^{(3)}$ are unrestricted in sign. Denote by W_1 the set of points $\mathbf{x}$ such that the components of $\mathbf{x}$ satisfy the above conditions, by W_2 the set of points $\boldsymbol{\lambda}$ such that the components of $\boldsymbol{\lambda}$ satisfy the above conditions, and by W the set of points $[\mathbf{x}, \boldsymbol{\lambda}]$ with $\mathbf{x} \in W_1$ and $\boldsymbol{\lambda} \in W_2$. The function $F(\mathbf{x}, \boldsymbol{\lambda})$ is then said to have a saddle point at $[\mathbf{x}_0, \boldsymbol{\lambda}_0]$ for $[\mathbf{x}, \boldsymbol{\lambda}] \in W$ if $[\mathbf{x}_0, \boldsymbol{\lambda}_0] \in W$, and there exists an $\epsilon > 0$ such that (6–1) holds for all $\mathbf{x} \in W_1$ in an ϵ-neighborhood of $\mathbf{x}_0$ and all $\boldsymbol{\lambda} \in W_2$ in an ϵ-neighborhood of $\boldsymbol{\lambda}_0$.

Suppose now that $F \in C^1$. If $F(\mathbf{x}, \boldsymbol{\lambda})$ has a saddle point at $[\mathbf{x}_0, \boldsymbol{\lambda}_0]$ for $[\mathbf{x}, \boldsymbol{\lambda}] \in W$, then from the definition of a saddle point and the material of Section 3–2, $[\mathbf{x}_0, \boldsymbol{\lambda}_0]$ must satisfy the equations

$$\begin{aligned} \frac{\partial}{\partial x_j} F(\mathbf{x}_0, \boldsymbol{\lambda}_0) &= 0, \quad j = t+1, \ldots, n; \\ \frac{\partial}{\partial \lambda_i} F(\mathbf{x}_0, \boldsymbol{\lambda}_0) &= 0, \quad i = v+1, \ldots, m, \end{aligned} \tag{6–2}$$

since components $t + 1, \ldots, n$ of $\mathbf{x}$ and components $v + 1, \ldots, m$ of $\boldsymbol{\lambda}$ are unrestricted in sign. In other words, if we plot F as a function of x_k when k has one of the values $t + 1, \ldots, n$, and set $x_j = x_j^0$, $j \neq k$, $\boldsymbol{\lambda} = \boldsymbol{\lambda}_0$, then in a neighborhood of x_k^0, F must have a shape something like that shown in Fig. 6–1. Under similar conditions, F as a function of λ_r, where r has one of the values $v + 1, \ldots, m$, would pass through a relative minimum. Note also that if $x_k^0 \neq 0$ for one of the first t components of $\mathbf{x}$, it must again be true that

$$\partial F(\mathbf{x}_0, \boldsymbol{\lambda}_0)/\partial x_k = 0,$$

and also if $\lambda_r^0 \neq 0$ for one of the first v components of $\boldsymbol{\lambda}$, it must be true that

$$\partial F(\mathbf{x}_0, \boldsymbol{\lambda}_0)/\partial \lambda_r = 0.$$

Let us now assume that $x_k^0 = 0$, where k has one of the values $1, \ldots, t$, and let us determine what can be said about $\partial F(\mathbf{x}_0, \boldsymbol{\lambda}_0)/\partial x_k$ in this case. Imagine first that k comes from the set $1, \ldots, s$, so that x_k must be nonnegative. Then, in order that $F(\mathbf{x}, \boldsymbol{\lambda}_0) \leq F(\mathbf{x}_0, \boldsymbol{\lambda}_0)$ for $[\mathbf{x}, \boldsymbol{\lambda}_0] \in W$, it must be true that

$$\frac{\partial}{\partial x_k} F(\mathbf{x}_0, \boldsymbol{\lambda}_0) \leq 0. \tag{6–3}$$

To prove this, assume on the contrary that $\partial F/\partial x_k > 0$ at $[\mathbf{x}_0, \boldsymbol{\lambda}_0]$. Since $\partial F/\partial x_k$ is continuous, we know by the theorem proved in Section 2–8 that

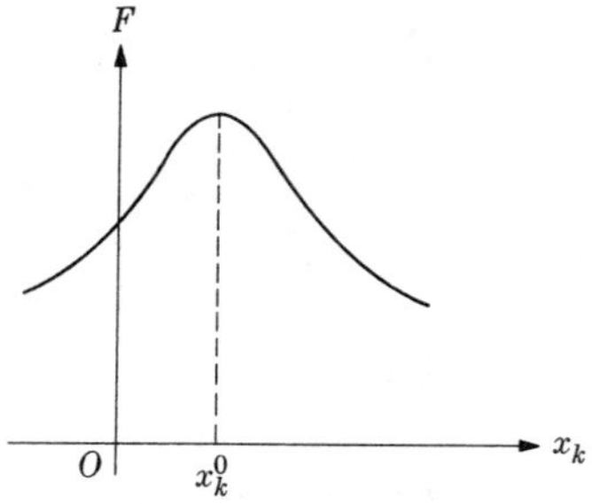

FIGURE 6-1

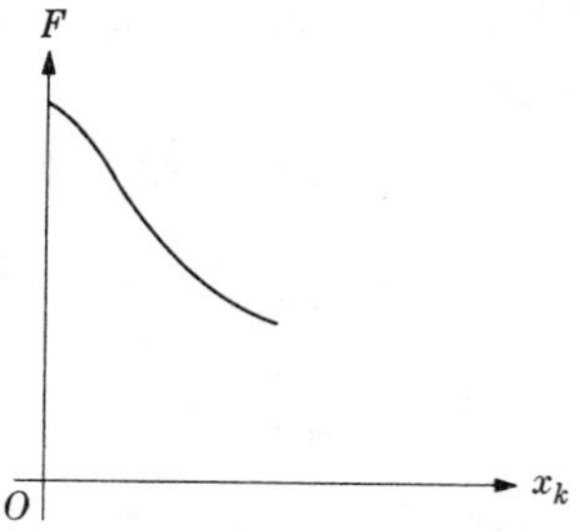

FIGURE 6-2

there exists an $\epsilon_0 > 0$ such that for all points $[\mathbf{x}, \boldsymbol{\lambda}]$ in this ϵ_0-neighborhood of $[\mathbf{x}_0, \boldsymbol{\lambda}_0]$, $\partial F/\partial x_k > 0$. Select any ϵ, $0 < \epsilon < \epsilon_0$, and consider points in an ϵ-neighborhood of $[\mathbf{x}_0, \boldsymbol{\lambda}_0]$ of the form $[\mathbf{x}_0 + h\mathbf{e}_k, \boldsymbol{\lambda}_0]$, $h > 0$. By Taylor's theorem for a single variable,

$$F(\mathbf{x}_0 + h\mathbf{e}_k, \boldsymbol{\lambda}_0) = F(\mathbf{x}_0, \boldsymbol{\lambda}_0) + h \frac{\partial}{\partial x_k} F(\mathbf{x}_0 + \theta h\mathbf{e}_k, \boldsymbol{\lambda}_0), \qquad 0 \leq \theta \leq 1.$$

But $[\mathbf{x}_0 + \theta h\mathbf{e}_k, \boldsymbol{\lambda}_0]$ is in the ϵ-neighborhood, and hence

$$\frac{\partial}{\partial x_k} F(\mathbf{x}_0 + \theta h\mathbf{e}_k, \boldsymbol{\lambda}_0) > 0;$$

so

$$F(\mathbf{x}_0 + h\mathbf{e}_k, \boldsymbol{\lambda}_0) > F(\mathbf{x}_0, \boldsymbol{\lambda}_0), \qquad \text{all } h, \qquad 0 < h < \epsilon. \tag{6-4}$$

Therefore, every ϵ-neighborhood of $[\mathbf{x}_0, \boldsymbol{\lambda}_0]$ contains points $[\mathbf{x}, \boldsymbol{\lambda}_0] \in W$ for which (6-4) holds. This contradicts the fact that $F(\mathbf{x}, \boldsymbol{\lambda})$ has a saddle point at $[\mathbf{x}_0, \boldsymbol{\lambda}_0]$ for $[\mathbf{x}, \boldsymbol{\lambda}] \in W$. Thus we conclude that (6-3) must hold. In other words, if we plot F as a function of x_k when setting $x_j = x_j^0$, $j \neq k$, $\boldsymbol{\lambda} = \boldsymbol{\lambda}_0$, we must obtain something like the curve shown in Fig. 6-2. A precisely similar argument shows that if k belongs to the set $s + 1, \ldots, t$ and $x_k^0 = 0$, then $\partial F(\mathbf{x}_0, \boldsymbol{\lambda}_0)/\partial x_k \geq 0$. Similarly, if $\lambda_r^0 = 0$, it must be true that

$$\begin{aligned} \frac{\partial F(\mathbf{x}_0, \boldsymbol{\lambda}_0)}{\partial \lambda_r} &\geq 0, \qquad r = 1, \ldots, u; \\ \frac{\partial F(\mathbf{x}_0, \boldsymbol{\lambda}_0)}{\partial \lambda_r} &\leq 0, \qquad r = u + 1, \ldots, v. \end{aligned} \tag{6-5}$$

Note that in the above discussion we have shown that it must be true that either $\partial F(\mathbf{x}_0, \boldsymbol{\lambda}_0)/\partial x_j = 0$ or $x_j^0 = 0$, and either $\partial F(\mathbf{x}_0, \boldsymbol{\lambda}_0)/\partial \lambda_i = 0$ or $\lambda_i^0 = 0$. Hence, if $F(\mathbf{x}, \boldsymbol{\lambda})$ has a saddle point at $[\mathbf{x}_0, \boldsymbol{\lambda}_0]$ for $[\mathbf{x}, \boldsymbol{\lambda}] \in W$, and if $F \in C^1$, then $[\mathbf{x}_0, \boldsymbol{\lambda}_0]$ must satisfy

$$\begin{aligned} &\frac{\partial}{\partial x_j} F(\mathbf{x}_0, \boldsymbol{\lambda}_0) \leq 0, \qquad j = 1, \ldots, s; \\ &\frac{\partial}{\partial x_j} F(\mathbf{x}_0, \boldsymbol{\lambda}_0) \geq 0, \qquad j = s+1, \ldots, t; \\ &\frac{\partial}{\partial x_j} F(\mathbf{x}_0, \boldsymbol{\lambda}_0) = 0, \qquad j = t+1, \ldots, n; \end{aligned} \tag{6-6}$$

$$\begin{aligned} &x_j^0 \geq 0, \quad j = 1, \ldots, s; \qquad x_j^0 \leq 0, \quad j = s+1, \ldots, t; \\ &x_j^0 \text{ unrestricted}, \qquad j = t+1, \ldots, n; \end{aligned} \tag{6-7}$$

$$x_j^0 \frac{\partial}{\partial x_j} F(\mathbf{x}_0, \boldsymbol{\lambda}_0) = 0, \qquad j = 1, \ldots, n; \tag{6-8}$$

$$\begin{aligned} &\frac{\partial}{\partial \lambda_i} F(\mathbf{x}_0, \boldsymbol{\lambda}_0) \geq 0, \qquad i = 1, \ldots, u; \\ &\frac{\partial}{\partial \lambda_i} F(\mathbf{x}_0, \boldsymbol{\lambda}_0) \leq 0, \qquad i = u+1, \ldots, v; \\ &\frac{\partial}{\partial \lambda_i} F(\mathbf{x}_0, \boldsymbol{\lambda}_0) = 0, \qquad i = v+1, \ldots, m; \end{aligned} \tag{6-9}$$

$$\begin{aligned} &\lambda_i^0 \geq 0, \quad i = 1, \ldots, u; \qquad \lambda_i^0 \leq 0, \quad i = u+1, \ldots, v; \\ &\lambda_i^0 \text{ unrestricted}, \qquad i = v+1, \ldots, m; \end{aligned} \tag{6-10}$$

$$\lambda_i^0 \frac{\partial}{\partial \lambda_i} F(\mathbf{x}_0, \boldsymbol{\lambda}_0) = 0, \qquad i = 1, \ldots, m. \tag{6-11}$$

Equations (6–6) *through* (6–11) *represent a set of necessary conditions which* $[\mathbf{x}_0, \boldsymbol{\lambda}_0]$ *must satisfy if* $F(\mathbf{x}, \boldsymbol{\lambda})$ *has a saddle point at* $[\mathbf{x}_0, \boldsymbol{\lambda}_0]$ *for* $[\mathbf{x}, \boldsymbol{\lambda}] \in W$, *provided that* $F \in C^1$.

Let us define the gradient of $F(\mathbf{x}, \boldsymbol{\lambda})$ with respect to $\mathbf{x}$ evaluated at $[\mathbf{x}_0, \boldsymbol{\lambda}_0]$ to be

$$\nabla_{\mathbf{x}} F(\mathbf{x}_0, \boldsymbol{\lambda}_0) = \left(\frac{\partial}{\partial x_1} F(\mathbf{x}_0, \boldsymbol{\lambda}_0), \ldots, \frac{\partial}{\partial x_n} F(\mathbf{x}_0, \boldsymbol{\lambda}_0)\right), \tag{6-12}$$

and the gradient of $F(\mathbf{x}, \boldsymbol{\lambda})$ with respect to $\boldsymbol{\lambda}$ evaluated at $[\mathbf{x}_0, \boldsymbol{\lambda}_0]$ to be

$$\nabla_{\boldsymbol{\lambda}} F(\mathbf{x}_0, \boldsymbol{\lambda}_0) = \left(\frac{\partial}{\partial \lambda_1} F(\mathbf{x}_0, \boldsymbol{\lambda}_0), \ldots, \frac{\partial}{\partial \lambda_m} F(\mathbf{x}_0, \boldsymbol{\lambda}_0)\right) \cdot \tag{6-13}$$

Then on summing (6–8) over j and (6–11) over i, we obtain

$$\nabla_{\mathbf{x}} F(\mathbf{x}_0, \boldsymbol{\lambda}_0)\mathbf{x}_0 = 0; \quad \nabla_{\boldsymbol{\lambda}} F(\mathbf{x}_0, \boldsymbol{\lambda}_0)\boldsymbol{\lambda}_0 = 0. \tag{6-14}$$

It is also possible to supply a set of sufficient conditions which, if satisfied, guarantee that $F(\mathbf{x}, \boldsymbol{\lambda})$ has a saddle point for $[\mathbf{x}, \boldsymbol{\lambda}] \in W$ at a point $[\mathbf{x}_0, \boldsymbol{\lambda}_0]$ satisfying (6–6) through (6–11). These conditions can be stated as follows. *Let* $[\mathbf{x}_0, \boldsymbol{\lambda}_0]$ *be a point satisfying* (6–6) *through* (6–11). *Then if there exists an* ϵ*-neighborhood about* $[\mathbf{x}_0, \boldsymbol{\lambda}_0]$ *such that for points* $[\mathbf{x}, \boldsymbol{\lambda}_0] \in W$ *in this neighborhood,*

$$F(\mathbf{x}, \boldsymbol{\lambda}_0) \leq F(\mathbf{x}_0, \boldsymbol{\lambda}_0) + \nabla_{\mathbf{x}} F(\mathbf{x}_0, \boldsymbol{\lambda}_0)(\mathbf{x} - \mathbf{x}_0), \tag{6–15}$$

and for points $[\mathbf{x}_0, \boldsymbol{\lambda}] \in W$ in this neighborhood,

$$F(\mathbf{x}_0, \boldsymbol{\lambda}) \geq F(\mathbf{x}_0, \boldsymbol{\lambda}_0) + \nabla_{\boldsymbol{\lambda}} F(\mathbf{x}_0, \boldsymbol{\lambda}_0)(\boldsymbol{\lambda} - \boldsymbol{\lambda}_0), \tag{6–16}$$

then $F(\mathbf{x}, \boldsymbol{\lambda})$ *has a saddle point at* $[\mathbf{x}_0, \boldsymbol{\lambda}_0]$ *for* $[\mathbf{x}, \boldsymbol{\lambda}] \in W$. *If* (6–15) *and* (6–16) *hold for all* $\mathbf{x} \in \mathbf{W}_1$, $\boldsymbol{\lambda} \in W_2$, *it follows that* $F(\mathbf{x}, \boldsymbol{\lambda})$ *has a global saddle point at* $[\mathbf{x}_0, \boldsymbol{\lambda}_0]$ *for* $[\mathbf{x}, \boldsymbol{\lambda}] \in W$.

To prove this, we note that since (6–14) holds at $[\mathbf{x}_0, \boldsymbol{\lambda}_0]$,

$$\nabla_{\mathbf{x}} F(\mathbf{x}_0, \boldsymbol{\lambda}_0)(\mathbf{x} - \mathbf{x}_0) = \nabla_{\mathbf{x}} F(\mathbf{x}_0, \boldsymbol{\lambda}_0)\mathbf{x}.$$

However, if $\mathbf{x} \in W_1$, then

$$x_j \geq 0, \qquad j = 1, \ldots, s; \qquad x_j \leq 0, \qquad j = s + 1, \ldots, t.$$

Furthermore, (6–6) holds. Thus $\nabla_{\mathbf{x}} F(\mathbf{x}_0, \boldsymbol{\lambda}_0)\mathbf{x} \leq 0$. Consequently, whenever (6–15) holds for $\mathbf{x} \in W_1$, $F(\mathbf{x}, \boldsymbol{\lambda}_0) \leq F(\mathbf{x}_0, \boldsymbol{\lambda}_0)$. Similarly,

$$\nabla_{\boldsymbol{\lambda}} F(\mathbf{x}_0, \boldsymbol{\lambda}_0)(\boldsymbol{\lambda} - \boldsymbol{\lambda}_0) = \nabla_{\boldsymbol{\lambda}} F(\mathbf{x}_0, \boldsymbol{\lambda}_0)\boldsymbol{\lambda} \geq 0.$$

Therefore, for any $\boldsymbol{\lambda} \in W_2$ such that (6–16) holds, $F(\mathbf{x}_0, \boldsymbol{\lambda}_0) \leq F(\mathbf{x}_0, \boldsymbol{\lambda})$. Combining these results, we conclude that for $\mathbf{x} \in W_1$, $\boldsymbol{\lambda} \in W_2$ such that (6–15) and (6–16) hold, $F(\mathbf{x}, \boldsymbol{\lambda}_0) \leq F(\mathbf{x}_0, \boldsymbol{\lambda}_0) \leq F(\mathbf{x}_0, \boldsymbol{\lambda})$, provided that $[\mathbf{x}_0, \boldsymbol{\lambda}_0]$ satisfies (6–6) through (6–11). Since (6–15) and (6–16) hold either in an ϵ-neighborhood of $[\mathbf{x}_0, \boldsymbol{\lambda}_0]$ (or everywhere), it follows that $F(\mathbf{x}, \boldsymbol{\lambda})$ has a saddle point (or a global saddle point) at $[\mathbf{x}_0, \boldsymbol{\lambda}_0]$ for $[\mathbf{x}, \boldsymbol{\lambda}] \in W$.

Recall from Section 3–10 that if $F(\mathbf{x}, \boldsymbol{\lambda}_0)$ is a concave function of $\mathbf{x}$, then (6–15) holds, and similarly, if $F(\mathbf{x}_0, \boldsymbol{\lambda})$ is a convex function of $\boldsymbol{\lambda}$, then (6–16) holds. Thus another (equivalent) sufficient condition that $F(\mathbf{x}, \boldsymbol{\lambda})$ have a saddle point at $[\mathbf{x}_0, \boldsymbol{\lambda}_0]$ is that $[\mathbf{x}_0, \boldsymbol{\lambda}_0]$ satisfy (6–6) through (6–11), and that for $\mathbf{x} \in W_1$ in an ϵ-neighborhood of $\mathbf{x}_0$, $F(\mathbf{x}, \boldsymbol{\lambda}_0)$ is a concave function of $\mathbf{x}$, and for $\boldsymbol{\lambda} \in W_2$ in an ϵ-neighborhood of $\boldsymbol{\lambda}_0$, $F(\mathbf{x}_0, \boldsymbol{\lambda})$ is a convex function of $\boldsymbol{\lambda}$. If $F(\mathbf{x}, \boldsymbol{\lambda}_0)$ is a concave function of $\mathbf{x}$ for all $\mathbf{x} \in W_1$ and $F(\mathbf{x}_0, \boldsymbol{\lambda})$ is a convex function of $\boldsymbol{\lambda}$ for all $\boldsymbol{\lambda} \in W_2$, then $F(\mathbf{x}, \boldsymbol{\lambda})$ has a global saddle point at $[\mathbf{x}_0, \boldsymbol{\lambda}_0]$ for $[\mathbf{x}, \boldsymbol{\lambda}] \in W$.

6–3 The Kuhn-Tucker theorem. We are now prepared to obtain the fundamental results first pointed out by Kuhn and Tucker. Consider the nonlinear programming problem

$$\begin{aligned} g_i(\mathbf{x}) &\leq b_i, & i &= 1, \ldots, u, \\ g_i(\mathbf{x}) &\geq b_i, & i &= u+1, \ldots, v, \\ g_i(\mathbf{x}) &= b_i, & i &= v+1, \ldots, m, \\ & \mathbf{x} \geq \mathbf{0}, \\ & \max z = f(\mathbf{x}). \end{aligned} \tag{6–17}$$

Let us assume that $f \in C^1$, $g_i \in C^1$, $i = 1, \ldots, m$, over the entire non-negative orthant. After adding non-negative slack and surplus variables, we obtain the equivalent problem

$$\begin{aligned} g_i(\mathbf{x}) + x_{si} &= b_i, & i &= 1, \ldots, u, \\ g_i(\mathbf{x}) - x_{si} &= b_i, & i &= u+1, \ldots, v, \\ g_i(\mathbf{x}) \qquad &= b_i, & i &= v+1, \ldots, m, \\ & [\mathbf{x}, \mathbf{x}_s] \geq \mathbf{0}, \\ & \max z = f(\mathbf{x}). \end{aligned} \tag{6–18}$$

Denote by Y the set of $\mathbf{x} \geq \mathbf{0}$ which satisfy the constraints. Assume that at $\mathbf{x}^*$, $f(\mathbf{x})$ takes on its absolute maximum for $\mathbf{x} \in Y$. Let us assume that $r(\mathbf{G}) = r(\mathbf{G}_f)$ at $\mathbf{x}^*$, where $\mathbf{G}$ contains columns only for positive x_j^*, x_{si}^*, so that without loss in generality we can form the Lagrangian function, assuming that $\lambda_0^* = 1$. Let J be the subset of the indices j, $j = 1, \ldots, n$, containing the indices j for which $x_j^* > 0$, and $\hat{J}$ be the subset containing the indices j for which $x_j^* = 0$. Similarly, let I be the subset of the indices i, $i = 1, \ldots, v$, containing the indices i for which constraint i is active at $\mathbf{x}^*$, and $\hat{I}$ the subset† containing the i for which constraint i is inactive at $\mathbf{x}^*$. We proved in Chapter 3 that there exists a set of m Lagrange multipliers λ_j^* which are unique if $r(\mathbf{G}) = m$ at $\mathbf{x}^*$, and not unique otherwise, such that

$$\frac{\partial f(\mathbf{x}^*)}{\partial x_j} - \sum_{i=1}^{m} \lambda_i^* \frac{\partial g_i(\mathbf{x}^*)}{\partial x_j} = 0, \quad j \in J, \quad \lambda_i^* = 0, \quad i \in \hat{I}. \tag{6–19}$$

We did not consider in Chapter 3 what could be said about

$$\frac{\partial f(\mathbf{x}^*)}{\partial x_j} - \sum_{i=1}^{m} \lambda_i^* \frac{\partial g_i(\mathbf{x}^*)}{\partial x_j}, \quad j \in \hat{J}. \tag{6–20}$$

---

† Note that one or more of the sets J, $\hat{J}$, I, and $\hat{I}$ may be empty.

Let us now investigate this. The simplest way to investigate the sign of (6–20) is to imagine that we explicitly include $\mathbf{x} \geq \mathbf{0}$ as a set of n additional constraints. After a surplus variable† $x_{s,v+j}$ is added, $x_j \geq 0$ becomes $x_j - x_{s,v+j} = 0$, $j = 1, \ldots, n$. We now have a problem with $m + n$ constraints and $2n + v$ variables. The slack and surplus variables are restricted to be non-negative, but the components of $\mathbf{x}$ are now unrestricted. Note that if $r(\mathbf{G}) = r(\mathbf{G}_f)$ at $\mathbf{x}^*$ for the original system of m constraints, the same relation must hold for the system of $m + n$ constraints where the $x_j \geq 0$ are treated as constraints. Hence the theory of Chapter 3 tells us that there exist $m + n$ Lagrange multipliers λ_i^*, $i = 1, \ldots, m + n$, such that at the point $\mathbf{x}^*$,

$$\frac{\partial f(\mathbf{x}^*)}{\partial x_j} - \sum_{i=1}^{m} \lambda_i^* \frac{\partial g_i(\mathbf{x}^*)}{\partial x_j} - \lambda_{m+j}^* = 0, \qquad j = 1, \ldots, n,$$

$$\lambda_i^* = 0, \qquad i \in \hat{I}, \qquad \lambda_{m+j}^* = 0, \qquad j \in J.$$

Since $\lambda_{m+j}^* = 0$, $j \in J$, we obtain once again (6–19).

However, let us now consider

$$\frac{\partial f(\mathbf{x}^*)}{\partial x_j} - \sum_{i=1}^{m} \lambda_i^* \frac{\partial g_i(\mathbf{x}^*)}{\partial x_j} - \lambda_{m+j}^* = 0, \qquad j \in \hat{J}. \tag{6–21}$$

We recall from Section 3–7 and Problem 3–16 that

$$\frac{\partial z^*}{\partial b_i} = \lambda_i^*, \qquad i = 1, \ldots, m + n.$$

It will be assumed that these derivatives exist. Problem 6–15 asks the reader to provide a sufficient condition for their existence. Consider the constraints $x_j \geq b_{m+j}$, where for our problem $b_{m+j} = 0$. Suppose that we now reduce b_{m+j} from zero to a negative number. Then z^* can only increase or remain unchanged since, due to the inequality sign, any feasible solution with $b_{m+j} = 0$ is also a feasible solution for $b_{m+j} < 0$. Therefore $\partial z^*/\partial b_{m+j} \leq 0$, thus implying that $\lambda_{m+j}^* \leq 0$. This immediately allows us to answer the question which we wished to answer. From (6–21) we see that

$$\frac{\partial f(\mathbf{x}^*)}{\partial x_j} - \sum_{i=1}^{m} \lambda_i^* \frac{\partial g_i(\mathbf{x}^*)}{\partial x_j} \leq 0, \qquad j \in \hat{J}. \tag{6–22}$$

This same analysis gives us some additional information. If we increase b_i for $i = 1, \ldots, u$, z^* can only increase or remain unchanged. Hence

† Note that in (6–18) we already have v slack and surplus variables.

$\partial z^*/\partial b_i \geq 0$, that is, $\lambda_i^* \geq 0$, $i = 1, \ldots, u$. Similarly, if b_i is decreased for $i = u + 1, \ldots, v$, z^* can only increase, and hence $\lambda_i^* \leq 0$, $i = u + 1, \ldots, v$. For $i = v + 1, \ldots, m$, the λ_i^* may have either sign. In certain razor's edge cases, where an active constraint becomes inactive for an infinitesimal change in b_i in a certain direction, it may be necessary to interpret $\partial z^*/\partial b_i$ as a one-sided derivative. However, as noted in Problem 3–16, this in no way changes the above analysis.

We can put the above results in the following form. If $\mathbf{x}^*$ is the absolute maximum of $f(\mathbf{x})$ for $\mathbf{x} \in Y$, it is necessary that there exist a $\boldsymbol{\lambda}^*$ such that

$$\nabla_{\mathbf{x}} F(\mathbf{x}^*, \boldsymbol{\lambda}^*) = \nabla f(\mathbf{x}^*) - \sum_{i=1}^{m} \lambda_i^* \nabla g_i(\mathbf{x}^*) \leq \mathbf{0}, \tag{6–23}$$

with the strict equality holding for $j \in J$, where $F(\mathbf{x}, \boldsymbol{\lambda})$ is the Lagrangian function

$$F(\mathbf{x}, \boldsymbol{\lambda}) = f(\mathbf{x}) + \sum_{j=1}^{m} \lambda_i [b_i - g_i(\mathbf{x})]. \tag{6–24}$$

Also

$$\nabla_{\mathbf{x}} F(\mathbf{x}^*, \boldsymbol{\lambda}^*)\mathbf{x}^* = \sum_{j=1}^{n} x_j^* \left\{ \frac{\partial f(\mathbf{x}^*)}{\partial x_j} - \sum_{i=1}^{m} \lambda_i^* \frac{\partial g_i(\mathbf{x}^*)}{\partial x_j} \right\} = 0. \tag{6–25}$$

Similarly, the first u components of

$$\nabla_{\lambda} F(\mathbf{x}^*, \boldsymbol{\lambda}^*) = (b_1 - g_1(\mathbf{x}^*), \ldots, b_m - g_m(\mathbf{x}^*)) \tag{6–26}$$

are non-negative, while components $u + 1, \ldots, v$ are nonpositive, and components $v + 1, \ldots, m$ vanish. Furthermore

$$\nabla_{\lambda} F(\mathbf{x}^*, \boldsymbol{\lambda}^*)\boldsymbol{\lambda}^* = \sum_{i=1}^{m} \lambda_i^* [b_i - g_i(\mathbf{x}^*)] = 0. \tag{6–27}$$

However, if we examine the conditions (6–6) through (6–11), we see by (6–19), (6–22), (6–25), and (6–27) that the point $[\mathbf{x}^*, \boldsymbol{\lambda}^*]$ satisfies the necessary conditions that the Lagrangian function $F(\mathbf{x}, \boldsymbol{\lambda})$ have a saddle point at $[\mathbf{x}^*, \boldsymbol{\lambda}^*]$ for $\mathbf{x} \geq \mathbf{0}$, $\boldsymbol{\lambda} \in W_2$.

We shall next prove that *if* $[\mathbf{x}^*, \boldsymbol{\lambda}^*]$ *satisfies the above conditions, and if* $f(\mathbf{x})$ *is concave over the non-negative orthant, while* $g_i(\mathbf{x})$ *is convex if* $\lambda_i^* > 0$ *and* $g_i(\mathbf{x})$ *is concave if* $\lambda_i^* < 0$, $i = 1, \ldots, m$, *then* $f(\mathbf{x}^*)$ *is the absolute maximum of* $f(\mathbf{x})$ *for* $\mathbf{x} \in Y$. To prove this note that if these conditions hold, then $F(\mathbf{x}, \boldsymbol{\lambda}^*)$ is a concave function of $\mathbf{x}$ for all $\mathbf{x} \geq \mathbf{0}$. Also, $F(\mathbf{x}^*, \boldsymbol{\lambda})$ is a linear, and hence convex, function of $\boldsymbol{\lambda}$ for all $\boldsymbol{\lambda}$. Therefore, by what we proved in Section 6–2, we know that $F(\mathbf{x}, \boldsymbol{\lambda})$ has a global saddle point at $[\mathbf{x}^*, \boldsymbol{\lambda}^*]$ for all $\mathbf{x} \geq \mathbf{0}$, $\boldsymbol{\lambda} \in W_2$, that is,

$$F(\mathbf{x}, \boldsymbol{\lambda}^*) \leq F(\mathbf{x}^*, \boldsymbol{\lambda}^*) \leq F(\mathbf{x}^*, \boldsymbol{\lambda}) \tag{6–28}$$

for all $\mathbf{x} \geq \mathbf{0}$, $\boldsymbol{\lambda} \in W_2$. Now by (6–27), $F(\mathbf{x}^*, \boldsymbol{\lambda}^*) = f(\mathbf{x}^*)$. However,

$$F(\mathbf{x}, \boldsymbol{\lambda}^*) = f(\mathbf{x}) + \sum_{i=1}^{m} \lambda_i^*[b_i - g_i(\mathbf{x})].$$

Consider any $\mathbf{x} \geq \mathbf{0}$ satisfying the constraints. Then $b_i = g_i(\mathbf{x})$, $i = v + 1, \ldots, m$, and $\lambda_i^*[b_i - g_i(\mathbf{x})] = 0$. For $i = 1, \ldots, u$, we have $b_i \geq g_i(\mathbf{x})$. Recall that for these constraints we showed that $\lambda_i^* \geq 0$. Hence $\lambda_i^*[b_i - g_i(\mathbf{x})] \geq 0$, $i = 1, \ldots, u$. When $i = u + 1, \ldots, v$, $b_i \leq g_i(\mathbf{x})$. However, in this case, $\lambda_i^* \leq 0$ and $\lambda_i^*[b_i - g_i(\mathbf{x})] \geq 0$. Therefore it must be true that for all $\mathbf{x} \in Y$,

$$\sum_{i=1}^{m} \lambda_i^*[b_i - g_i(\mathbf{x})] \geq 0,$$

so that for all $\mathbf{x} \in Y$, $f(\mathbf{x}) \leq F(\mathbf{x}, \boldsymbol{\lambda}^*)$, and hence $f(\mathbf{x}) \leq f(\mathbf{x}^*)$. Consequently, $f(\mathbf{x})$ takes on its absolute maximum at $\mathbf{x}^*$ for $\mathbf{x} \in Y$.

It may be well to reiterate at this point what we have proved above. We have obtained a set of necessary conditions which a point $\mathbf{x}^*$ where $f(\mathbf{x})$ takes on its global maximum for $\mathbf{x} \in Y$ must satisfy. Of course, any point $\mathbf{x}_0$ at which $f(\mathbf{x})$ takes on a relative maximum for $\mathbf{x} \in Y$ will also satisfy these necessary conditions. We then showed that if $f(\mathbf{x})$ is concave over the non-negative orthant, and the $g_i(\mathbf{x})$ are either convex or concave as required by the sign of λ_i^*, then at any point $\mathbf{x}^*$ which satisfies the necessary conditions, $f(\mathbf{x})$ will indeed take on its global maximum for $\mathbf{x} \in Y$, that is, with these restrictions on the concavity of $f(\mathbf{x})$ and the convexity or concavity of the $g_i(\mathbf{x})$, the necessary conditions are also sufficient. Finally, we showed that when $f(\mathbf{x})$ is concave and the $g_i(\mathbf{x})$ are either convex or concave as required, then at a point $[\mathbf{x}^*, \boldsymbol{\lambda}^*]$ satisfying the necessary conditions, the Lagrangian function $F(\mathbf{x}, \boldsymbol{\lambda})$ has a global saddle point at $[\mathbf{x}^*, \boldsymbol{\lambda}^*]$ for $\mathbf{x} \geq \mathbf{0}$ and $\boldsymbol{\lambda} \in W_2$.

One final observation of interest can be made. Let us assume that $f(\mathbf{x})$ is concave, that $g_i(\mathbf{x})$ is convex if $\lambda_i^* > 0$, and $g_i(\mathbf{x})$ is concave if $\lambda_i^* < 0$. Then at a point $[\mathbf{x}^*, \boldsymbol{\lambda}^*]$ satisfying the necessary conditions that $\mathbf{x}^*$ maximize f for $\mathbf{x} \in Y$, we must have (6–28) hold for all $\mathbf{x} \geq \mathbf{0}$ and all $\boldsymbol{\lambda} \in W_2$, that is,

$$F(\mathbf{x}^*, \boldsymbol{\lambda}^*) = f(\mathbf{x}^*) \leq F(\mathbf{x}^*, \boldsymbol{\lambda}).$$

Then $\boldsymbol{\lambda}^*$ must be the minimum of $F(\mathbf{x}^*, \boldsymbol{\lambda})$ for $\boldsymbol{\lambda}$ satisfying

$$\sum_{i=1}^{m} \lambda_i \frac{\partial g_i(\mathbf{x}^*)}{\partial x_j} \begin{cases} = \dfrac{\partial f(\mathbf{x}^*)}{\partial x_j}, & j \in J, \\ \geq \dfrac{\partial f(\mathbf{x}^*)}{\partial x_j}, & j \in \hat{J}; \end{cases} \tag{6–29}$$

$$\lambda_i \geq 0, \quad i = 1, \ldots, u; \quad \lambda_i \leq 0, \quad i = u + 1, \ldots, v;$$

$$\lambda_i \text{ unrestricted}, \quad i = v + 1, \ldots, m.$$

Here we have a linear programming problem which has $\boldsymbol{\lambda}^*$ as the optimal solution.

6–4 Kuhn and Tucker's derivation of the necessary conditions. Kuhn and Tucker used a different sort of argument to obtain the necessary conditions that we derived in the previous section. They restricted their attention to nonlinear programming problems of the type

$$\mathscr{g}_i(\mathbf{x}) \geq 0, \quad i = 1, \ldots, M; \quad \mathbf{x} \geq \mathbf{0}; \quad \max z = \mathrm{f}(\mathbf{x}). \tag{6–30}$$

We can transform the inequalities of (6–17) into this form by writing

$$\mathscr{g}_i(\mathbf{x}) = b_i - g_i(\mathbf{x}), \qquad i = 1, \ldots, u, \tag{6–31}$$

$$\mathscr{g}_i(\mathbf{x}) = g_i(\mathbf{x}) - b_i, \qquad i = u + 1, \ldots, v. \tag{6–32}$$

To transform an equation $g_i(\mathbf{x}) = b_i$ into the form (6–30), we note that this equation is equivalent to the two inequalities $g_i(\mathbf{x}) \geq b_i$, $g_i(\mathbf{x}) \leq b_i$. Thus the $m - v$ equations $g_i(\mathbf{x}) = b_i$ of (6–17) are equivalent to $2(m - v)$ inequalities

$$\begin{aligned} \mathscr{g}_{i1}(\mathbf{x}) &= g_i(\mathbf{x}) - b_i \geq 0; \\ \mathscr{g}_{i2}(\mathbf{x}) &= b_i - g_i(\mathbf{x}) \geq 0, \\ i &= v + 1, \ldots, m. \end{aligned} \tag{6–33}$$

Consequently, it is seen that the problem studied by Kuhn and Tucker is equivalent to the one discussed in the previous section. It is also possible to generalize Kuhn and Tucker's development to include constraints of the form $\mathscr{g}_i(\mathbf{x}) = 0$, so that transformations of the form (6–33) are not necessary. We ask the reader to do this in Problem 6–4.

The most important concept in Kuhn and Tucker's derivation of the necessary conditions is what is referred to as the *constraint qualification.* This qualification places some very important restrictions on the nature of the set of feasible solutions in the immediate vicinity of $\mathbf{x}^*$. Before specifically introducing the constraint qualification, we must make some additional observations.

Let us note first of all that if any constraints are inactive or any variables positive at $\mathbf{x}^*$, then there is a sufficiently small neighborhood about $\mathbf{x}^*$ such that for all $\mathbf{x} = \mathbf{x}^* + \mathbf{h}$ in this neighborhood, these constraints will remain inactive and these variables will remain positive. Thus, if $I, \hat{I}, J, \hat{J}$ are defined as in the previous section, then in the analysis to follow, we need not consider the constraints for which $i \in \hat{I}$ and variables for which $j \in J$. Let us then restrict our attention to the constraints for which $i \in I$ and the variables for which $j \in \hat{J}$. For $j \in \hat{J}$, $x_j^* = 0$, so that if we consider points $\mathbf{x} = \mathbf{x}^* + \mathbf{h} \geq \mathbf{0}$, it must be true that $h_j \geq 0, j \in \hat{J}$. To introduce the constraint qualification, recall that the tangent hyperplanes at $\mathbf{x}^*$ to the surfaces $\mathscr{g}_i(\mathbf{x}) = 0$, $i \in I$, can be written

$$\nabla \mathscr{g}_i(\mathbf{x}^*)\mathbf{x} = \nabla \mathscr{g}_i(\mathbf{x}^*)\mathbf{x}^*. \tag{6–34}$$

Consider then the set of points $\mathbf{y}$, lying in the intersection of the closed half-spaces

$$\nabla \mathscr{g}_i(\mathbf{x}^*)\mathbf{y} \geq \nabla \mathscr{g}_i(\mathbf{x}^*)\mathbf{x}^*, \quad i \in I; \qquad y_j \geq 0, \quad j \in \hat{J}. \tag{6–35}$$

If for any point $\mathbf{y}$ lying in the convex set (6–35), we write $\mathbf{y} = \mathbf{x}^* + \mathbf{h}$, then all such $\mathbf{h}$ must satisfy the inequalities

$$\nabla \mathscr{g}_i(\mathbf{x}^*)\mathbf{h} \geq 0, \quad i \in I; \qquad h_j \geq 0, \quad j \in \hat{J}. \tag{6–36}$$

Suppose now that we select any point $\mathbf{y}$ satisfying (6–35), and examine the line originating at $\mathbf{x}^*$ and drawn through $\mathbf{y}$. This entire line lies in the convex set (6–35), and any point $\mathbf{w}$ on this line can be written $\mathbf{w} = \mathbf{x}^* + \tau\mathbf{h}_0$, $\tau \geq 0$, where $\mathbf{h}_0 = \mathbf{y} - \mathbf{x}^*$. Furthermore $\mathbf{h}_0$ and $\mathbf{h} = \tau\mathbf{h}_0$ satisfy (6–36). We can then think of $\mathbf{h}_0$ or $\mathbf{h} = \tau\mathbf{h}_0$, $\tau > 0$, as defining the direction in which we move along the line going from $\mathbf{x}^*$ to $\mathbf{y}$.

The constraint qualification introduced by Kuhn and Tucker then requires that *for each line originating at* $\mathbf{x}^*$ *and lying in the convex set* (6–35) *or, in other words, for each* $\mathbf{h}$ *satisfying* (6–36), *there is in some* ϵ*-neighborhood of* $\mathbf{x}^*$ *a continuous, differentiable curve, every point* $\mathbf{x}$ *of which satisfies* $\mathscr{g}_i(\mathbf{x}) \geq 0$, $i \in I$, and $x_j \geq 0$, $j \in \hat{J}$, *such that at* $\mathbf{x}^*$, *this curve is tangent to the line lying in the set* (6–35). By a continuous, differentiable curve we mean that we can write $\mathbf{x} = \boldsymbol{\phi}(\tau)$, with τ being a parameter, such that $dx_j/d\tau$, $j = 1, \ldots, n$, exists. We shall imagine that the parametric representation is chosen so that $\mathbf{x}^* = \boldsymbol{\phi}(0)$ and τ increases as one moves from $\mathbf{x}^*$ along the curve. The constraint qualification requires that for every line lying in (6–35) such a curve exist in an ϵ-neighborhood of $\mathbf{x}^*$, with the properties that every point $\mathbf{x} = \boldsymbol{\phi}(\tau)$ is contained in the set of feasible solutions, and the curve is tangent to the line at $\mathbf{x}^*$. By the curve being tangent to the line it is meant that if

$$\frac{d\phi_j(0)}{d\tau} = h_j^0, \qquad j = 1, \ldots, n, \tag{6–37}$$

then the equation of the line is given by $\mathbf{w} = \mathbf{x}^* + \tau\mathbf{h}_0$, $\tau \geq 0$, or conversely, if we write any point on the line as $\mathbf{w} = \mathbf{x}^* + \mathbf{h}$, where $\mathbf{h}$ satisfies (6–36), then

$$\frac{d\phi_j(0)}{d\tau} = \mu h_j, \qquad \mu > 0, \quad j = 1, \ldots, n. \tag{6–38}$$

This is illustrated geometrically in Fig. 6–3. The derivative $d\phi_j(0)/d\tau$ may be defined only as $\tau \to 0$ from $\tau > 0$, since the curve may terminate at $\mathbf{x}^*$ and may not be defined for $\tau < 0$. Note that in the above discussion the curve $\boldsymbol{\phi}(\tau)$ will change as the line lying in (6–35) is changed. The constraint qualification can be stated in another way by saying that for *each* $\mathbf{h}$ satisfying (6–36) there exists at least one curve $\mathbf{x} = \boldsymbol{\phi}(\tau)$ in some ϵ-neighborhood of $\mathbf{x}^*$, with $\mathbf{x} = \boldsymbol{\phi}(\tau)$ being a feasible solution to the problem for each τ, such that (6–38) holds.

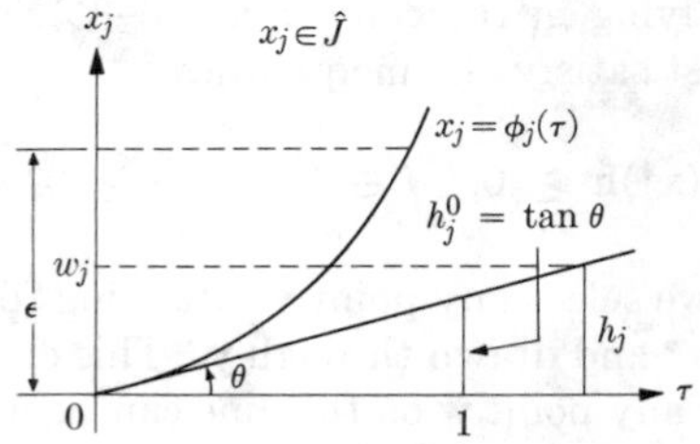

FIGURE 6–3

We can now prove that *when the constraint qualification holds, then if* $\mathbf{x}^*$ *maximizes* $f(\mathbf{x})$ *for* $\mathbf{x} \geq \mathbf{0}$ *satisfying the constraints, it is necessary that* $\nabla f(\mathbf{x}^*)\mathbf{h} \leq 0$ *for all* $\mathbf{h}$ *satisfying* (6–36). This can be proved by contradiction. Assume that there exists some $\mathbf{h}$, call it $\mathbf{h}_1 = [h_{11}, \ldots, h_{n1}]$ satisfying (6–36) for which $\nabla f(\mathbf{x}^*)\mathbf{h}_1 > 0$. But then $\nabla f(\mathbf{x}^*)\hat{\mathbf{h}} > 0$ for all $\hat{\mathbf{h}}(\rho) = \rho\mathbf{h}_1$, $\rho > 0$. Since $\nabla f(\mathbf{x})\mathbf{h}_1$ is a continuous function of $\mathbf{x}$, we know that for all $\mathbf{x}$ in some δ-neighborhood of $\mathbf{x}^*$, $\nabla f(\mathbf{x})\mathbf{h}_1 > 0$, and hence $\nabla f(\mathbf{x})\hat{\mathbf{h}}(\rho) > 0$.

Consider now the curve in the set of feasible solutions tangent to the line emanating from $\mathbf{x}^*$ in the direction $\mathbf{h}_1$. Because of (6–38), we can write

$$\phi_j(\tau) - x_j^* = \tau\mu h_{j1} + \tau\mu\gamma_j(\tau\mu),$$

where $\gamma_j(\tau\mu) \to 0$ as $\tau \to 0$, or

$$\mathbf{x} = \mathbf{x}^* + \tau\mu\mathbf{h}_1 + \tau\mu\boldsymbol{\gamma}(\tau\mu) = \mathbf{x}^* + \rho\mathbf{h}_1 + \rho\boldsymbol{\gamma}(\rho), \qquad \rho > 0, \tag{6–39}$$

and $\mathbf{x} \geq \mathbf{0}$ satisfies the constraints. Write $\mathbf{h}(\rho) = \rho[\mathbf{h}_1 + \boldsymbol{\gamma}(\rho)]$. We can then choose a ρ_0 so small that for all ρ, $0 \leq \rho \leq \rho_0$, $\mathbf{x}$ given by (6–39) lies in the δ-neighborhood referred to above, so that $\nabla f[\mathbf{x}^* + \mathbf{h}(\rho)]\mathbf{h}_1 > 0$. If we choose a specific ρ, $0 \leq \rho \leq \rho_0$, so that $\mathbf{h}(\rho)$ is determined, then $\nabla f[\mathbf{x}^* + \mathbf{h}(\rho)]\mathbf{y}$ becomes a continuous function of $\mathbf{y}$, and hence there is a σ_ρ-neighborhood about $\mathbf{h}_1$ such that for all $\mathbf{y}$ in this neighborhood, $\nabla f[\mathbf{x}^* + \mathbf{h}(\rho)]\mathbf{y} > 0$. Note that σ_ρ will depend on ρ. Let

$$\sigma = \min_{\rho} \sigma_\rho, \qquad 0 \leq \rho \leq \rho_0. \tag{6–40}$$

Then for all $\mathbf{y}$ in a σ-neighborhood of $\mathbf{h}_1$, and for all $\mathbf{x}$ in a ρ_0-neighborhood of $\mathbf{x}^*$, we must have $\nabla f(\mathbf{x})\mathbf{y} > 0$. Consequently, we can select ρ sufficiently small that $\mathbf{h}_1 + \boldsymbol{\gamma}(\rho)$ lies in the σ-neighborhood of $\mathbf{h}_1$, and $\mathbf{x}^* + \theta\mathbf{h}(\rho)$ lies in the ρ_0-neighborhood of $\mathbf{x}^*$ for any θ, $0 \leq \theta \leq 1$. Therefore, for such ρ,

$$\nabla f[\mathbf{x}^* + \theta\mathbf{h}(\rho)][\mathbf{h}_1 + \boldsymbol{\gamma}(\rho)] > 0,$$

and on multiplying by ρ, we have

$$\nabla f[\mathbf{x}^* + \theta\mathbf{h}(\rho)]\mathbf{h}(\rho) > 0.$$

But for some θ, $0 \leq \theta \leq 1$, we know from Taylor's theorem that

$$f(\mathbf{x}) = f(\mathbf{x}^*) + \nabla f[\mathbf{x}^* + \theta\mathbf{h}(\rho)]\mathbf{h}(\rho) > f(\mathbf{x}^*), \tag{6–41}$$

and $\mathbf{x} = \mathbf{x}^* + \mathbf{h}(\rho) \geq \mathbf{0}$ and satisfies the constraints. Thus we have arrived at a contradiction. Hence for *all* $\mathbf{h}$ satisfying (6–36) it must be true that $\nabla f(\mathbf{x}^*)\mathbf{h} \leq 0$.

Kuhn and Tucker did not go through the above analysis. They merely stated that if the constraint qualification holds, then it must be true that $\nabla f(\mathbf{x}^*)\mathbf{h} \leq 0$ for all $\mathbf{h}$ satisfying (6–36). The above provides the proof of this statement.

The purpose of the constraint qualification is to rule out exceptional behavior on the boundaries of a set of feasible solutions. Suppose that the constraints were

$$g_1(\mathbf{x}) = (3 - x_1)^3 - (x_2 - 2) \geq 0,$$
$$g_2(\mathbf{x}) = (3 - x_1)^3 + (x_2 - 2) \geq 0.$$

The set of feasible solutions is shown in Fig. 6–4.† Assume that $\mathbf{x}^* = [3, 2]$. Then $\nabla g_1(\mathbf{x}^*)\mathbf{h} \geq 0$ becomes $-h_2 \geq 0$ and $\nabla g_2(\mathbf{x}^*)\mathbf{h} \geq 0$ becomes $h_2 \geq 0$. These two constraints require that $h_2 = 0$ while h_1 can have any

† It is convenient here and in some of the following figures to have the gradient vectors drawn from the point at which they are evaluated rather than from the origin.

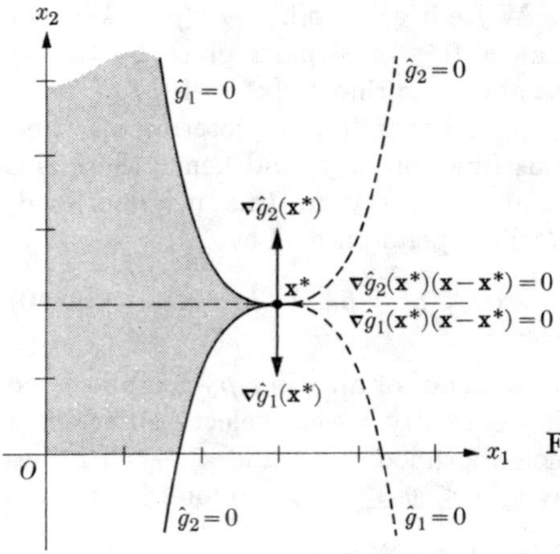

FIGURE 6-4

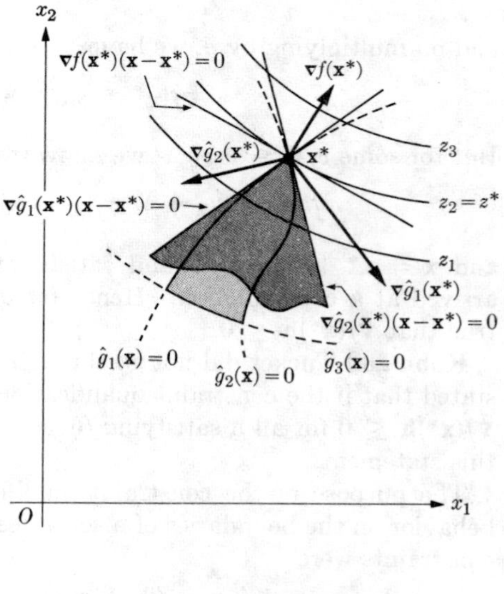

FIGURE 6-5

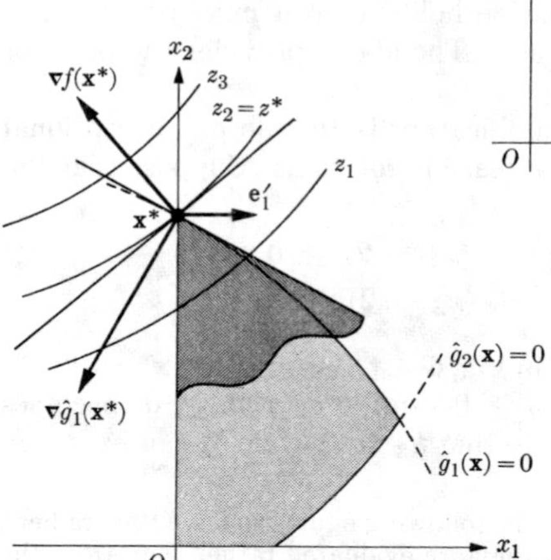

FIGURE 6-6

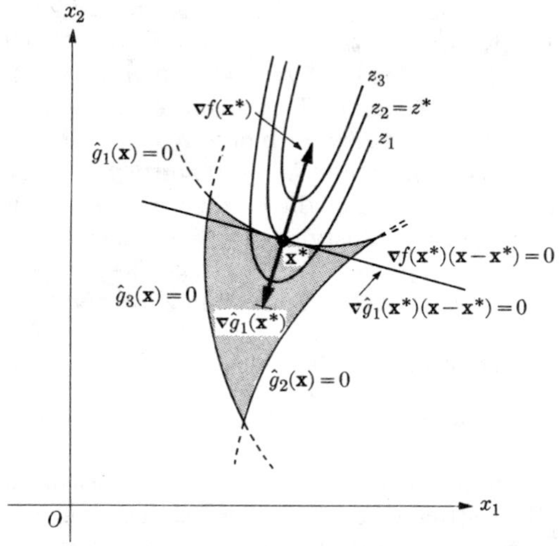

FIGURE 6–7

value. Consequently, the points $\mathbf{y}$ satisfying (6–35) must lie on the line shown in Fig. 6–4, and hence the vectors $\mathbf{h}$ drawn from $\mathbf{x}^*$ must be along this line. However, for $\mathbf{h}$ such that $h_1 > 0$, there is no curve lying in the set of feasible solutions which is tangent to the line at $\mathbf{x}^*$, since there are no points in the set of feasible solutions with $x_1 > x_1^*$. Here we have a case where the constraint qualification is not satisfied. Furthermore, in this case, it need not be true that $\nabla f(\mathbf{x}^*)\mathbf{h} \leq 0$ for all $\mathbf{h}$ satisfying (6–36), as can be seen if we take $f(\mathbf{x}) = x_1$, so that $\nabla f(\mathbf{x}^*)\mathbf{h} = h_1$. Certainly it is not necessary that $h_1 \leq 0$ for all h_1. This need be true only for $h_1 \leq 0$. This example shows that the constraint qualification is important in the sense that if the constraint qualification does not hold, it does not follow that necessarily $\nabla f(\mathbf{x}^*)\mathbf{h} \leq 0$ for all $\mathbf{h}$ satisfying (6–36). There is a very close connection between the constraint qualification introduced here and the requirements introduced in the previous section that $\partial z^*/\partial b_i$ exist and $r(\mathbf{G}_f) = r(\mathbf{G})$. However, a considerable amount of analysis is needed to establish a precise relationship, and we shall not attempt to provide it.

Figures 6–5 through 6–7 illustrate several cases where the constraint qualification is satisfied. In Fig. 6–5, the set $\hat{J}$ is empty, but two constraints are active. The convex set formed by the intersection of the two half-spaces $\nabla g_i(\mathbf{x}^*)\mathbf{h} \geq 0$ is the darkly shaded region. For each point in the convex set, $\nabla f(\mathbf{x}^*)\mathbf{h} \leq 0$. In Fig. 6–6, $x_1^* = 0$, and the convex set formed by the intersection of $h_1 \geq 0$ and $\nabla g_1(\mathbf{x}^*)\mathbf{h} \geq 0$ is the darkly shaded region. Again for any point in this convex set, $\nabla f(\mathbf{x}^*)\mathbf{h} \leq 0$.

At this point Kuhn and Tucker convert the necessary condition that $\nabla f(\mathbf{x}^*)\mathbf{h} \leq 0$ for all $\mathbf{h}$ satisfying (6–36) to the form given in the previous section, by making use of what is known as Farkas' lemma. Farkas' lemma states the following: *A vector* $\mathbf{b}$ *will satisfy* $\mathbf{b}'\mathbf{y} \geq 0$ *for all* $\mathbf{y}$ *satisfying* $\mathbf{Ay} \geq \mathbf{0}$ *if and only if there exists a* $\mathbf{w} \geq \mathbf{0}$ *such that* $\mathbf{A}'\mathbf{w} = \mathbf{b}$. It is not difficult to prove this lemma. To prove the sufficiency, assume that there exists a $\mathbf{w} \geq \mathbf{0}$ such that $\mathbf{A}'\mathbf{w} = \mathbf{b}$ or $\mathbf{w}'\mathbf{A} = \mathbf{b}'$. Thus for any $\mathbf{y}$, $\mathbf{w}'\mathbf{Ay} = \mathbf{b}'\mathbf{y}$. Hence, if $\mathbf{Ay} \geq \mathbf{0}$, then $\mathbf{w}'\mathbf{Ay} \geq \mathbf{0}$ and $\mathbf{b}'\mathbf{y} \geq 0$ as desired. To prove the necessity, we make use of the duality theorem of linear programming. If $\mathbf{b}'\mathbf{y} \geq 0$ for every $\mathbf{y}$ satisfying $\mathbf{Ay} \geq \mathbf{0}$, then the linear programming problem

$$\mathbf{Ay} \geq \mathbf{0}; \qquad \min Z = \mathbf{b}'\mathbf{y}$$

has an optimal solution $\mathbf{y} = \mathbf{0}$. Hence the dual problem

$$\mathbf{A}'\mathbf{w} = \mathbf{b}; \quad \mathbf{w} \geq \mathbf{0}; \qquad \max z = \mathbf{0w}$$

also has an optimal solution, i.e., there exists at least one $\mathbf{w} \geq \mathbf{0}$ satisfying $\mathbf{A}'\mathbf{w} = \mathbf{b}$. The strict equality holds for the dual constraints since the primal variables are unrestricted in sign. However, this is precisely what we wanted to prove. Farkas' lemma can also be proved without using the results of linear programming, but then the proof becomes more difficult.

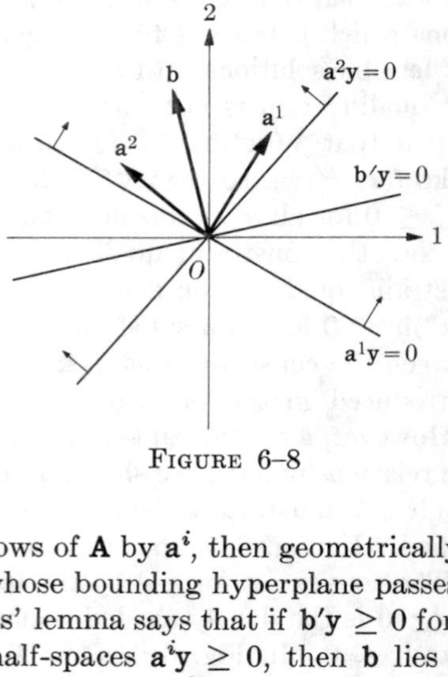

FIGURE 6–8

If we denote the rows of $\mathbf{A}$ by $\mathbf{a}^i$, then geometrically $\mathbf{a}^i\mathbf{y} \geq 0$ represents a closed half-space whose bounding hyperplane passes through the origin. Consequently, Farkas' lemma says that if $\mathbf{b}'\mathbf{y} \geq 0$ for every $\mathbf{y}$ lying in the intersection of the half-spaces $\mathbf{a}^i\mathbf{y} \geq 0$, then $\mathbf{b}$ lies in the convex polyhedral cone generated by the $\mathbf{a}^i$, $i = 1, \ldots, M$. This is illustrated geometrically in Fig. 6–8; $\mathbf{b}$ lies in the cone generated by $\mathbf{a}^1$ and $\mathbf{a}^2$.

We can now apply Farkas' lemma to the situation at hand. It must be true that $-\nabla f(\mathbf{x}^*)\mathbf{h} \geq 0$ for all $\mathbf{h}$ satisfying (6–36). Hence there exist

$\lambda_i^* \geq 0$, $i = 1, \ldots, M$, and $\mu_j^* \geq 0$, $j \in \hat{J}$ such that

$$\sum_{i \in I} \lambda_i^* \frac{\partial \hat{g}_i(\mathbf{x}^*)}{\partial x_j} + \mu_j^* = -\frac{\partial f(\mathbf{x}^*)}{\partial x_j}, \qquad j \in \hat{J}, \tag{6–42}$$

$$\sum_{i \in I} \lambda_i^* \frac{\partial \hat{g}_i(\mathbf{x}^*)}{\partial x_j} = -\frac{\partial f(\mathbf{x}^*)}{\partial x_j}, \qquad j \in J. \tag{6–43}$$

Note that in applying Farkas' lemma, the conditions $h_j \geq 0$, $j \in \hat{J}$, were included as constraints. Equations (6–42) and (6–43) state that a necessary condition for $\mathbf{x}^*$ to be an optimal solution to (6–30) is that $-\nabla f(\mathbf{x}^*)$ be in the convex polyhedral cone generated by the vectors $\nabla g_i(\mathbf{x}^*)$, $i \in I$, and $\mathbf{e}_j$, $j \in \hat{J}$. This should be checked in Figs. 6–5 through 6–7. The two equations can be combined to read

$$\sum_{i=1}^{M} \lambda_i^* \frac{\partial \hat{g}_i(\mathbf{x}^*)}{\partial x_j} \leq -\frac{\partial f(\mathbf{x}^*)}{\partial x_j}, \qquad j = 1, \ldots, n, \tag{6–44}$$

where $\lambda_i^* = 0$ for $i \in \hat{I}$ and the strict equality holds for $j \in J$. A convenient way of indicating that the strict equality holds for $j \in J$ is to write

$$\nabla_{\mathbf{x}} F(\mathbf{x}^*, \boldsymbol{\lambda}^*)\mathbf{x}^* = 0, \tag{6–45}$$

where $F(\mathbf{x}, \boldsymbol{\lambda})$ is the Lagrangian function

$$F(\mathbf{x}, \boldsymbol{\lambda}) = f(\mathbf{x}) + \sum_{i=1}^{M} \lambda_i \hat{g}_i(\mathbf{x}). \tag{6–46}$$

Similarly, a convenient way to indicate that $\lambda_i^* = 0$ for $i \in \hat{I}$ is to write

$$\nabla_{\boldsymbol{\lambda}} F(\mathbf{x}^*, \boldsymbol{\lambda}^*)\boldsymbol{\lambda}^* = 0. \tag{6–47}$$

When Eqs. (6–44), (6–45), and (6–47) are applied to the problem being studied here they represent precisely the same necessary conditions that we obtained in the previous section.

When the constraints (6–30) are linear, then the constraint qualification is always satisfied, the reason being that if the constraints are linear, there is a neighborhood of $\mathbf{x}^*$ such that any point satisfying (6–35) also satisfies the constraints. Thus, for any line emanating from $\mathbf{x}^*$ and lying in the set (6–35), we can use the line itself as the curve referred to in the constraint qualification. Therefore, when the constraints are linear, the necessary conditions obtained in this and the preceding section must hold, the only restriction being that f is differentiable.

In the derivations of the necessary conditions both in this section and the previous one, it has been assumed that all the relevant functions were differentiable. In practice, this condition seems to be frequently satisfied. However, the fact that the Lagrangian function has a saddle point at $[\mathbf{x}^*, \boldsymbol{\lambda}^*]$ can be proved under more general conditions, provided that one assumes that $f(\mathbf{x})$ and the $\mathscr{g}_i(\mathbf{x})$, $i = 1, \ldots, M$, are concave. This proof is left to the problems.

6–5 A special case and an example. Assume that the nonlinear programming problem under consideration has linear constraints and an objective function which is concave over the non-negative orthant, i.e., the problem has the form

$$
\begin{aligned}
\sum_{j=1}^{n} a_{ij}x_j &\leq b_i, \qquad i = 1, \ldots, u, \\
\sum_{j=1}^{n} a_{ij}x_j &\geq b_i, \qquad i = u+1, \ldots, v, \\
\sum_{j=1}^{n} a_{ij}x_j &= b_i, \qquad i = v+1, \ldots, m, \\
\mathbf{x} &\geq \mathbf{0}, \\
\max z = f(\mathbf{x}), &\qquad f(\mathbf{x}) \text{ concave.}
\end{aligned}
\tag{6–48}
$$

Since the constraints are linear, and hence can be considered to be either convex or concave, and since $f(\mathbf{x})$ is concave, a necessary and sufficient condition that f take on its global optimum at $\mathbf{x}^*$ is that there exist a $\boldsymbol{\lambda}^*$ with $\lambda_i^* \geq 0$, $i = 1, \ldots, u$; $\lambda_i^* \leq 0$, $i = u+1, \ldots, v$; and λ_i^* unrestricted in sign such that

$$
\sum_{i=1}^{m} \lambda_i^* a_{ij} \geq \frac{\partial f(\mathbf{x}^*)}{\partial x_j}, \qquad j = 1, \ldots, n,
\tag{6–49}
$$

and

$$
\sum_{j=1}^{n} x_j^* \left[\frac{\partial f(\mathbf{x}^*)}{\partial x_j} - \sum_{i=1}^{m} \lambda_i^* a_{ij}\right] = 0,
\tag{6–50}
$$

and

$$
\sum_{i=1}^{m} \lambda_i^* \left[b_i - \sum_{j=1}^{n} a_{ij}x_j^*\right] = 0.
\tag{6–51}
$$

Furthermore the Lagrangian function

$$
F(\mathbf{x}, \boldsymbol{\lambda}) = f(\mathbf{x}) + \sum_{i=1}^{m} \lambda_i \left[b_i - \sum_{j=1}^{n} a_{ij}x_j\right]
\tag{6–52}
$$

has a global saddle point at $[\mathbf{x}^*, \boldsymbol{\lambda}^*]$ for $\mathbf{x} \geq \mathbf{0}$ and $\boldsymbol{\lambda}$ such that components 1 through u are non-negative, whereas components $u + 1$ through v are nonpositive.

At first glance it seems peculiar that $F(\mathbf{x}^*, \boldsymbol{\lambda})$ should take on its minimum at $\boldsymbol{\lambda}^*$. The reason for this lies in the restrictions on the signs of the components of $\boldsymbol{\lambda}$. By (6–51) we see that $F(\mathbf{x}^*, \boldsymbol{\lambda})$ will take on its minimum at $\boldsymbol{\lambda}^*$ if

$$\sum_{i=1}^{m} \lambda_i \left[b_i - \sum_{j=1}^{n} a_{ij} x_j^* \right] \geq 0$$

for all $\boldsymbol{\lambda} \in W_2$. This must be true, however, as can be seen by noting that $\mathbf{x}^*$ satisfies the constraints and $\lambda_i^* \geq 0$, $i = 1, \ldots, u$; $\lambda_i^* \leq 0$, $i = u + 1, \ldots, v$. It might be noted that the $\boldsymbol{\lambda}$ which minimizes $F(\mathbf{x}^*, \boldsymbol{\lambda})$ is not necessarily unique; $\boldsymbol{\lambda} = \mathbf{0}$ also minimizes $F(\mathbf{x}^*, \boldsymbol{\lambda})$.

Observe that (6–50) can be written

$$\sum_{j=1}^{n} x_j^* \frac{\partial f(\mathbf{x}^*)}{\partial x_j} = \sum_{i=1}^{m} \lambda_i^* \left(\sum_{j=1}^{n} a_{ij} x_j^* \right). \tag{6–53}$$

However, $\lambda_i^* = 0$ when a constraint is inactive. Thus we can replace $\sum_j a_{ij} x_j^*$ in (6–53) by b_i without changing the value of the expression. Consequently, it must be true that

$$\sum_{j=1}^{n} x_j^* \frac{\partial f(\mathbf{x}^*)}{\partial x_j} = \sum_{i=1}^{m} \lambda_i^* b_i. \tag{6–54}$$

Let us now suppose that $f(\mathbf{x}) = \mathbf{c}\mathbf{x}$, so that (6–48) reduces to a linear programming problem. Then (6–49) and (6–54) become respectively

$$\sum_{i=1}^{m} \lambda_i^* a_{ij} \geq c_j, \qquad j = 1, \ldots, n, \tag{6–55}$$

$$\sum_{i=1}^{m} \lambda_i^* b_i = \sum_{j=1}^{n} c_j x_j^*. \tag{6–56}$$

Next note that for any $\boldsymbol{\lambda} \in W_2$ satisfying $\sum_i \lambda_i a_{ij} \geq c_j$, and for any $\mathbf{x} \geq \mathbf{0}$ satisfying the constraints, it must be true that

$$\lambda_i \sum_{j=1}^{n} a_{ij} x_j \leq \lambda_i b_i, \qquad i = 1, \ldots, v,$$

$$\lambda_i \sum_{j=1}^{n} a_{ij} x_j = \lambda_i b_i, \qquad i = v + 1, \ldots, m,$$

so that

$$\sum_{i=1}^{m} \lambda_i b_i \geq \sum_{i=1}^{m} \lambda_i \left(\sum_{j=1}^{n} a_{ij} x_j \right) = \sum_{j=1}^{n} \left(\sum_{i=1}^{m} \lambda_i a_{ij} \right) x_j \geq \sum_{j=1}^{n} c_j x_j. \tag{6-57}$$

Therefore

$$\sum_{i=1}^{m} \lambda_i b_i \geq \sum_{j=1}^{n} c_j x_j^*. \tag{6-58}$$

Consequently, by (6–56), $\boldsymbol{\lambda}^*$ must be an optimal solution to the linear programming problem

$$\sum_{i=1}^{m} \lambda_i a_{ij} \geq c_j, \quad j = 1, \ldots, n,$$

$$\lambda_i \geq 0, \quad i = 1, \ldots, u; \qquad \lambda_i \leq 0, \quad i = u+1, \ldots, v;$$

$$\lambda_i \text{ unrestricted}, \qquad i = v+1, \ldots, m, \tag{6-59}$$

$$\min Z = \sum_{i=1}^{m} \lambda_i b_i.$$

This problem is precisely the dual of the given linear programming problem. The relations (6–50) and (6–51) express the familiar complementary slackness property of dual linear programming problems. Thus, by applying the Kuhn-Tucker theory we have shown that if the primal linear programming problem has an optimal solution, then the dual must also have an optimal solution, and in addition, (6–56) must hold.

EXAMPLE. Let us consider the example presented in Chapter 1 whose constraint set is that given in (1–14) and whose objective function is (1–15). The solution to this problem is illustrated geometrically in Fig. 1–2. To put the problem in the form of a maximization problem, let us recall that

$$\min z = -\max - z.$$

Thus an equivalent problem is one in which we wish to maximize

$$\bar{z} = -10(x_1 - 3.5)^2 - 20(x_2 - 4)^2,$$

and $\min z = -\max \bar{z}$.

Thus

$$\frac{\partial \bar{z}}{\partial x_1} = -20(x_1 - 3.5); \qquad \frac{\partial \bar{z}}{\partial x_2} = -40(x_2 - 4).$$

If $\mathbf{x}^*$ is the optimal solution, then there must exist a five-component vector

$\boldsymbol{\lambda}^*$ with $\lambda_1, \lambda_2 \geq 0$, and $\lambda_3, \lambda_4, \lambda_5 \leq 0$, such that

$$\begin{aligned} \lambda_1^* + \lambda_2^* + 2\lambda_3^* + 0.5\lambda_4^* + \lambda_5^* &\geq -20(x_1^* - 3.5) = 20, \\ \lambda_1^* - \lambda_2^* + \lambda_3^* - \lambda_4^* &\geq -40(x_2^* - 4) = 20, \end{aligned} \tag{6–60}$$

since we found in Chapter 1 that the optimal solution was $x_1^* = 2.50$, $x_2^* = 3.50$. Furthermore, we know $\lambda_i^* = 0$ if the ith constraint is inactive at $\mathbf{x}^*$. Only the first constraint is active in this problem. Thus $\lambda_2^* = \lambda_3^* = \lambda_4^* = \lambda_5^* = 0$. It must also be true that the strict equality must hold for each constraint of (6–60) for which $x_j^* > 0$. Since both $x_1^*, x_2^* > 0$, the strict equality must hold in both constraints, and therefore $\lambda_1^* = 20$. From (6–54) it must be true that

$$\lambda_1^* b_1 = -20x_1^*(x_1^* - 3.5) - 40x_2^*(x_2^* - 4)$$

or

$$20(6) = 20(2.5) + 20(3.5) = 20(6),$$

which does indeed check out. Since $\bar{z}$ is a concave function for all $\mathbf{x}$, and since the constraints are linear, the necessary conditions that must be satisfied by $\mathbf{x}^*$ if $f(\mathbf{x}^*)$ is the global maximum of $f(\mathbf{x})$ subject to the constraint are also sufficient. Since we have found a $\boldsymbol{\lambda}^*$ such that $[\mathbf{x}^*, \boldsymbol{\lambda}^*]$ satisfies the necessary conditions, then we know that $f(\mathbf{x})$ assumes its global maximum at $\mathbf{x}^*$ subject to the constraints.

References

1. Arrow, K. J., and L. Hurwicz, "Reduction of Constrained Maxima to Saddle-Point Problems," in *Proceedings of the Third Berkeley Symposium on Mathematical Statistics and Probability*, J. Neyman, editor, Vol. V, pp. 1–20. Berkeley and Los Angeles, California: University of California Press, 1956.
2. Arrow, K. J., L. Hurwicz, and H. Uzawa, *Studies in Linear and Nonlinear Programming*. Stanford, California: Stanford University Press, 1958.
3. Burger, E., "On Extrema with Side Conditions," *Econometrica*, **23**, 1955, pp. 451–452.
4. Forsythe, G., "Computing Constrained Minima with Lagrange Multipliers," *Journal of the Society for Industrial and Applied Mathematics*, **3**, 1955, pp. 173–178.
5. John, F., "Extremum Problems with Inequalities as Subsidiary Conditions," in *Studies and Essays, Courant Anniversary Volume*. New York: Interscience, 1948.
6. Karlin, S., *Mathematical Methods and Theory in Games, Programming, and Economics*, Vol. I. Reading, Mass.: Addison-Wesley, 1959.

7. KUHN, H. W., and A. W. TUCKER, "Nonlinear Programming," in *Proceedings of the Second Berkeley Symposium on Mathematical Statistics and Probability*, J. Neyman, editor. Berkeley and Los Angeles, California: University of California Press, 1951, pp. 481–492.

8. PHIPPS, C. G., "Maxima and Minima under Restraint," *American Mathematical Monthly*, **59**, 1952, pp. 230–235.

9. SLATER, M., "Lagrange Multipliers Revisited: A Contribution to Nonlinear Programming," *Cowles Commission Discussion Paper, Math. 403*, November, 1950.

10. TUCKER, A. W., "Linear and Nonlinear Programming," *Operations Research*, **5**, 1957, pp. 244–257. This paper gives an elementary discussion, without proofs, of the Kuhn-Tucker theory as applied to problems with linear constraints.

11. VAJDA, S., *Mathematical Programming*. Reading, Mass.: Addison-Wesley, 1961.

PROBLEMS

6–1. Give the Kuhn-Tucker necessary conditions corresponding to Eqs. (6–6) through (6–11) for minimization problems. For what convexity conditions are the necessary conditions also sufficient? What form should the Lagrangian function assume in this case and what is the nature of the saddle point?

6–2. Generalize the material in Section 6–3 to include the case where $x_j \geq 0$, $j = 1, \ldots, s$; $x_j \leq 0$, $j = s + 1, \ldots, t$; x_j is unrestricted in sign, $j = t + 1, \ldots, n$.

6–3. Prove the following variants of Farkas' lemma:

(a) A given vector $\mathbf{b}$ will have the property that $\mathbf{b}'\mathbf{y} \geq 0$ for all $\mathbf{y} \geq \mathbf{0}$ satisfying $\mathbf{A}\mathbf{y} \geq \mathbf{0}$ if and only if there exists a $\mathbf{w} \geq \mathbf{0}$ such that $\mathbf{A}'\mathbf{w} \leq \mathbf{b}$.

(b) A given vector $\mathbf{b}$ will satisfy $\mathbf{b}'\mathbf{y} \geq 0$ for all $\mathbf{y}$ satisfying $\mathbf{a}^i\mathbf{y} \geq 0$, $i = 1, \ldots, v$; $\mathbf{a}^i\mathbf{y} = 0$, $i = k + 1, \ldots, m$, if and only if there exists a $\mathbf{w}$ whose first v components are non-negative and the remainder of whose components are unrestricted in sign such that $\mathbf{A}'\mathbf{w} = \mathbf{b}$.

6–4. Generalize the material in Section 6–4 to problems of the form

$$\hat{g}_i(\mathbf{x}) \geq 0, \quad i = 1, \ldots, v; \qquad \hat{g}_i(\mathbf{x}) = 0, \quad i = v + 1, \ldots, M;$$
$$\mathbf{x} \geq \mathbf{0}; \qquad \max z = f(\mathbf{x}).$$

How should the Kuhn-Tucker constraint qualification be interpreted in this case? [*Hint:* For constraints of the form $\hat{g}_i(\mathbf{x}) = 0$, show that at $\mathbf{x}^*$, there appear in (6–36) constraints of the form $\nabla g_i(\mathbf{x}^*)\mathbf{h} = 0$. Then apply the results of Problem 6–3.

6–5. For each of the problems given at the end of Chapter 1 for which the variables are not required to be integers, illustrate the application of the Kuhn-Tucker conditions. For those cases where the appropriate concavity or convexity conditions hold, verify from the Kuhn-Tucker conditions that the graphical solution obtained is indeed optimal.

6–6. Consider the problem

$$(1 - x_1)^3 - x_2 \geq 0, \qquad \mathbf{x} \geq \mathbf{0}, \qquad \max z = x_1.$$

Solve this problem geometrically and show that the Kuhn-Tucker necessary conditions do not hold in this case. Show also that the constraint qualification is violated.

6–7. Consider the problem of finding the minimum distance from the origin to the convex set

$$x_1 + x_2 \geq 4; \qquad 2x_1 + x_2 \geq 5.$$

Solve the problem graphically and show that the Kuhn-Tucker necessary conditions hold at the minimizing point.

6–8. Apply the Kuhn-Tucker theory to the general transportation problem of linear programming. Write down the Lagrangian function and obtain the dual problem.

6–9. If V and W are two convex sets with no interior point in common, prove that there is a hyperplane $\mathbf{cx} = z$ which separates V and W, so that $\mathbf{cv} \geq z$ for all $\mathbf{v} \in W$, and $\mathbf{cw} \leq z$ for all $\mathbf{w} \in W$. Illustrate this geometrically. [*Hint:* Consider the set $X = \{\mathbf{v} - \mathbf{w} | \mathbf{v} \in V, \mathbf{w} \in W\}$.] Show that X is convex and that either $\mathbf{0}$ lies on the boundary of X or is not an element of X at all. Then by the theorems on separating or supporting hyperplanes (Section 2–6), there exists a hyperplane containing $\mathbf{0}$ such that all of X lies in one closed half-space produced by this hyperplane, that is, $\mathbf{c}(\mathbf{v} - \mathbf{w}) \geq 0$ for all $(\mathbf{v} - \mathbf{w}) \in X$. In other words, $\mathbf{cv} \geq \mathbf{cw}$ for all $\mathbf{v} \in V$, $\mathbf{w} \in W$. If the sets V and W have a boundary point $\mathbf{y}$ in common, set $z = \mathbf{cy}$. How can one select z if they do not have a point in common?

6–10. Let W be a convex set which has no point in common with the non-negative orthant. Prove that there exists a vector $\mathbf{c} \geq \mathbf{0}$, $\mathbf{c} \neq \mathbf{0}$ such that $\mathbf{cw} \leq 0$ for all $\mathbf{w} \in W$. [*Hint:* Apply the results of Problem 6–9.]

6–11. Consider the problem $\hat{g}_i(\mathbf{x}) \geq 0$, $i = 1, \ldots, M$, $\mathbf{x} \geq \mathbf{0}$, $\max z = f(\mathbf{x})$. Assume that f and the $\hat{g}_i$ are concave functions over the non-negative orthant. Let $F(\mathbf{x}, \boldsymbol{\lambda}) = f(\mathbf{x}) + \sum_{i=1}^{M} \lambda_i \hat{g}_i(\mathbf{x})$. Let the global maximum of $f(\mathbf{x})$ subject to the constraints be taken on at $\mathbf{x}^*$. Assume that for any $\boldsymbol{\lambda} \geq \mathbf{0}$, $\boldsymbol{\lambda} \neq \mathbf{0}$, there exists an $\mathbf{x} \geq \mathbf{0}$ such that $\sum \lambda_i \hat{g}_i(\mathbf{x}) > 0$. Prove that there exists a $\boldsymbol{\lambda}^* \geq \mathbf{0}$ such that (6–1) holds for all $\mathbf{x} \geq \mathbf{0}$, $\boldsymbol{\lambda} \geq \mathbf{0}$, and $\sum \lambda^* \hat{g}_i(\mathbf{x}^*) = 0$. Conversely, prove that if $[\mathbf{x}^*, \boldsymbol{\lambda}^*]$ satisfies (6–1) for all $[\mathbf{x}, \boldsymbol{\lambda}] \geq \mathbf{0}$, then $\mathbf{x}^*$ maximizes $f(\mathbf{x})$ subject to the constraints. {*Hint:* Assume that $[\mathbf{x}^*, \boldsymbol{\lambda}^*]$ is a saddle point of $F(\mathbf{x}, \boldsymbol{\lambda})$, for $[\mathbf{x}, \boldsymbol{\lambda}] \geq \mathbf{0}$. Set $\boldsymbol{\lambda} = \mathbf{0}$ and conclude that $\sum \lambda_i^* \hat{g}_i(\mathbf{x}^*) = 0$. Set all components of $\boldsymbol{\lambda}$ equal to zero except λ_i. Hence conclude that $\hat{g}_i(\mathbf{x}^*) \geq 0$. But from the left-hand inequality, $f(\mathbf{x}) \leq f(\mathbf{x}^*)$. Now assume that $\mathbf{x}^*$ is optimal. Consider the following two convex sets in E^{M+1}: $Y = \{\hat{\mathbf{y}}\}$, where $\hat{\mathbf{y}} = [y_0, \mathbf{y}]$, $\hat{\mathbf{y}}$ being an $(M + 1)$-component vector such that there is at least one $\mathbf{x} \geq \mathbf{0}$ for which $\hat{\mathbf{y}} \leq [f(\mathbf{x}), \hat{g}_1(\mathbf{x}), \ldots, \hat{g}_M(\mathbf{x})]$, and $W = \{\hat{\mathbf{w}}\}$, where $\hat{\mathbf{w}} = [w_0, \mathbf{w}]$, $\hat{\mathbf{w}}$ being an $(M + 1)$-component vector such that $[w_0, \mathbf{w}] > [f(\mathbf{x}^*), \mathbf{0}]$, that is, the strict inequality holds for each component. Show that Y and W are convex, and have no points in common. Hence by Problem 6–9, there exists a $[v_0, \mathbf{v}] \neq 0$ such that

$$v_0 y_0 + \mathbf{v}'\mathbf{y} \leq v_0 w_0 + \mathbf{v}'\mathbf{w}$$

for all $\hat{\mathbf{y}} \in Y$, $\hat{\mathbf{w}} \in W$. However, on taking $\hat{\mathbf{y}} = [f(\mathbf{x}^*), \ldots, \hat{g}_M(\mathbf{x}^*)]$ and noting that in the limit we can set $w_0 = f(\mathbf{x}^*)$, conclude that $\mathbf{v} \geq \mathbf{0}$. Set $\hat{\mathbf{y}} = [f(\mathbf{x}), \ldots, \hat{g}_M(\mathbf{x})]$, $\hat{\mathbf{w}} = [f(\mathbf{x}^*), \mathbf{0}]$. Thus show that $v_0 > 0$, for otherwise $\mathbf{v} \geq \mathbf{0}$, $\mathbf{v} \neq \mathbf{0}$, and $\sum v_i\hat{g}_i(\mathbf{x}) \leq 0$ for all $\mathbf{x} \geq \mathbf{0}$, which contradicts the hypothesis of the theorem. Let $\boldsymbol{\lambda}^* = \mathbf{v}/v_0$. Hence $\sum \lambda_i^*\hat{g}_i(\mathbf{x}^*) = 0$, since $\hat{g}_i(\mathbf{x}^*) \geq 0$. Thus show that $F(\mathbf{x}, \boldsymbol{\lambda})$ has a saddle point at $[\mathbf{x}^*, \boldsymbol{\lambda}^*]$. This argument can be found in [2] and [6].}

6–12. Consider the problem $\hat{g}(x) = -x^2 \geq 0$, $x \geq 0$, $\max z = f(x) = x$. Do the Kuhn-Tucker conditions apply at the optimizing point? Show that $F(x, \lambda)$ does not have a saddle point at the optimizing point. Why not? Explain why not in terms of the theorem proved in Problem 6–11.

6–13. Consider the problem

$$\hat{g}(x) = -x_1 + (x_2 - 1)^2 \geq 0, \qquad \mathbf{x} \geq \mathbf{0}, \qquad \max z = (x_1 - 3)^2 + x_2^2.$$

Are the Kuhn-Tucker conditions satisfied at the optimizing point? Show that while $\nabla f(\mathbf{x}^*)\mathbf{h}$ must be ≤ 0 for all $\mathbf{h}$ such that $\mathbf{x}^* + \mathbf{h}$ satisfies the constraint, it is not true here that $\nabla f(\mathbf{x}^*)\mathbf{h} \leq 0$ for all $\mathbf{h}$ satisfying Eq. (6–36). Why? Which of the hypotheses made in deriving the necessary conditions is violated?

6–14. Consider Fig. 6–9. Are the Kuhn-Tucker conditions satisfied at the optimizing point?

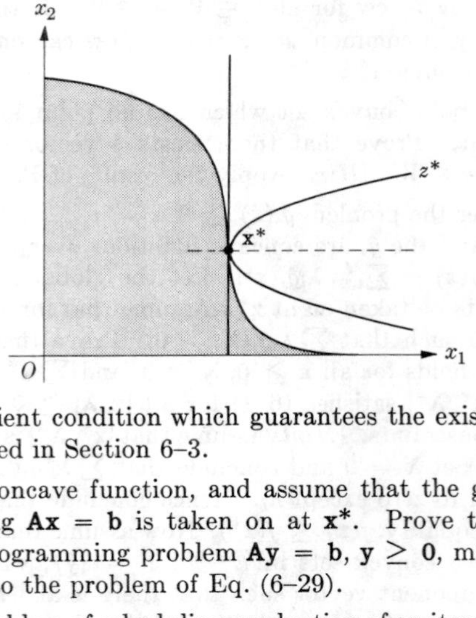

FIGURE 6–9

6–15. Provide a sufficient condition which guarantees the existence of all the derivatives $\partial z^*/\partial b_i$ needed in Section 6–3.

6–16. Let $f(\mathbf{x})$ be a concave function, and assume that the global optimum of f for $\mathbf{x} \geq \mathbf{0}$ satisfying $\mathbf{A}\mathbf{x} = \mathbf{b}$ is taken on at $\mathbf{x}^*$. Prove that an optimal solution to the linear programming problem $\mathbf{A}\mathbf{y} = \mathbf{b}$, $\mathbf{y} \geq \mathbf{0}$, $\max z = \nabla f(\mathbf{x}^*)\mathbf{y}$ is $\mathbf{y} = \mathbf{x}^*$. Relate this to the problem of Eq. (6–29).

6–17. Consider the problem of scheduling production of an item over n periods. Assume that the item can be inventoried, but that the warehouse has a maximum capacity of A units of the item. The demand for the item can be treated as deterministic. However, it does fluctuate from period to period. All demands occurring in a period must be met by the end of the period. They can be met either from inventory existing at the beginning of the period or from production during the period. There is a cost of carrying inventory, and the cost per period per unit in inventory at the beginning of the period is D. Imagine that the production cost in period j is a convex, differentiable function of the quantity produced in period j. Plans call for s units in inventory at the end of the last period. Set up the problem of scheduling production so as to minimize the sum of production and carrying costs over the n periods as a nonlinear programming problem. Use the Kuhn-Tucker conditions to determine a set of relations which must be satisfied by the optimizing schedule.

6–18. Let $\mathbf{f}(\mathbf{x}) = [f_1(\mathbf{x}), \ldots, f_r(\mathbf{x})]$ be an r-component vector each component of which is a differentiable function of $\mathbf{x}$. Consider the problem of maximizing $\mathbf{f}(\mathbf{x})$ for $\mathbf{x} \geq \mathbf{0}$ subject to the differentiable constraints $\hat{g}_i(\mathbf{x}) \geq 0$, $i = 1, \ldots, M$, for which the constraint qualification holds. By maximizing $\mathbf{f}(\mathbf{x})$ we mean that $\mathbf{x}^* \geq \mathbf{0}$ is a point at which the global optimum of $\mathbf{f}(\mathbf{x})$ is taken on if $\mathbf{x}^*$ satisfies the constraints, and for all $\mathbf{x} \geq \mathbf{0}$ which satisfy the constraints, there is no $\mathbf{x} \geq \mathbf{0}$, $\mathbf{x} \neq \mathbf{x}^*$ satisfying the constraints such that $\mathbf{f}(\mathbf{x}) \geq \mathbf{f}(\mathbf{x}^*)$. Let I, $\hat{I}$, J, $\hat{J}$ be defined as in Section 6–3. Suppose we restrict our attention to problems such that $\nabla f_k(\mathbf{x}^*)\mathbf{h} \geq 0$, $k = 1, \ldots, r$, with a strict inequality holding for at least one k, for no $\mathbf{h}$ satisfying Eq. (6–36). Prove that if $\mathbf{x}^*$ is optimal it is necessary that there exist a $\boldsymbol{\psi}^*$ with each component positive, and a $\boldsymbol{\lambda}^*$, such that if $F(\mathbf{x}, \boldsymbol{\lambda}) = \sum \psi_k^* f_k(\mathbf{x}) + \sum \lambda_i \hat{g}_i(\mathbf{x})$ then, with the appropriate interpretation, the conditions expressed by Eqs. (6–6) through (6–11) hold at $[\mathbf{x}^*, \boldsymbol{\lambda}^*]$. [*Hint:* The restriction given above is equivalent to saying that for *every* $\mathbf{h}$ which satisfies Eq. (6–36) and $\nabla f_k(\mathbf{x}^*)\mathbf{h} \geq 0$, $k = 1, \ldots, r$, it must be true that $\nabla f_p(\mathbf{x}^*)\mathbf{h} = 0$, or equivalently $\nabla f_p(\mathbf{x}^*)\mathbf{h} \leq 0$ for each $p = 1, \ldots, r$. Apply Farkas' lemma r times, where $\mathbf{b} = \nabla f_p(\mathbf{x}^*)$, and include $\nabla f_k(\mathbf{x}^*)\mathbf{h} \geq 0$, $k = 1, \ldots, r$, in $\mathbf{A}$.]

6–19. Show by an example that in Problem 6–18, the requirement that $\mathbf{f}(\mathbf{x}) \geq \mathbf{f}(\mathbf{x}^*)$ for no $\mathbf{x} \geq \mathbf{0}$, $\mathbf{x} \neq \mathbf{x}^*$, which satisfy the constraints is not equivalent to the requirement that $\mathbf{f}(\mathbf{x}) \leq \mathbf{f}(\mathbf{x}^*)$ for *all* $\mathbf{x} \geq \mathbf{0}$ which satisfy the constraints.

6–20. Show that the necessary conditions of Problem 6–18 are also sufficient if $F(\mathbf{x}, \boldsymbol{\lambda})$ satisfies Eqs. (6–15) and (6–16).

6–21. Let the functions $f_k(\mathbf{x})$, $k = 1, \ldots, r$, and $\hat{g}_i(\mathbf{x})$, $i = 1, \ldots, M$, introduced in Problem 6–18 be concave. Then show that the necessary conditions for a global optimum are also sufficient.

6–22. Assume that all the functions $f_k(\mathbf{x})$ and $\hat{g}_i(\mathbf{x})$ introduced in Problem 6–18 are linear. What form do the necessary conditions and $F(\mathbf{x}, \boldsymbol{\lambda})$ take in this case?

6–23. Consider a special case of the type of problem discussed in Problem 6–18 where there is only a single constraint of the form $x \geq 1$ and $\mathbf{f}(x)$ is a two-component vector with $f_1 = x - 1$ and $f_2 = 2(x - 1) - (x - 1)^2$. Show that any $x \geq 2$ can be considered to be optimal according to the definition given in Problem 6–18. Show, however, that the restriction introduced does not hold when $x^* = 2$.

6–24. For $\mathbf{f}(\mathbf{x})$ as defined in Problem 6–18, let $v(\mathbf{x})$ be defined for each $\mathbf{x}$ as $v(\mathbf{x}) = \min_k f_k(\mathbf{x})$. Consider the problem of maximizing $v(\mathbf{x})$ for $\mathbf{x} \geq \mathbf{0}$ subject to the constraints $\hat{g}_i(\mathbf{x}) \geq 0$, $i = 1, \ldots, M$, where the g_i are differentiable, and the constraint qualification is assumed to hold. In other words, we wish to maximize the minimum component of $\mathbf{f}(\mathbf{x})$. Prove that if $\mathbf{x}^*$ maximizes $v(\mathbf{x})$, there exists a $\boldsymbol{\psi}^* \geq \mathbf{0}$ whose components sum to unity such that

$$v(\mathbf{x}^*) = \sum \psi_k^* f_k(\mathbf{x}^*),$$

and there exists a $\boldsymbol{\lambda}^*$ such that if $F(\mathbf{x}, \boldsymbol{\lambda}) = \sum \psi_k^* f_k(\mathbf{x}) + \sum \lambda_i \hat{g}_i(\mathbf{x})$, then at $[\mathbf{x}^*, \boldsymbol{\lambda}^*]$, Eqs. (6–6) through (6–11) hold. [*Hint:* At $\mathbf{x}^*$, let K contain the set of indices k for which $v(\mathbf{x}^*) = f_k(\mathbf{x}^*)$ and let $\hat{K}$ contain the set of indices k for which $v(\mathbf{x}^*) < f_k(\mathbf{x}^*)$. Then if I, J, $\hat{I}$, $\hat{J}$ are defined as in Section 6–3, show that there can be no $\mathbf{h}$ satisfying Eq. (6–36) such that $\nabla f_k(\mathbf{x}^*)\mathbf{h} \geq 0$, $k \in K$, and the strict inequality holding for at least one k. Hence for all $\mathbf{h}$ satisfying Eq. (6–36) and $\nabla f_k(\mathbf{x}^*)\mathbf{h} \geq 0$, $k \in K$, it must be true that $\nabla f_p(\mathbf{x}^*)\mathbf{h} \leq 0$ for each $p \in K$. Now proceed as in Problem 6–18.]

6–25. Show that the necessary conditions obtained in Problem 6–24 are sufficient if $F(\mathbf{x}, \boldsymbol{\lambda})$ satisfies Eqs. (6–15) and (6–16). Then show that the necessary conditions are sufficient for the existence of the global maximum if the f_k and $\hat{g}_i$ are concave functions.

6–26. Specialize the general type of problem considered in Problem 6–24 to the case where the f_k and $\hat{g}_i$ are linear functions. What set of necessary and sufficient conditions will ensure that $\mathbf{x}^*$ maximized $v(\mathbf{x})$?

6–27. Consider a function of two variables which has a saddle point at $[x_0, \lambda_0]$. Sketch in E^3 one possible surface which might represent this function in a neighborhood of $[x_0, \lambda_0]$.

6–28. Show that the objective function of the first example of Section 3–9 is strictly convex. Thus use the Kuhn-Tucker theory developed in this chapter to prove that the answer obtained in Section 3–9 does indeed yield the global optimum.

6–29. Consider the constraint set shown in Fig. 6–10 which consists only of a discrete set of points (the dots shown). Show that the constraint qualification is not satisfied in this case. Write down the equations for the constraints that would yield such a constraint set.

6–30. Show that the Kuhn-Tucker conditions are satisfied both at extreme points 2 and 4 of Fig. 1–4.

6–31. Consider the linear programming problem

$$\mathbf{A}\mathbf{x} = \mathbf{b}, \qquad \mathbf{x} \geq \mathbf{0}, \qquad \max z = \mathbf{c}\mathbf{x}.$$

Denote by $z^*(\mathbf{b})$ the optimal value of the objective function for the specified $\mathbf{b}$, and let $\mathbf{x}^*$ be an optimal solution. Suppose now that we replace $\mathbf{b}$ by $\mathbf{b} + \epsilon\mathbf{a}_j$. Note that $\mathbf{x}^* + \epsilon\mathbf{e}_j$ is a feasible solution to the new problem provided that $x_j^* + \epsilon \geq 0$. Thus $z^*(\mathbf{b} + \epsilon\mathbf{a}_j) \geq \mathbf{c}\mathbf{x}^* + \epsilon c_j$. Now use Taylor's theorem to express the function $z^*(\mathbf{b} + \epsilon\mathbf{a}_j)$ in terms of $z^*(\mathbf{b})$ and terms involving ϵ. Assume

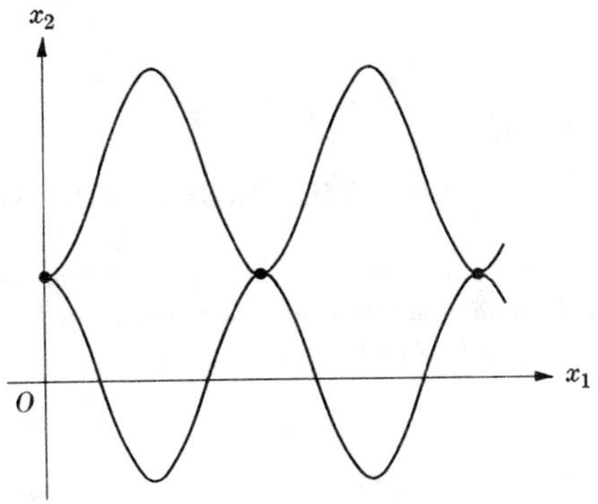

FIGURE 6–10

that z^* is differentiable everywhere. Show that this leads to the conclusion that

$$\sum_i \frac{\partial z^*}{\partial b_i} a_{ij} = c_j \qquad \text{if} \quad x_j^* > 0,$$

and

$$\sum_i \frac{\partial z^*}{\partial b_i} a_{ij} \geq c_j \qquad \text{if} \quad x_j^* = 0,$$

where $\partial z_i^*/\partial b_i$ is evaluated at some appropriate point. Write $\lambda_i^* = \partial z^*/\partial b_i$. In this way derive the Kuhn-Tucker conditions and the dual linear programming problem. Use this approach to obtain the Kuhn-Tucker necessary conditions for a problem with linear constraints and a nonlinear objective function. Can you generalize it to obtain the Kuhn-Tucker necessary conditions for a problem with nonlinear constraints? The approach of this problem has been suggested by Dreyfus and Freimer in Appendix 2 of *Applied Dynamic Programming* by Bellman and Dryfus, Princeton Univ. Press 1962.

6–32. Assume that we have a feasible solution $\mathbf{x}_0$ to the problem studied in Problem 4–52, and imagine that for this solution the solution to the approximating problem is $\boldsymbol{\mu} = \mathbf{0}$. Are the Kuhn-Tucker conditions satisfied at $\mathbf{x}_0$?

CHAPTER 7

QUADRATIC PROGRAMMING

Every valley shall be exalted, and every mountain and hill shall be made low: and the crooked shall be made straight, and the rough places plain.

Isaiah, XL, 4

7–1 Introduction. It will be recalled from Section 1–2 that a quadratic programming problem is a nonlinear programming problem having linear constraints and an objective function which is the sum of a linear and a quadratic form. The objective function can be written as in (1–10). After introducing slack and surplus variables into the constraints as needed (in the manner discussed in Section 2–3), and on introducing matrix-vector notation, we can write the general quadratic programming problem as

$$\begin{aligned} \mathbf{Ax} &= \mathbf{b}, \\ \mathbf{x} &\geq \mathbf{0}, \\ \max z &= \mathbf{cx} + \mathbf{x}'\mathbf{Dx}. \end{aligned} \tag{7–1}$$

It will be assumed that there are m constraints and n variables, so that $\mathbf{A}$ is an $m \times n$ matrix, $\mathbf{D}$ an $n \times n$ matrix, $\mathbf{b}$ an m-component vector, and $\mathbf{x}$, $\mathbf{c}$ are n-component vectors. Recall from Section 2–7 that without loss of generality, $\mathbf{D}$ can be taken to be a symmetric matrix. Hence, in the following, $\mathbf{D}$ will be assumed to be symmetric. It suffices to consider only maximization problems, since a minimization problem can be converted to a maximization problem merely by changing the sign of the objective function, i.e.,

$$\min f(\mathbf{x}) = -\max - f(\mathbf{x}).$$

As is generally true with nonlinear programming problems, it has not been found possible to develop a numerical technique for finding a global optimum for a quadratic programming problem unless it is known that any local optimum is also a global optimum. The set of feasible solutions to the constraints is a convex set. Hence from Section 3–12, we know that if the objective function is a concave function, then any relative maximum is a global maximum. Now z is the sum of a linear form (which is concave) and a quadratic form. Since the sum of two concave functions is concave, the objective function will be concave if $\mathbf{x}'\mathbf{Dx}$ is a concave function. However, from Section 3–10, $\mathbf{x}'\mathbf{Dx}$ will be concave if $\mathbf{x}'\mathbf{Dx}$ is a negative semidefinite or negative definite form. If $\mathbf{x}'\mathbf{D}\mathbf{x}$ is negative definite, $\mathbf{x}'\mathbf{D}\mathbf{x}$ and z are strictly concave (the proof that z is strictly concave is to be given in Problem 7–19) and the global maximum is unique. *In the ensuing discussion, attention will be restricted to the case where* $\mathbf{x}'\mathbf{D}\mathbf{x}$ *is concave,* i.e., to situations where $\mathbf{x}'\mathbf{D}\mathbf{x}$ is either negative semidefinite or negative definite.

Inasmuch as the constraints are linear, the Kuhn-Tucker constraint qualification is automatically satisfied, and therefore the results of Chapter 6 can be used to provide a set of necessary and sufficient conditions for an optimal solution. For quadratic programming problems, the functions $g_i(\mathbf{x})$, $f(\mathbf{x})$ of Chapter 6 are

$$g_i(\mathbf{x}) = \mathbf{a}^i\mathbf{x}; \qquad f(\mathbf{x}) = \mathbf{c}\mathbf{x} + \mathbf{x}'\mathbf{D}\mathbf{x}, \tag{7–2}$$

where $\mathbf{a}^i$ is the ith row of $\mathbf{A}$. Then

$$\frac{\partial g_i}{\partial x_j} = a_{ij}; \qquad \nabla g_i(\mathbf{x}) = \mathbf{a}^i, \tag{7–3}$$

$$\frac{\partial f}{\partial x_j} = c_j + 2\sum_{i=1}^{n} x_i d_{ij}; \qquad \nabla f(\mathbf{x}) = \mathbf{c} + 2\mathbf{x}'\mathbf{D}. \tag{7–4}$$

From the results of Chapter 6, we know that if $\mathbf{x}^* \geq \mathbf{0}$ is an optimal solution to the quadratic programming problem, then there must exist a $\boldsymbol{\lambda}^*$ such that $\mathbf{x}^*$, $\boldsymbol{\lambda}^*$ satisfy (6–23), (6–25), (6–26), (6–27). Consider (6–23) first. On using (7–3), (7–4), we find that it becomes

$$\mathbf{c} + 2(\mathbf{x}^*)'\mathbf{D} - (\boldsymbol{\lambda}^*)'\mathbf{A} \leq \mathbf{0}. \tag{7–5}$$

Let us now take the transpose of (7–5), note that $\mathbf{D}' = \mathbf{D}$, and introduce the n-component slack vector

$$\mathbf{v}^* = \mathbf{A}'\boldsymbol{\lambda}^* - \mathbf{c}' - 2\mathbf{D}\mathbf{x}^* \geq \mathbf{0}.$$

Then (7–5) can be written

$$\mathbf{c}' + 2\mathbf{D}\mathbf{x}^* - \mathbf{A}'\boldsymbol{\lambda}^* + \mathbf{v}^* = \mathbf{0}. \tag{7–6}$$

Making use of $\mathbf{v}^*$, we can write (6–25) as

$$(\mathbf{x}^*)'\mathbf{v}^* = 0 \qquad \text{or} \qquad x_j^* v_j^* = 0, \qquad j = 1, \ldots, n. \tag{7–7}$$

Equation (6–26) becomes simply

$$\mathbf{A}\mathbf{x}^* = \mathbf{b}, \tag{7–8}$$

while (6–27) is satisfied automatically by any feasible solution and hence need not be included. We thus conclude that if $\mathbf{x}^* \geq \mathbf{0}$ is an optimal solution to the problem, it is necessary that there exist a $\boldsymbol{\lambda}^*$ and a $\mathbf{v}^* \geq \mathbf{0}$ such that (7–6), (7–7), and (7–8) are satisfied. These represent the Kuhn-Tucker conditions as applied to quadratic programming problems.

However, since $g_i(\mathbf{x}) = \mathbf{a}^i\mathbf{x}$ can be considered to be either convex or concave, and since we are assuming that $f(\mathbf{x})$ is concave, it follows from Section 6–3 that the necessary conditions are also sufficient, i.e., if we can find an $\mathbf{x} \geq \mathbf{0}$, $\mathbf{v} \geq \mathbf{0}$, $\boldsymbol{\lambda}$ which satisfy

$$\begin{aligned} \mathbf{Ax} &= \mathbf{b}, \\ 2\mathbf{Dx} - \mathbf{A}'\boldsymbol{\lambda} + \mathbf{v} &= -\mathbf{c}', \\ x_j v_j &= 0, \qquad j = 1, \ldots, n, \end{aligned} \tag{7–9}$$

then $\mathbf{x}$ is an optimal solution to the quadratic programming problem.

To sum up the above discussion, if the quadratic programming problem has an optimal solution, there exist an $\mathbf{x} \geq \mathbf{0}$, $\mathbf{v} \geq \mathbf{0}$, $\boldsymbol{\lambda}$ satisfying (7–9), and if an $\mathbf{x} \geq \mathbf{0}$, $\mathbf{v} \geq \mathbf{0}$, $\boldsymbol{\lambda}$ satisfying (7–9) is found, then $\mathbf{x}$ is an optimal solution to the quadratic programming problem. The task of solving a quadratic programming problem then reduces to finding an $\mathbf{x} \geq \mathbf{0}$, $\mathbf{v} \geq \mathbf{0}$, $\boldsymbol{\lambda}$ satisfying (7–9). In the next section we shall see how this can be done.

7–2 Solution of quadratic programming problems when x Dx is negative definite. We shall now consider the method developed by Wolfe [16] for finding an $\mathbf{x} \geq \mathbf{0}$, $\mathbf{v} \geq \mathbf{0}$, $\boldsymbol{\lambda}$ which satisfy (7–9). The great advantage of this procedure over the other numerical techniques which have been suggested is that the simplex method can be used to obtain the solution.

The first important observation to make in developing a numerical technique is that if $[\mathbf{x}, \boldsymbol{\lambda}, \mathbf{v}]$ is a solution to the $m + n$ equations

$$\begin{bmatrix} \mathbf{A} & \mathbf{0} & \mathbf{0} \\ 2\mathbf{D} & -\mathbf{A}' & \mathbf{I}_n \end{bmatrix} \begin{bmatrix} \mathbf{x} \\ \boldsymbol{\lambda} \\ \mathbf{v} \end{bmatrix} = \begin{bmatrix} \mathbf{b} \\ -\mathbf{c}' \end{bmatrix} \tag{7–10}$$

such that $\mathbf{x} \geq \mathbf{0}$, $\mathbf{v} \geq \mathbf{0}$, $\mathbf{x}'\mathbf{v} = 0$, then no more than $m + n$ components of $[\mathbf{x}, \boldsymbol{\lambda}, \mathbf{v}]$ can be different from zero. This follows since $\mathbf{x}'\mathbf{v} = 0$. If k components of $\mathbf{x}$ are positive, at least k components of $\mathbf{v}$ are zero, and hence no more than $n - k$ components of $\mathbf{v}$ are positive. Thus no more than n components of the $2n$-component vector $[\mathbf{x}, \mathbf{v}]$ can be positive. However, $\boldsymbol{\lambda}$ contains only m components, and, consequently, no more than $n + m$ components of $[\mathbf{x}, \boldsymbol{\lambda}, \mathbf{v}]$ can differ from zero. What we have thus concluded is that a vector $[\mathbf{x}, \boldsymbol{\lambda}, \mathbf{v}]$ which satisfies (7–9) and $\mathbf{x} \geq \mathbf{0}$, $\mathbf{v} \geq \mathbf{0}$ must be a basic solution to (7–10). Therefore it is only necessary to examine basic solutions to (7–10) to find a solution satisfying (7–9), provided that such a solution exists. This result was first obtained by Barankin and Dorfman [1].

We shall for the remainder of this section confine our attention to the case where **x'Dx** *is negative definite.* The semidefinite case can cause difficulties in the computational procedure to be considered. The means for resolving these difficulties will be considered later, but for the present it will be assumed that **x'Dx** is negative definite.

When **x'Dx** is negative definite, it is easy to show that the quadratic programming problem cannot have an unbounded solution. Consider any point **x** lying on the hypersphere of radius σ with center at the origin, i.e., $|\mathbf{x}| = \sigma$. Then $\mathbf{x} = \sigma\mathbf{r}$, where **r** is a point on the hypersphere with radius unity and center at the origin (the unit hypersphere). Furthermore, $\mathbf{x}'\mathbf{D}\mathbf{x} = \sigma^2\mathbf{r}'\mathbf{D}\mathbf{r}$. Let the maximum of $\mathbf{r}'\mathbf{D}\mathbf{r}$ over the unit hypersphere be taken on at $\mathbf{r}_0$. Then $\mathbf{r}_0'\mathbf{D}\mathbf{r}_0 = d < 0$ and $\mathbf{x}'\mathbf{D}\mathbf{x} \leq \sigma^2 d < 0$ for any point **x** on the hypersphere of radius σ. Consequently, as $|\mathbf{x}| \to \infty$, $\mathbf{x}'\mathbf{D}\mathbf{x} \to -\infty$. Next note that when $\mathbf{x} \neq \mathbf{0}$, then

$$z = \mathbf{x}'\mathbf{D}\mathbf{x}\left[1 + \frac{\mathbf{c}\mathbf{x}}{\mathbf{x}'\mathbf{D}\mathbf{x}}\right].$$

Let the maximum of $|\mathbf{c}\mathbf{r}/\mathbf{r}'\mathbf{D}\mathbf{r}|$ over the unit hypersphere be taken on at $\mathbf{r}_1$. This value will be finite, since $\mathbf{r}_1'\mathbf{D}\mathbf{r}_1 \neq 0$. Then

$$\left|\frac{\mathbf{c}\mathbf{x}}{\mathbf{x}'\mathbf{D}\mathbf{x}}\right| \leq \frac{1}{\sigma}\left|\frac{\mathbf{c}\mathbf{r}_1}{\mathbf{r}_1'\mathbf{D}\mathbf{r}_1}\right|,$$

and as $|\mathbf{x}| \to \infty$, $\mathbf{c}\mathbf{x}/\mathbf{x}'\mathbf{D}\mathbf{x} \to 0$ and $z \to -\infty$. Thus, regardless of the direction in which one moves, $z \to -\infty$ as $|\mathbf{x}| \to \infty$, and the maximum value of z cannot be made arbitrarily large. When **x'Dx** is semidefinite, it is possible to have unbounded solutions. These may occur if the convex set of feasible solutions is not bounded from above, and it is possible to move without limit from a given point in a direction such that **x'Dx** remains constant and **cx** is increasing.

Since there cannot be an unbounded solution when **x'Dx** is negative definite, there is either no feasible solution or a unique optimal solution (recall that uniqueness also follows when **x'Dx** is negative definite). Consequently, if we know that there is a feasible solution, then there will be at least one basic solution $[\mathbf{x}, \boldsymbol{\lambda}, \mathbf{v}]$ to (7–10) with the property that $\mathbf{x} \geq \mathbf{0}$, $\mathbf{v} \geq \mathbf{0}$, $\mathbf{x}'\mathbf{v} = 0$. The first n components are unique and provide the optimal solution to the quadratic programming problem.

The computational procedure for finding the desired basic solution to (7–10) involves a slight modification of the artificial variable technique used to obtain initial basic feasible solutions to linear programming problems. The first step is to determine a basic feasible solution to the constraints $\mathbf{A}\mathbf{x} = \mathbf{b}$, if one exists. This is done using the usual Phase I of the simplex method. Once a feasible solution to $\mathbf{A}\mathbf{x} = \mathbf{b}$ has been found, then it is certain (when **x'Dx** is negative definite) that there will exist a basic solution to (7–10) with $\mathbf{x} \geq \mathbf{0}, \mathbf{v} \geq \mathbf{0}, \mathbf{x}'\mathbf{v} = 0$. The problem is to find it. The procedure for doing this will be very similar to a Phase I computation in linear programming. The set of equations (7–10) will be augmented by adding some non-negative artificial variables. Then the negative of the sum of the artificial variables is maximized while the condition $\mathbf{x}'\mathbf{v} = 0$ is maintained, and, when the sum of the artificial variables is zero, the desired basic solution to (7–10) will have been found.

In carrying out the procedure just outlined, one will find it very convenient, in determining the initial basic feasible solution to the augmented constraints, to make use of the basic feasible solution to $\mathbf{A}\mathbf{x} = \mathbf{b}$ obtained in the first step referred to above. Let $\mathbf{B}$ be the basis matrix and $\mathbf{x}_B$ contain the basic variables so that $\mathbf{B}\mathbf{x}_B = \mathbf{b}$. Note that this basic solution satisfies the first m constraints of (7–10). We shall therefore make use of this and only add artificial variables to the last n constraints of (7–10). This will be done as follows. In place of (7–10), consider the augmented system of equations.

$$\begin{aligned} \mathbf{A}\mathbf{x} \qquad\qquad\qquad\qquad &= \mathbf{b}, \\ 2\mathbf{D}\mathbf{x} - \mathbf{A}'\boldsymbol{\lambda} + \mathbf{v} + \mathbf{E}\mathbf{u} &= -\mathbf{c}', \end{aligned} \tag{7–11}$$

where we require that $\mathbf{u} \geq \mathbf{0}$, and $\mathbf{E} = \|\Delta_j \delta_{ij}\|$ is a diagonal matrix whose diagonal elements are $\Delta_j = \pm 1$.

Consider now the determination of the sign of Δ_j. Let $\mathbf{D}_B$ contain the columns of $\mathbf{D}$ corresponding to the columns of $\mathbf{A}$ in $\mathbf{B}$, and denote by $\mathbf{d}_B^j$ the jth row of $\mathbf{D}_B$. Then

$$\Delta_j = \begin{cases} +1 & \text{if} \quad -c_j - 2\mathbf{d}_B^j\mathbf{x}_B \geq 0, \\ -1 & \text{if} \quad -c_j - 2\mathbf{d}_B^j\mathbf{x}_B < 0. \end{cases} \tag{7–12}$$

With the Δ_j defined in this way, we see that if we set

$$u_j = |-c_j - 2\mathbf{d}_B^j\mathbf{x}_B| \geq 0, \; j = 1, \ldots, n; \qquad \boldsymbol{\lambda} = \mathbf{0}; \quad \mathbf{v} = \mathbf{0}, \tag{7–13}$$

we have a feasible solution to (7–11). This solution contains no more than $n + m$ positive variables. It can be written

$$\begin{bmatrix} \mathbf{B} & \mathbf{0} \\ 2\mathbf{D}_B & \mathbf{E} \end{bmatrix} \begin{bmatrix} \mathbf{x}_B \\ \mathbf{u} \end{bmatrix} = \begin{bmatrix} \mathbf{b} \\ -\mathbf{c}' \end{bmatrix}.$$

This is, in fact, a basic solution to (7–11), since the matrix of the coefficients, which will be denoted by $\mathbf{B}_Q$, is nonsingular. Indeed, when

$$\mathbf{B}_Q = \begin{bmatrix} \mathbf{B} & \mathbf{0} \\ 2\mathbf{D}_B & \mathbf{E} \end{bmatrix}, \quad \text{then} \quad \mathbf{B}_Q^{-1} = \begin{bmatrix} \mathbf{B}^{-1} & \mathbf{0} \\ -2\mathbf{E}\mathbf{D}_B\mathbf{B}^{-1} & \mathbf{E} \end{bmatrix}. \tag{7–14}$$

This follows from the observation that $\mathbf{E}$ is nonsingular and $\mathbf{E}^{-1} = \mathbf{E}$. The fact that the $\mathbf{B}_Q^{-1}$ shown is indeed the inverse of $\mathbf{B}_Q$ is easily verified by multiplication of $\mathbf{B}_Q$ and $\mathbf{B}_Q^{-1}$ to show that the identity matrix is obtained. The expression for $\mathbf{B}_Q^{-1}$ can be obtained directly by means of the partitioning method for computing the inverse, as discussed in Section 2–1 and {LA 3–20}.

Having found a basic solution to (7–11) with $\mathbf{x}_B \geq \mathbf{0}$, $\mathbf{u} \geq \mathbf{0}$, we then use the simplex method to reduce $-\sum_j u_j$ to zero, i.e., by maximizing $Z = -\sum_j u_j$. We introduce only one variation from the standard simplex procedure, i.e., if $x_j > 0$, we do not allow v_j to enter the basis and vice versa.* Let us now set down more specifically the new nonlinear programming problem whose solution also yields an optimal solution to the quadratic programming problem. Recall that the components of $\boldsymbol{\lambda}$ are unrestricted in sign. For all variables to be non-negative in the new programming problem, we write $\boldsymbol{\lambda} = \boldsymbol{\zeta} - \boldsymbol{\xi}$, $\boldsymbol{\zeta} \geq \mathbf{0}$, $\boldsymbol{\xi} \geq \mathbf{0}$. Then if

$$\mathbf{Q} = \begin{bmatrix} \mathbf{A} & \mathbf{0} & \mathbf{0} & \mathbf{0} & \mathbf{0} \\ 2\mathbf{D} & -\mathbf{A}' & \mathbf{A}' & \mathbf{I}_n & \mathbf{E} \end{bmatrix}, \qquad \mathbf{f} = [\mathbf{b}, -\mathbf{c}'],$$
$$\mathbf{w} = [\mathbf{x}, \boldsymbol{\zeta}, \boldsymbol{\xi}, \mathbf{v}, \mathbf{u}], \tag{7–15}$$

the nonlinear programming problem we wish to solve is

$$\mathbf{Q}\mathbf{w} = \mathbf{f}; \qquad \mathbf{w} \geq \mathbf{0}; \qquad \mathbf{x}'\mathbf{v} = 0, \qquad \max Z = -\sum_j u_j. \tag{7–16}$$

This problem is linear except for the restriction $\mathbf{x}'\mathbf{v} = 0$. It can be solved by using the simplex method, with the modification described above. The revised simplex method provides a convenient way of solving this problem. We have already shown how to determine an initial basic solution for (7–16). The procedure is to first obtain a basic solution $\mathbf{x}_B$ with basis matrix $\mathbf{B}$ to the constraints $\mathbf{A}\mathbf{x} = \mathbf{b}$ by means of Phase I of the simplex method. Then if

$$\mathbf{u} = \mathbf{E}(-\mathbf{c}' - 2\mathbf{D}_B\mathbf{x}_B) \geq \mathbf{0}, \tag{7–17}$$

it follows that $\mathbf{q}_B = [\mathbf{x}_B, \mathbf{u}]$ is a basic feasible solution to (7–16) with basis matrix $\mathbf{B}_Q$ given by (7–14). We have also found an expression for $\mathbf{B}_Q^{-1}$ in terms of $\mathbf{B}^{-1}$, $\mathbf{E}$, $\mathbf{D}_B$, which is needed for the first tableau of the revised simplex method. This completes the details of the solution technique. The computational effort required to solve a quadratic programming problem involving m constraints and n variables is then roughly the same as that involved in the solution of a linear programming problem with $n + m$ constraints. Markowitz [12] was the first to suggest finding a basic solution to

* More generally, we can allow x_j and v_j in the basis, but only if $x_jv_j = 0$.

(7–10) with $\mathbf{x} \geq \mathbf{0}$, $\mathbf{v} \geq \mathbf{0}$, $\mathbf{x}'\mathbf{v} = 0$ by starting with constraints looser than (7–10), but with $\mathbf{x}'\mathbf{v} = 0$, and altering the variables while keeping $\mathbf{x}'\mathbf{v} = 0$ until the desired solution is obtained. He did not use the simplex method, however. Wolfe modified his technique so that the simplex method could be applied.

There is one question concerning the computational technique which so far remains unanswered. We have not proved that when additional iterations in the simplex method (when using $x_j v_j = 0$) cannot be made, we shall have $Z = 0$ and obtain the desired solution. This will be demonstrated in the next section.

7–3 Proof of termination for the negative definite case. We now wish to prove that when solving (7–16) under the condition $\mathbf{x}'\mathbf{v} = 0$, it is true that $Z = 0$, that is, $\mathbf{u} = \mathbf{0}$ when a point is reached where one cannot make additional iterations which do not violate the simplex rules or $\mathbf{x}'\mathbf{v} = 0$. We shall continue to assume, of course, that $\mathbf{x}'\mathbf{D}\mathbf{x}$ is negative definite.

Consider the state of affairs when no additional simplex iterations can be made. Let $\mathbf{x}_1$ contain the components of $\mathbf{x}$ which are positive, and $\mathbf{v}_1$ contain the corresponding components of $\mathbf{v}$. Then $\mathbf{v}_1 = \mathbf{0}$, since $\mathbf{x}_1'\mathbf{v}_1 = 0$. Let $\mathbf{v}_2$ contain the components of $\mathbf{v}$ which are positive, and $\mathbf{x}_2$ contain the corresponding components of $\mathbf{x}$. Then $\mathbf{x}_2 = \mathbf{0}$. With these definitions an optimal solution to the linear programming problem

$$\mathbf{Q}\mathbf{w} = \mathbf{f}; \quad \mathbf{v}_1 = \mathbf{0}; \quad \mathbf{x}_2 = \mathbf{0}; \quad \mathbf{w} \geq \mathbf{0};$$
$$\max Z = -\sum_j u_j = \mathbf{h}\mathbf{w} \tag{7–18}$$

will yield precisely the solution we obtained to (7–16) when restricting the basis entry using $\mathbf{x}'\mathbf{v} = 0$, since the manner in which (7–16) was solved yielded a solution with all $Z_j - h_j \geq 0$ (the price h_j of all legitimate variables is zero and is -1 for the u_j) for variables not contained in $\mathbf{v}_1$ or $\mathbf{x}_2$.

In $\mathbf{x}_1$ and $\mathbf{x}_2$ we may not have included all the components of $\mathbf{x}$. Let $\mathbf{x}_3$ contain those components of $\mathbf{x}$ which are zero, but are not required to be zero because the corresponding component of $\mathbf{v}$ is positive. Similarly, let $\mathbf{v}_3$ contain the components of $\mathbf{v}$ which are zero, but are not required to be zero. We shall then partition the set of constraints $\mathbf{Q}\mathbf{w} = \mathbf{f}$ and write them as follows:

$$\begin{array}{llllllllll}
\mathbf{A}_1\mathbf{x}_1 + & \mathbf{A}_2\mathbf{x}_2 + & \mathbf{A}_3\mathbf{x}_3 & \mathbf{0} & \mathbf{0} & \mathbf{0} & \mathbf{0} & \mathbf{0} & \mathbf{0} = & \mathbf{b}, \\
2\mathbf{D}_{11}\mathbf{x}_1 + & 2\mathbf{D}_{12}\mathbf{x}_2 + & 2\mathbf{D}_{13}\mathbf{x}_3 & - \mathbf{A}_1'\boldsymbol{\zeta} & + \mathbf{A}_1'\boldsymbol{\xi} & + \mathbf{I}\mathbf{v}_1 & & & + \mathbf{E}_1\mathbf{u} = & -\mathbf{c}_1', \\
2\mathbf{D}_{21}\mathbf{x}_1 + & 2\mathbf{D}_{22}\mathbf{x}_2 + & 2\mathbf{D}_{23}\mathbf{x}_3 & - \mathbf{A}_2'\boldsymbol{\zeta} & + \mathbf{A}_2'\boldsymbol{\xi} & & + \mathbf{I}\mathbf{v}_2 & & + \mathbf{E}_2\mathbf{u} = & -\mathbf{c}_2', \\
2\mathbf{D}_{31}\mathbf{x}_1 + & 2\mathbf{D}_{32}\mathbf{x}_2 + & 2\mathbf{D}_{33}\mathbf{x}_3 & - \mathbf{A}_3'\boldsymbol{\zeta} & + \mathbf{A}_3'\boldsymbol{\xi} & & & + \mathbf{I}\mathbf{v}_3 & + \mathbf{E}_3\mathbf{u} = & -\mathbf{c}_3'.
\end{array} \tag{7–19}$$

The last n constraints are partitioned exactly as $\mathbf{x}$ and $\mathbf{v}$ are.

Consider now the dual of the linear programming problem (7–18). Let the row vector $(\mathbf{s}, \mathbf{t}_1, \mathbf{t}_2, \mathbf{t}_3)$ be an optimal solution to the dual, where this $(m + n)$-component vector has been partitioned in the same way as the rows of (7–19). In the analysis to follow, it is unnecessary to include dual variables corresponding to the constraints $\mathbf{v}_1 = \mathbf{0}$, $\mathbf{x}_2 = \mathbf{0}$ in (7–18). Instead, we can merely think of these latter constraints as having the effect of removing from $\mathbf{Q}$ the columns corresponding to $\mathbf{v}_1$ and $\mathbf{x}_2$, that is, one has precisely the same linear programming problem he would obtain if he imagined that the variables in $\mathbf{v}_1$ and $\mathbf{x}_2$ did not exist. Thus the constraints which the solution to the dual must satisfy are:

$$\begin{aligned}
\mathbf{sA}_1 + 2\mathbf{t}_1\mathbf{D}_{11} + 2\mathbf{t}_2\mathbf{D}_{21} + 2\mathbf{t}_3\mathbf{D}_{31} &= \mathbf{0},\\
\mathbf{sA}_3 + 2\mathbf{t}_1\mathbf{D}_{13} + 2\mathbf{t}_2\mathbf{D}_{23} + 2\mathbf{t}_3\mathbf{D}_{33} &\geq \mathbf{0},\\
\mathbf{t}_1\mathbf{A}_1' + \mathbf{t}_2\mathbf{A}_2' + \mathbf{t}_3\mathbf{A}_3' &= \mathbf{0},\\
\mathbf{t}_2 &= \mathbf{0},\\
\mathbf{t}_3 &\geq \mathbf{0},\\
\mathbf{t}_1\mathbf{E}_1 + \mathbf{t}_2\mathbf{E}_2 + \mathbf{t}_3\mathbf{E}_3 &\geq -\mathbf{1},
\end{aligned} \tag{7–20}$$

and since the solution to the dual is optimal, it must be true that the primal and dual objective functions are equal, that is,

$$\max Z = \mathbf{sb} - \mathbf{t}_1\mathbf{c}_1' - \mathbf{t}_2\mathbf{c}_2' - \mathbf{t}_3\mathbf{c}_3'. \tag{7–21}$$

In the first set of constraints in (7–20), an equality sign appears because of the complementary slackness principle mentioned in Section 2–5. Since the components of $\mathbf{x}_1$ are positive, the corresponding dual constraints must hold as strict equalities; for the same reason, $\mathbf{t}_2 = \mathbf{0}$. The third set of constraints holds as strict equalities because the two sets of constraints corresponding to $\boldsymbol{\zeta}$ and $\boldsymbol{\xi}$ were combined, or, since the components of $\boldsymbol{\lambda}$ are unrestricted in sign, the corresponding dual constraints hold as strict equalities. The vector $\mathbf{1}$ is a column vector each of whose elements is unity.

Let us now examine the constraints (7–20) in more detail to see what must be true of the optimal solution to the dual. Multiplying the first set of constraints in (7–20) on the right by $\mathbf{t}_1'$ and the second set by $\mathbf{t}_3'$, we obtain, after using $\mathbf{t}_2 = \mathbf{0}$, $\mathbf{t}_3 \geq \mathbf{0}$,

$$\begin{aligned}
\mathbf{sA}_1\mathbf{t}_1' + 2\mathbf{t}_1\mathbf{D}_{11}\mathbf{t}_1' + 2\mathbf{t}_3\mathbf{D}_{31}\mathbf{t}_1' &= 0,\\
\mathbf{sA}_3\mathbf{t}_3' + 2\mathbf{t}_1\mathbf{D}_{13}\mathbf{t}_3' + 2\mathbf{t}_3\mathbf{D}_{33}\mathbf{t}_3' &\geq 0.
\end{aligned}$$

Adding these two relations, we can write

$$\mathbf{s}[\mathbf{A}_1\mathbf{t}_1' + \mathbf{A}_3\mathbf{t}_3'] + 2(\mathbf{t}_1, \mathbf{t}_3)\begin{bmatrix}\mathbf{D}_{11} & \mathbf{D}_{13}\\ \mathbf{D}_{31} & \mathbf{D}_{33}\end{bmatrix}\begin{bmatrix}\mathbf{t}_1'\\ \mathbf{t}_3'\end{bmatrix} \geq 0, \tag{7–22}$$

but, from the third set of constraints in (7–20), it follows that the first term in (7–22) vanishes. Furthermore, the second term is $2\mathbf{x}'\mathbf{D}\mathbf{x}$ evaluated for a particular $\mathbf{x}$ determined by $\mathbf{t}_1$, $\mathbf{t}_2$, $\mathbf{t}_3$. However, recall that $\mathbf{x}'\mathbf{D}\mathbf{x}$ is negative definite. Hence, if (7–22) is to hold, it must be true that $\mathbf{t}_1 = \mathbf{0}$, $\mathbf{t}_3 = \mathbf{0}$. It is at this point that we need the fact that $\mathbf{x}'\mathbf{D}\mathbf{x}$ is negative definite. If $\mathbf{x}'\mathbf{D}\mathbf{x}$ was only negative semidefinite, we could not be certain that $\mathbf{t}_1 = \mathbf{0}$, $\mathbf{t}_3 = \mathbf{0}$, since there exist $\mathbf{x} \neq \mathbf{0}$ for which

$$\mathbf{x}'\mathbf{D}\mathbf{x} = 0.$$

We now know that $\mathbf{t}_1 = \mathbf{0}$, $\mathbf{t}_2 = \mathbf{0}$, $\mathbf{t}_3 = \mathbf{0}$. Consequently, from the first set of constraints in (7–20), we see that $\mathbf{s}\mathbf{A}_1 = \mathbf{0}$, or on multiplying on the right by $\mathbf{x}_1$, $\mathbf{s}\mathbf{A}_1\mathbf{x}_1 = 0$. However, $\mathbf{A}_1\mathbf{x}_1 = \mathbf{b}$. Therefore $\mathbf{s}\mathbf{b} = 0$. But from (7–21) this implies that $\max Z = 0$, that is, $u_j = 0$, $j = 1, \ldots, n$, and the solution we obtained to (7–16) when it was impossible to make any additional iterations while holding $\mathbf{x}'\mathbf{v} = 0$ is the solution we wished to obtain. Thus we have shown that the computational procedure does terminate in the manner desired. In the above we have implicitly assumed that degeneracy was no problem and that cycling did not occur. This can be guaranteed by using one of the standard procedures for resolving the degeneracy problem in linear programming (see {LP 6–1} through {LP 6–8}).

7–4 Charnes' resolution of the semidefinite case. The case of $\mathbf{x}'\mathbf{D}\mathbf{x}$ negative semidefinite rather than negative definite troubled us in two different ways in the computational scheme introduced in Section 7–2. First, when $\mathbf{x}'\mathbf{D}\mathbf{x}$ is semidefinite, there exists the possibility that the quadratic programming problem has an unbounded solution, so that there may not be any solution to (7–9) with $\mathbf{x} \geq \mathbf{0}$; $\mathbf{v} \geq \mathbf{0}$. Secondly, even if the quadratic programming problem has an optimal solution, it is not certain that when the computational procedure terminates, the desired solution has been obtained.

The interesting thing to note about the semidefinite case is that it is a razor's edge case. By this we mean that a negative semidefinite form $\mathbf{x}'\mathbf{D}\mathbf{x}$ can be converted into a negative definite form by making an arbitrarily small change in the diagonal elements of $\mathbf{D}$. In particular, if $\mathbf{x}'\mathbf{D}\mathbf{x}$ is negative semidefinite, then $\mathbf{x}'(\mathbf{D} + \epsilon\mathbf{I})\mathbf{x}$ is negative definite for any $\epsilon < 0$, however small $|\epsilon|$. To prove this, note that $\mathbf{x}'\mathbf{D}\mathbf{x} \leq 0$ for any $\mathbf{x}$ and $\epsilon\mathbf{x}'\mathbf{I}\mathbf{x} < 0$ for any $\mathbf{x} \neq \mathbf{0}$. Thus $\mathbf{x}'(\mathbf{D} + \epsilon\mathbf{I})\mathbf{x} < 0$ for any $\mathbf{x} \neq \mathbf{0}$, and the form is negative definite. Consequently, if we have a quadratic programming problem in which we know that $\mathbf{x}'\mathbf{D}\mathbf{x}$ is either negative semidefinite or negative definite, we can make sure that the form is negative definite by subtracting a unit in perhaps the fourth or fifth decimal place of each diagonal element of **D**. In this fashion, the perturbation can be made small enough that it in no way affects the numerical results obtained. The one case where such a perturbation could influence the numerical answer is that where $\mathbf{x}'\mathbf{D}\mathbf{x}$ was originally indefinite and the problem had an unbounded solution. However, just as in linear programming, properly formulated problems should not have unbounded solutions, and hence no difficulty should arise.

Generally, the method developed in Section 7–2 will work even if $\mathbf{x}'\mathbf{D}\mathbf{x}$ is semidefinite, and consequently the usual procedure is to try it without attempting first to perturb **D**.

Charnes has suggested this perturbation technique for resolving the semidefinite case in [4]. The reader may have been wondering how one determines ahead of time whether or not $\mathbf{x}'\mathbf{D}\mathbf{x}$ might be indefinite, positive definite, or positive semidefinite instead of negative definite or negative semidefinite. In simple cases, this can be done by inspection. In general, however, one must determine the characteristic values of **D**. This can be a very difficult task, and thus the nature of $\mathbf{x}'\mathbf{D}\mathbf{x}$ is usually ascertained by economic or physical arguments concerning the nature of the problem.

7–5 Wolfe's approach for treating the parametric objective function.

Wolfe [16] introduced a much more intricate procedure for handling the semidefinite case than the one considered above. From a practical point of view, the technique discussed in the previous section is more appropriate for treating the problems arising from the semidefinite case. Wolfe's procedure is of interest, not so much for the way in which it handles the semidefinite case, but rather for the parametric procedure it introduces for solving, for all values of $\theta \geq 0$, the quadratic programming problem whose objective function is

$$z = \theta \mathbf{c}\mathbf{x} + \mathbf{x}'\mathbf{D}\mathbf{x}. \tag{7–23}$$

Problems for which one wishes to obtain a solution for all $\theta \geq 0$ have been discussed by Markowitz in his work on portfolio selection [13].

We shall concern ourselves in the following only with the problem of solving for all $\theta \geq 0$ the quadratic programming problem whose objective function is (7–23), in the case where $\mathbf{x}'\mathbf{D}\mathbf{x}$ is negative definite. The procedure will usually work also when $\mathbf{x}'\mathbf{D}\mathbf{x}$ is semidefinite, but to guarantee its success we must imagine that $\mathbf{x}'\mathbf{D}\mathbf{x}$ has been perturbed, if necessary, to make it negative definite. No attempt will be made to show how Wolfe generalized the procedure to handle the semidefinite case without perturbing $\mathbf{x}'\mathbf{D}\mathbf{x}$. Since we are assuming that $\mathbf{x}'\mathbf{D}\mathbf{x}$ is negative definite, there will exist a unique optimal solution for every $\theta \geq 0$. The first step in the process then is to solve the problem for $\theta = 0$, i.e., in the case where $z = \mathbf{x}'\mathbf{D}\mathbf{x}$.

Consider next the method for increasing θ. What we would like to do is trace out the sequence of basic solutions to

$$\begin{bmatrix} \mathbf{A} & \mathbf{0} & \mathbf{0} & \mathbf{0} \\ 2\mathbf{D} & -\mathbf{A}' & \mathbf{A}' & \mathbf{I} \end{bmatrix} \begin{bmatrix} \mathbf{x} \\ \boldsymbol{\zeta} \\ \boldsymbol{\xi} \\ \mathbf{v} \end{bmatrix} = \begin{bmatrix} \mathbf{b} \\ -\theta\mathbf{c}' \end{bmatrix} = \begin{bmatrix} \mathbf{b} \\ \mathbf{0} \end{bmatrix} + \theta \begin{bmatrix} \mathbf{0} \\ -\mathbf{c}' \end{bmatrix} \tag{7–24}$$

with non-negative variables and $\mathbf{x}'\mathbf{v} = 0$ as θ varies from 0 to ∞, when we have such a basic solution for $\theta = 0$. This is very similar to a problem in parametric programming where the requirements vector is to be parametrized (see {LP 11–4}).

Write $\mathbf{r} = [\mathbf{x}, \boldsymbol{\zeta}, \boldsymbol{\xi}, \mathbf{v}]$ and let $\mathbf{B}_Q^{-1}$ be the inverse of the basis matrix obtained by solving the problem for $\theta = 0$. It will be assumed that if any of the u_j appeared in the final basis at a zero level, they have been removed. This can always be done (why?). Denote by $\mathbf{r}_B$ the basic solution so that $\mathbf{r}_B = \mathbf{B}_Q^{-1}[\mathbf{b}, \mathbf{0}]$. Also write

$$\mathbf{h} = \mathbf{B}_Q^{-1}[\mathbf{0}, -\mathbf{c}']. \tag{7–25}$$

Denote by $\hat{\mathbf{r}}_B$ the values of the basic variables for the basic solution under consideration for the case where $\theta > 0$. Then

$$\hat{\mathbf{r}}_B = \mathbf{B}_Q^{-1}\{[\mathbf{b}, \mathbf{0}] + \theta[\mathbf{0}, -\mathbf{c}']\} = \mathbf{r}_B + \theta\mathbf{h}. \tag{7–26}$$

This basic solution will be feasible if

$$\hat{r}_{Bi} = r_{Bi} + \theta h_i \geq 0, \qquad i = 1, \ldots, m + n. \tag{7–27}$$

In the event that $h_i \geq 0$ for all i, the initial basic solution will be feasible for all $\theta \geq 0$, and the optimal basis for the quadratic programming problem will be independent of θ. However, if one or more $h_i < 0$, the solution will no longer be feasible when

$$\theta > \theta_1 = \min_i \left\{ -\frac{r_{Bi}}{h_i} \right\}, \qquad h_i < 0. \tag{7–28}$$

To maintain feasibility as θ passes through θ_1, it is necessary to make a change in the basis. Note that when $\theta = \theta_1$, at least one of the basic variables will be zero. Let us agree always to replace the basic variable (or one of the basic variables), call it x_{B_u}, which has been driven to zero at $\theta = \theta_1$. The new vector will enter the basis at a zero level. We must next decide how to choose the vector to enter the basis. After changing the basis, we would like to be able to increase θ some more. If $\mathbf{q}_j$ is to enter the basis, and if $\mathbf{y}_j = \mathbf{B}_Q^{-1}\mathbf{q}_j$, the new value of the uth component of $\mathbf{h}$ will be h_u/y_{uj}. However, $h_u < 0$, and hence, to be able to increase

θ above θ_1, it is necessary that $y_{uj} < 0$, so that the new value of the uth component of $\mathbf{h}$ is positive. The reason for this is as follows. When $\theta = \theta_1$, the value of the uth basic variable for the new basis is 0, since the vector enters the basis at a zero level. Hence its value for $\theta > \theta_1$ is $(\theta - \theta_1)h_u/y_{uj}$ which will be negative unless $y_{uj} < 0$. Any vector with $y_{uj} < 0$ which when its level in the basis becomes positive does not violate $\mathbf{x}'\mathbf{v} = 0$ will do. We can then proceed using the new basic solution to increase θ until one of the basic variables becomes zero, at which point another change of basis must be made, etc. Thus we obtain a sequence of critical values of θ, $\theta_0 = 0, \theta_1, \theta_2, \ldots, \theta_k < \theta_{k+1}$ such that for all θ lying in the interval $\theta_k \leq \theta \leq \theta_{k+1}$, the same basis matrix will be optimal. Since there is only a finite number of different bases, the above procedure can terminate in only one of two ways: (a) a point is reached where no vector allowed to enter basis has $y_{uj} < 0$, or (b) θ can be increased arbitrarily and the given basis will remain optimal. We shall show below that only case (b) can occur.

For each of the critical values θ_k, there exists an optimal solution $\mathbf{x}_k^*$ to the quadratic programming problem. It is easy to determine the optimal solution $\mathbf{x}^*$ for any θ, $\theta_k \leq \theta \leq \theta_{k+1}$, using only $\mathbf{x}_k^*$ and $\mathbf{x}_{k+1}^*$. From what we obtained above, if $\mathbf{B}_Q$ is the basis matrix for θ in the range $\theta_k \leq \theta \leq \theta_{k+1}$, $\mathbf{r}_{Bk}$ is the basic solution at θ_k appropriate to $\mathbf{B}_Q$, and $\mathbf{r}_{B,k+1}$ is the corresponding basic solution at θ_{k+1} (before the change to a new basis is made), then

$$\mathbf{r}_{Bk} = \mathbf{B}_Q^{-1}\{[\mathbf{b}, \mathbf{0}] + \theta_k[\mathbf{0}, -\mathbf{c}']\}; \quad \mathbf{r}_{B,k+1} = \mathbf{B}_Q^{-1}\{[\mathbf{b}, \mathbf{0}] + \theta_{k+1}[\mathbf{0}, -\mathbf{c}']\},$$

or

$$\mathbf{r}_{B,k+1} = \mathbf{r}_{Bk} + (\theta_{k+1} - \theta_k)\mathbf{h}, \qquad \text{where} \qquad \mathbf{h} = \mathbf{B}_Q^{-1}[\mathbf{0}, -\mathbf{c}'].$$

Similarly, for any θ, $\theta_k \leq \theta \leq \theta_{k+1}$, the corresponding basic solution $\mathbf{r}_B$ is

$$\mathbf{r}_B = \mathbf{r}_{Bk} + (\theta - \theta_k)\mathbf{h}$$
$$= \left[\left(1 - \frac{\theta - \theta_k}{\theta_{k+1} - \theta_k}\right)\mathbf{r}_{Bk} + \left(\frac{\theta - \theta_k}{\theta_{k+1} - \theta_k}\right)\mathbf{r}_{B,k+1}\right]. \tag{7-29}$$

Hence

$$\mathbf{x}^* = \left[\left(1 - \frac{\theta - \theta_k}{\theta_{k+1} - \theta_k}\right)\mathbf{x}_k^* + \left(\frac{\theta - \theta_k}{\theta_{k+1} - \theta_k}\right)\mathbf{x}_{k+1}^*\right], \tag{7-30}$$

since $\mathbf{x}_{k+1}^*$ is the same before and after the change of basis at θ_{k+1}. If after the change of basis at θ_k is made, the new basis remains optimal for all $\theta > \theta_k$, then for any $\theta > \theta_k$,

$$\mathbf{r}_B = \mathbf{r}_{Bk} + (\theta - \theta_k)\mathbf{h} \qquad \text{or} \qquad \mathbf{x}^* = \mathbf{x}_k^* + (\theta - \theta_k)\mathbf{t}, \tag{7-31}$$

where $t_j = 0$ if x_j is not a basic variable and $t_j = h_i$ if $x_j = r_{Bi}$.

We can now make the interesting observation that in generating the sequence of θ_k by a series of basis changes in (7–24), we are really proceeding as though we were solving the linear programming problem

$$\begin{bmatrix} \mathbf{A} & \mathbf{0} & \mathbf{0} & \mathbf{0} & \mathbf{0} \\ 2\mathbf{D} & -\mathbf{A}' & \mathbf{A}' & \mathbf{I} & \mathbf{c}' \end{bmatrix} \begin{bmatrix} \mathbf{x} \\ \boldsymbol{\zeta} \\ \boldsymbol{\xi} \\ \mathbf{v} \\ \theta \end{bmatrix} = \begin{bmatrix} \mathbf{b} \\ \mathbf{0} \end{bmatrix}, \tag{7–32}$$

$$[\mathbf{x}, \boldsymbol{\zeta}, \boldsymbol{\xi}, \mathbf{v}, \theta] \geq \mathbf{0},$$

$$\max Z_\theta = \theta,$$

under the restriction $\mathbf{x}'\mathbf{v} = 0$. This is precisely what we were doing above. Note that there is no contradiction here in the fact that θ now appears in the basis, since we noted previously that for the critical values of θ, at least one variable in a basic solution to (7–24) would be zero. Hence for the critical values of θ, a basic solution to (7–24) contained no more than $m + n - 1$ positive variables. Since for (7–32) there can be $m + n$ positive values, one of which will be θ, the other $m + n - 1$ are nothing but the values of the basic variables for the corresponding basic solution to (7–24). The solution of (7–32), beginning with the basic feasible solution corresponding to $\theta = 0$, provides a convenient way of determining the set of critical values of θ as iterations are made to increase θ.

Let us now show that (7–32) has an unbounded solution and that we must always end in what was referred to above as case (b). Suppose on the contrary that a point was reached where for all vectors allowed to enter the basis under the restriction $\mathbf{x}'\mathbf{v} = 0$, the optimality criterion was satisfied. Then proceed exactly as in Section 7–3, considering the associated linear programming problem and its dual. The dual will have the form (7–20), except that the last constraint will read

$$\mathbf{t}_1\mathbf{c}_1 + \mathbf{t}_2\mathbf{c}_2 + \mathbf{t}_3\mathbf{c}_3 \geq 1, \tag{7–33}$$

instead of

$$\mathbf{t}_1\mathbf{E}_1 + \mathbf{t}_2\mathbf{E}_2 + \mathbf{t}_3\mathbf{E}_3 \geq -1. \tag{7–34}$$

The analysis of Section 7–3 shows that an optimal solution to the dual must have $\mathbf{t}_1 = \mathbf{t}_2 = \mathbf{t}_3 = \mathbf{0}$. But this solution must also satisfy (7–33), which is impossible. Thus the computation involving (7–32) must terminate with an unbounded solution.

7–6 Example. As an example of the computational procedure developed in Section 7–2, we shall solve again the problem considered in Section 4–8, since it is a quadratic programming problem. Recall that the problem is

$$\begin{aligned} 2x_1 + 3x_2 + x_3 &= 6, \\ 2x_1 + x_2 + x_4 &= 4, \\ x_1, x_2, x_3, x_4 &\geq 0, \\ \max z &= 2x_1 + x_2 - x_1^2. \end{aligned} \tag{7–35}$$

In the notation of Section 7–2, $\mathbf{x}'\mathbf{D}\mathbf{x} = -x_1^2$, and the quadratic form is clearly negative semidefinite. Furthermore

$$\mathbf{A} = \begin{bmatrix} 2 & 3 & 1 & 0 \\ 2 & 1 & 0 & 1 \end{bmatrix}; \qquad \mathbf{D} = \begin{bmatrix} -1 & 0 & 0 & 0 \\ 0 & 0 & 0 & 0 \\ 0 & 0 & 0 & 0 \\ 0 & 0 & 0 & 0 \end{bmatrix}$$

$$\mathbf{c} = (2, 1, 0, 0); \qquad \mathbf{b} = [6, 4].$$

For this example, the set of augmented equations (7–16) with which we begin is (7–36). Even though $\mathbf{x}'\mathbf{D}\mathbf{x}$ is only negative semidefinite, we shall see that the computational procedure of Section 7–2 will work without difficulty even if no perturbation of the type discussed in Section 7–4 is used. In this case, it is easy to provide a basic feasible solution to the constraints $\mathbf{A}\mathbf{x} = \mathbf{b}$ without going through a Phase I computation. Such a solution is $x_1 = \frac{3}{2}$, $x_2 = 1$, $x_3 = x_4 = 0$. For this solution,

$$\mathbf{B} = \begin{bmatrix} 2 & 3 \\ 2 & 1 \end{bmatrix}; \qquad \mathbf{B}^{-1} = \begin{bmatrix} -\frac{1}{4} & \frac{3}{4} \\ \frac{1}{2} & -\frac{1}{2} \end{bmatrix}; \qquad 2\mathbf{D}_B = \begin{bmatrix} -2 & 0 \\ 0 & 0 \\ 0 & 0 \\ 0 & 0 \end{bmatrix}$$

Next it is necessary to determine the values of Δ_j and the initial values of the u_j. On setting $\boldsymbol{\zeta} = \boldsymbol{\xi} = \mathbf{0}$, $\mathbf{v} = \mathbf{0}$, we find from the third constraint of (7–36), using $x_1 = \frac{3}{2}$, that $\Delta_1 u_1 = 1$. Thus $\Delta_1 = 1$, $u_1 = 1$. From the fourth constraint, $\Delta_2 u_2 = -1$ so that $\Delta_2 = -1$, $u_2 = 1$. Finally from the fifth and sixth constraints $\Delta_3 u_3 = \Delta_4 u_4 = 0$ so that we can take $\Delta_3 = \Delta_4 = 1$ and $u_3 = u_4 = 0$. At this point we might note that, instead of having u_3 and u_4, we can equally well have v_3 and v_4 in the initial basic solution at a zero level. Since this approach does no harm and might quite possibly eliminate some iterations, we shall insert v_3 and v_4 at a zero level instead of u_3 and u_4. This means that in reality we never need to consider the variables u_3 and u_4. They may be omitted completely.

The initial basis matrix $\mathbf{B}_Q$ will then have as its first two columns the vectors corresponding to x_1 and x_2, respectively, as its third and fourth columns the vectors corresponding to u_1 and u_2, respectively, and as its last two columns the vectors corresponding to v_3, v_4, respectively.

$$\begin{aligned}
&2x_1 + 3x_2 + x_3 &&= 6\\
&2x_1 + x_2 + x_4 &&= 4\\
&-2x_1 - 2\zeta_1 + 2\xi_1 - 2\zeta_2 + 2\xi_2 + v_1 + \Delta_1 u_1 &&= -2\\
&- 3\zeta_1 + 3\xi_1 - \zeta_2 + \xi_2 + v_2 + \Delta_2 u_2 &&= -1\\
&- \zeta_1 + \xi_1 + v_3 + \Delta_3 u_3 &&= 0\\
&- \zeta_2 + \xi_2 + v_4 + \Delta_4 u_4 &&= 0
\end{aligned} \tag{7-36}$$

$$\mathbf{B}_Q = \begin{bmatrix} 2 & 3 & 0 & 0 & 0 & 0\\ 2 & 1 & 0 & 0 & 0 & 0\\ -2 & 0 & 1 & 0 & 0 & 0\\ 0 & 0 & 0 & -1 & 0 & 0\\ 0 & 0 & 0 & 0 & 1 & 0\\ 0 & 0 & 0 & 0 & 0 & 1 \end{bmatrix}; \quad \mathbf{B}_Q^{-1} = \begin{bmatrix} -\frac{1}{4} & \frac{3}{4} & 0 & 0 & 0 & 0\\ \frac{1}{2} & -\frac{1}{2} & 0 & 0 & 0 & 0\\ -\frac{1}{2} & \frac{3}{2} & 1 & 0 & 0 & 0\\ 0 & 0 & 0 & -1 & 0 & 0\\ 0 & 0 & 0 & 0 & 1 & 0\\ 0 & 0 & 0 & 0 & 0 & 1 \end{bmatrix} \tag{7-37}$$

This $\mathbf{B}_Q$ is shown in (7–37). Also, $\mathbf{B}_Q^{-1}$ computed using (7–14) is shown in (7–37). The initial basic feasible solution to the set of augmented constraints is then $x_1 = \frac{3}{2}$, $x_2 = 1$, $u_1 = 1$, $u_2 = 1$, $v_3 = v_4 = 0$, with all other variables at a zero level. It is desired to maximize $Z = -u_1 - u_2$; the value of Z corresponding to the initial basic feasible solution is -2. The revised simplex method will be used for maximizing Z. The only unusual thing about its application is that we maintain $x_j v_j = 0$.

The vectors corresponding to the variables not in the basis are

$$\mathbf{q}_{x_3} = \mathbf{e}_1; \quad \mathbf{q}_{x_4} = \mathbf{e}_2; \quad \mathbf{q}_{\zeta_1} = [0, 0, -2, -3, -1, 0] = -\mathbf{q}_{\xi_1};$$
$$\mathbf{q}_{\zeta_2} = [0, 0, -2, -1, 0, -1] = -\mathbf{q}_{\xi_2}; \quad \mathbf{q}_{v_1} = \mathbf{e}_3; \quad \mathbf{q}_{v_2} = \mathbf{e}_4.$$

The price of each variable not in the basis is zero, and hence for all vectors that will be considered for entrance into the basis, one must examine only the sign of the Z_j. For the initial basic solution,

$$\mathbf{c}_B = (0, 0, -1, -1, 0, 0), \qquad \mathbf{c}_B\mathbf{B}_Q^{-1} = (\tfrac{1}{2}, -\tfrac{3}{2}, -1, 1, 0, 0),$$

and, since $Z_j = \mathbf{c}_B\mathbf{B}_Q^{-1}\mathbf{q}_j$,

$$Z_{x_3} = \tfrac{1}{2}; \quad Z_{x_4} = -\tfrac{3}{2}; \quad Z_{\zeta_1} = -1; \quad Z_{\xi_1} = 1;$$
$$Z_{\zeta_2} = 1; \quad Z_{\xi_2} = -1; \quad Z_{v_1} = -1; \quad Z_{v_2} = 1.$$

TABLEAUX FOR SOLUTION OF EXAMPLE

Table 7–1. Tableau 1

Variables in basis	$\boldsymbol{\beta}_1$	$\boldsymbol{\beta}_2$	$\boldsymbol{\beta}_3$	$\boldsymbol{\beta}_4$	$\boldsymbol{\beta}_5$	$\boldsymbol{\beta}_6$	$\mathbf{q}_B^{(1)}$	$\mathbf{y}_k^{(1)}$
Z	$\frac{1}{2}$	$-\frac{3}{2}$	-1	1	0	0	-2	$-\frac{3}{2}$
x_1	$-\frac{1}{4}$	$\frac{3}{4}$	0	0	0	0	$\frac{3}{2}$	$\frac{3}{4}$
x_2	$\frac{1}{2}$	$-\frac{1}{2}$	0	0	0	0	1	$-\frac{1}{2}$
u_1	$-\frac{1}{2}$	$\frac{3}{2}$	1	0	0	0	1	$\textcircled{\frac{3}{2}}$
u_2	0	0	0	-1	0	0	1	0
v_3	0	0	0	0	1	0	0	0
v_4	0	0	0	0	0	1	0	0

Table 7–2. Tableau 2

Z	0	0	0	1	0	0	-1	-3
x_1	0	0	$-\frac{1}{2}$	0	0	0	1	1
x_2	$\frac{1}{3}$	0	$\frac{1}{3}$	0	0	0	$\frac{4}{3}$	$-\frac{2}{3}$
x_4	$-\frac{1}{3}$	1	$\frac{2}{3}$	0	0	0	$\frac{2}{3}$	$-\frac{4}{3}$
u_2	0	0	0	-1	0	0	1	$\textcircled{3}$
v_3	0	0	0	0	1	0	0	-1
v_4	0	0	0	0	0	1	0	0

The minimum value of the Z_j is $-\frac{3}{2}$, the minimum being taken on for the variable x_4. Now v_4 is in the basis, but at a zero level. Thus it is permissible to allow x_4 to become positive if v_4 remains at a zero level. This will indeed be the case. Therefore at the first iteration $\mathbf{q}_{x_4}$ enters the basis. The initial tableau is shown in Table 7–1. It is seen that $\mathbf{q}_{u_1}$ must leave the basis so that u_1 is driven to zero. The new tableau is given in Table 7–2. Note that v_4 does remain at a zero level. The new values of the Z_j are

$$Z_{x_3} = 0;\; Z_{\zeta_1} = -3;\; Z_{\xi_1} = 3;\; Z_{\zeta_2} = -1;\; Z_{\xi_2} = 1;\; Z_{v_1} = 0;\; Z_{v_2} = 1.$$

At the next iteration $\mathbf{q}_{\zeta_1}$ enters the basis. From Table 7–2 it is seen that

$\mathbf{q}_{u_2}$ leaves the basis and u_2 is driven to zero. Consequently, all the artificial variables have been driven to zero, Z has been maximized, and the desired solution has been obtained. It is thus unnecessary to transform all of Table 7–2. Only the $\mathbf{q}_B^{(1)}$-column needs to be transformed. The new values of basic variables after u_2 is driven to zero are $x_1 = \frac{2}{3}$, $x_2 = \frac{14}{9}$, $x_4 = \frac{10}{9}$, $\lambda_1 = \frac{1}{3}$, $v_3 = \frac{1}{3}$, $v_4 = 0$. Thus a solution to (7–9) has been found with $\mathbf{x} \geq \mathbf{0}$, $\mathbf{v} \geq \mathbf{0}$. It is $x_1 = \frac{2}{3}$, $x_2 = \frac{14}{9}$, $x_3 = 0$, $x_4 = \frac{10}{9}$, $\lambda_1 = \frac{1}{3}$, $\lambda_2 = 0$, $v_1 = v_2 = 0$, $v_3 = \frac{1}{3}$, $v_4 = 0$. The unique optimal solution to the quadratic programming problem is $x_1^* = \frac{2}{3}$, $x_2^* = \frac{14}{9}$, $x_3^* = 0$, $x_4^* = \frac{10}{9}$. This is, of course, the same result that was obtained by the graphical technique in Chapter 4. In addition to illustrating how to solve quadratic programming problems by the technique presented in Section 7–2, this example also points out that even the most trivial quadratic programming problems lead to sizable problems to which the simplex method is to be applied. In solving a quadratic programming problem in practice, one should give careful consideration to the question of whether the approximate techniques of Chapter 4 would yield a sufficiently accurate answer with less computational effort than the method discussed here.

To illustrate the parametric technique discussed in Section 7–5, we shall solve (7–36) when the objective function is replaced by

$$z = 2\theta x_1 + \theta x_2 - x_1^2$$

for all $\theta \geq 0$. We shall see that for $\theta = 1$, precisely the same solution will be obtained as above.

The procedure in this case is to first solve the problem by the method of Section 7–2 when $\theta = 0$. We then wish to maximize $z = -x_1^2$. It is clear that an optimal solution is $x_1 = 0$ and x_2 having any value between 0 and 2. We can immediately write down an optimal basic feasible solution to (7–36). The values of the basic variables are $x_2 = x_4 = 2$, $v_1 = 0$, $u_2 = 0$, $v_3 = 0$, $u_4 = 0$. The revised simplex tableau corresponding to this basic solution is shown in Table 7–3. Before we can attempt to increase θ, we must remove u_2, u_4 from the basis. This is done by making arbitrary insertions, as shown in Tables 7–4 and 7–5. Note that ζ_1 replaced u_2 and ζ_2 replaced u_4. In making the insertions, the rule was followed that if x_j was in the basis, v_j was not allowed to enter, and vice versa.

Having obtained Table 7–5, we now proceed to maximize θ. Note that the price of every vector except $[\mathbf{0}, \mathbf{c}']$ is zero, and the price of $[\mathbf{0}, \mathbf{c}']$ is 1. At the first iteration, θ goes into the basis at a zero level to yield Table 7–6. Next x_1 enters the basis and replaces x_4. The value of θ increases from 0 to $\frac{9}{4}$. On attempting to insert v_4 into the basis, one sees that there is an unbounded solution, and the computation terminates. We see that $x_1 = \frac{3}{2}$, $x_2 = 1$, $\theta = \frac{9}{4} + \delta$, $\zeta_1 = \frac{3}{4}$, $v_3 = \frac{3}{4}$, $\zeta_2 = \delta$, $v_4 = \delta$ is a solution to (7–32) for any $\delta \geq 0$. Furthermore, the variables exclusive of

SOLUTION FOR ALL $\theta \geq 0$

TABLE 7-3. TABLEAU 1

Variables in basis	$\boldsymbol{\beta}_1$	$\boldsymbol{\beta}_2$	$\boldsymbol{\beta}_3$	$\boldsymbol{\beta}_4$	$\boldsymbol{\beta}_5$	$\boldsymbol{\beta}_6$	$\mathbf{r}_B^{(1)}$	$\mathbf{y}_k^{(1)}$
Z_θ	0	0	0	0	0	0	0	0
x_2	$\frac{1}{3}$	0	0	0	0	0	2	0
x_4	$-\frac{1}{3}$	1	0	0	0	0	2	0
v_1	0	0	1	0	0	0	0	-2
u_2	0	0	0	1	0	0	0	-3 (circled)
v_3	0	0	0	0	1	0	0	-1
u_4	0	0	0	0	0	1	0	0

TABLE 7-4. TABLEAU 2

Variables in basis	$\boldsymbol{\beta}_1$	$\boldsymbol{\beta}_2$	$\boldsymbol{\beta}_3$	$\boldsymbol{\beta}_4$	$\boldsymbol{\beta}_5$	$\boldsymbol{\beta}_6$	$\mathbf{r}_B^{(1)}$	$\mathbf{y}_k^{(1)}$
Z_θ	0	0	0	0	0	0	0	0
x_2	$\frac{1}{3}$	0	0	0	0	0	2	0
x_4	$-\frac{1}{3}$	1	0	0	0	0	2	0
v_1	0	0	1	$-\frac{2}{3}$	0	0	0	$-\frac{4}{3}$
ζ_1	0	0	0	$-\frac{1}{3}$	0	0	0	$\frac{1}{3}$
v_3	0	0	0	$-\frac{1}{3}$	1	0	0	$\frac{1}{3}$
u_4	0	0	0	0	0	1	0	-1 (circled)

TABLE 7-5. TABLEAU 3

Variables in basis	$\boldsymbol{\beta}_1$	$\boldsymbol{\beta}_2$	$\boldsymbol{\beta}_3$	$\boldsymbol{\beta}_4$	$\boldsymbol{\beta}_5$	$\boldsymbol{\beta}_6$	$\mathbf{r}_B^{(1)}$	$\mathbf{y}_k^{(1)}$
Z_θ	0	0	0	0	0	0	0	-1
x_2	$\frac{1}{3}$	0	0	0	0	0	2	0
x_4	$-\frac{1}{3}$	1	0	0	0	0	2	0
v_1	0	0	1	$-\frac{2}{3}$	0	$-\frac{4}{3}$	0	$\frac{4}{3}$ (circled)
ζ_1	0	0	0	$-\frac{1}{3}$	0	$\frac{1}{3}$	0	$-\frac{1}{3}$
v_3	0	0	0	$-\frac{1}{3}$	1	$\frac{1}{3}$	0	$-\frac{1}{3}$
ζ_2	0	0	0	0	0	-1	0	0

θ provide a basic feasible solution to (7–24) with $\mathbf{x}'\mathbf{v} = 0$ for any $\delta \geq 0$. Therefore $x_1 = \frac{3}{2}$, $x_2 = 1$, $x_3 = x_4 = 0$ is an optimal solution to the quadratic programming problem for any $\theta \geq \frac{9}{4}$. This is an extreme point of the convex set of feasible solutions. The case of $\theta = 4$ is illustrated in Fig. 7–1. For this example, there is only one critical value of θ other than 0, namely $\theta = \frac{9}{4}$. Note that $\mathbf{x}_0^* = [0, 2, 0, 2]$. Although there are alternative optimal solutions for $\theta = 0$, θ cannot be increased until the basic solution has $x_2 = x_4 = 2$, $x_3 = 0$. Then x_1 can be brought in. Also $\mathbf{x}_1^* = [\frac{3}{2}, 1, 0, 0]$ when $\theta = \frac{9}{4}$. The solution appropriate to $\theta = 1$ should then be

$$\mathbf{x}^* = (1 - \tfrac{4}{9})\mathbf{x}_0^* + \tfrac{4}{9}\mathbf{x}_1^* = [\tfrac{2}{3}, \tfrac{14}{9}, 0, \tfrac{10}{9}],$$

which is precisely what was obtained above.

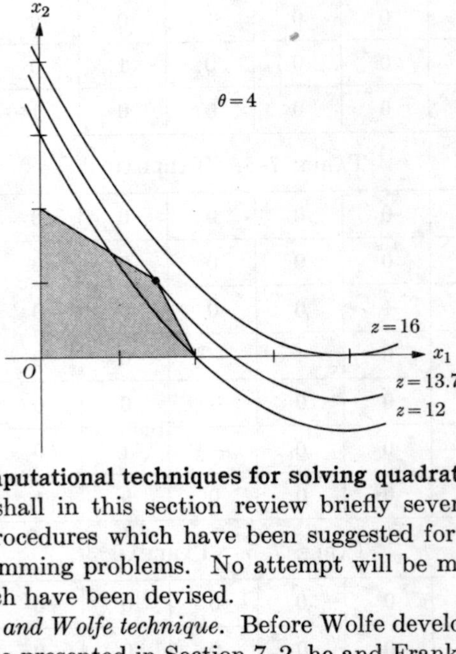

FIGURE 7–1

7–7 Other computational techniques for solving quadratic programming problems. We shall in this section review briefly several of the other computational procedures which have been suggested for solving exactly quadratic programming problems. No attempt will be made to cover all the schemes which have been devised.

(a) *The Frank and Wolfe technique.* Before Wolfe developed the computational technique presented in Section 7–2, he and Frank [8] developed a somewhat different procedure for solving quadratic programming problems in which $\mathbf{x}'\mathbf{D}\mathbf{x}$ is negative definite or negative semidefinite. They also begin with the Kuhn-Tucker conditions (7–9). However, they initiate the computation by applying a Phase I of the simplex method for finding a basic feasible solution to (7–10), without attempting to maintain $\mathbf{x}'\mathbf{v} = 0$. If there is no feasible solution to (7–10), they test $\mathbf{A}\mathbf{x} = \mathbf{b}$ for feasibility. If $\mathbf{A}\mathbf{x} = \mathbf{b}$ is feasible but there is no feasible solution to (7–10), then there

TABLE 7–6. TABLEAU 4

Variables in basis	$\boldsymbol{\beta}_1$	$\boldsymbol{\beta}_2$	$\boldsymbol{\beta}_3$	$\boldsymbol{\beta}_4$	$\boldsymbol{\beta}_5$	$\boldsymbol{\beta}_6$	$\mathbf{r}_B^{(1)}$	$\mathbf{y}_k^{(1)}$
Z_θ	0	0	$\frac{3}{4}$	$-\frac{1}{2}$	0	-1	0	$-\frac{3}{2}$
x_2	$\frac{1}{3}$	0	0	0	0	0	2	$\frac{2}{3}$
x_4	$-\frac{1}{3}$	1	0	0	0	0	2	$\frac{4}{3}$ (circled)
θ	0	0	$\frac{3}{4}$	$-\frac{1}{2}$	0	-1	0	$-\frac{3}{2}$
ζ_1	0	0	$\frac{1}{4}$	$-\frac{1}{2}$	0	0	0	$-\frac{1}{2}$
v_3	0	0	$\frac{1}{4}$	$-\frac{1}{2}$	1	0	0	$-\frac{1}{2}$
ζ_2	0	0	0	0	0	-1	0	0

TABLE 7–7. TABLEAU 5

Variables in basis	$\boldsymbol{\beta}_1$	$\boldsymbol{\beta}_2$	$\boldsymbol{\beta}_3$	$\boldsymbol{\beta}_4$	$\boldsymbol{\beta}_5$	$\boldsymbol{\beta}_6$	$\mathbf{r}_B^{(1)}$	$\mathbf{y}_k^{(1)}$
Z_θ	$-\frac{3}{8}$	$\frac{9}{8}$	$\frac{3}{4}$	$-\frac{1}{2}$	0	-1	$\frac{9}{4}$	-1
x_2	$\frac{1}{2}$	$-\frac{1}{2}$	0	0	0	0	1	0
x_1	$-\frac{1}{4}$	$\frac{3}{4}$	0	0	0	0	$\frac{3}{2}$	0
θ	$-\frac{3}{8}$	$\frac{9}{8}$	$\frac{3}{4}$	$-\frac{1}{2}$	0	-1	$\frac{9}{4}$	-1
ζ_1	$-\frac{1}{8}$	$\frac{3}{8}$	$\frac{1}{4}$	$-\frac{1}{2}$	0	0	$\frac{3}{4}$	0
v_3	$-\frac{1}{8}$	$\frac{3}{8}$	$\frac{1}{4}$	$-\frac{1}{2}$	1	0	$\frac{3}{4}$	0
ζ_2	0	0	0	0	0	-1	0	-1

is an unbounded solution to the problem. If (7–10) has a feasible solution (not necessarily with $\mathbf{x}'\mathbf{v} = 0$), then (7–1) will have an optimal solution (and not an unbounded solution). This is to be proved in Problem 7–46.

Suppose now that a basic feasible solution to (7–10) has been found. Frank and Wolfe then begin with this basic solution and move from it to a basic solution for which $\mathbf{x}'\mathbf{v} = 0$. Let us consider how this is done. Write $\boldsymbol{\Phi} = [\mathbf{x}, \mathbf{v}] \geq \mathbf{0}$, $\boldsymbol{\Phi}^+ = (\mathbf{v}', \mathbf{x}') \geq \mathbf{0}$. Then

$$\tfrac{1}{2}\boldsymbol{\Phi}^+\boldsymbol{\Phi} = \tfrac{1}{2}(\mathbf{v}'\mathbf{x} + \mathbf{x}'\mathbf{v}) = \mathbf{x}'\mathbf{v} \geq 0.$$

Thus a feasible solution for which $Z = -\boldsymbol{\Phi}^+\boldsymbol{\Phi}$ is maximal (that is, 0) is optimal.

To maximize Z, a sequence of linear programming problems is solved. Let $\mathbf{\Phi}_0^+$ be the $\mathbf{\Phi}^+$ corresponding to the initial basic feasible solution to (7–10) obtained by a Phase I computation. Then the simplex method is used to maximize the linear function $Z_1 = -\mathbf{\Phi}_0^+\mathbf{\Phi}$ where the variables are the x_j and v_j of $\mathbf{\Phi}$, the price of x_j is the negative of the jth component of $\mathbf{\Phi}_0$, and the price of v_j is the negative of the $(n + j)$-component. The application of the simplex method gives a sequence of basic feasible solutions $\mathbf{\Phi}(1)$, $\mathbf{\Phi}(2)$, etc., such that if degeneracy is removed, $-\mathbf{\Phi}_0^+\mathbf{\Phi}(1) < -\mathbf{\Phi}_0^+\mathbf{\Phi}(2) < \cdots$, etc. We stop the iteration procedure at the first $\mathbf{\Phi}(k)$ such that:

$$\text{(a)}\quad \mathbf{\Phi}^+(k)\mathbf{\Phi}(k) = 0 \qquad \text{or} \qquad \text{(b)}\quad -\mathbf{\Phi}_0^+\mathbf{\Phi}(k) \geq -\tfrac{1}{2}\mathbf{\Phi}_0^+\mathbf{\Phi}_0.$$

Then when the procedure terminates in (a), an optimal solution has been found. When it terminates in (b), a new set of prices $-\mathbf{\Phi}_1^+$ is determined, as described below, and we proceed to maximize $Z_2 = -\mathbf{\Phi}_1^+\mathbf{\Phi}$, using the last basic feasible solution as the initial new one. Imagine now that we have gone through r such stages and at the end of the rth stage we have terminated with $-\mathbf{\Phi}_r^+\mathbf{\Phi}(k) \geq -\frac{1}{2}\mathbf{\Phi}_r^+\mathbf{\Phi}_r$. The vector $\mathbf{\Phi}_{r+1}$ is determined as follows. Let

$$\mu = \min\left\{\frac{\mathbf{\Phi}_r^+[\mathbf{\Phi}_r - \mathbf{\Phi}(k)]}{[\mathbf{\Phi}^+(k) - \mathbf{\Phi}_r^+][\mathbf{\Phi}(k) - \mathbf{\Phi}_r]}, 1\right\}. \tag{7–38}$$

Then

$$\mathbf{\Phi}_{r+1} = \mu\mathbf{\Phi}(k) + (1 - \mu)\mathbf{\Phi}_r. \tag{7–39}$$

It is left for the reader to show in the problems that this procedure does converge in a finite number of iterations.

(b) *Beale's technique.* Beale in [2, 3] has proposed a technique for solving quadratic programming problems which does not begin with the Kuhn-Tucker conditions. Suppose that we select from $\mathbf{A}$ a nonsingular matrix $\mathbf{B}$. Denote by $\mathbf{x}_B = [x_{B1}, \ldots, x_{Bm}]$ the variables associated with the columns of $\mathbf{A}$ in $\mathbf{B}$. Let $\mathbf{R}$ contain the columns of $\mathbf{A}$ not in $\mathbf{B}$, and let $\mathbf{x}_R = [x_{R1}, \ldots, x_{R,n-m}]$ be the variables associated with the columns of $\mathbf{A}$ not in $\mathbf{B}$. Then any solution to the constraints $\mathbf{Ax} = \mathbf{b}$ can be written

$$\mathbf{x}_B = \mathbf{B}^{-1}\mathbf{b} - \mathbf{B}^{-1}\mathbf{R}\mathbf{x}_R.$$

A basic solution is obtained by setting $\mathbf{x}_R = \mathbf{0}$. The basic solution will be feasible if $\mathbf{B}^{-1}\mathbf{b} \geq \mathbf{0}$. Let $\mathbf{B}^{-1}\mathbf{b} = \mathbf{y}_0$ and denote the jth column of $\mathbf{B}^{-1}\mathbf{R}$ by $\mathbf{y}_j$; then any solution must satisfy

$$x_{Bi} = y_{i0} - \sum_{j=1}^{n-m} y_{ij}x_{Rj}, \qquad i = 1, \ldots, m. \tag{7–40}$$

By use of (7–40) it is possible to eliminate the variables x_{Bi} in $z = \mathbf{cx} + \mathbf{x}'\mathbf{Dx}$ to yield

$$z = z_0 + \boldsymbol{\alpha}\mathbf{x}_R + \mathbf{x}'_R\mathbf{G}\mathbf{x}_R. \tag{7–41}$$

In Problem 7–37 we ask the reader to express the α_j, g_{kj} in terms of the c_j and d_{kj}. Then

$$\frac{\partial z}{\partial x_{Rj}} = \alpha_j + 2\sum_{k=1}^{n-m} g_{jk}x_{Rk}. \tag{7–42}$$

Suppose now that $\mathbf{x}_B = \mathbf{y}_0$ is a basic feasible solution to the constraints, so that $\mathbf{x}_R = \mathbf{0}$. However, from (7–42), it will pay to increase x_{Rj} if $\alpha_j > 0$ since $\partial z/\partial x_{Rj} = \alpha_j$ when $\mathbf{x}_R = \mathbf{0}$. The value of x_{Rj} cannot usually be increased indefinitely, though. It cannot be increased above the point where one of the basic variables becomes negative, and it is not desirable to increase it beyond the point where $\partial z/\partial x_{Rj}$ becomes zero if this derivative decreases as x_{Rj} is increased. The critical value $x_{Rj}^{(1)}$ of x_{Rj} which drives the first basic variable to zero is

$$x_{Rj}^{(1)} = \min_i \frac{y_{i0}}{y_{ij}} = \frac{y_{s0}}{y_{sj}}, \qquad y_{ij} > 0, \quad \text{or} \quad \infty \quad \text{if all } y_{ij} \leq 0.$$

When $g_{jj} < 0$, it will not be desirable to increase x_{Rj} above $-\alpha_j/2g_{jj}$. Thus if

$$x_{Rj}^{(2)} = \begin{cases} \dfrac{-\alpha_j}{2g_{jj}}, & g_{jj} < 0, \\ \infty, & g_{jj} = 0, \end{cases}$$

the desired maximum increase in $x_{Rj} = \min\{x_{Rj}^{(1)}, x_{Rj}^{(2)}\}$.

Suppose now that the desired increase in x_{Rj} is finite and $x_{Rj} = x_{Rj}^{(1)}$. In this case, a new basic solution is obtained with x_{Rj} in the basis and x_{Bs} being driven to zero. Now the coefficients of $\mathbf{y}_0$, $\mathbf{y}_j$, $\boldsymbol{\alpha}$, $\mathbf{G}$ are recomputed for the new basic feasible solution, and the computational procedure is repeated. If, on the other hand, $x_{Rj} = x_{Rj}^{(2)}$, we no longer have a basic solution to the original constraints; we now have $m + 1$ positive variables (in the absence of degeneracy). However, we have $\partial z/\partial x_{Rj} = 0$. To proceed, we introduce a new unrestricted variable $u_j = \partial z/\partial x_{Rj}$. We have increased x_{Rj} to the point where $u_j = 0$. We can now imagine that we have a basic feasible solution to the set of $m + 1$ constraints $\mathbf{Ax} = \mathbf{b}$ and $\partial z/\partial x_{Rj} = 0$. Note that from (7–42)

$$x_{Rj} = -\frac{\alpha_j}{2g_{jj}} - \sum_{k\neq j} \frac{g_{jk}}{g_{jj}}\, x_{jk} + \frac{1}{2g_{jj}}\, u_j. \tag{7–43}$$

We use (7–43) to replace x_{Rj} in (7–40) and (7–41) and introduce u_j. Then (7–43), along with (7–40), represents the new basic feasible solution to the $m + 1$ constraints $\mathbf{Ax} = \mathbf{b}$, $\partial z/\partial x_{Rj} = 0$.

Having obtained a new basic solution, we repeat the procedure discussed above. When considering $\partial z/\partial u_j$ one should remember that u_j is unrestricted so that both increases or decreases in u_j must be examined. It is possible that at a later stage, u_j will enter the basis and become nonzero. If this happens, we could drop the constraint for u_j, since it is unrestricted. The variable could later be introduced if u_j is driven to zero again. Note that as the computation proceeds, the size of the basis can increase and perhaps decrease again (if u_j in the basis are deleted). When a point is reached where it is not possible to change any of the nonbasic variables in such a way that z can be increased, then the solution is a local optimum. To prove this we shall assume that degeneracy has been eliminated by a suitable perturbation. For the final solution, let $\mathbf{x}_{NB}$ contain the $n - m$ nonbasic variables (both x_{Rj} and u_j); then $\mathbf{x}_{NB} = \mathbf{0}$ for this solution. However, there is an $\epsilon > 0$ such that for all $\mathbf{x}_{NB}$ in an ϵ-neighborhood of the origin with $x_{Rj} \geq 0$, the $\mathbf{x}$ determined from (7–40), (7–43) is a feasible solution to the constraints, and furthermore for any $\mathbf{x}_{NB}$ in this neighborhood,

$$\nabla z[(1 - \theta)\mathbf{x}_{NB}]\mathbf{x}_{NB} \leq 0, \qquad \text{any } \theta, \quad 0 \leq \theta \leq 1,$$

or the computational procedure would not have terminated. But then by Taylor's theorem, (2–31), $z(\mathbf{x}_{NB}) \leq z(\mathbf{0})$ for $\mathbf{x}_{NB}$ in this ϵ-neighborhood, and we have a local optimum. Note, however, that z is a concave function of the nonbasic variables as well as of the original variables. Thus the local optimum also yields a global optimum. There still remains the question of whether or not the computational procedure converges in a finite number of steps. The reader is asked to prove in the problems that convergence is obtained in a finite number of iterations.

(c) *Hildreth's Method.* Hildreth [9] developed an interesting computational technique for solving quadratic programming problems. He first reduces the problem with constraints to a problem of minimizing a quadratic objective function in non-negative variables without constraints. This is done as follows. Let us imagine that if in the original problem any of the variables are required to be non-negative, then these non-negativity restrictions are included in the constraints. Let us assume that, in addition, the constraints are converted to a form where a $\leq$ sign appears in each constraint. Then the original problem has the form

$$\mathbf{Hx} \leq \mathbf{h}, \qquad \max z = \mathbf{cx} + \mathbf{x}'\mathbf{Dx}, \tag{7–44}$$

where no additional restrictions are placed on the signs of the x_j. Thus from Section 6–3 we know that $\mathbf{x}^*$ will be an optimal solution to (7–44) if and only if there exists a $\boldsymbol{\lambda}^* \geq \mathbf{0}$ such that

$$F(\mathbf{x}, \boldsymbol{\lambda}) = \mathbf{cx} + \mathbf{x}'\mathbf{Dx} + \boldsymbol{\lambda}'[\mathbf{h} - \mathbf{Hx}] \tag{7–45}$$

has a saddle point at $[\mathbf{x}^*, \boldsymbol{\lambda}^*]$ for $\boldsymbol{\lambda} \geq \mathbf{0}$. We shall restrict our attention to the case where $\mathbf{x}'\mathbf{D}\mathbf{x}$ is negative definite so that $\mathbf{D}$ is nonsingular. For any $\boldsymbol{\lambda}$, $F(\mathbf{x}, \boldsymbol{\lambda})$ is a strictly concave function of $\mathbf{x}$ and assumes its unique absolute maximum at a point $\mathbf{x}(\boldsymbol{\lambda})$. Inasmuch as the components of $\mathbf{x}$ are unrestricted in sign, $\mathbf{x}(\boldsymbol{\lambda})$ must be the unique solution to

$$\nabla_{\mathbf{x}} F = \mathbf{0} = \mathbf{c} + 2\mathbf{x}'\mathbf{D} - \boldsymbol{\lambda}'\mathbf{H},$$

that is,

$$\mathbf{x}'(\boldsymbol{\lambda}) = \tfrac{1}{2}[\boldsymbol{\lambda}'\mathbf{H} - \mathbf{c}]\,\mathbf{D}^{-1} \quad \text{or} \quad \mathbf{x}(\boldsymbol{\lambda}) = \tfrac{1}{2}\,\mathbf{D}^{-1}[\mathbf{H}'\boldsymbol{\lambda} - \mathbf{c}'], \tag{7–46}$$

since the inverse of a symmetric matrix is symmetric. Furthermore, the Kuhn-Tucker conditions guarantee that $\mathbf{x}^*, \boldsymbol{\lambda}^*$ satisfy (7–46). Substitution of $\mathbf{x}(\boldsymbol{\lambda})$ into $F(\mathbf{x}, \boldsymbol{\lambda})$ yields a function $\hat{F}(\boldsymbol{\lambda})$ of $\boldsymbol{\lambda}$ only, which is

$$\hat{F}(\boldsymbol{\lambda}) = \mathbf{d}\boldsymbol{\lambda} + \boldsymbol{\lambda}'\mathbf{E}\boldsymbol{\lambda} - \tfrac{1}{4}\mathbf{c}\,\mathbf{D}^{-1}\mathbf{c}', \tag{7–47}$$

where

$$\mathbf{E} = -\tfrac{1}{4}\mathbf{H}\,\mathbf{D}^{-1}\mathbf{H}'; \qquad \mathbf{d} = \tfrac{1}{2}\mathbf{c}\,\mathbf{D}^{-1}\mathbf{H}' + \mathbf{h}'. \tag{7–48}$$

Let us next note that if $\mathbf{x}'\mathbf{D}\mathbf{x}$ is negative definite, then $\mathbf{u}'\mathbf{H}\mathbf{D}^{-1}\mathbf{H}'\mathbf{u}$ is negative definite or negative semidefinite. To see this, let $\mathbf{D}\mathbf{x} = \mathbf{H}'\mathbf{u}$ for any $\mathbf{u}$. Then $\mathbf{u}'\mathbf{H}\mathbf{D}^{-1}\mathbf{H}'\mathbf{u} = \mathbf{x}'\mathbf{D}\mathbf{x} \leq 0$. Thus $\boldsymbol{\lambda}'\mathbf{E}\boldsymbol{\lambda}$ is positive definite or positive semidefinite and $\hat{F}(\boldsymbol{\lambda})$ is a convex function of $\boldsymbol{\lambda}$. Note that $\hat{F}(\boldsymbol{\lambda}^*) = F(\mathbf{x}^*, \boldsymbol{\lambda}^*)$. Also note that for all $\boldsymbol{\lambda} \geq \mathbf{0}$,

$$F(\mathbf{x}^*, \boldsymbol{\lambda}^*) \leq F(\mathbf{x}^*, \boldsymbol{\lambda}) \leq \hat{F}(\boldsymbol{\lambda}), \tag{7–49}$$

where the first inequality follows, because F has a saddle point at $[\mathbf{x}^*, \boldsymbol{\lambda}^*]$ and the second, because $\hat{F}(\boldsymbol{\lambda})$ is the maximum over $\mathbf{x}$ of $F(\mathbf{x}, \boldsymbol{\lambda})$ for a given $\boldsymbol{\lambda}$. Thus $F(\mathbf{x}^*, \boldsymbol{\lambda}^*)$ is the absolute minimum of $\hat{F}(\boldsymbol{\lambda})$ for $\boldsymbol{\lambda} \geq \mathbf{0}$. Consequently, if we determine the absolute minimum of

$$Z = \mathbf{d}\boldsymbol{\lambda} + \boldsymbol{\lambda}'\mathbf{E}\boldsymbol{\lambda} \tag{7–50}$$

for $\boldsymbol{\lambda} \geq \mathbf{0}$, this minimum yields a $\boldsymbol{\lambda}^*$ such that $\mathbf{x}^*$ computed from (7–46) is an optimal solution to the original problem.

Any one of the procedures considered previously can be used to minimize (7–50) for $\boldsymbol{\lambda} \geq \mathbf{0}$. Hildreth suggested a method which might require an infinite number of steps for convergence. We shall not consider this technique. Lemke [11] developed a finite algorithm especially for minimizing (7–50) for $\boldsymbol{\lambda} \geq \mathbf{0}$. We shall not consider it here either, although it is discussed in the problems. Instead, we shall consider Houthakker's method for solving this problem.

(d) *Houthakker's procedure when the only constraint is a capacity constraint.* Houthakker [10] has presented a technique for solving quadratic programming problems, which is somewhat similar to Beale's. Houthakker's technique can be subdivided into two parts. First is the method for solving the problem

$$\max z = \mathbf{cx} + \mathbf{x}'\mathbf{Dx}, \qquad \mathbf{x} \geq \mathbf{0}, \qquad \sum_j x_j \leq \beta. \tag{7–51}$$

Here the only constraint is a capacity constraint. Houthakker solves this problem parametrically, generating the optimal $\mathbf{x}$ for every non-negative value of β. Secondly, there is the method for solving (7–51) when, in addition, there are other linear constraints of the form $\mathbf{Ax} \leq \mathbf{b}$, where all $a_{ij} \geq 0$ and $b_i > 0$. We shall consider only the technique for solving (7–51). It provides an interesting method of minimizing (7–50).

On applying a suitable perturbation, we can assume that $\mathbf{x}'\mathbf{Dx}$ is negative definite. The solution procedure generates a finite set of critical values of β, $\beta_0 = 0, \beta_1, \beta_2, \ldots, \beta_k = \infty$ such that for all β in the interval $\beta_i < \beta < \beta_{i+1}$ it will be optimal to have a certain set of variables positive and the remainder zero. However, as β increases through a critical value, the set of positive values of the variables changes. Consider then the details of generating the optimal solution to (7–51) for all values of β.

We begin with $\beta = 0$. Then the optimal solution is $\mathbf{x} = \mathbf{0}$. When $\mathbf{x} = \mathbf{0}$, $\partial z/\partial x_j = c_j$. As we allow β to become positive but small, it is clearly optimal to allow only that variable x_r to become positive for which $c_r > 0$ is the largest of the c_j; that is, initially we set $x_r = \beta$ while keeping all other variables at a zero level. Assume for the moment that c_r is unique. The case where it is not will be considered below. As x_r increases, the values of $\partial z/\partial x_j$ will, in general, change. The partial derivatives will now have the form

$$\frac{\partial z}{\partial x_j} = c_j + 2\, d_{rr} x_r. \tag{7–52}$$

As x_r is increased, one will usually reach a point such that for one or more x_s,

$$\frac{\partial z}{\partial x_s} = \frac{\partial z}{\partial x_r} \cdot \tag{7–53}$$

The smallest value of β where this occurs is a critical value of β, call it β_1. It can be determined directly from (7–52). For $\beta > \beta_1$, we also allow the one or more x_s to be positive. It is conceivable that (7–53) may never occur and, instead, x_r can be increased until $\partial z/\partial x_r = 0$. In such a case, the value of β at which this occurs is β_1, and the solution obtained is optimal for all $\beta \geq \beta_1$, since then $\partial z/\partial x_j \leq 0$ for all other x_j.

Consider the case where (7-53) is reached and now two or more variables are to become positive. If in the original step, c_r was not unique, we would allow all variables with price c_r to become positive, and we would be immediately reduced to the case now to be considered. To be specific, suppose that two variables x_r and x_s are to be positive. The optimal values of these variables as functions of β, with all other variables being held at a zero level, are determined by means of the Lagrange multiplier approach of Chapter 3. The Lagrangian will be

$$F = c_r x_r + c_s x_s + d_{rr} x_r^2 + d_{ss} x_s^2 + 2\, d_{rs} x_r x_s + \lambda(\beta - x_r - x_s), \quad (7\text{-}54)$$

where λ is the Lagrange multiplier. The necessary conditions which must be satisfied are

$$\begin{aligned} c_r + 2\, d_{rr} x_r + 2\, d_{rs} x_s &= \lambda, \\ c_s + 2\, d_{rs} x_r + 2\, d_{ss} x_s &= \lambda, \\ x_r + \phantom{2\, d_{rs}} x_s &= \beta. \end{aligned}$$

These equations are then solved explicitly for x_r, x_s, λ in terms of β to yield

$$x_r = \alpha_r + \gamma_r \beta, \qquad x_s = \alpha_s + \gamma_s \beta, \qquad \lambda = \alpha_0 + \gamma_0 \beta. \quad (7\text{-}55)$$

We now proceed again to determine the largest value β_2 of β for which this solution can remain optimal. To determine β_2 we first compute a set β_{2a}, β_{2bi}, β_{2cj}, where β_{2a} is the value of β such that for all $\beta \geq \beta_{2a}$ the capacity constraint is inactive, so that x_r, x_s evaluated at β_{2a} represent the absolute minimum of F in (7-54); β_{2a} is found from the last equation of (7-55) by setting $\lambda = 0$. Next, for each positive variable x_i which decreases as β is increased, we determine β_{2bi}, the value of β at which x_i is driven to zero. Finally, for each variable x_j required to be zero, we determine $\partial z/\partial x_j$ in terms of the variables x_i which are allowed to be positive. We then determine how much β can be increased before $\partial z/\partial x_j = \lambda$. This is done by using (7-55) to express λ and $\partial z/\partial x_j$ in terms of β. Let β_{2cj} be the value so obtained. Then β_2 is the minimum of all the β_{2a}, β_{2bi}, β_{2cj} obtained above, where any values $\leq \beta_1$ are ignored in computing the minimum.

If $\beta_2 = \beta_{2a}$, the optimal solution for all $\beta \geq \beta_2$ is found by setting $\beta = \beta_{2a}$. When $\beta_2 = \beta_{2bi}$, the variable x_i is removed from the set allowed to be positive as β passes through β_2. If $\beta_2 = \beta_{2cj}$, x_j is allowed to become positive as β passes through β_2. Having determined the new set of variables which are allowed to be positive, we repeat the whole procedure. Ultimately the case will be reached when $\beta_k = \beta_{ka}$, and the solution for β_k will be optimal for all $\beta \geq \beta_k$. To prove that the solution obtained by the above procedure is optimal for any β, the Kuhn-Tucker conditions may be applied. The reader is asked to do this in Problem 7–29. Note that although the number of positive variables can fluctuate as one moves from one critical value of β to the next, the number will tend to grow as β is increased, so that the size of the set of equations which must be solved to yield (7–55) increases.

Although no detailed tests have been made to compare the various methods for solving quadratic programming problems, it would appear on an *a priori* basis that the method suggested in Section 7–2 should be as efficient as any of the others considered in this section.

7–8 Duality in quadratic programming. We shall now investigate the notion of duality as applied to quadratic programming. The key to deriving the dual of a quadratic programming problem lies in the material of Sections 3–8 and 6–5. It was seen in Section 3–8 that if certain conditions were satisfied, then the dual of a programming problem $g_i(\mathbf{x}) = b_i$, $i = 1, \ldots, m$; $\max z = f(\mathbf{x})$ was $\partial F/\partial x_j = 0$, $j = 1, \ldots, n$; $\min Z = F(\mathbf{x}, \boldsymbol{\lambda})$, where

$$F(\mathbf{x}, \boldsymbol{\lambda}) = f(\mathbf{x}) + \sum_{i=1}^{m} \lambda_i[b_i - g_i(\mathbf{x})].$$

If we consider a quadratic programming problem $\mathbf{Ax} = \mathbf{b}$, $\max z = \mathbf{cx} + \mathbf{x'Dx}$, where the components of $\mathbf{x}$ are unrestricted in sign, then, since

$$F(\mathbf{x}, \boldsymbol{\lambda}) = \mathbf{cx} + \mathbf{x'Dx} + \boldsymbol{\lambda}'[\mathbf{b} - \mathbf{Ax}],$$

the above would imply the dual

$$\mathbf{c} + 2\mathbf{x'D} - \boldsymbol{\lambda}'\mathbf{A} = \mathbf{0}, \tag{7–56}$$
$$\min Z = \mathbf{cx} + \mathbf{x'Dx} + \boldsymbol{\lambda}'\mathbf{b} - \boldsymbol{\lambda}'\mathbf{Ax}.$$

Multiplying (7–56) on the right by $\mathbf{x}$, we see that

$$\boldsymbol{\lambda}'\mathbf{Ax} = \mathbf{cx} + 2\mathbf{x'Dx}, \tag{7–57}$$

so that for any $\mathbf{x}, \boldsymbol{\lambda}$ satisfying (7–56), Z becomes

$$Z = -\mathbf{x'Dx} + \boldsymbol{\lambda}'\mathbf{b}, \tag{7–58}$$

and the dual problem would be

$$-2\mathbf{Dx} + \mathbf{A}'\boldsymbol{\lambda} = \mathbf{c}',$$
$$\min Z = -\mathbf{x'Dx} + \boldsymbol{\lambda}'\mathbf{b}. \tag{7–59}$$

In the above we have not taken account of the fact that, in general, we want $\mathbf{x} \geq \mathbf{0}$. The results of Section 6–3 can then be used to obtain the appropriate form of the dual. Suppose that $\mathbf{x}^* \geq \mathbf{0}$ is an optimal solution to

$$\mathbf{Ax} = \mathbf{b}, \quad \mathbf{x} \geq \mathbf{0}, \quad \max z = \mathbf{cx} + \mathbf{x}'\mathbf{Dx}. \tag{7–60}$$

Then from the Kuhn-Tucker theory we know that there exists a $\boldsymbol{\lambda}^*$ such that

$$-2\mathbf{Dx}^* + \mathbf{A}'\boldsymbol{\lambda}^* \geq \mathbf{c}',$$

and

$$\max z = F(\mathbf{x}^*, \boldsymbol{\lambda}^*) = \mathbf{cx}^* + (\mathbf{x}^*)'\mathbf{Dx}^* + (\boldsymbol{\lambda}^*)'[\mathbf{b} - \mathbf{Ax}^*] = \mathbf{cx}^* + (\mathbf{x}^*)'\mathbf{Dx}^*, \tag{7–61}$$

since by (6–51),

$$(\boldsymbol{\lambda}^*)'[\mathbf{b} - \mathbf{Ax}^*] = 0.$$

Also from (6–50),

$$-2(\mathbf{x}^*)'\mathbf{Dx}^* + (\boldsymbol{\lambda}^*)'\mathbf{Ax}^* = \mathbf{cx}^*. \tag{7–62}$$

Now let us note that for any $\mathbf{x} \geq \mathbf{0}$ and $\boldsymbol{\lambda}$ satisfying $-2\mathbf{Dx} + \mathbf{A}'\boldsymbol{\lambda} \geq \mathbf{c}'$, we obtain, on multiplying on the left by $\mathbf{x}$ and taking the transpose,

$$-\boldsymbol{\lambda}'\mathbf{Ax} \leq -\mathbf{cx} - 2\mathbf{x}'\mathbf{Dx};$$

so

$$F(\mathbf{x}, \boldsymbol{\lambda}) \leq -\mathbf{x}'\mathbf{Dx} + \boldsymbol{\lambda}'\mathbf{b} = Z. \tag{7–63}$$

However, by (7–62),

$$F(\mathbf{x}^*, \boldsymbol{\lambda}^*) = -(\mathbf{x}^*)'\mathbf{Dx}^* + (\boldsymbol{\lambda}^*)'\mathbf{b} = \max z.$$

Therefore $[\mathbf{x}^*, \boldsymbol{\lambda}^*]$ is an optimal solution to the quadratic programming problem

$$\begin{gathered} -2\mathbf{Dx} + \mathbf{A}'\boldsymbol{\lambda} \geq \mathbf{c}', \\ \mathbf{x} \geq \mathbf{0}, \\ \min Z = -\mathbf{x}'\mathbf{Dx} + \boldsymbol{\lambda}'\mathbf{b}. \end{gathered} \tag{7–64}$$

Furthermore $\max z = \min Z$. We shall call the quadratic programming problem (7–64) a dual of (7–60). We have already proved that if (7–60) has an optimal solution, then so does (7–64). In fact, an optimal solution $\mathbf{x}^*$ to (7–60) forms part of an optimal solution to (7–64). To determine the remainder of the optimal solution to the dual, we can solve the linear programming problem (6–29). Note that if z is a concave function of $\mathbf{x}$, then Z is a convex function of $[\mathbf{x}, \boldsymbol{\lambda}]$.

Let us now assume that there exists an optimal solution to (7–64). We can then show that (7–60) also has an optimal solution. In doing this, we shall assume, without any essential loss of generality, that $\mathbf{x}'\mathbf{D}\mathbf{x}$ is negative definite so that $\mathbf{D}$ is nonsingular. Then all we need to do in order to show that (7–60) has an optimal solution is to demonstrate that there exists a feasible solution to the constraints $\mathbf{A}\mathbf{x} = \mathbf{b}$. Let $[\mathbf{x}^*, \boldsymbol{\lambda}^*]$ be an optimal solution to (7–64). The Kuhn-Tucker conditions applied to (7–64) must be satisfied. This implies (derivation?) that there exists a $\boldsymbol{\delta}^*$ such that

$$-2\mathbf{D}\mathbf{x}^* + 2\mathbf{D}\boldsymbol{\delta}^* \geq \mathbf{0}, \tag{7–65}$$

$$\mathbf{A}\boldsymbol{\delta}^* = \mathbf{b}. \tag{7–66}$$

However, from (7–65) $\boldsymbol{\delta}^* \geq \mathbf{x}^* \geq \mathbf{0}$ so that $\boldsymbol{\delta}^*$ yields a feasible solution to the constraints of (7–60), and thus (7–60) has an optimal solution.

Essentially the same type of dual problems obtained here have been presented by Dorn [6]. He did not, however, indicate how they may be obtained directly from the Kuhn-Tucker conditions. Duality in a somewhat different form has been considered by Dennis [5]. His results are to be studied in the problems.

References

1. Barankin, E. W., and R. Dorfman, *Towards Quadratic Programming.* Office of Naval Research Logistics Project at Columbia University and University of California, Berkeley, 1955.

2. Beale, E. M. L., "On Minimizing a Convex Function Subject to Linear Inequalities," *Journal of the Royal Statistical Society* (*B*), **17,** 1955, pp. 173–184.

3. Beale, E. M. L., "On Quadratic Programming," *Naval Research Logistics Quarterly,* **6,** 1959, pp. 227–243.

4. Charnes, A., and W. W. Cooper, *Management Models and Industrial Applications of Linear Programming,* Vol. II, pp. 682–687. New York: Wiley, 1961.

5. Dennis, J. B., *Mathematical Programming and Electrical Networks,* New York: Wiley (Technology Press), 1959.

6. Dorn, W. S., "Duality in Quadratic Programming," *Quarterly of Applied Mathematics,* **18,** 1960, pp. 155–162.

7. Dorn, W. S., "Self-Dual Quadratic Programs," *Journal of the Society for Industrial and Applied Mathematics,* **9,** 1961, pp. 51–54.

8. Frank, M., and P. Wolfe, "An Algorithm for Quadratic Programming," *Naval Research Logistics Quarterly,* **3,** 1956, pp. 95–110.

9. Hildreth, C., "A Quadratic Programming Procedure," *Naval Research Logistics Quarterly,* **14,** 1957, pp. 79–85.

10. Houthakker, H. S., "The Capacity Method of Quadratic Programming," *Econometrica,* **28,** 1960, pp. 62–87.

11. Lemke, C. E., "A Method for Solution of Quadratic Programs," *Management Science,* **8,** 1962, pp. 442–453.

12. Markowitz, H., "The Optimization of a Quadratic Function Subject to Linear Constraints," *Naval Research Logistics Quarterly*, **3**, 1956, pp. 111–133.

13. Markowitz, H., *Portfolio Selection* (Cowles Foundation Monograph No. 16). New York: Wiley, 1959.

14. Theil, H., and C. van de Panne, "Quadratic Programming as an Extension of Classical Quadratic Maximization," *Management Science*, **7**, 1960, pp. 1–20.

15. Vajda, S., *Mathematical Programming*. Reading, Mass.: Addison-Wesley, 1961.

16. Wolfe, P., "The Simplex Method for Quadratic Programming," *Econometrica*, **27**, 1959, pp. 382–398.

Problems

7–1. Consider the quadratic programming problem

$$3x_1 + 2x_2 \leq 6, \qquad \mathbf{x} \geq \mathbf{0}, \qquad \max z = 8x_1 + 10x_2 - x_1^2 - x_2^2.$$

Solve this problem by the method of Section 7–2, and also provide a graphic solution.

7–2. Solve Problem 7–1 by the method of Frank and Wolfe.

7–3. Solve Problem 7–1 by Beale's technique.

7–4. Solve Problem 7–1 by Houthakker's capacity method. Note that a constraint $\sum p_j x_j \leq \beta$ with all $p_j > 0$ can, with the substitution of variables $y_j = p_j x_j$, be converted to the form $\sum y_j \leq \beta$.

7–5. In Problem 7–1, suppose that the objective function is

$$z = 8\theta x_1 + 10\theta x_2 - x_1^2 - x_2^2.$$

Determine an optimal solution for every $\theta \geq 0$.

7–6. Consider the following quadratic programming problem:

$$\begin{aligned} x_1 + 4x_2 &\leq 4, \\ x_1 + x_2 &\leq 2, \\ x_1, x_2 &\geq 0, \\ \max z &= 2x_1 + 3x_2 - 2x_2^2. \end{aligned}$$

Solve this problem by the method of Section 7–2.

7–7. Solve Problem 7–6 by the method of Frank and Wolfe.

7–8. Solve Problem 7–6 by the method of Beale.

7–9. Solve Problem 7–6 by a combination of Hildreth's and Houthakker's method.

7–10. Suppose that the objective function in Problem 7–6 is

$$z = 2\theta x_1 + 3\theta x_2 - 2x_2^2.$$

Determine an optimal solution for every $\theta \geq 0$.

7–11. Consider the quadratic programming problem

$$3x_1 + 2x_2 \leq 6, \qquad \mathbf{x} \geq \mathbf{0}, \qquad \max z = x_1^2 + x_2^2.$$

Note that the objective function does not have the proper concavity properties. Solve the problem graphically and point out what might cause difficulties if one of the methods developed in the chapter is used to solve the problem.

7–12. Does the method of Section 7–2 when used to solve Problem 7–11 yield the optimal solution?

7–13. Solve the following quadratic programming problem by the method of Section 7–2.

$$\begin{aligned} x_1 + 3x_2 &\geq 5, \\ 2x_2 + 0.5x_1 &\geq 2, \\ x_1, x_2 &\geq 0, \\ \min z &= 4x_1^2 + 3x_2^2. \end{aligned}$$

7–14. Solve the following quadratic programming problem by the method of Section 7–2.

$$\begin{aligned} x_1 - x_2 &\geq 0, \\ -x_1 + 2x_2 &\leq 2, \\ x_1, x_2 &\geq 0, \\ \max z &= 2x_1 + 3x_2 - x_1^2. \end{aligned}$$

7–15. Suppose that in Problem 7–14 the objective function is

$$z = 2\theta x_1 + 3\theta x_2 - x_1^2.$$

Find an optimal solution for every $\theta \geq 0$.

7–16. Solve the following quadratic programming problem for every $\theta \geq 0$.

$$\begin{aligned} x_1 - x_2 &\geq 0, \\ -x_1 + 2x_2 &\leq 2, \\ x_1, x_2 &\geq 0, \\ \max z &= 2\theta x_1 - x_2^2. \end{aligned}$$

7–17. Solve the example of Section 7–6, using Charnes' perturbation technique to convert the quadratic form into a negative definite one. Take $\epsilon = -0.001$. Is the computational effort required to solve the problem increased by making this perturbation?

7–18. Imagine that we have a quadratic programming problem in which it is desired to minimize the objective function. Assume that the objective function is convex. Write down the Kuhn-Tucker conditions for this case, and obtain the equivalent of Eq. (7–16) for the minimization problem.

7–19. Prove that if $\mathbf{x'Dx}$ is strictly concave, then $\mathbf{cx} + \mathbf{x'Dx}$ is also strictly concave.

7–20. In economics it is often assumed that the preferences of a consumer for n goods can be represented by a numerical utility function $U(\mathbf{x})$, where x_j is the quantity of good j he buys. If the consumer has an income β to spend, and if if p_j is the unit price of good j, then the quantity of each good that the consumer should purchase is found by solving the problem

$$\max z = U(\mathbf{x}), \qquad \sum p_j x_j \leq \beta, \qquad \mathbf{x} \geq \mathbf{0}.$$

Note that if $U(\mathbf{x}) = \mathbf{cx} + \mathbf{x}'\mathbf{Dx}$ and is concave, we have a quadratic programming problem. For the case of only two goods, imagine that

$$U(\mathbf{x}) = 18x_1 + 16x_2 - 3x_1^2 - x_1x_2 - 5x_2^2.$$

In the x_1x_2-plane, sketch the curves of constant utility. If $p_1 = 1$, $p_2 = 2$, $\beta = 10$, determine the optimal quantity of each good the consumer should procure.

7–21. In {LP 13–3} the linear programming approach to the theory of the firm was considered. It was noted there that such a theory was appropriate to the case of pure competition (where the market price of any product is independent of the amount which the firm produces), where, in addition, the marginal costs of production are constant. Recall that the firm is allowed to produce several products. Quite possibly, any given product may be produced in a number of different ways (perhaps on several different combinations of machines). It is assumed, however, that the number of different processes of production for a given product is finite. We assume that the number of limited resources used per unit time by the firm is m, and that b_i is the upper limit to the quantity of resource i which can be used; let $\mathbf{b} = [b_1, \ldots, b_m]$. For a given process of production j, let a_{ij} be the quantity of resource i required to produce one unit of the product; let $\mathbf{a}_j = [a_{1j}, \ldots, a_{mj}]$, and $\mathbf{A} = (\mathbf{a}_1, \ldots, \mathbf{a}_n)$, where n is the total number of processes. The quantities of each resource required in process j are assumed to be directly proportional to the number of units produced by this process. Let x_j be the number of units produced by process j; x_j refers to the number of units of a given product produced by a given process. Several different j may refer to the same product. Write $\mathbf{x} = [x_1, \ldots, x_n]$. Then, if the profit per unit on j is p_j, the problem of determining the optimal level for each x_j is that of solving the linear programming problem

$$\mathbf{Ax} \leq \mathbf{b}, \qquad \mathbf{x} \geq \mathbf{0}, \qquad \max z = \mathbf{px}.$$

Suppose now that the cost of production per unit of j is a constant c_j, i.e., the cost for x_j units is $c_j x_j$, but the price which the firm can charge if it hopes to sell its entire output decreases linearly with the quantity produced. If a quantity y_k of good k is produced, the unit price p_k at which y_k can be sold is $p_k = \alpha_k - \beta_k y_k$, $\alpha_k, \beta_k > 0$. Now note that $y_k = \sum x_j$, the sum being taken over all processes of production which refer to product k. Write down the profit expression in this case and note that the objective function has the form $z = \mathbf{fx} + \mathbf{x}'\mathbf{Dx}$, so that the problem of optimizing the firm's operations now becomes a quadratic programming problem. Is z concave, as desired?

7–22. Generalize Problem 7–21 to the case where the price which can be charged for product i varies not only with the quantity of i produced, but linearly with the quantity of all other products as well. Imagine that the price of i must decrease or remain unchanged as the quantity of any other product is increased. This occurs when there is substitutability among products. Is z concave? Now continue the generalization of Problem 7–21 and allow for the possibility that the unit cost of resource i will decrease linearly as the quantity of this resource is increased. Note that the problem remains a quadratic programming problem. Is z concave? Suppose instead that costs are increasing. Is z concave?

7–23. In Problem 7–21 we implicitly assumed that only one good was associated with any process of production. Imagine now that there are joint products so that it is not possible to produce one good without producing some of one or more other goods. Define a process of production as before. Imagine, however, that when the process of production i is used at a level x_j, it produces $g_{kj}x_j$ units of good k. Answer Problems 7–21 and 7–22 for this case.

7–24. A firm produces two products, using two limited resources. The maximum amount of resource 1 available per week is 2000, and the maximum amount of resource 2 is 500. The production of one unit of product 1 requires two units of resource 1 and 0.4 unit of resource 2. The production of one unit of product 2 requires one unit of resource 1 and one unit of resource 2. The unit cost of resource 1 is $0.75 - 0.0001\,u_1$, where u_1 is the number of units of resource 1 used. The unit cost of resource 2 is $1.50 - 0.0002\,u_2$, where u_2 is the number of units of resource 2 used. The two products are partial substitutes for each other, and the maximum price which the firm can charge if it is to sell all units decreases as the quantity product of either product is increased. The prices for the two products are

$$p_1 = 4.00 - 0.001x_1 - 0.0003x_2; \quad p_2 = 7.00 - 0.0004x_1 - 0.003x_2.$$

Assume that there are no costs of production other than the costs of the resources. Determine the optimal weekly output of x_1, x_2.

7–25. Consider a situation in which it is believed that some physical variable y is linearly related to n other variables x_j, that is,

$$y = \beta_0 + \beta_1 x_1 + \cdots + \beta_n x_n.$$

The β_j must, however, be determined from experimental data which are not too accurate. Imagine that $M > n + 1$ sets of experimental data $[y_k, x_{1k}, \ldots, x_{nk}]$ are available, with y determined for a given set of x_j-values. It is then desired to find the best values of the β_j estimated from these experimental data. By "best" we mean the values of the β_j which minimize

$$z = \sum_{k=1}^{M} (y_k - \beta_0 - \beta_1 x_{1k} - \cdots - \beta_n x_{nk})^2.$$

Suppose, furthermore, that certain physical principles indicate *a priori* that some of the β_j must be non-negative. Show that the resulting problem is a quadratic programming problem. Is z a convex function?

7–26. Imagine a security portfolio is to be formed by making selections in proper proportions from n different stocks and bonds. Assume that historical data are available which give a record of the price and dividend behavior of the securities. Define the return $r_j(k)$ from security j in year k to be

$$r_j(k) = \frac{p_j(k) - p_j(k-1) + d_j(k)}{p_j(k-1)},$$

where $p_j(k)$ is the average price in year k and $d_j(k)$ is the dividends received in year k. For each j, let us now compute over the period for which data are available (say m years), the average return

$$\mu_j = \frac{1}{m}\sum_k r_j(k),$$

the variance of the return

$$\sigma_j^2 = \frac{1}{m}\sum_k [r_j(k) - \mu_j]^2,$$

and for each ij pair, the covariance

$$\sigma_{ij} = \frac{1}{m}\sum_k [r_i(k) - \mu_i][r_j(k) - \mu_j].$$

Now, over the historical period under consideration, imagine that one had a portfolio of securities such that initially the fraction of its total value accounted for by j was x_j. Show that the average return in year k is then $\sum_j r_j(k)x_j$, and that for the period is $\sum \mu_j x_j = \mu$. The variance of the return is

$$\sigma^2 = \sum_k \left[\sum_j (r_j(k) - \mu_j)x_j\right]^2 = \mathbf{x}'\mathbf{D}\mathbf{x}, \qquad \text{where} \qquad \mathbf{D} = \| \sigma_{ij} \|.$$

It is possible for σ^2 to be less than any one of the σ_j^2, although the average return must lie between the largest and smallest of the μ_j. For any given allowable average return μ, there will, in general, be an infinite number of points $\mathbf{x} \geq \mathbf{0}$, $\sum x_j = 1$, satisfying $\sum \mu_j x_j = \mu$. We can then obtain a legitimate quadratic programming problem which seeks to determine an $\mathbf{x}$ which minimizes the variance for a given return, i.e.,

$$\sum \mu_j x_j = \mu, \qquad \sum x_j = 1, \qquad \mathbf{x} \geq \mathbf{0}, \qquad \min z = \mathbf{x}'\mathbf{D}\mathbf{x}.$$

Note that z is convex (why?). After we have finished this computation, it might turn out that if we now use the minimum variance σ_m^2 so obtained and consider a problem that seeks to maximize the average rate of return, given that $\sigma^2 = \sigma_m^2$, we might find that μ could be increased over the value assumed initially without an increase in the variance. Certainly, then, this latter return would be preferred to the initial one. This suggests that we introduce the notion of *efficient pairs* (μ, σ^2). Such a pair will be called efficient if σ^2 is the minimum variance, given μ, and μ is the maximum average return, given σ^2. We would like to determine all the efficient pairs (μ, σ^2) and the corresponding $\mathbf{x}$ which yield them. Show that these will be obtained by solving the following problem for all $\theta \geq 0$:

$$\sum x_j = 1, \qquad \mathbf{x} \geq \mathbf{0}, \qquad \max z = \theta \sum \mu_j x_j - \mathbf{x}'\mathbf{D}\mathbf{x}.$$

The above computational technique could be used to make portfolio selections based on historical data, given the assumption that the future would be like the past. Another approach would be simply to use assumed values for the μ_j, σ_{ij}. H. Markowitz [13] first proposed and gave a detailed discussion of this type of analysis. [*Hint:* To carry out the above proof, note that when z is maximized for a given θ to yield an $\mathbf{x}^*$, then $\sum \mu_j x_j^* = \mu^*$, and $\mathbf{x}'\mathbf{D}\mathbf{x}$ is minimized for $\mathbf{x}$ such that $\sum \mu_j x_j = \mu^*$. This follows since $z^* \geq z(\mathbf{x})$ for all $\mathbf{x} \geq \mathbf{0}$, $\sum x_j = 1$, and this in particular holds for all $\mathbf{x}$ satisfying $\sum \mu_j x_j = \mu^*$. Similarly, if σ^2 is set equal to $(\mathbf{x}^*)'\mathbf{D}\mathbf{x}^*$, then μ^* is the maximum of all $\sum \mu_j x_j$ with this variance. Hence the (μ, σ^2)-pair is efficient.]

7–27. Over the years 1933 to 1951 the mean returns on U.S. Steel and American Tobacco common were \$0.144 and \$0.073 respectively. The standard deviations were \$0.26 for U.S. Steel and \$0.15 for American Tobacco. The correlation coefficient $\rho = \sigma_{12}/\sigma_1\sigma_2 = 0.19$ for these two stocks. Determine the set of efficient pairs (μ, σ^2) and the corresponding optimal portfolio combinations $\mathbf{x}$. Refer to Problem 7–26 for the necessary background.

7–28. Consider the quadratic programming problem

$$\mathbf{A}\mathbf{x} = \mathbf{b}, \qquad \mathbf{x} \geq \mathbf{0}, \qquad \max z = \theta\mathbf{c}\mathbf{x} + \mathbf{x}'\mathbf{D}\mathbf{x},$$

where $\mathbf{x}'\mathbf{D}\mathbf{x}$ is negative semidefinite. Write $F(\theta) = \max z$. Prove that the set of $\mathbf{x}$ for which $F(\theta) = \theta\mathbf{c}\mathbf{x} + \mathbf{x}'\mathbf{D}\mathbf{x}$ is convex, and that $\mathbf{c}\mathbf{x}$ is constant over this set. [*Hint:* If $\mathbf{x}_1$, $\mathbf{x}_2$, are two points in the set, show by the concavity of z that this is also true of $\lambda\mathbf{x}_1 + (1 - \lambda)\mathbf{x}_2$, $0 \leq \lambda \leq 1$. Let $\mathbf{w} = \mathbf{x}_1 - \mathbf{x}_2$. Thus conclude that

$$(\theta\mathbf{c}\mathbf{w} + 2\mathbf{x}_2'\mathbf{D}\mathbf{w})\lambda + \mathbf{w}'\mathbf{D}\mathbf{w}\lambda^2 \equiv 0, \qquad \text{all } \lambda, \qquad 0 \leq \lambda \leq 1.$$

Thus $\mathbf{w}'\mathbf{D}\mathbf{w} = 0$; so $\mathbf{D}\mathbf{w} = \mathbf{0}$, and therefore $\mathbf{c}\mathbf{w} = 0$.]

7–29. Apply the Kuhn-Tucker conditions to show that for each $\beta \geq 0$, Houthakker's method discussed in Section 7–7 yields an optimal solution to the problem.

7–30. Prove that if (7–1) has an unbounded solution then there is no solution to (7–10) with $\mathbf{x} \geq \mathbf{0}$, $\mathbf{v} \geq \mathbf{0}$. [*Hint:* Write $z = f(\mathbf{x})$. Since f is concave, (3–65) holds for any $\mathbf{x}_1$, $\mathbf{x}_2$. Assume that $\mathbf{x}_1$, $\boldsymbol{\lambda}$ satisfies (7–10), and $\mathbf{x}_2$ is any point satisfying $\mathbf{A}\mathbf{x} = \mathbf{b}$, $\mathbf{x} \geq \mathbf{0}$. Thus $f(\mathbf{x}_2) - f(\mathbf{x}_1) \leq -F(\mathbf{x}_1, \boldsymbol{\lambda})$. But this is impossible if $f(\mathbf{x}_2)$ can be arbitrarily large.

7–31. Show that the computational scheme of Frank and Wolfe discussed in Section 7–7 does converge in a finite number of iterations. [*Hint:* First show that

$-\mathbf{\Phi}_r^+\mathbf{\Phi} \geq -\frac{1}{2}\mathbf{\Phi}_r^+\mathbf{\Phi}_r$ can always be obtained. To do this note that $-\mathbf{\Phi}_r^+\mathbf{\Phi} \leq 0$; so the maximum is finite. Furthermore, the optimal solution $\mathbf{\Phi}_*$ is a feasible solution, and $\mathbf{\Phi}_*^+\mathbf{\Phi}_* = 0$. In addition, $\mathbf{\Phi}_r^+\mathbf{\Phi}_r - 2\mathbf{\Phi}_r^+\mathbf{\Phi}_* = (\mathbf{\Phi}_r^+ - \mathbf{\Phi}_*^+)(\mathbf{\Phi}_r - \mathbf{\Phi}_*) \geq 0$, so that the maximum of $-\mathbf{\Phi}_r^+\mathbf{\Phi}$ is not less than $-\frac{1}{2}\mathbf{\Phi}_r^+\mathbf{\Phi}_r$. This also implies that

$$\mathbf{\Phi}_r^+[\mathbf{\Phi}_r - \mathbf{\Phi}(k)] \geq \tfrac{1}{2}\mathbf{\Phi}_r^+\mathbf{\Phi}_r > 0,$$

and we conclude that $0 < \mu \leq 1$. Next show that

$$\mathbf{\Phi}_{r+1}^+\mathbf{\Phi}_{r+1} \leq (1 - \tfrac{1}{2}\mu)\mathbf{\Phi}_r^+\mathbf{\Phi}_r.$$

Since the prices are changed from one problem to another, a basis may be repeated, and the convergence proof cannot be founded on the fact that the number of basic solutions is finite. Instead, let W be the convex polyhedron generated by the basic feasible solutions to $\mathbf{Qw} = \mathbf{f}$. Let $L = \max\,[(\mathbf{\Phi}_2^+ - \mathbf{\Phi}_1^+)(\mathbf{\Phi}_2 - \mathbf{\Phi}_1)]$ for all $\mathbf{\Phi}_1$ and $\mathbf{\Phi}_2$ in W. Then $L > 0$ and if $\mu < 1$,

$$\frac{1}{2}\,\mu \geq \frac{1}{2L}\,\mathbf{\Phi}_r^+\,[\mathbf{\Phi}_r - \mathbf{\Phi}(k)] \geq \frac{1}{4L}\,\mathbf{\Phi}_r^+\mathbf{\Phi}_r.$$

Thus in every case,

$$1 - \frac{\mu}{2} \leq \max\left\{1 - \frac{1}{4L}\,\mathbf{\Phi}_r^+\mathbf{\Phi}_r,\ \frac{1}{2}\right\} = \gamma_r,$$

or if

$$\Delta_r = \frac{1}{4L}\,\mathbf{\Phi}_r^+\mathbf{\Phi}_r,$$

then

$$\Delta_{r+1} \leq \gamma_r\,\Delta_r.$$

If $\Delta_r \geq 1/2$, $\Delta_{r+1} \leq \Delta_r/2$. Thus there exists an R such that $\Delta_r < 1/2$ for all $r \geq R$. But then

$$\frac{1}{\Delta_{r+1}} \geq \frac{1}{\Delta_r} + 1 \qquad \text{or} \qquad \frac{1}{\Delta_r} \geq \frac{1}{\Delta_R} + (r - R), \qquad r \geq R.$$

Therefore Δ_r approaches zero at worst as $1/r$. Show that the limit must be reached in a finite number of steps. To do this note that from the above there is a limiting value $\Delta_\infty = 0$. But $\mathbf{\Phi}_\infty$ is a convex combination of the extreme point solutions $\mathbf{\Phi}(k)$ that were obtained. [This is a contradiction.]

7–32. Give the dual of the following quadratic programming problem. Assume that z is concave.

$$\mathbf{Ax} \leq \mathbf{b}, \qquad \mathbf{x} \geq \mathbf{0}, \qquad \max z = \mathbf{cx} + \mathbf{x}'\mathbf{Dx}.$$

7–33. Give the dual of the following quadratic programming problem. Assume that z is convex.

$$\mathbf{Ax} = \mathbf{b}, \qquad \mathbf{x} \geq \mathbf{0}, \qquad \min z = \mathbf{cx} + \mathbf{x}'\mathbf{Dx}.$$

7–34. Assume that $\mathbf{x}'\mathbf{D}\mathbf{x}$ is positive definite. Show that the following quadratic programming problems can be considered to be dual problems. This is the form considered by Dennis [5].

$$(1)\quad \mathbf{A}\mathbf{x} \geq \mathbf{b}, \qquad \mathbf{x} \geq \mathbf{0}, \qquad \min z = \mathbf{c}\mathbf{x} + \mathbf{x}'\mathbf{D}\mathbf{x}.$$

$$(2)\quad -\mathbf{y} \leq \mathbf{c}', \qquad \max z = \mathbf{y}'\mathbf{D}^{-1}\mathbf{y}.$$

7–35. For the duality theory given in Section 7–8, is it true that the dual of the dual is the primal?

7–36. Show that for a critical value of θ (Section 7–5), $[\mathbf{0}, \mathbf{c}]$ can replace the vector corresponding to the variable driven to zero in the basic solution to (7–24) and thus yield a basic solution to (7–32).

7–37. In obtaining Eq. (7–41), show how to express the α_j, g_{js} in terms of the c_i and d_{ij}.

7–38. With Beale's method, show how you obtain the new y_{ij}, that is, the $\hat{y}_{ij}$, and the new α_j, g_{jk}, that is, $\hat{\alpha}_j$, $\hat{g}_{jk}$, on changing the basic solution in terms of the previous values. In particular, imagine that if x_{Rr} (imagine that this might be a u_j also) is to enter the basis and x_{Bs} is to leave (x_{Bs} might be a u_j also), then

$$x_{Rr} = \frac{y_{s0}}{y_{sr}} - \sum_{j \neq r} \frac{y_{sj}}{y_{sr}} - \frac{x_{Bs}}{y_{sr}} = v_0 + v_s x_{Bs} + \sum_{j \neq r} v_j x_j.$$

Show that

$$\hat{g}_{ss} = g_{rr} v_s^2; \qquad \hat{g}_{sj} = g_{rj} v_s + g_{rr} v_s v_j;$$

$$\hat{g}_{js} = g_{jr} v_s + g_{rr} v_{sx} v_j; \qquad \hat{g}_{jk} = g_{jk} + g_{jr} v_k + g_{rk} v_j + g_{rr} v_j v_k,\ k \neq s,$$

where $\hat{\alpha}_j = \hat{g}_{j0}$. Thus show that the new matrix is also symmetric. Does the number of nonbasic variables change from one iteration to the next?

7–39. Prove that Beale's computational method converges in a finite number of steps. [*Hint:* First note that if in Problem 7–38, the variable leaving the basis is an unrestricted variable u_j, then $v_s = 1/g_{rr}$, $v_j = -g_{rj}/g_{rr}$, $j \neq s$, so that $\hat{g}_{sj} = \hat{g}_{js} = 0$, $j \neq s$. Also note that if $g_{jk} = g_{kj} = 0$ for all $k \neq j$, and if an unrestricted variable is being removed from the basis so that $v_j = 0$, then $\hat{g}_{jk} = \hat{g}_{kj} = 0$ for all $k \neq j$. Define z as being in standard form if it contains no linear term in any free variable. Since z increases at each step, we can never return to the same standard form, even with a different set of unrestricted variables, since this would imply that the same basic solution to $\mathbf{A}\mathbf{x} = \mathbf{b}$ yields two different values of z. Of course, there is only a finite number of basic solutions to $\mathbf{A}\mathbf{x} = \mathbf{b}$. Thus the iterative procedure must terminate in a finite number of steps if it always reaches a standard form in a finite number of steps when it is not in standard form. Use the results to Problem 7–38 to show that this is the case. Show that so long as the expression is not in standard form, the number of nonbasic unrestricted variables cannot increase, provided that so long as it is not in standard form, we always choose an unrestricted variable to enter the basis.

7–40. Attempt to set up a tableau format for numerically solving a quadratic programming problem by Beale's method.

7–41. Suppose that in using the method of Section 7–2, we have allowed x_j (or v_j) to enter the basis at a positive level when v_j (or x_j) is in the basis at a zero level. Imagine that at a later iteration, if the standard rules are followed, v_j as well as x_j will become positive when some vector is inserted into the basis and a variable different from x_j or v_j is driven to zero. Show that one can always avoid this problem by removing v_j (which is at a zero level) from the basis, and thus insert the new vector at a zero level.

7–42. Are any simplifications introduced into the method of Section 7–2 when some variables are unrestricted in sign?

7–43. What will be the order of the matrix $\mathbf{E}$ in Eq. (7–50) when all the original variables are required to be non-negative? Obtain the Kuhn-Tucker conditions for the problem represented by Eq. (7–50) and compare them with those for the original form of the problem. Compare the effort required to solve the problem in its original form by the method of Section 7–2 with that of solving Eq. (7–50) by the same method. Thus show that the transformation to the form of Eq. (7–50) will not reduce the computational effort required to solve the problem.

7–44. For the parametric method discussed in Section 7–5, show that if one or more u_j appear in the final basis corresponding to $\theta = 0$, it is not necessary to remove these variables from the basis. Show how they can be maintained at a zero level. [*Hint:* Recall what is done when one uses the two-phase technique with the revised simplex method in linear programming.]

7–45. Prove directly that when $u_j = 0$, the procedure suggested in Beale's method discussed in part (b) of Section 7–7 does yield a basic solution to $\mathbf{Ax} = \mathbf{b}$ and $\partial z/\partial x_{rj} = 0$, i.e., show that the matrix of the coefficients of the basic variables is nonsingular.

7–46. Suppose that $\mathbf{x}'\mathbf{Dx}$ can be semidefinite. Show that if there is a feasible solution to Eq. (7–10), i.e., one with $\mathbf{x} \geq \mathbf{0}$, $\mathbf{v} \geq \mathbf{0}$, there must be a feasible solution with $\mathbf{x}'\mathbf{v} = 0$. This implies that if Eq. (7–10) has a feasible solution, Eq. (7–1) must have an optimal solution (not an unbounded solution), since if Eq. (7–10) has a feasible solution, $\mathbf{Ax} = \mathbf{b}$ has a feasible solution. [*Hint:* Use Eq. (3–65), where $\mathbf{x}_2$ is the $\mathbf{x}$-part of the solution to Eq. (7–10).]

7–47. If using Beale's method, we are going to increase x_{Rj}, we first determine the value of x_{Rj}, call it ρ, at which one or more of the basic variables is driven to zero. Then we increase x_{Rj} up to the point where $\partial z/\partial x_{Rj} = 0$ or to ρ. Show that if $\partial z/\partial x_{Rj}$ vanishes over the interval $0 \leq x_{Rj} \leq \alpha$, then z assumes its maximum value over the interval at the point where $\partial z/\partial x_{Rj}$ vanishes. Thus, in Beale's method, we find the maximum allowable increase in z, given that we are going to change only a single variable at a time.

7–48. Lemke [11] has devised a finite iterative procedure for minimizing (7–50) for $\boldsymbol{\lambda} \geq \mathbf{0}$. Let $\boldsymbol{\lambda}$ contain N components. Then at each iteration k he makes use of the solution $\boldsymbol{\lambda} \geq \mathbf{0}$, the inverse of an Nth-order matrix (which he calls a basis matrix) $\mathbf{B}^{-1}$, and $\mathbf{r} = (\mathbf{d} + 2\boldsymbol{\lambda}'\mathbf{E})'$, which is the tranpose of ∇z. Initially, $\boldsymbol{\lambda} = \mathbf{0}$, $\mathbf{B}^{-1} = \mathbf{I}$, and $\mathbf{r} = \mathbf{d}'$. An iteration can then be described as follows. Assume that for the current feasible solution $\lambda_i = 0$, $i \in I$. Then for each $i \in I$, there will be a column of $\mathbf{B}$ which is $\mathbf{e}_i$. These are called restricted columns.

Denote the columns of $\mathbf{B}$ by $\mathbf{b}_j$. Let J contain the j corresponding to the restricted columns. Let $\mathbf{w} = \mathbf{B}^{-1}\mathbf{r}$. If $\mathbf{w} \geq \mathbf{0}$ and $w_j = 0, j \notin J$, then the current solution is optimal. Use the Kuhn-Tucker theory to prove this. If this is not the case, then either $w_j \neq 0$ for one or more $j \notin J$, or all $w_j = 0, j \notin J$, but $w_j < 0$ for one or more $j \in J$. Consider now the iterative procedure. Select a column $\mathbf{b}_r$ of $\mathbf{B}$ for which $w_j \neq 0, j \notin J$ or $w_j < 0, j \in J$. To be definite, select the one for which $|w_j|$ is maximized. Then $\mathbf{b}_r$ will leave the basis. To determine the vector to enter the basis, consider $\hat{\boldsymbol{\lambda}} = \boldsymbol{\lambda} - \theta\boldsymbol{\beta}_r$, where $\boldsymbol{\beta}_r$ is the rth column of $(\mathbf{B}^{-1})'$. Select θ such that $Z(\hat{\boldsymbol{\lambda}})$ will be maximized for $\hat{\boldsymbol{\lambda}} \geq \mathbf{0}$. Show that the value of θ which accomplishes this can be determined as follows. Compute $\mathbf{q} = \mathbf{E}\boldsymbol{\beta}_r$. If $\mathbf{q} \neq \mathbf{0}$, compute $\theta_0 = w_r/\mathbf{q}'\boldsymbol{\beta}_r$. Next compute

$$t_0 = \min \begin{cases} \min\limits_i \dfrac{\mathbf{e}_i'\boldsymbol{\lambda}}{\theta_0\mathbf{e}_i'\boldsymbol{\beta}_r}, & \theta_0\mathbf{e}_i'\boldsymbol{\beta}_r > 0. \\ \infty \end{cases}$$

Take $\theta = \theta_0$ if $t_0 > 1$, and $\theta = t_0\theta_0$ if $t_0 \leq 1$. If $\theta = t_0\theta_0$, then for some k, $\theta = \mathbf{e}_k'\boldsymbol{\lambda}/\mathbf{e}_k'\boldsymbol{\beta}_r$. If $\mathbf{q} = \mathbf{0}$, $Z(\hat{\boldsymbol{\lambda}}) = Z(\boldsymbol{\lambda}) - \theta w_r$. In this case, take $\theta_0 = 1$ if $w_r > 0$, and $\theta_0 = -1$ if $w_r < 0$, and $\theta = t_0\theta_0$. The new vector $\mathbf{b}_k$ to replace $\mathbf{b}_r$ in $\mathbf{B}$ is then $\mathbf{b}_k = \mathbf{q}$ if $\theta = \theta_0$, and $\mathbf{b}_k = \mathbf{e}_k$ otherwise. The new solution is $\hat{\boldsymbol{\lambda}}$, $\hat{Z} = Z - \theta\mathbf{q}$. The matrix $\hat{\mathbf{B}}^{-1}$ is obtained from $\mathbf{B}^{-1}$ by the usual transformation formulas of the simplex method.

7–49. Use Lemke's algorithm to maximize $U(\mathbf{x})$ in Problem 7–20 when there is no capacity restriction.

7–50. Can you show that Lemke's algorithm discussed in Problem 7–48 must converge in a finite number of iterations?

7–51. In Beale's method, imagine that (7–42) represents $\partial z/\partial u_j$, rather than $\partial z/\partial x_{Rj}$. Show that if $\alpha_j \neq 0$, z can be increased by allowing u_j to be different from 0. What sign should u_j have?

7–52. In Beale's method, if the constant term α_j in $\partial z/\partial x_{Rj}$ or $\partial z/\partial u_j$ is zero, z cannot be increased by allowing the corresponding variable to become basic. Why is this the case?

7–53. Initiate the parametric solution for the example of Section 7–6, using as basic variables $x_3, x_4, v_1, v_2, \xi_1$, and ξ_2 rather than the basic solution of Table 7–5. Attempt to carry out the solution. What happens? How do you explain this?

7–54. In Section 7–5, prove that when $\theta = 0$, the computational method of Section 7–2 will terminate with $Z = 0$ even when $\mathbf{x}'\mathbf{D}\mathbf{x}$ is only negative semidefinite. [*Hint:* Use fact (proof?) that if $\mathbf{x}'\mathbf{D}\mathbf{x} = 0$, $\mathbf{x}'\mathbf{D} = \mathbf{0}$.]

CHAPTER 8

INTEGER LINEAR PROGRAMMING

Seven swans aswimming,
Six geese alaying,
Five gold rings,
Four colly birds,
Three French hens,
Two turtle doves, and
A partridge in a pear tree.

The Twelve Days of Christmas, English Carol

8–1 Introduction. This chapter will be devoted to the study of integer linear programming problems. An *integer linear programming problem* is a nonlinear programming problem which would be linear if it were not for the fact that some or all the variables are restricted to integral values. The problem is called an *all integer* problem if all variables are restricted to integral values, and a *mixed integer-continuous variable* problem if some variables are restricted to integers while others are allowed to vary continuously. The most general problem of the type to be considered in this chapter can be written

$$\mathbf{Ax} = \mathbf{b}; \qquad \mathbf{x} \geq \mathbf{0}; \qquad x_j \text{ an integer}, \quad j \in J_1; \qquad \max z = \mathbf{cx}. \tag{8–1}$$

If J_1 contains all j, we have an all integer problem, and if J_1 is empty, (8–1) is a linear programming problem.

We shall begin by explaining why it is of so much interest to be able to solve problems of the form (8–1). It is fairly obvious that for many practical problems the variables are required to be integers. However, the reader might feel that one could simply solve (8–1), ignoring the integrality requirements and then round the values in the resulting solution to the nearest integers satisfying the constraints. This is frequently done in practice and is a perfectly valid approach when the values of the variables are sufficiently large that rounding has a negligible effect. However, the most interesting integer programming problems are those for which the integer variables must be small whole numbers, often 0 or 1. We shall see below that a number of nonlinear programming problems which at first glance would seem to be in no way connected with integer programming can be formulated as integer programming problems in which the integer variables can assume only the values 0 or 1.

It is possible to develop algorithms for solving (8–1) either for the all integer case or for the mixed integer-continuous variable case which converge in a finite number of iterations. This has been done by Gomory [8, 9, 10, 11]. We shall develop these algorithms and prove that they converge in a finite number of steps. Unfortunately, computational experience with these algorithms has been rather disappointing. Although they converge in a finite number of steps, the number of iterations required may be huge even for problems (8–1) of rather modest size. Thus it cannot be claimed at the present time that efficient numerical techniques are available for solving integer programming problems.

In this chapter we shall restrict our attention to solving problems of the form (8–1). We shall not attempt to consider how to solve problems having some variables required to be integers which would be nonlinear even if the integrality restrictions were dropped. In Chapter 10, however, we shall see that dynamic programming can be used to solve certain problems of this type.

Let us now show how a number of interesting problems can be formulated as integer linear programming problems. In studying these, the reader should note that most turn out to be mixed integer-continuous variable problems. The basic ideas for the integer programming formulations developed in Sections 8–2 through 8–6 and 8–9 are to be found in the survey paper by Dantzig [5].

8–2 The fixed-charge problem. In Section 4–10 we studied the fixed-charge problem

$$\mathbf{Ax} = \mathbf{b}; \qquad \mathbf{x} \geq \mathbf{0}, \qquad \min z = \sum_{j=1}^{n} [A_j\delta_j + c_jx_j], \tag{8–2}$$

where

$$\delta_j = \begin{cases} 0 & \text{if} \quad x_j = 0, \\ 1 & \text{if} \quad x_j > 0. \end{cases} \tag{8–3}$$

We showed that at least one extreme point of the convex set of feasible solutions will be optimal, but we noted that the methods of Chapter 4 were of little value in solving fixed-charge problems. We shall now illustrate how to convert the fixed-charge problem to an integer programming problem.

To do this it is fairly obvious that we wish to use the same variables appearing in (8–1) and to require that the δ_j assume only integral values. To ensure that each δ_j can have only the values 0 or 1, given that they are integers, all we need to do is introduce the constraints

$$0 \leq \delta_j \leq 1, \qquad j = 1, \ldots, n. \tag{8–4}$$

As yet, we have not guaranteed that δ_j will take on the values 0 or 1 in accordance with (8–3). This can be done by requiring that x_j be less than, or equal to, a scalar multiple times δ_j. More specifically, assume that we can determine an upper bound d_j on each variable x_j. Then, if we introduce the constraints

$$x_j \leq d_j\delta_j$$

or

$$x_j - d_j\delta_j \leq 0, \qquad j = 1, \ldots, n, \tag{8–5}$$

we are sure that x_j cannot be positive unless $\delta_j = 1$, since if $\delta_j = 0$, $x_j \leq 0$, that is, $x_j = 0$, whereas if $\delta_j = 1$, $x_j \leq d_j$, so that x_j is really unconstrained. Furthermore, an optimal solution will not have $\delta_j = 1$ if $x_j = 0$, because costs could be reduced by having $\delta_j = 0$ also.

Consequently, (8–2) and (8–3) are equivalent to

$$\begin{gathered}
\mathbf{Ax} = \mathbf{b}, \\
x_j - d_j\delta_j \leq 0, \qquad j = 1, \ldots, n, \\
0 \leq \delta_j \leq 1, \qquad j = 1, \ldots, n; \qquad \delta_j \text{ integers}, \\
\mathbf{x} \geq \mathbf{0}, \\
\min z = \sum_{j=1}^{n} (A_j\delta_j + c_jx_j),
\end{gathered} \tag{8–6}$$

which is a mixed integer-continuous variable programming problem of the form (8–1). Consequently, if it is possible to solve problems of the form (8–1), it is possible to solve fixed-charge problems.

Let us note, that if $\mathbf{A}$ is $m \times n$, problem (8–6) has $m + 2n$ constraints, or $m + n$ if one assumes that the upper bounds on the δ_j can be handled in a special way. Consequently, (8–6) will have a very large number of constraints if m and n are at all sizable, and there is a fixed charge associated with each variable. As we shall see later, to apply the integer programming algorithm, we must first solve (8–6) as a linear programming problem ignoring the integrality restrictions. For $m = 100$ and $n = 1000$ (which, in the absence of fixed charges, would yield a linear programming problem which could be solved readily), it would not even be possible to carry out the first step of the integer algorithm and solve (8–6) as a linear programming problem if there were a fixed charge associated with each variable. In the event that some variables do not have fixed charges associated with them, the size of the resulting integer programming problem is correspondingly reduced. We shall see repeatedly in the following sections that in converting a problem to an integer programming problem it is, in general, necessary to increase greatly the number of constraints.

8–3 Determination of global optimum for δ-form of approximating problem. It will be recalled from Section 4–4 that the δ-form of the approximating problem for (4–1) can be written

$$\sum_{j=1}^{n}\sum_{k=1}^{r_j} (\Delta g_{kij})\delta_{kj}\{\leq, =, \geq\}b_i - \sum_{j=1}^{n} g_{0ij}, \qquad i = 1, \ldots, m,$$

$$0 \leq \delta_{kj} \leq 1, \qquad \text{all } k, j, \tag{8–7}$$

$$\text{If} \quad \delta_{kj} > 0, \quad \delta_{uj} = 1, \quad u = 1, \ldots, k-1,$$

$$\max z = \sum_{j=1}^{n}\sum_{k=1}^{r_j} (\Delta f_{kj})\delta_{kj}.$$

We proved in Chapter 4 that by using the simplex method with restricted entry, a local maximum of (8–7) could be determined. However, unless the problem had the appropriate convexity and concavity properties, there was no guarantee that the local optimum so obtained was a global optimum. We shall now show how to convert (8–7) to an integer linear programming problem. By solving this problem we can determine a global optimum for (8–7) in all cases.

To convert (8–7) to an integer programming problem all that needs to be done is represent the conditions

$$\text{If} \quad \delta_{kj} > 0, \quad \delta_{uj} = 1, \quad u = 1, \ldots, k-1, \tag{8–8}$$

within this framework. Note that (8–8) is equivalent to saying that $\delta_{k+1,j} = 0$ unless $\delta_{kj} = 1$. To represent these restrictions, let us introduce a new set of variables ψ_{kj} which are allowed to take on only the integer values 0 or 1. Suppose that for each k and j, we introduce the constraints

$$\delta_{kj} \geq \psi_{kj}, \qquad \delta_{k+1,j} \leq \psi_{kj}. \tag{8–9}$$

Then if $\psi_{kj} = 1$, (8–9) requires that $\delta_{kj} \geq 1$, that is, $\delta_{kj} = 1$ and $\delta_{k+1,j} \leq 1$, i.e., no new restriction is placed on $\delta_{k+1,j}$. On the other hand, if $\psi_{kj} = 0$, (8–9) requires that $\delta_{kj} \geq 0$, i.e., no new restriction is placed on δ_{kj}, and $\delta_{k+1,j} \leq 0$ so that $\delta_{k+1,j} = 0$. This is precisely what we wanted. Note that if $\psi_{kj} = 1$, it must be true that $\psi_{uj} = 1$, $u = 0, \ldots, k-1$, for if $\psi_{uj} = 1$ and $\psi_{u-1,j} = 0$, it follows from (8–9) that $\delta_{uj} \leq 0$ and $\delta_{uj} \geq 1$, which is a contradiction. To make sure that the integer variables ψ_{kj} are restricted to the values 0 or 1, we need to require only that $\psi_{kj} \geq 0$ for all k and j. It is not necessary to impose the conditions $0 \leq \psi_{kj} \leq 1$, because the restrictions $\delta_{kj} \geq \psi_{kj}$ and $0 \leq \delta_{kj} \leq 1$ ensure that ψ_{kj} cannot be greater than unity. Consequently, (8–7) can be replaced by the mixed integer-continuous variable problem

$$\sum_{j=1}^{n} \sum_{k=1}^{r_j} (\Delta g_{kij}) \delta_{kj} \{\leq, =, \geq\} b_i - \sum_{j=1}^{n} g_{0ij}, \qquad i = 1, \ldots, m,$$

$$\begin{aligned} \delta_{kj} - \psi_{kj} &\geq 0, \qquad \text{all } k, j, \\ \delta_{k+1,j} - \psi_{kj} &\leq 0, \qquad \text{all } k, j, \\ 0 \leq \delta_{kj} &\leq 1, \qquad \text{all } k, j, \end{aligned} \tag{8-10}$$

$$\psi_{kj} \geq 0, \qquad \psi_{kj} \text{ integers}, \quad \text{all } k, j,$$

$$\max z = \sum_{j=1}^{n} \sum_{k=1}^{r_j} (\Delta f_{kj}) \delta_{kj}.$$

The conversion of (8–7) to an integer programming problem (8–10) necessitated a considerable increase in the number of constraints. Even if m and n were as absurdly small as 5 and 20, respectively, and if five δ_{kj}-variables were used for each original variable, (8–10) would have 305 constraints including the upper bounds, or 205 not including the upper bounds. For values of m and n that would be of interest in practice, (8–10) would have 2000 or more constraints. In the event that some of the variables enter the problem in a strictly linear fashion, the size of the integer programming problem will be correspondingly reduced; because for such variables x_j it is unnecessary to introduce variables δ_{kj}.

8–4 Determination of global optimum for λ-form of approximating problem. As might be expected, it is also possible to represent the λ-form of the approximating problem for (4–1) as an integer linear programming problem, and thus, in principle, a means is available for determining a global optimum for this problem. It was shown in Section 4–2 that the λ-form of the approximating problem for (4–1) is

$$\sum_{j=1}^{n} \sum_{k=0}^{r_j} g_{kij} \lambda_{kj} \{\leq, =, \geq\} b_i, \qquad i = 1, \ldots, n,$$

$$\sum_{k=0}^{r_j} \lambda_{kj} = 1, \qquad j = 1, \ldots, n, \tag{8-11}$$

$$\lambda_{kj} \geq 0, \qquad \text{all } k, j,$$

$$\max z = \sum_{j=1}^{n} \sum_{k=0}^{r_j} f_{kj} \lambda_{kj},$$

where we require in addition that for each j, no more than two λ_{kj} shall be positive, and two can be positive only if they are adjacent.

To convert (8–11) to an integer programming problem, we only need to represent properly the restrictions indicating which λ_{kj} can be positive. To do this, we again introduce a new set of variables ψ_{kj} which are allowed to take on only the integer values 0 and 1. Next let us require that

$$\sum_k \psi_{kj} = 1, \qquad j = 1, \ldots, n. \tag{8–12}$$

Because each $\psi_{kj} = 0$ or 1, (8–12) implies that for a given j, all ψ_{kj} will be zero except one of the set which will be unity. Next let us introduce the constraints

$$\lambda_{0j} \leq \psi_{0j}; \qquad \lambda_{kj} \leq \psi_{k-1,j} + \psi_{kj}, \qquad k = 1, \ldots, r_j - 1;$$
$$\lambda_{r_j,j} \leq \psi_{r_j-1,j}; \qquad j = 1, \ldots, n. \tag{8–13}$$

We now have the representation desired, for if $\psi_{kj} = 1$, we know from (8–12) that $\psi_{uj} = 0$, $u \neq k$, and (8–13) requires that $\lambda_{uj} \leq 0$, that is, $\lambda_{uj} = 0$, $u \neq k, k+1$. Furthermore, $\lambda_{kj} \leq 1$, $\lambda_{k+1,j} \leq 1$, so that no new restrictions are placed on the values of these two variables. Thus the above constraints do imply that no more than two λ_{kj} can be positive for a given j, and two can be positive only if they are adjacent. Therefore (8–11) is equivalent to the mixed integer-continuous variable problem

$$\sum_{j=1}^{n} \sum_{k=0}^{r_j} g_{kij}\lambda_{kj}\{\leq, =, \geq\}b_i, \qquad i = 1, \ldots, m,$$

$$\sum_{k=0}^{r_j} \lambda_{kj} = 1, \qquad j = 1, \ldots, n,$$

$$\sum_{k=0}^{r_j-1} \psi_{kj} = 1, \qquad j = 1, \ldots, n, \tag{8–14}$$

$$\lambda_{0j} \leq \psi_{0j}; \qquad \lambda_{kj} \leq \psi_{k-1,j} + \psi_{kj}, \quad k = 1, \ldots, r_j - 1;$$

$$\lambda_{r_j,j} \leq \psi_{r_j-1,j}, \quad j = 1, \ldots, n,$$

$$\psi_{kj} \geq 0, \qquad \psi_{kj} \text{ integers}, \qquad \text{all } k, j,$$

$$\lambda_{kj} \geq 0, \qquad \text{all } k, j,$$

$$\max z = \sum_{j=1}^{n} \sum_{k=0}^{r_j} f_{kj}\lambda_{kj}.$$

It is unnecessary to place an upper bound of unity on each ψ_{kj} to be sure that it can assume only the values 0 or 1, since (8–12) automatically guarantees that no $\psi_{kj} > 1$. The variables $\psi_{r_j,j}$ are not needed. However, they could be included without changing anything. In fact, one could also introduce the integer variables ψ_{-1j}, and then (8–13) could be written as

$$\lambda_{kj} \leq \psi_{k-1,j} + \psi_{kj}$$

for all $k = 0, 1, \ldots, r_j$. Note that once again a large number of new constraints are required to convert (8–11) to an integer programming problem.

8–5 Representation of certain surfaces. In Section 4–5, we showed that the function $u = \min [x_1, x_2]$ could be represented as

$$x_1 = \lambda_1 + \lambda_2; \quad x_2 = \lambda_2 + \lambda_3; \quad u = \lambda_2; \quad \lambda_i \geq 0, \quad i = 1, 2, 3, \tag{8–15}$$

where we require in addition that no more than two λ_i shall be positive, and two can be positive only if they are adjacent. These restrictions on the λ_i can be represented within the integer linear programming framework by introducing the two variables ψ_1, ψ_2 each of which can assume only the values 0 and 1. Let us suppose that we can determine a number d such that $x_1 \leq d$, $x_2 \leq d$. Then if we write

$$\begin{gathered} \psi_1 + \psi_2 = 1, \\ \lambda_1 \leq d\psi_1; \quad \lambda_3 \leq d\psi_2, \\ \psi_1 \geq 0, \quad \psi_2 \geq 0, \quad \psi_1, \psi_2 \text{ integers}, \end{gathered} \tag{8–16}$$

these equations guarantee that no more than two λ_i will be positive, and then only if they are adjacent. Therefore $u = \min [x_1, x_2]$ can be represented in an integer linear programming framework by (8–15) and (8–16), and so can the surface shown in Fig. 4–7.

8–6 Discrete alternatives. Consider a linear programming problem in which the solution $\mathbf{x}$ must satisfy one of two constraints $\mathbf{a}^u\mathbf{x} - b_u \leq 0$ or $\mathbf{a}^v\mathbf{x} - b_v \leq 0$, but not both. We are free to impose either one or the other, depending on which allows us to obtain the largest value of the objective function. As a practical example, suppose that the manufacturer of a variety of products wishes to determine an optimal product mix and the processes of production to be used. For one particular product, it must be true that if he produces it at all, he must produce at least an amount b. Suppose that the product can be made by several different processes of production, and let x_j be the quantity produced by process j. Then we must have either $\sum_j x_j \geq b$ or $\sum_j x_j = 0$. A straightforward way of handling a situation of this kind would be to first solve the problem, assuming that the product will be made so that $\sum_j x_j \geq b$ will be included as a constraint. Next one would solve the problem, assuming that the product was not made, i.e., $\sum_j x_j = 0$. An optimal solution would then be that one of the two just obtained which yielded the largest profit.

We would now like to show that the two alternatives $\mathbf{a}^u\mathbf{x} - b_u \leq 0$ or $\mathbf{a}^v\mathbf{x} - b_v \leq 0$ can be handled simultaneously by the introduction of an integer variable. We proceed by assuming that upper bounds L_u and L_v can be determined for the functions $\mathbf{a}^u\mathbf{x} - b_u$ and $\mathbf{a}^v\mathbf{x} - b_v$, respectively, for all relevant $\mathbf{x}$. Now we introduce the variable δ which can take on only the value 0 or 1. Then the conditions $\mathbf{a}^u\mathbf{x} - b_u \leq 0$ or $\mathbf{a}^v\mathbf{x} - b_v \leq 0$ can be replaced by

$$\begin{gathered} \mathbf{a}^u\mathbf{x} - b_u \leq \delta L_u; \qquad \mathbf{a}^v\mathbf{x} - b_v \leq (1 - \delta)L_v, \\ 0 \leq \delta \leq 1, \qquad \delta \text{ an integer.} \end{gathered} \tag{8-17}$$

This follows, since if $\delta = 0$, $\mathbf{a}^u\mathbf{x} - b_u \leq 0$ so that constraint u must be satisfied, whereas $\mathbf{a}^v\mathbf{x} - b_v \leq L_v$, and hence constraint v need not be satisfied. Just the reverse is true when $\delta = 1$. Thus, instead of solving two linear programming problems, one could solve a single mixed integer-continuous variable programming problem with one integer-valued variable.

The "either/or" approach just introduced can be generalized to more complicated situations. Assume, for example, that there are q constraints $\mathbf{a}^i\mathbf{x} - b_i \leq 0, i = 1, \ldots, q$, and it is stipulated that at least k, $k = 1, \ldots, q - 1$, of these constraints must be satisfied, but no restriction is made as to which set of k. This problem could be handled as above by solving $q!/k!(q - k)!$ different linear programming problems and selecting the solution yielding the largest value of the objective function. However, we are able to take account of all the possibilities simultaneously by introducing integer-valued variables.

Assume that for each i, we can determine an upper bound L_i for $\mathbf{a}^i\mathbf{x} - b_i$. Next let us introduce q integer-valued variables δ_i which can take on only the values 0 or 1. Then it is clear that the condition that at least k of the constraints $\mathbf{a}^i\mathbf{x} \leq b_i$ must hold can be represented by

$$\begin{gathered} \mathbf{a}^i\mathbf{x} - b_i \leq \delta_i L_i, \qquad i = 1, \ldots, q, \\ \sum \delta_i = q - k, \\ 0 \leq \delta_i \leq 1, \qquad \delta_i \text{ an integer}, \qquad i = 1, \ldots, q. \end{gathered} \tag{8-18}$$

We set $\sum \delta_i = q - k$, since we want $q - k$ of the δ_i to be unity, the reason being that when $\delta_i = 1$, then the ith constraint is not required to hold.

Discrete alternatives of the type considered above can be used to represent certain types of nonconvex regions. Consider, for example, the region shown in Fig. 8–1. Note that any point $\mathbf{x}$ in this nonconvex region lies

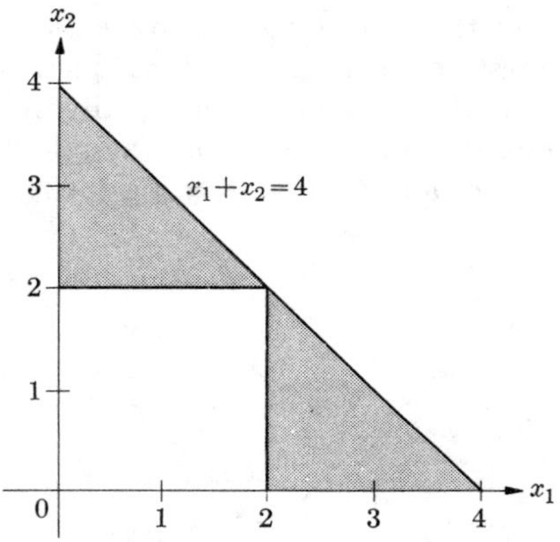

FIGURE 8-1

either in the convex set

$$x_1 + x_2 \leq 4, \qquad x_2 \geq 2, \qquad x_1 \geq 0 \tag{8-19}$$

or

$$x_1 + x_2 \leq 4, \qquad x_1 \geq 2, \qquad x_2 \geq 0. \tag{8-20}$$

We can then represent the region as

$$\begin{gathered} x_1 + x_2 \leq 4, \\ x_1 \geq 2 \qquad \text{or} \qquad x_2 \geq 2, \\ \mathbf{x} \geq \mathbf{0}, \end{gathered} \tag{8-21}$$

and hence, using an integral-valued variable, as

$$\begin{aligned} x_1 + x_2 &\leq 4, \\ x_1 - 2 + 2\delta &\geq 0, \\ x_2 - 2 + 2(1 - \delta) &\geq 0, \\ 0 \leq \delta \leq 1, \qquad \delta &\text{ an integer}, \\ \mathbf{x} &\geq \mathbf{0}. \end{aligned} \tag{8-22}$$

To maximize a linear objective function over the nonconvex region of Fig. 8-1 one could simply solve two linear programming problems; in the first, one maximizes the objective function over the convex set (8-19), and in the second, one maximizes the objective function over the convex set (8-20), i.e., one solves

$$x_1 + x_2 \leq 4, \qquad x_2 \geq 2, \qquad x_1 \geq 0, \qquad \max z = \mathbf{cx} \tag{8-23}$$

and

$$x_1 + x_2 \leq 4, \qquad x_1 \geq 2, \qquad x_2 \geq 0, \qquad \max z = \mathbf{cx}. \tag{8-24}$$

An optimal solution for the nonconvex region would then be the solution which yielded the largest value of the objective function for the two linear programming problems. However, one could equally well solve the problem by solving a single mixed integer-continuous variable linear programming problem with one integer-valued variable, using (8–22).

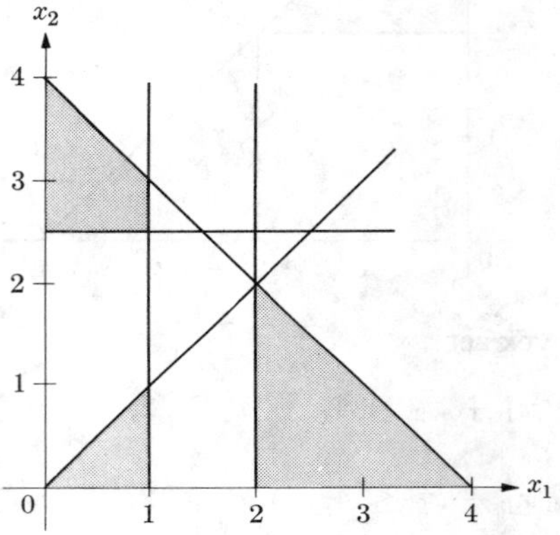

FIGURE 8–2

As an example of a case where at least k of a set of q constraints must be active, we can represent the nonconvex set shown in Fig. 8–2 as follows. The constraints are

$$x_1 + x_2 \leq 4, \quad x_2 \geq 2.5, \quad x_1 \leq 1, \quad x_1 \geq 2, \quad x_1 - x_2 \geq 0. \tag{8–25}$$

The disconnected sets of Fig. 8–2 can be represented by the constraints (8–25), along with $\mathbf{x} \geq \mathbf{0}$, when it is specified that $x_1 + x_2 \leq 4$ always holds and two or more of the remaining constraints in (8–25) must be satisfied simultaneously (check this by considering all the possibilities). By introducing the integer-valued variables δ_i, the disconnected sets of Fig. 8–2 can be represented by the relations

$$\begin{gathered} x_1 + x_2 \leq 4, \qquad x_2 - 3 \geq -3\delta_1, \qquad x_1 - 1 \leq 3\delta_2, \\ x_1 - 2.5 \geq -2.5\delta_3, \qquad x_1 - x_2 \geq -4\delta_4, \qquad \sum_{i=1}^{4} \delta_i = 2, \\ 0 \leq \delta_i \leq 1, \qquad \delta_i \text{ an integer}, \qquad i = 1, \ldots, 4, \end{gathered} \tag{8–26}$$

where, in addition, it is required that $\mathbf{x} \geq \mathbf{0}$, and the fact has been used that there is an upper bound of 4 on each variable.

Another situation similar to that which we have been discussing occurs when it is required that $\mathbf{x}$ lie in at least one of r of the convex sets

$$\mathbf{A}_u \mathbf{x} \leq \mathbf{b}_u, \qquad u = 1, \ldots, r. \tag{8–27}$$

To optimize a linear objective function subject to the restriction that $\mathbf{x}$ be in at least one of the convex sets (8-27), one could proceed by optimizing the objective function over each of the convex sets separately, and then selecting from the solutions so obtained the one which yielded the largest value of the objective function. This would be an optimal solution to the given problem. We shall now show that instead of following this procedure, one can solve a mixed integer-continuous variable linear programming problem.

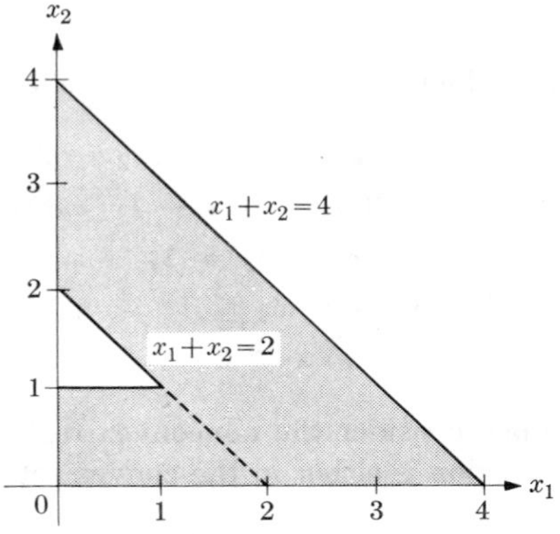

FIGURE 8-3

To obtain the desired representation, assume that we have found an $\mathbf{a}_1$, $\mathbf{a}_2$ such that if $\mathbf{x}$ is in any of the regions (8-27), then $\mathbf{a}_1 \leq \mathbf{x} \leq \mathbf{a}_2$. With respect to these bounds on $\mathbf{x}$, assume that vectors $\mathbf{L}_u$ have been determined such that for all $\mathbf{x}$, $\mathbf{a}_1 \leq \mathbf{x} \leq \mathbf{a}_2$, it is true that $\mathbf{A}_u\mathbf{x} - \mathbf{b}_u \leq \mathbf{L}_u$. Then, if we introduce r integer-valued variables δ_u, the condition that $\mathbf{x}$ must lie in at least one of the convex sets (8-27) can be written

$$\begin{gathered} \mathbf{A}_u\mathbf{x} - \mathbf{b}_u \leq (1 - \delta_u)\mathbf{L}_u, \qquad u = 1, \ldots, r, \\ \sum_u \delta_u = 1, \\ 0 \leq \delta_u \leq 1, \qquad \delta_u \text{ an integer}, \qquad u = 1, \ldots, r. \end{gathered} \tag{8-28}$$

As an example of how one might use the material just discussed, consider the nonconvex region shown in Fig. 8-3. Note that any point $\mathbf{x}$ in this region is either in the convex set

$$x_1 + x_2 \leq 4, \qquad x_1 + x_2 \geq 2, \qquad x_1 \geq 0, \qquad x_2 \geq 0 \tag{8-29}$$

or in the convex set

$$x_1 + x_2 \leq 2, \qquad x_2 \leq 1, \qquad x_1 \geq 0, \qquad x_2 \geq 0. \tag{8-30}$$

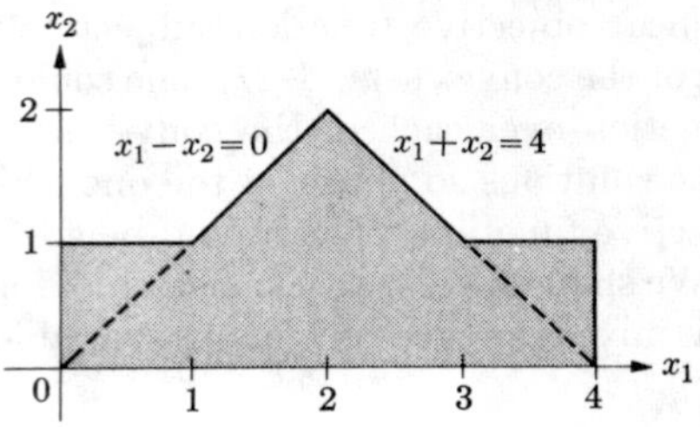

FIGURE 8–4

The representation of the region of Fig. 8–3 in the format of (8–28) is then

$$\begin{gathered} x_1 + x_2 - 4 \le 4\delta_1, \qquad x_1 + x_2 - 2 \ge -2\delta_1, \\ x_1 + x_2 - 2 \le 6\delta_2, \qquad x_2 - 1 \le 3\delta_2, \\ \delta_1 + \delta_2 = 1, \\ 0 \le \delta_1 \le 1, \qquad 0 \le \delta_2 \le 1, \qquad \delta_1, \delta_2 \text{ integers}, \\ \mathbf{x} \ge \mathbf{0}. \end{gathered} \tag{8–31}$$

As another example, consider the nonconvex region shown in Fig. 8–4. Any point $\mathbf{x}$ in this region is either in the convex set

$$x_1 - x_2 \ge 0, \qquad x_1 + x_2 \le 4, \qquad \mathbf{x} \ge \mathbf{0} \tag{8–32}$$

or in the set

$$x_1 \le 4, \qquad x_2 \le 1, \qquad \mathbf{x} \ge \mathbf{0}. \tag{8–33}$$

Some points are in both sets, but this is perfectly all right. In the format of (8–28), this region can be represented as

$$\begin{gathered} x_1 - x_2 \ge -4\delta_1, \qquad x_1 + x_2 - 4 \le 4\delta_1, \\ x_1 - 4 \le 0, \qquad x_2 - 1 \le 3\delta_2, \\ \delta_1 + \delta_2 = 1, \\ 0 \le \delta_1 \le 1, \qquad 0 \le \delta_2 \le 1, \qquad \delta_1, \delta_2 \text{ integers}, \\ \mathbf{x} \ge \mathbf{0}. \end{gathered} \tag{8–34}$$

In this section we have studied situations involving linear programming problems with a discrete number of alternatives. We have seen that problems of this type can be solved by solving (1) a sequence of linear programming problems or (2) a single mixed integer-continuous variable linear programming problem. Although the fact that the problems can be formulated as integer programming problems is interesting, it is probably true that, at present, solving the sequence of linear programming problems is usually at least as efficient as solving the integer programming problem.

8–7 Sequencing problems. Many practical problems have the characteristic that certain operations or events must occur in a definite sequence or must at least satisfy certain ordering restrictions. Often it is difficult or impossible to represent these sequencing requirements within a linear programming format. However, problems of this type which would be linear programming problems if it were not for the ordering requirements can usually be formulated as integer linear programming problems. In the next two sections, we shall provide two examples of this type. Others will be considered in the problems.

8–8 Project planning and manpower scheduling. Consider some project, such as the construction of a building, the turnaround of a catalytic cracker in a refinery, or the periodic overhaul of an airliner. The types of projects that are of interest to us are those involving a large number of jobs which require a number of different types of skilled labor and equipment, and having the property that there is a certain order in which the various jobs must be carried out. We would like to set up a schedule for carrying out the project which minimizes the total costs involved. From this schedule we shall determine how long it will take to finish the project and how much of each kind of skilled labor, equipment, etc., will be needed each day.

The problem will be treated as deterministic, so that there will be no uncertainty in the time estimates, etc. It will be assumed that a day is the smallest time period that needs to be considered, so that scheduling will be done on a daily basis. As is typical in economics, we shall refer to the various kinds of labor, materials, equipment, etc., as factors of production. It will be assumed that the daily availabilities of these factors may be limited. Furthermore, it will be assumed that each day work can be done either on regular time or overtime, and availabilities of each of the factors are specified for both time categories. Let a_{kj} and b_{kj} be the availability of factor k on day j for regular time and overtime use, respectively. It will be assumed that in all there are K factors of production.

Imagine that it has been decided that a maximum of N days and a minimum of n days will be needed to complete the project. In all, I different jobs must be completed (we assume that the entire effort has been broken down into these I jobs). We shall suppose that a table is available giving the order in which the jobs must be completed. It is not necessarily true that only one job can be worked on at a time. Normally, a number of jobs can be worked on simultaneously, but a certain subset of jobs $I(i)$ must be completed before job i can be started.

Let α_{ik} be the quantity of factor k required to do job i on regular time, and β_{ik} the quantity of factor k required to do job i on overtime. For generality, we allow α_{ik} to be different from β_{ik}. The fundamental variables which we shall use in formulating the problem will then be x_{ij} and y_{ij}, the fraction of job i done in day j on regular time and overtime, respectively. We shall assume that the quantity of factor k used on job i in day j on regular time is simply $\alpha_{ik}x_{ij}$, and that used on overtime is $\beta_{ik}y_{ij}$. We can then immediately write down the constraints which must be satisfied if we are not to use any more of a given factor than is available. They are

$$\sum_{i=1}^{I} \alpha_{ik}x_{ij} \leq a_{kj}; \qquad k = 1, \ldots, K; \qquad j = 1, \ldots, N, \tag{8–35}$$

$$\sum_{i=1}^{I} \beta_{ik}y_{ij} \leq b_{kj}; \qquad k = 1, \ldots, K; \qquad j = 1, \ldots, N. \tag{8–36}$$

It must also be true that ultimately all jobs are completed. Thus

$$\sum_{j=1}^{N} (x_{ij} + y_{ij}) = 1, \qquad i = 1, \ldots, I. \tag{8–37}$$

Furthermore job i cannot be started until all jobs in $I(i)$ are finished. Let us now see how these restrictions should be represented. It must be true that $x_{ij} = 0$ unless

$$\sum_{u=1}^{j-1} (x_{i'u} + y_{i'u}) = 1, \qquad i' \in I(i), \tag{8–38}$$

and $y_{ij} = 0$ unless

$$\sum_{u=1}^{j} x_{i'u} + \sum_{u=1}^{j-1} y_{i'u} = 1, \qquad i' \in I(i). \tag{8–39}$$

Here we have an either/or situation of the type similar to the one studied in Section 8–6. To represent it within the integer programming framework, let us introduce the integer-valued variables $\delta_{i'j}$ which will be allowed to assume only the values 0 or 1. Then the condition that $x_{ij} = 0$ unless (8–38) holds can be represented as follows:

$$x_{ij} \leq \delta_{i'j}, \qquad i' \in I(i), \qquad \text{all } i, j, \tag{8–40}$$

$$\sum_{u=1}^{j-1} (x_{i'u} + y_{i'u}) \geq \delta_{i'j}, \qquad \text{all } i', j, \tag{8–41}$$

$$\delta_{i'j} \geq 0, \qquad \delta_{i'j} \text{ an integer}, \qquad \text{all } i', j. \tag{8–42}$$

Note that if $\delta_{i'j} = 1$, it follows from (8–41) that (8–38) must hold. This corresponding constraint in (8–40) then only requires that $x_{ij} \leq 1$. However, if any one of the $\delta_{i'j} = 0$, Eq. (8–40) yields $x_{ij} \leq 0$, that is, $x_{ij} = 0$.

Thus x_{ij} cannot be positive unless (8–38) holds for each $i' \in I(i)$. We need not explicitly introduce upper bounds of unity on the $\delta_{i'j}$ to ensure that they take on only the values 0 or 1, since (8–41) and (8–37) guarantee that $\delta_{i'j}$ cannot be greater than unity.

Similarly, if we introduce a set of integer-valued variables $\psi_{i'j}$, we can represent the fact that $y_{ij} = 0$, unless (8–39) holds, by

$$y_{ij} \leq \psi_{i'j}, \qquad i' \in I(i), \qquad \text{all } i, j, \tag{8–43}$$

$$\sum_{u=1}^{j} x_{i'u} + \sum_{u=1}^{j-1} y_{i'u} \geq \psi_{i'j}, \qquad \text{all } i', j, \tag{8–44}$$

$$\psi_{i'j} \geq 0, \qquad \psi_{i'j} \text{ an integer}, \qquad \text{all } i', j. \tag{8–45}$$

All that remains to be done in the problem formulation is to consider the cost structure. Let c_{kj} be the cost per unit of resource k used on day j during regular time, and d_{kj} the cost per unit of resource k used on day j during overtime. It will be assumed that the cost of any resource on a given day will be directly proportional to the quantity of the resource used, so that the cost of resource k on day j will be

$$c_{kj} \sum_{i=1}^{I} \alpha_{ik} x_{ij} + d_{kj} \sum_{i=1}^{I} \beta_{ik} y_{ij}. \tag{8–46}$$

In certain cases, one would wish to always charge a full shift for each man regardless of the amount of time he worked. This can be done, but it requires a somewhat more complicated formulation.

We shall also assume that there can be a cost associated with a change from one day to the next in the quantity of some resource used, say with a change in the size of the work force. In particular, we shall imagine that there are costs, e_{kj} and g_{kj}, per unit increase in the quantity of factor k required from day $j - 1$ to j on regular time and overtime, respectively, and costs, f_{kj} and h_{kj}, per unit decrease in the quantity of factor k required from day $j - 1$ to j on regular time and overtime, respectively. To represent these costs, note first that the change in the quantity of factor k required from day $j - 1$ to j on regular time is

$$\sum_{i=1}^{I} \alpha_{ik}(x_{ij} - x_{i,j-1}),$$

with a similar expression for overtime. Let us then write

$$v'_{kj} - v''_{kj} = \sum_{i=1}^{I} \alpha_{ik}(x_{ij} - x_{i,j-1}),$$

$$v'_{kj}, v''_{kj} \geq 0; \qquad k = 1, \ldots, K; \qquad j = 2, \ldots, N, \tag{8–47}$$

and

$$w'_{kj} - w''_{kj} = \sum_{i=1}^{I} \beta_{ik}(y_{ij} - y_{i,j-1}),$$

$$w'_{kj}, w''_{kj} \geq 0; \quad k = 1, \ldots, K; \quad j = 2, \ldots, N. \tag{8-48}$$

Then the cost for day j of having the quantity of factor k used changed from that used on the previous day is

$$e_{kj}v'_{kj} + f_{kj}v''_{kj} + g_{kj}w'_{kj} + h_{kj}w''_{kj}. \tag{8-49}$$

The final cost to be included will be an opportunity cost which is incurred every day that the project is being worked on. It may be the lost profits per day of having the catalytic cracker off stream or the lost profits per day for not having the airliner in service, etc. Let D be the opportunity cost incurred per day. A cost D will be incurred every day until the project is completed. We assumed previously that the project could not be completed in less than n days and should not require more than N days. The cost nD for the first n days cannot be avoided, and hence need not be included in the objective function. A cost D will be incurred on day $j > n$ if work is still to be done on day j or on a future day, i.e., if

$$\sum_{u=j}^{N} \sum_{i=1}^{I} (x_{iu} + y_{iu}) > 0.$$

To represent these opportunity costs properly, we shall introduce some additional integer-valued variables ρ_j which can take on only the values 0 or 1. Let us write

$$\sum_{u=j}^{N} \sum_{i=1}^{I} (x_{iu} + y_{iu}) \leq I\rho_j, \quad j = n+1, \ldots, N, \tag{8-50}$$

$$0 \leq \rho_j \leq 1, \quad \rho_j \text{ an integer}, \quad j = n+1, \ldots, N. \tag{8-51}$$

When $\rho_j = 0$, (8–50) requires that

$$\sum_{u=j}^{N} \sum_{i=1}^{I} (x_{iu} + y_{iu}) = 0, \tag{8-52}$$

and no opportunity cost should be incurred on day j. If $\rho_j = 1$, no restriction is placed on $\sum_{u,i}(x_{iu} + y_{iu})$. If we then take the opportunity cost in day j to be

$$D\rho_j, \tag{8-53}$$

we can never omit charging this cost if work is done on day j or a later day. However, the above restrictions do not prohibit charging a cost D

on day j even if the project is finished. This will never occur when the objective function has been minimized, since costs can be reduced by setting $\rho_j = 0$ in this case. This would not violate any of the above constraints. Therefore the opportunity cost for day j can be correctly represented by (8-53). On combining (8-46), (8-49), and (8-53), we see that the objective function which we desire to minimize is

$$z = \sum_{k=1}^{K} \sum_{j=1}^{N} \sum_{i=1}^{I} (c_{kj}\alpha_{ik}x_{ij} + d_{kj}\beta_{ik}y_{ij})$$

$$+ \sum_{k=1}^{K} \sum_{j=2}^{N} (e_{kj}v'_{kj} + f_{kj}v''_{kj} + g_{kj}w'_{kj} + h_{kj}w''_{kj}) + D \sum_{j=n+1}^{N} \rho_j. \qquad (8\text{-}54)$$

We thus wish to minimize (8-54) subject to (8-35), (8-36), (8-37), (8-40), (8-41), (8-42), (8-43), (8-44), (8-45), (8-47), (8-48), (8-50), and (8-51) where, of course, all x_{ij} and y_{ij} must be non-negative. Here we have a mixed integer-continuous variable linear programming problem. For any realistic problem, the number of constraints will be huge, and a solution is at present quite impossible. However, it is interesting to show that the problem can be formulated as an integer programming problem. The number of constraints, such as (8-41), can often be reduced considerably by noting that if i'' must be finished before i' which must be finished before i, it is unnecessary to include a constraint requiring that i'' be finished before i is started. This will be automatically accounted for by requiring that i' be finished before i is begun, because we must also have a constraint requiring that i'' be finished before i' is started. However, this reduction is not sufficient to make problems of practical interest computationally feasible.

8-9 The traveling salesman problem. Suppose that a salesman has a territory which covers n cities. He wishes to start from his home in a particular city, call it 1, visit each of the other $n - 1$ cities, and return home again. He would like to select the sequence in which the cities are visited in such a way as to minimize the total distance to be traveled. The distance from city i to city j will be denoted by d_{ij}. In the formulation of the problem which we shall give it is not required that $d_{ij} = d_{ji}$. It is clear that there are $(n - 1)!$ different sequences in which the cities can be visited. The round trip can then be thought of as a sequence of n legs, where on leg k of the trip, the salesman travels from city i to city j. On leg 1 he travels from his home, city 1, to some other city, and on leg n, he travels from some city to his home.

To formulate the problem whose solution will yield the sequence of cities for which the distance traveled is a minimum, let us introduce the variables δ_{ijk} which have the value 1 if the salesman travels from city i to city j on leg k of the trip and 0 otherwise. Since there can only be one pair of cities appropriate to leg k, it must be true that

$$\sum_{i,j} \delta_{ijk} = 1, \quad k = 2, \ldots, n - 1$$
$$\sum_{j} \delta_{1j1} = 1, \tag{8-55}$$
$$\sum_{i} \delta_{i1n} = 1.$$

It must also be true that from any given city i, there is only one leg of the trip which begins at i and terminates in some other city. Thus

$$\sum_{j,k} \delta_{ijk} = 1, \quad i = 2, \ldots, n, \tag{8-56}$$

where in carrying out the summation, we require that if $j = 1$, then $k = n$ and vice versa. The restriction for $i = 1$ is contained in (8-55). Similarly, it must be true that only one leg of the trip ends at city j. Consequently

$$\sum_{i,k} \delta_{ijk} = 1, \quad j = 2, \ldots, n, \tag{8-57}$$

where we require that if $i = 1$, then $k = 1$ and vice versa. The case of $j = 1$ is contained in (8-55). Finally, it must be true that if leg k ends in city j, then leg $k + 1$ must begin in city j. This implies that

$$\sum_{i} \delta_{ijk} = \sum_{j'} \delta_{jj',k+1};$$
$$j = 2, \ldots, n;$$
$$k = 2, \ldots, n - 1, \tag{8-58}$$
$$\delta_{1j1} = \sum_{j'} \delta_{jj'2},$$
$$\sum_{i} \delta_{ij,n-1} = \delta_{j1n}.$$

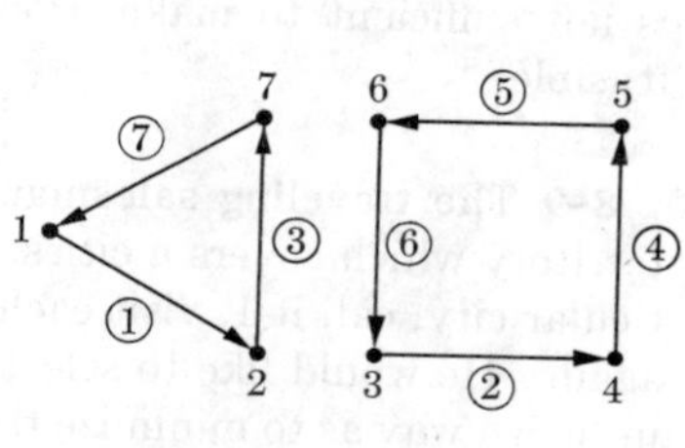

FIGURE 8-5

The constraints (8-58) eliminate the possibility of disconnected trips such as that illustrated in Fig. 8-5 for the case of seven cities. Note that the set of δ_{ijk} appropriate to the disconnected trip shown in Fig. 8-5 would satisfy the constraints (8-55) through (8-57).

We now have formulated all the constraints in the problem. It is unnecessary to include constraints $\delta_{ijk} \leq 1$, since (8-55) through (8-58) automatically guarantee that no $\delta_{ijk} > 1$. We then wish to determine non-negative integers δ_{ijk} satisfying (8-55) through (8-58) which minimize

$$z = \sum_{i,j,k} d_{ij}\, \delta_{ijk}. \tag{8-59}$$

It might be noted that we could have written the constraints in a more symmetric form, not treating $i = 1$ and $j = 1$ as special cases, simply by writing

$$\sum_{i,j} \delta_{ijk} = 1, \qquad k = 1, \ldots, n; \qquad \sum_{j,k} \delta_{ijk} = 1, \qquad i = 1, \ldots, n;$$

$$\sum_{i,k} \delta_{ijk} = 1, \qquad j = 1, \ldots, n; \tag{8-60}$$

$$\sum_{i} \delta_{ijk} = \sum_{j'} \delta_{jj',k+1}, \qquad j = 1, \ldots, n; \qquad k = 1, \ldots, n-1. \tag{8-61}$$

However, this approach introduces a number of variables which we know are zero, as well as some unnecessary constraints.

8-10 Capital budgeting in a firm. Certain simple types of problems concerned with the manner in which a firm should allocate available capital to various projects can be formulated as integer programming problems. Consider first the simplest imaginable case. A firm has available an amount D of investment capital. There are n different projects which are competing for these funds. Project j requires an investment of d_j dollars. Let p_j be the present worth of all future profits from project j. It is desired to determine which projects should be undertaken to maximize the present worth of all future profits without having the capital requirements exceed D. A project must either be undertaken or not; it is not permissible to invest less than d_j if project j is started. Similarly, only one of project j can be undertaken; it is not possible to embark on two or more projects j. To formulate the problem as an integer programming problem let us introduce the integer-valued variables δ_j which can take on only the values 0 or 1. It is then clear that the solution to the following integer programming problem will determine the projects to select in order to maximize the present worth of future profits.

$$\sum_{j=1}^{n} d_j \delta_j \leq D,$$

$$0 \leq \delta_j \leq 1, \qquad \delta_j \text{ an integer}, \qquad j = 1, \ldots, n, \tag{8-62}$$

$$\max z = \sum_{j=1}^{n} p_j \delta_j.$$

Here is the first problem we have encountered which is an all-integer problem. Even this case could conceivably be a mixed integer-continuous variable problem, since the slack variable that would be added to the budget constraint is not required to be an integer. However, the d_j and D will normally be integers, and therefore the slack variable will also be integer-valued when the δ_j are. Problem (8–62) can be solved by dynamic programming, as will be seen in Chapter 10. The dynamic programming method of solution would probably be more efficient than the use of an integer programming algorithm.

Several simple generalizations of problem (8–62) might be noted. For example, for a certain group of projects, say $j \in J$, only one of the group may be selected. In particular, one project may correspond to installing a catalytic cracker in a refinery and another might correspond to installing a thermal cracker. It would not be permissible to install both. To account for this, it is only necessary to add the constraint

$$\sum_{j \in J} \delta_j \leq 1. \tag{8–63}$$

For $j \in J$, it is then unnecessary to include the constraints $\delta_j \leq 1$, since they are automatically included in (8–63).

As another possibility, suppose that if project j is undertaken, then one must also undertake i; however, i may be undertaken without j. To represent this situation, all we need to do is add the constraint

$$\delta_i - \delta_j \geq 0. \tag{8–64}$$

Finally, in addition to a budget constraint, there may be some sort of manpower constraint. Denote by M the total manpower available, and by m_j the manpower required to undertake project j. To take account of manpower restrictions, we would simply annex the constraint

$$\sum_{j=1}^{n} m_j \delta_j \leq M \tag{8–65}$$

to (8–62).

The simple model represented by (8–62) did not consider in any detail the time sequencing for flows of funds in each project. It might be true that, in addition to an initial investment, further investments would be required in later periods. Let us suppose that there is a limitation D_k on capital investment in each of K periods, and let d_{kj} be the capital required for project j in period k. Then the integer programming problem which must be solved to select the projects which maximize the present worth of future profits without violating the budget constraint in any period is

$$\sum_{j=1}^{n} d_{kj}\delta_j \leq D_k, \qquad k = 1, \ldots, K,$$

$$0 \leq \delta_j \leq 1, \qquad \delta_j \text{ an integer}, \qquad j = 1, \ldots, n, \tag{8-66}$$

$$\max z = \sum_{j=1}^{n} p_j\delta_j.$$

Other obvious generalizations are possible. These include making the capital available for investment in period k depend on funds generated by the projects in previous periods. Also, one might consider starting new projects at later periods. The reader will be asked to develop in more detail some of these generalizations in the problems. Applications of integer programming to capital budgeting have been considered by Weingartner [20].

8-11 Solution of integer programming problems—cuts. After having given a number of examples illustrating the wide variety of problems which can be formulated as integer linear programming problems, we would now like to turn our attention to the means of solving integer programming problems of the form (8-1). The basic technique for solving such problems which was originally suggested by Dantzig, Fulkerson, and Johnson [7] is to first solve (8-1), ignoring the integrality requirements. If the solution so obtained has the proper integrality properties, then it must be an optimal solution to (8-1), since every feasible solution to (8-1) is a feasible solution to the linear programming problem obtained from (8-1) by ignoring the integrality requirements. Let us refer to the linear programming problem obtained from (8-1) by ignoring the integrality restrictions as LP (8-1). If an optimal solution to LP (8-1) is not a feasible solution to (8-1), because some of the integrality restrictions are violated, new constraints are added to LP (8-1), one at a time, to yield a sequence of new linear programming problems. The first constraint added to LP (8-1) has the property that the set of feasible solutions to the new linear programming problem does not include the optimal solution to LP (8-1), but does include every feasible solution to (8-1). The new linear programming problem with this one additional constraint is then solved. If the solution is a feasible solution to (8-1), it is an optimal solution to (8-1). If not, one adds another constraint with the property that the set of feasible solutions to the new problem includes every feasible solution to (8-1), but excludes the optimal solution obtained to the previous linear programming problem. These additional constraints that are added as one moves from one problem to the next are referred to as *cuts*. Geometrically, each of these cuts cuts off part of the set of feasible solutions to LP (8–1). In general, we have no guarantee that the introduction of cuts in the manner described above will lead to an optimal solution to (8–1) in a finite number of steps. However, as we shall see below, it is possible to select the cuts in a manner that will guarantee convergence to an optimal solution to (8–1), if there is one, in a finite number of steps.

8–12 Gomory's algorithm for the all-integer problem. We shall begin by considering cases where in (8–1) the set J_1 contains all j, that is, we shall initially restrict our attention to all integer problems. Assume that we have solved LP (8–1), and let $\mathbf{B}$ be the basis matrix for the optimal solution so obtained. Denote by R the set of j corresponding to the nonbasic variables. Then if $\mathbf{y}_j = \mathbf{B}^{-1}\mathbf{a}_j$, $j = 1, \ldots, n$, and $\mathbf{y}_0 = \mathbf{B}^{-1}\mathbf{b}$, $\mathbf{x}_B = \mathbf{y}_0$ is a vector containing the values of the basic variables for the optimal solution to LP (8–1). Furthermore, any feasible solution $\mathbf{x}$ must satisfy

$$\mathbf{x}_B = \mathbf{y}_0 - \sum_{j \in R} \mathbf{y}_j x_j, \tag{8–67}$$

as we noted in Section 2–2. Now there is only one solution to (8–67) with $x_j = 0, j \in R$, which is the basic solution $\mathbf{x}_B = \mathbf{y}_0$, $\mathbf{x}_R = \mathbf{0}$. If this solution does not have the property that all components of $\mathbf{y}_0$ are non-negative integers, then it is certain that any optimal solution to (8–1) must have at least one $x_j > 0, j \in R$. However, since any such x_j must be an integer, it is necessary that at least one $x_j \geq 1, j \in R$. Consider then the constraint

$$\sum_{j \in R} x_j \geq 1. \tag{8–68}$$

Every feasible solution to (8–1) must satisfy (8–68), as we have just shown. Furthermore, $\mathbf{x}_R = \mathbf{0}$ does not satisfy (8–68). Consequently, if we consider a new linear programming problem formed by annexing (8–68) to the constraints of LP (8–1), we have a new linear programming problem whose set of feasible solutions is "smaller" than that of LP (8–1), but which nonetheless contains all feasible solutions to (8–1). Assume that we now solve the new linear programming problem obtained by annexing (8–68) to LP (8–1). If the optimal solution (which will have as many as $m + 1$ positive values) obtained to this linear programming problem happens to have the property that all positive variables are integral, it is an optimal solution to (8–1). If not, we introduce a new constraint of the form (8–68) for the new set of nonbasic variables and repeat the process. Dantzig [6] originally suggested this procedure for solving all-integer problems based on the introduction of cuts of the form (8–68). In the few instances where this procedure has been tried, convergence was obtained. However, it has been proved [14], that there exist cases where convergence cannot occur. Markowitz and Manne [16] have discussed other ways of obtaining cuts; however, these were not systematic procedures, but required the use of intuition and ingenuity. On the other hand, Gomory [8, 9] has developed a systematic procedure for obtaining cuts which can be shown to lead to an optimal solution to (8–1) in a finite number of steps. We shall now consider Gomory's technique.

As above, assume that we have solved LP (8–1) and let the optimal solution so obtained be $\mathbf{x}_B = \mathbf{y}_0$, $\mathbf{y}_0$ being defined as above. Suppose that not all components of $\mathbf{y}_0$ are integers. Let us suppose that y_{u0} is not integral. Then consider the uth equation of (8–67), which reads

$$x_{Bu} = y_{u0} - \sum_{j \in R} y_{uj} x_j. \tag{8–69}$$

Now write

$$y_{uj} = \delta_{uj} + f_{uj}, \qquad j \in R; \qquad y_{u0} = \delta_{u0} + f_{u0}, \tag{8–70}$$

where δ_{uj} is the largest integer less than or equal to y_{uj}, $j \in R$ and $j = 0$. Then by assumption, $f_{u0} > 0$, since y_{u0} is not integral. Furthermore, $f_{uj} \geq 0$. Substitution of (8–70) into (8–69) yields

$$x_{Bu} = \delta_{u0} - \sum_{j \in R} \delta_{uj} x_j + f_{u0} - \sum_{j \in R} f_{uj} x_j. \tag{8–71}$$

Now for any solution in integers to (8–67),

$$x_{Bu} - \delta_{u0} + \sum_{j \in R} \delta_{uj} x_j$$

will be an integer (not necessarily non-negative). Consequently, from (8–71), for any integer solution to (8–67),

$$f_{u0} - \sum_{j \in R} f_{uj} x_j \tag{8–72}$$

must be an integer. Now $\sum_{j \in R} f_{uj} x_j$ cannot be negative. Thus, since $0 < f_{u0} < 1$, (8–72) cannot be a positive integer. Therefore, every feasible solution to (8–1) must satisfy

$$f_{u0} - \sum_{j \in R} f_{uj} x_j \leq 0 \tag{8–73}$$

or

$$\sum_{j \in R} (-f_{uj}) x_j \leq -f_{u0}. \tag{8–74}$$

Clearly, the optimal solution obtained to LP (8–1) does not satisfy (8–74), since $x_j = 0, j \in R$. Thus if we add (8–74) to the constraints of LP (8–1), the new set of feasible solutions will be smaller than that for LP (8–1), but will still contain all feasible solutions to (8–1). Equation (8–74) is the form of the cuts introduced by Gomory.

The procedure then is to annex (8–74) to LP (8–1) and solve the resulting problem having $m + 1$ constraints. In {LP 11–5} it is shown that it is easy to add a single new constraint to a problem without having to solve the problem all over to obtain an optimal solution to the augmented system. Let s_1 be the slack variable for (8–74); the subscript 1 indicates that it is the slack variable for the first cut annexed to LP (8–1). Note from (8–74) that

$$s_1 = -f_{u0} + \sum_{j \in R} f_{uj} x_j.$$

However, we observed previously that for any integer solution to (8–67), (8–72) must be an integer, and thus s_1 will be an integer, and we need not be concerned about the fact that the new variable introduced may not need to be integral. Note that a basis matrix for the augmented problem is

$$\mathbf{B}_1 = \begin{bmatrix} \mathbf{B} & \mathbf{0} \\ \mathbf{0} & 1 \end{bmatrix} \quad \text{and} \quad \mathbf{B}_1^{-1} = \begin{bmatrix} \mathbf{B}^{-1} & \mathbf{0} \\ \mathbf{0} & 1 \end{bmatrix}, \tag{8–75}$$

where $\mathbf{e}_{m+1} = [\mathbf{0}, 1]$ is the activity vector corresponding to s_1. Thus a basic solution to the augmented problem is

$$\mathbf{B}_1^{-1}[\mathbf{b}, -f_{u0}] = [\mathbf{y}_0, -f_{u0}]. \tag{8–76}$$

This basic solution is not feasible, since $-f_{u0} < 0$. The vector containing the prices appropriate to $\mathbf{B}_1$ is $(\mathbf{c}_B, 0)$. Thus, the $z_j - c_j$ for the augmented problem are precisely the same as those for the optimal solution to LP (8–1), since the $\mathbf{y}_j, j \in R$, for the augmented problem, call them $\mathbf{y}_j^{(1)}$, are

$$\mathbf{y}_j^{(1)} = \mathbf{B}_1^{-1}[\mathbf{a}_j, -f_{uj}] = [\mathbf{y}_j, -f_{uj}]. \tag{8–77}$$

Therefore we have a basic but nonfeasible solution to the augmented problem with all $z_j - c_j \geq 0$. Hence the dual simplex algorithm, {LP 8–7} and Section 2–5, can be applied to obtain an optimal solution to the augmented problem. Because of (8–77), we can immediately write down the initial simplex tableau for the augmented problem. We simply add another row and column to the tableau corresponding to the optimal solution obtained to LP (8–1). In the $\mathbf{y}_0$-column for this row we enter $-f_{u0}$ and in the $j \in R$-columns, we enter $-f_{uj}$. In the new column corresponding to s_1 we enter zeros everywhere except in the new row where we enter unity. The remainder of the new row is filled out with zeros. We then apply the dual simplex algorithm. Normally only a relatively small number of iterations (often only one) will be required to carry out the reoptimization. If the solution to the new linear programming problem does not have the desired integrality properties, we repeat the entire procedure, adding another cut. This is continued until a feasible, and hence optimal, solution to (8–1) has been obtained.

In the above procedure, we gave no rule for deciding which equation of (8–67) should be selected for use in determining the cut (8–74) in cases where more than a single component of $\mathbf{y}_0$ is nonintegral. If convergence in a finite number of steps is to be ensured, a special method must be employed for making the selection. This will be discussed in the next section. However, this rule is not especially convenient in practice, and hence a simpler rule is needed. Intuitively, it would seem desirable to select that cut which cuts as deeply as possible, i.e., excludes as much of the set of feasible solutions to the previous problem as possible. It is hard to define precisely what this means, however. Roughly, we would like the intersection of the plane

$$\sum_{j \in R} (-f_{uj})x_j = -f_{u0}$$

with the x_j-axis, $j \in R$, to be as large as possible, so that the x_j, $j \in R$, will have to be as large as possible to satisfy (8–74). This, in essence, corresponds to moving as far into the set from $\mathbf{x} = [\mathbf{y}_0, \mathbf{0}]$ as we can. Thus we want all the ratios f_{u0}/f_{uj} to be as large as possible. Unfortunately, it frequently turns out that for each possible u, some ratios will be large while others are small. A rule which has been adopted in practice is simply to select the equation from (8–67) for which f_{u0} is largest. This has worked. Clearly one could formulate many other, relatively simple, selection rules. Indeed, one could develop a cut for each nonintegral variable and annex all these cuts to obtain the augmented problem. It would still be easy to find a new basic solution, but the number of negative variables would be equal to the number of constraints added, and, on using the dual simplex method, one would have to expect that the number of iterations required for reoptimization would increase rapidly with the number of constraints added. It is not known whether there would be any advantages to this approach.

The procedure we have just described is an iterative process where we first solve LP (8–1). We shall refer to this problem as P_0. If the solution so obtained is a feasible solution to (8–1), it is an optimal solution to (8–1). If not, we determine a cut (8–74) and obtain a new linear programming problem P_1 which has one additional constraint and one more variable than P_0. The dual simplex method is applied to solve P_1. Then there are two alternatives: either we have obtained a feasible and optimal solution to (8–1) or we determine another cut and a new problem P_2. As the procedure is continued, the number of constraints for problem v will initially tend to increase as v is increased. Let us now note, however, that regardless of how large v is, problem P_v never need have more than $n+1$ constraints. To see this note that if any slack variable s_j is basic in the optimal solution obtained to P_{v-1}, then the constraint for which s_j is a slack variable can be omitted when forming problem P_v, since it is not required that this constraint always be satisfied. We can obtain a basic solution to the resulting problem, using the same x_j as were obtained in the optimal solution to P_{v-1}. To delete this constraint, we simply cross off the row in the optimal tableau for P_{v-1} where s_j appears in the listing of the basic variables and delete the column for s_j. In Problem 8–10, we ask that the reader prove this to be the correct procedure. Now, since (8–1) contains only n variables, it follows that after deleting from P_{v-1} those constraints whose s_j appear in the optimal basis, we cannot be left with a problem having more than n constraints. Call the resulting problem P'_{v-1}. To obtain P_v we add one cut to P'_{v-1}. Therefore, P_v can never have more than $n+1$ constraints, which is what we wished to show. This result demonstrates that there is a limit to how large the problems P_v can become.

We have yet to prove that only a finite number of problems P_v will need to be solved before we obtain an optimal solution to (8–1), if there is one. We shall do this next. It might be noted, however, that other algorithms have been devised for solving the all-integer problem. Gomory [10] has constructed a different algorithm which requires that all the elements of **A** and **b** in (8–1) must be integers. With this algorithm, we do not begin by solving LP (8–1). Instead it is necessary to assume that we start out with all $z_j - c_j \geq 0$ and a basic, but not feasible, solution. Then the dual simplex method can be applied. Now, however, a cut is added at each iteration. Land and Doig [15] have also developed a method for solving the all-integer problem. Neither of these alternative methods seems to have any clear-cut advantages over the algorithm presented here.

8–13 Finiteness proof. To obtain a process which can be proved to converge after the solution of a finite number of problems P_v, we must modify somewhat the procedure outlined in the preceding section. First, we shall assume that the c_j in (8–1) are integers, so that when the x_j are integers, then z will also be an integer. We can always achieve this to an arbitrary degree of accuracy by properly selecting the physical dimensions in which the c_j are measured. In carrying out this proof, we shall also require that z have both an upper and a lower bound.

Now we shall include with (8–67) the equation for z to yield

$$z = y_{00} - \sum_{j \in R} y_{0j} x_j, \qquad \mathbf{x}_B = \mathbf{y}_0 - \sum_{j \in R} \mathbf{y}_j x_j, \tag{8–78}$$

where $y_{00} = \mathbf{c}_B\mathbf{y}_0$ is the value of z corresponding to the optimal solution obtained to LP (8–1) and $y_{0j} = z_j - c_j$. If we denote by $\mathbf{x}_R$ the vector containing x_j, $j \in R$, then we can write

$$\mathbf{x}_R = \mathbf{0} - \sum_{j\in R} (-\mathbf{e}_j)x_j, \tag{8–79}$$

where $\mathbf{e}_j$ is the unit vector containing $n - m$ components with unity in the appropriate position. Let us annex (8–79) to (8–78) to yield

$$\begin{aligned} z &= y_{00} - \sum_{j\in R} y_{0j}x_j, \\ \mathbf{x}_B &= \mathbf{y}_0 - \sum_{j\in R} \mathbf{y}_jx_j, \\ \mathbf{x}_R &= \mathbf{0} - \sum_{j\in R} (-\mathbf{e}_j)x_j. \end{aligned} \tag{8–80}$$

In (8–80) let us write

$$\mathbf{p}_j = [y_{0j}, \mathbf{y}_j, -\mathbf{e}_j], \qquad j \in R; \qquad \mathbf{p}_0 = [y_{00}, \mathbf{y}_0, \mathbf{0}]. \tag{8–81}$$

We shall assume that the first n rows following the z-row in (8–80) have been arranged so that each $\mathbf{p}_j$, $j \in R$, is lexicographically positive. A column vector $\mathbf{p}_j$ is lexicographically positive, written $\mathbf{p}_j \succ \mathbf{0}$, if the first nonvanishing component, reading from the top down, is positive. Furthermore, $\mathbf{p}_j \succ \mathbf{p}_k$ if $\mathbf{p}_j - \mathbf{p}_k \succ \mathbf{0}$. It is not immediately clear that the rows of (8–80) can be arranged so that $\mathbf{p}_j \succ \mathbf{0}, j \in R$. We can always guarantee that this can be done, however, if we assume that the convex set of feasible solutions to LP (8–1) is strictly bounded. All we need to do is add the redundant constraint

$$\sum_{j\in R} x_j + x_{n+1} = M, \tag{8–82}$$

where M is an integer so large that every feasible solution to (8–1) will satisfy (8–82) with $x_{n+1} > 0$. Thus x_{n+1} will be in every basic solution. If we imagine that x_{n+1} is always the first basic variable, and write the equation for x_{n+1} immediately following the z-equation in (8–80), this equation will have the form

$$x_{n+1} = M - \sum_{j\in R} x_j,$$

so that the second component of each $\mathbf{p}_j$ will be unity, and thus $\mathbf{p}_j \succ \mathbf{0}$, $j \in R$, since on finding an optimal solution to LP (8–1), we have $y_{0j} \geq 0$. We shall assume, then, that (8–82) has been included in (8–80) if it is needed to yield $\mathbf{p}_j \succ \mathbf{0}, j \in R$.

We shall now apply the method described in Section 8–12 to (8–80), with the following modifications. First, if y_{00} is not an integer, we use the equation for z to determine a cut. Note that we did not do this in Section 8–12. Furthermore, we shall agree always to annex cut constraints to the bottom of (8–80). We shall select the equation to be used for determining a cut according to the following rule: we shall examine the equations in the order written in (8–80), and use the equation corresponding to the first y_{i0}, $i = 0, \ldots, m$, which is not an integer. Thus as long as y_{00} is not an integer, the z-equation will be used to determine the cut.

We are now ready to show that matters can be arranged so that only a finite number of problems P_v need to be solved before a feasible solution to (8–1) is found, if there is one. Assume that $\mathbf{p}_0$ is not a feasible solution to (8–1). Then, using the rule of selection described above, we determine a cut and consider the resulting problem P_1. We solve P_1 by the dual simplex algorithm. However, we shall use a special procedure for selecting the vector to enter the basis. This procedure is really equivalent to solving directly the dual problem by means of vector variables and the generalized simplex method {LP 6–7 and 6–8}, where the vector variables of interest are simply the $\mathbf{p}_j$. The procedure which we shall use is then the following. If x_{Br} is the most negative primal variable, so that it is to be driven to zero, we first compute

$$\frac{y_{0k}}{y_{rk}} = \max_{j \in R} \frac{y_{0j}}{y_{rj}}, \qquad y_{rj} < 0. \tag{8–83}$$

When k is unique, then column k enters the primal basis. If k is not unique, we compute for those j where the maximum was taken on in (8–83):

$$\max \frac{y_{1j}}{y_{rj}}. \tag{8–84}$$

When this is unique, the column to enter the basis is determined. When it is not, we compute max y_{2j}/y_{rj} for those j for which the maximum was taken on in (8–84). Ultimately, we must uniquely determine the column to enter the basis, because, otherwise, one vector $\mathbf{p}_j$ would be a scalar multiple of another, and we see from (8–81) that this is not possible. What we are really doing in the above procedure is finding the vector $(-1/y_{rk})\mathbf{p}_k \succ \mathbf{0}$ such that

$$\left(\frac{-1}{y_{rj}}\right)\mathbf{p}_j - \left(\frac{-1}{y_{rk}}\right)\mathbf{p}_k \succ \mathbf{0}, \qquad y_{rj} < 0, \qquad j \in R. \tag{8–85}$$

Thus

$$\mathbf{p}_j - \frac{y_{rj}}{y_{rk}}\,\mathbf{p}_k \succ \mathbf{0}, \qquad \text{all } j \neq k \in R \tag{8–86}$$

However, (8–86) is, except for its rth component, $\hat{\mathbf{p}}_j$, the new column j after x_{Br} has been driven to zero and x_k has become a basic variable.

The rth component of $\hat{\mathbf{p}}_j$ is y_{rj}/y_{rk}. The vector corresponding to x_{Br} which is driven to zero and so becomes a nonbasic variable is

$$\frac{-1}{y_{rk}}\, y_{ik}, \qquad i \neq r, \qquad \frac{1}{y_{rk}} < 0, \qquad i = r. \tag{8-87}$$

However, since $\mathbf{p}_k$ was lexicographically positive, the first nonzero component was positive, and this will also hold for (8-87), because $y_{rk} < 0$ and hence could not have been the first nonvanishing component of $\mathbf{p}_k$. Thus the vector corresponding to x_{Br} will be lexicographically positive. The fact that y_{rk} is not the first nonvanishing component of $\mathbf{p}_k$, coupled with (8-86), shows that $\hat{\mathbf{p}}_j \succ \mathbf{0}$, $j \neq k \in R$ (detailed proof?). Consequently, for all j in the new set $\hat{R}$ obtained from R by deleting $j = k$ and adding the j corresponding to x_{Br}, it follows that $\hat{\mathbf{p}}_j \succ \mathbf{0}$.

Next note that

$$\hat{\mathbf{p}}_0 = \mathbf{p}_0 - \frac{x_{Br}}{y_{rk}}\, \mathbf{p}_k + \frac{x_{Br}}{y_{rk}}\, \mathbf{e}_r,$$

so that

$$\mathbf{p}_0 - \hat{\mathbf{p}}_0 \succ \mathbf{0}. \tag{8-88}$$

At each iteration of the dual simplex method, $\mathbf{p}_0$ will decrease lexicographically. This holds for each iteration when we are solving a given P_v and also on moving to P_{v+1}, since the initial $n + 1$ components of $\mathbf{p}_0$ for P_{v+1} are those of the terminal $\mathbf{p}_0$ for P_v. The lexicographic scheme we have just described guarantees that cycling will never occur while we are solving P_v {LP 6-7}. It will also be used to show that we shall reach a feasible and optimal solution to (8-1) if there is one, after solving a finite number of P_v.

As cuts are annexed to (8-80), the number of components in the $\mathbf{p}_j$ increase. It is important to remember, however, that the procedure for dropping a cut if its slack variable becomes basic will not change the fact that all $\mathbf{p}_j \succ \mathbf{0}$, $j \in R$. To see this note that in (8-80), the matrix whose columns are the $n - m$ vectors $\mathbf{p}_j$ has rank $n - m$. Now for every iteration the first $n + 1$ equations [or $n + 2$ if (8-82) is added] will have precisely the same form as (8-80), so that it is impossible for the first $n + 1$ components of some $\mathbf{p}_j$ to vanish at a later iteration. Consequently, the lexicographic properties of the $\mathbf{p}_j$ will always be determined by the first $n + 1$ components, and thus it will always be true that $\mathbf{p}_j \succ \mathbf{0}$, $j \in R$. This also shows that in selecting the vector to enter the basis we will never have a tie for more than n rows.

If, in solving a P_v, we should ever encounter a situation where all $y_{rj} \geq 0$, we know that the dual problem has an unbounded solution and the primal problem has no solution. In this case, there does not exist any feasible solution to (8-1). It is perfectly possible to have feasible solutions to LP (8-1) but no feasible solution to (8-1). We ask the reader to provide an example of this case in Problem 8-11.

Let us now show that if we never encounter a case where $y_{rj} \geq 0$, all $j \in R$, the process will terminate in a finite number of steps. By continually applying the dual simplex method to the problems P_v, we obtain a sequence of $\mathbf{p}_0$ which we shall denote by $\mathbf{p}_0(l)$. Here we shall imagine that l is increased by one each time we perform an iteration of the dual simplex method and not merely when we go from problem P_v to P_{v+1}. Then we have shown that $\mathbf{p}_0(l) \succ \mathbf{p}_0(l+1)$. We shall prove by contradiction that the sequence $\mathbf{p}_0(l)$ is finite.

Assume that the sequence $\mathbf{p}_0(l)$ is not finite. However, the first components of the $\mathbf{p}_0(l)$ must then satisfy $y_{00}(l) \geq y_{00}(l+1)$. But we have assumed that z is bounded from below. Thus the sequence $y_{00}(l)$ forms a monotone nonincreasing sequence which is bounded from below and must have a limit point z^*, such that every ϵ-neighborhood of z^* contains all but a finite number of the $y_{00}(l)$, and $z^* \leq y_{00}(l)$ for all l. Let δ_{00} be the largest integer such that $\delta_{00} \leq y_{00}(l)$ for all l. We shall show that $y_{00}(l) = \delta_{00}$ for all $l \geq l_0$ for some l_0.

From the definition of δ_{00}, it follows that after a certain l, we can write $y_{00}(l) = \delta_{00} + f_{00}(l)$, $0 \leq f_{00}(l) < 1$. Assume that this occurs when we solve problem P_v. After P_v has been solved, we have

$$y_{00}(l') = \delta_{00} + f_{00}(l'); \qquad f_{00}(l') \leq f_{00}(l). \tag{8-89}$$

If $f_{00}(l') \neq 0$, then, according to our method of selecting the equation to be used in forming a cut, the z-equation would be used and the cut would have the form

$$\sum_{j \in R(l')} -f_{0j}(l')x_j \leq -f_{00}(l'). \tag{8-90}$$

This constraint would be introduced to form problem P_{v+1} from P_v. The only negative variable initially in P_{v+1} would be s_{v+1}. Thus, at the first step in the application of the dual simplex method to P_{v+1}, s_{v+1} would be driven to zero, and $y_{00}(l'+1)$ is given by

$$y_{00}(l'+1) = y_{00}(l') - \frac{y_{0k}(l')}{f_{0k}(l')} f_{00}(l'). \tag{8-91}$$

Since $f_{0k}(l') > 0$, $y_{0k}(l') > 0$, and hence it follows that

$$y_{0k}(l') \geq f_{0k}(l'),$$

or

$$y_{00}(l'+1) \leq y_{00}(l') - f_{00}(l') = \delta_{00}.$$

Hence, for all $l \geq l' + 1$, $y_{00}(l) = \delta_{00}$.

The first component of the $\mathbf{p}_0(l)$ is fixed for $l \geq l' + 1$. It is only under special circumstances that not all variables are integer-valued when z

reaches δ_{00}. If z is not to change on future iterations, then it must be true that if x_k is to become positive at the next step, $y_{0k}(l) = 0$, for otherwise z would change. Let us suppose that when z reaches δ_{00}, the basic variable in the first equation following the z-equation is not integral. We then use this equation to form a cut. If x_k is to enter the basis, then $y_{1k}(l) \neq 0$, and since $y_{0k}(l) = 0$ and $\mathbf{p}_k \succ \mathbf{0}$, it must be true that $y_{1k}(l) > 0$. Hence the second component of $\mathbf{p}_0(l)$ will form a nonincreasing sequence which is bounded from below by zero. We now repeat precisely the same argument given above to conclude that the second component of the $\mathbf{p}_0(l)$ will reach an integer value in a finite number of additional iterations, since $y_{1k}(l)$ will be positive. Then we move to the third component, noting that if x_k is to enter the basis, $y_{0k}(l) = y_{1k}(l) = 0$ and $y_{2k}(l) > 0$, so that the same argument can be repeated, etc. But the $\mathbf{p}_j(l)$ have only a finite number of components. Thus we conclude that all components reach integer values in a finite number of steps, which contradicts the assumption that the sequence was infinite. Therefore in a finite number of steps, we obtain either an optimal solution to (8–1) or an indication that there is no feasible solution to (8–1).

The procedure introduced in this section to ensure convergence in a finite number of steps is inconvenient in practice, just as are the methods designed to eliminate degeneracy problems in the simplex method. The computational procedure described in the previous section is much more convenient for practical purposes. However, for that procedure there does not exist any proof of convergence in a finite number of steps, although convergence certainly seems reasonable, provided that cycling does not occur in the application of the dual simplex method.

It has been noted at the beginning of the chapter that computational experience with Gomory's method has been somewhat disappointing. Although with the proper precautions the algorithm can be made finite, it seems that in many cases the number of iterations required is so large that for practical purposes convergence is not obtained. Problems of the form (8–1) which require less than 20 iterations to solve LP (8–1) have been run for 2000 or more iterations without converging to an integer solution. This behavior, coupled with the fact that one must frequently introduce a large number of additional constraints to represent a problem as an integer programming problem, makes, at present, practical solutions of empirical interest usually not feasible.

We wish to point out that in developing an integer programming code for a digital computer, one may be confronted with roundoff difficulties. The actual solution if computed exactly might be an optimal solution to (8–1), but due to roundoff, the numbers determined by the computer might not be integers. To avoid these difficulties, one must modify the manner in which the arithmetic operations are performed.

8–14 The mixed integer-continuous variable algorithm. Gomory [11] has also developed an algorithm for solving (8–1) when J_1 does not contain all j, that is, for the mixed integer-continuous variable problem. We shall now study this algorithm. To initiate the algorithm, we proceed as in the all-integer case and solve LP (8–1). If the solution so obtained is a feasible solution to (8–1), it must be an optimal solution. If not, we proceed as before to introduce cuts. The differences between the present problem and the all integer case arise in the way the cuts are determined.

To determine a cut in the mixed case, consider the solution to LP (8–1) and assume that x_{Bu} is not an integer, but that it must be an integer in order to have a feasible solution to (8–1). Then consider

$$x_{Bu} = y_{u0} - \sum_{j \in R} y_{uj} x_j.$$

As in Section 8–12, write $y_{u0} = \delta_{u0} + f_{u0}$. Now, for any feasible solution to (8–1),

$$f_{u0} - \sum_{j \in R} y_{uj} x_j = \text{integer} = x_{Bu} - \delta_{u0}. \tag{8–92}$$

Next let R_+ be the subset of R for which $y_{uj} \geq 0$ and R_- the subset of R for which $y_{uj} < 0$. Then

$$\sum_{j \in R_+} y_{uj} x_j + \sum_{j \in R_-} y_{uj} x_j - f_{u0} = \text{integer}. \tag{8–93}$$

It is convenient to distinguish two cases, depending on whether $\sum_{j \in R} y_{uj} x_j$ is non-negative or negative. Consider first the case where the term is non-negative. Then it must be true that

$$\sum_{j \in R} y_{uj} x_j = \delta + f_{u0}, \tag{8–94}$$

where $\delta = 0$ or 1 or 2, etc. Consequently any feasible solution to (8–1) must satisfy

$$\sum_{j \in R} y_{uj} x_j \geq f_{u0},$$

or by the definition of R_-, it is also true that

$$\sum_{j \in R_+} y_{uj} x_j \geq f_{u0}. \tag{8–95}$$

Now consider the case where $\sum_{j \in R} y_{uj} x_j$ is negative. Then from (8–93), it must be true that

$$\sum_{j \in R} y_{uj} x_j = f_{u0} - \delta, \tag{8–96}$$

where $\delta = 1$, or 2, or 3, etc. Therefore for any feasible solution to (8-1), it must be true that

$$\sum_{j \in R_+} y_{uj} x_j + \sum_{j \in R_-} y_{uj} x_j \leq f_{u0} - 1, \tag{8-97}$$

or, since $\sum_{j \in R_+} y_{uj} x_j \geq 0$,

$$\sum_{j \in R_-} y_{uj} x_j \leq f_{u0} - 1. \tag{8-98}$$

Now multiply (8-98) by $f_{u0}/(f_{u0} - 1)$, which is a negative number. This yields

$$\sum_{j \in R_-} \frac{f_{u0}}{1 - f_{u0}} |y_{uj}| x_j \geq f_{u0}. \tag{8-99}$$

If we combine (8-95) and (8-99), we see that regardless of which case holds, any feasible solution to (8-1) must satisfy

$$\sum_{j \in R_+} y_{uj} x_j + \sum_{j \in R_-} \frac{f_{u0}}{1 - f_{u0}} |y_{uj}| x_j \geq f_{u0}, \tag{8-100}$$

since the left-hand sides of (8-95) and (8-99) are both positive, and at least one must be greater than, or equal to, f_{u0}. Note that the optimal solution obtained to LP (8-1) does not satisfy (8-100).

One can, therefore, use (8-100) as the cut. However, in obtaining it, use was made only of the fact that x_{Bu} was required to be an integer. If one or more x_j, $j \in R$, are also required to be integers, one can utilize this information to obtain what is hopefully a "better" cut. Consider the x_j, $j \in R \cap J_1$. As in Section 8-12, write $y_{uj} = \delta_{uj} + f_{uj}$, $0 \leq f_{uj} < 1$. Denote by R^* the subset of R not in $R \cap J_1$. Then (8-92) can be replaced by

$$f_{u0} - \sum_{j \in R \cap J_1} f_{uj} x_j - \sum_{j \in R^*} y_{uj} x_j = \text{integer}.$$

Now $\sum f_{uj} x_j \geq 0$, so that on introducing sets R_+^* and R_-^* to be the subsets of R^* for which $y_{uj} \geq 0$ and $y_{uj} < 0$, respectively, we can go through the same arguments set forth above to show that

$$\sum_{j \in R \cap J_1} f_{uj} x_j + \sum_{j \in R_+^*} y_{uj} x_j + \sum_{j \in R_-^*} \frac{f_{u0}}{1 - f_{u0}} |y_{uj}| x_j \geq f_{u0} \tag{8-101}$$

is satisfied by any feasible solution to (8-1), but not by the optimal solution obtained to LP (8-1), and hence (8-101) can be used for a cut.

Furthermore, we can obtain a different cut by letting δ_{uj}^* be the smallest integer greater than y_{uj} so that

$$y_{uj} = \delta_{uj}^* - (1 - f_{uj}). \tag{8–102}$$

Then (8–92) can be replaced by

$$f_{u0} + \sum_{j \in R \cap J_1} (1 - f_{uj})x_j - \sum_{j \in R^*} y_{uj}x_j = \text{integer}. \tag{8–103}$$

Now $-\sum (1 - f_{uj})x_j \leq 0$. Thus, applying the same arguments as above, we see that

$$\sum_{j \in R_+^*} y_{uj}x_j + \sum_{j \in R \cap J_1} \frac{f_{u0}}{1 - f_{u0}} (1 - f_{uj})x_j + \sum_{j \in R_-^*} \frac{f_{u0}}{1 - f_{u0}} |y_{uj}|x_j \geq f_{u0} \tag{8–104}$$

is also a cut.

We can improve things even further by making the intercepts of the bounding hyperplane of a cut with the x_j-axes as large as possible, so that we cut as deeply as we can. By combining (8–101) and (8–104) we see that the coefficient of x_j, $j \in R \cap J_1$, can be taken to be either

$$f_{uj} \quad \text{or} \quad \frac{f_{u0}}{1 - f_{u0}} (1 - f_{uj}).$$

We will then agree to select the smaller of these. Note that f_{uj} will be smaller if

$$(1 - f_{u0})f_{uj} < f_{u0} - f_{u0}f_{uj} \quad \text{or} \quad f_{uj} < f_{u0}.$$

What would then appear to be the best of the cuts generated above can be written

$$\sum_{j \in R} (-d_{uj})x_j \leq -f_{u0}, \tag{8–105}$$

where

$$d_{uj} = \begin{cases} y_{uj}, & j \in R_+^*, \\ \dfrac{f_{u0}}{1 - f_{u0}} |y_{uj}|, & j \in R_-^*, \\ f_{uj}, & j \in R \cap J_1, \quad f_{uj} \leq f_{u0}, \\ \dfrac{f_{u0}}{1 - f_{u0}} (1 - f_{uj}), & j \in R \cap J_1, \quad f_{uj} > f_{u0}. \end{cases} \tag{8–106}$$

Once the method for obtaining a cut has been determined, the solution to the mixed integer-continuous variable problem proceeds precisely as for the all-integer case discussed in Section 8–12. It might be noted that the cut (8–105) could also be used in the all-integer case.

The algorithm just described is not the only method developed for solving mixed integer-continuous variable linear programming problems. Beale [3] has also developed an algorithm, and the method of Land and Doig [15] can be applied. However, neither of these appears to be any more efficient than Gomory's approach.

8–15 Proof of finiteness for mixed case. Gomory [11] has provided a proof that if we use the cuts (8–105) in the mixed integer-continuous variable case, then, provided z is one of the variables restricted to be an integer and z has both upper and lower bounds, only a finite number of problems P_v will have to be solved to obtain an optimal solution to (8–1), if there is one. To carry out the proof we shall adopt the same conventions and procedures that were used in Section 8–13, with the modification that in (8–80), we assume that the equations for which the variables appearing on the left-hand side must be integers are written down before the equations corresponding to variables which are not required to be integers. We imagine that these equations are arranged so that the vectors $\mathbf{p}_j$ in (8–80) satisfy $\mathbf{p}_j \succ \mathbf{0}$. This can always be achieved by annexing the additional constraint $\sum_{j \in R \cap J_1} x_j \leq M$ as the first constraint after the z-equation, with its slack variable (an integer) being the basic variable associated with this constraint. Then we simply follow each step of the proof given in Section 8–13. We ask the reader to prove in Problem 8–12 that the equivalent of (8–91) which leads to $y_{00}(l'+1) \leq \delta_{00}$ goes through in precisely the same way when (8–105) is used instead of (8–90).

It will be noted that the proofs in Section 8–13 and in this section are not completely general because of the restrictions requiring z to have a lower bound and to be an integer. Furthermore, the cuts had to be selected in a special way. It would seem that the finiteness proofs should hold under much more general conditions, especially with respect to the selection of the equations to be used in determining cuts. However, such proofs are not yet available.

8–16 Example. To illustrate by an example the procedure of solving integer linear programming problems numerically, let us solve problem (1–19), illustrated geometrically in Fig. 1–6. After slack and surplus variables are added, (1–19) becomes

$$\begin{aligned} 0.50x_1 + x_2 + x_3 &= 1.75, \\ x_1 + 0.30x_2 + x_4 &= 1.50, \\ x_j \geq 0, \quad j = 1, \ldots, 4; &\quad x_1, x_2 \text{ integers}, \\ \max z &= 0.25x_1 + x_2. \end{aligned} \tag{8–107}$$

TABLE 8–1

OPTIMAL SOLUTION TO LP (8–107)

	c_j		0.25	1	0	0
$\mathbf{c}_B$	Basic variables	b	$\mathbf{a}_1$	$\mathbf{a}_2$	$\mathbf{a}_3$	$\mathbf{a}_4$
1	x_2	1.75	0.50	1	1	0
0	x_4	0.975	0.85	0	−0.30	1
		1.75	0.25	0	1	0

Here we have a mixed integer-continuous variable problem, since, although x_1 and x_2 must be integers, it is not necessarily true that the slack variables x_3 and x_4 will be integral. The solution to LP (8–107) is given in Table 8–1. In this solution, x_2 is not an integer, and hence additional computations must be made.

We obtain the first cut, using the ($x_{B1} = x_2$)-row in Table 8–1. We note that $y_{10} = 1.75$, $y_{11} = 0.50$, $y_{13} = 1$, the nonbasic variables being x_1 and x_3, with only x_1 required to be an integer. We see that $f_{10} = 0.75$, $f_{11} = 0.50$. Thus by (8–105) and (8–106), the cut is

$$-0.50\,x_1 - x_3 \leq -0.75. \tag{8–108}$$

To obtain the problem P_1, we annex (8–108) to LP (8–107).

When we begin by making use of the solution to LP (8–107) as described in Section 8–12, we obtain the first tableau for problem P_1 (Table 8–2). The remaining tableaux used in the solution of P_1 by the dual simplex algorithm are given in Tables 8–3 and 8–4. Note that two iterations were required to solve P_1. In Table 8–4, x_2 is an integer as desired, but x_1 is not integral. Thus another cut must be introduced.

The x_1-line in Table 8–4 is used to determine the new cut. We see that $f_{30} = 0.20$. Now $y_{34} = 1 > 0$, so $d_{34} = 1$, but $y_{35} = -0.30 < 0$ (position 5 corresponding to s_1); hence

$$d_{35} = \frac{f_{30}}{1 - f_{30}}\,|y_{35}| = \frac{0.20}{0.80}\,(0.30) = 0.075,$$

and the new cut takes the form

$$-x_4 - 0.075\,s_1 \leq -0.20. \tag{8–109}$$

To obtain problem P_2 we annex (8–109) to P_1. The initial tableau for

SOLUTION OF P_1

Table 8–2. Tableau 1

	c_j		0.25	1	0	0	0
$\mathbf{c}_B$	Basic variables	$\mathbf{b}$	$\mathbf{a}_1$	$\mathbf{a}_2$	$\mathbf{a}_3$	$\mathbf{a}_4$	$\mathbf{e}_3$
1	x_2	1.75	0.50	1	1	0	0
0	x_4	0.975	0.85	0	—0.30	1	0
0	s_1	—0.75	—0.50	0	—1	0	1
		1.75	0.25	0	1	0	0

Table 8–3. Tableau 2

1	x_2	1	0	1	0	0	1
0	x_4	—0.30	0	0	—2	1	1.70
0.25	x_1	1.50	1	0	2	0	—2
		1.375	0	0	0.50	0	0.50

Table 8–4. Tableau 3

1	x_2	1	0	1	0	0	1
0	x_3	0.15	0	0	1	—0.50	—0.85
0.25	x_1	1.20	1	0	0	1	—0.30
		1.30	0	0	0	0.25	0.925

P_2 is given in Table 8–5. On applying the dual simplex algorithm, we obtain an optimal solution to P_2 in a single iteration. For this solution, given in Table 8–6, x_1 and x_2 are both unity and hence integers. Thus we have obtained the optimal solution to (8–107). It is $x_1^* = x_2^* = 1$, $z^* = 1.25$. This is precisely the solution that was obtained graphically in Fig. 1–6. For this example, the integer algorithm converged quite quickly, and only two P_v problems had to be solved to obtain the optimal solution. Nonetheless, the amount of computational effort required was close to four times that needed to solve LP (8–107).

SOLUTION OF P_2

TABLE 8–5. TABLEAU 1

	c_j		0.25	1	0	0	0	0
$\mathbf{c}_B$	Basic variables	$\mathbf{b}$	$\mathbf{a}_1$	$\mathbf{a}_2$	$\mathbf{a}_3$	$\mathbf{a}_4$	$\mathbf{e}_3$	$\mathbf{e}_4$
1	x_2	1	0	1	0	0	1	0
0	x_3	0.15	0	0	1	—0.50	—0.85	0
0.25	x_1	1.20	1	0	0	1	—0.30	0
0	s_2	—0.20	0	0	0	—1	—0.075	1
		1.30	0	0	0	0.25	0.925	0

TABLE 8–6. TABLEAU 2

1	x_2	1	0	1	0	0	1	0
0	x_3	0.25	0	0	1	0	—0.8125	—0.50
0.25	x_1	1	1	0	0	0	—0.375	1
0	x_4	0.20	0	0	0	1	0.075	—1
		1.25	0	0	0	0	0.90625	0.25

The geometric interpretation of the cuts introduced is given in Fig. 8–6. Consider first the cut (8–108). If we eliminate x_3, using (8–107), we obtain

$$-0.50\,x_1 - 1.75 + 0.50\,x_1 + x_2 \leq -0.75,$$

or

$$x_2 \leq 1. \tag{8–110}$$

Thus the cut (8–108) is equivalent to $x_2 \leq 1$. The first cut then reduces the set of feasible solutions to LP (8–107) to the shaded area in Fig. 8–6. Consider now the second cut (8–109). Because of (8–110), $s_1 = 1 - x_2$, so that on using (8–107) to eliminate x_4, we obtain

$$x_1 + 0.30\,x_2 - 1.50 - 0.075 + 0.075\,x_2 \leq -0.20,$$

or

$$x_1 + 0.375\,x_2 \leq 1.375.$$

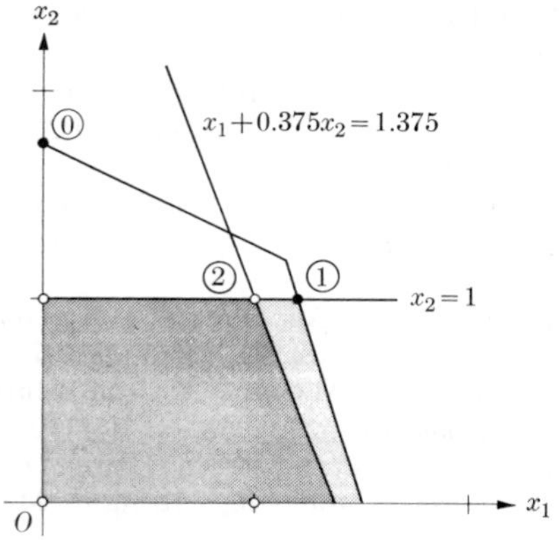

FIGURE 8–6

This second cut reduces the set of feasible solutions to the darkly shaded area in Fig. 8–6. The sequence of solutions to P_0, P_1, and P_2 are labeled 0, 1, and 2, respectively, in Fig. 8–6.

REFERENCES

1. BOWMAN, E. H., "The Schedule Sequencing Problem," *Operations Research* **7,** 1959, pp. 621–624.

2. BOWMAN, E. H., "Assembly-Line Balancing by Linear Programming," *Operations Research,* **8,** 1960, pp. 385–389.

3. BEALE, E. M. L., "A Method of Solving Linear Programming Problems When Some but Not All of the Variables Must Take Integral Values," *Statistical Techniques Research Group Technical Report No. 19*, Princeton, N. J., July 1958.

4. CHARNES, A., and W. W. COOPER, *Management Models and Industrial Applications of Linear Programming*, Vol. II. New York: Wiley, 1961.

5. DANTZIG, G. B., "On the Significance of Solving Linear Programming Problems with Some Integer Variables," *Econometrica,* **28,** 1960, pp. 30–44.

6. DANTZIG, G. B., "Note on Solving Linear Programs in Integers," *Naval Research Logistics Quarterly*, **6,** 1959, pp. 75–76.

7. DANTZIG, G. B., D. R. FULKERSON, and S. JOHNSON, "Solution of a Large-Scale Traveling-Salesman Problem," *Journal of the Operations Research Society of America*, **2,** 1954, pp. 393–410.

8. GOMORY, R. E., "Outline of an Algorithm for Integer Solutions to Linear Programs," *Bulletin of the American Mathematical Society*, **64,** 1958, pp. 275–278.

9. GOMORY, R. E., "An Algorithm for Integer Solutions to Linear Programming," *Princeton-IBM Mathematics Research Project, Technical Report No. 1*, November 1958.

10. GOMORY, R. E., "All-Integer Programming Algorithm," *IBM Research Center, Research Report RC-189*, 1960.

11. GOMORY, R. E., "An Algorithm for the Mixed Integer Problem," *P-1885*, The RAND Corp., June 1960.

12. GOMORY, R. E., and W. J. BAUMOL, "Integer Programming and Pricing," *Econometrica*, **28,** 1960, pp. 521–550.

13. GOMORY, R. E., "An Algorithm for Integer Solutions to Linear Programs," in *Recent Advances in Mathematical Programming*, R. Graves and P. Wolfe, editors, New York: McGraw-Hill, 1963.

14. GOMORY, R. E., and A. J. HOFFMAN, "On the Convergence of An Integer-Programming Process," *Naval Research Logistics Quarterly*, **10,** 1963, pp. 121–123.

15. LAND, A. H., and A. DOIG, "An Automatic Method of Solving Discrete Programming Problems," *Econometrica*, **28,** 1960, pp. 497–520.

16. MARKOWITZ, H., and A. S. MANNE, "On the Solution of Discrete Programming Problems," *Econometrica*, **25,** 1957, pp. 84–110.

17. SIMONNARD, M., *Programmation Lineaire*. Paris: Dunod, 1962.

18. VAJDA, S., *Mathematical Programming*. Reading, Mass.: Addison-Wesley, 1961.

19. WAGNER, H., "An Integer Linear Programming Model for Machine Scheduling," *Naval Research Logistics Quarterly*, **6,** 1959, pp. 131–140.

20. WEINGARTNER, H. M., *Mathematical Programming and the Analysis of Capital Budgeting Problems*. Ford Thesis, Englewood Cliffs, N. J.: Prentice-Hall, 1963.

PROBLEMS

8–1. Solve the example of Section 8–16, using cuts of the form of Eq. (8–100).

8–2. Solve the example of Section 8–16, using cuts of the form of Eq. (8–101).

8–3. Solve the example of Section 8–16, using cuts of the form of Eq. (8–104).

8–4. Solve the following problem, using the all integer algorithm:

$$\begin{aligned} 3x_1 + 2x_2 &\le 8, \\ x_1 + 4x_2 &\le 10, \\ x_1, x_2 \ge 0, &\qquad x_1, x_2 \text{ integers}, \\ \max z &= 3x_1 + 4x_2. \end{aligned}$$

8–5. Solve the following problem, using the all integer algorithm:

$$\begin{aligned} 3x_1 + 2x_2 &\le 5, \\ x_2 &\le 2, \\ x_1, x_2 \ge 0, &\qquad x_1, x_2 \text{ integers}, \\ \max z &= x_1 + x_2. \end{aligned}$$

8–6. Solve the following mixed integer-continuous variable problem:

$$\begin{aligned} 3x_1 + 5x_2 &\le 11, \\ 4x_1 + x_2 &\le 8, \\ x_1, x_2 \ge 0, &\qquad x_1 \text{ an integer} \\ \max z &= 8x_1 + 6x_2. \end{aligned}$$

8–7. Solve the following mixed integer-continuous variable problem:

$$4.5x_1 + 3x_2 + 5x_3 \leq 14,$$
$$2x_1 + 6.3x_2 + x_3 \leq 11,$$
$$x_1, x_2, x_3 \geq 0, \qquad x_1, x_3 \text{ integers},$$
$$\max z = 2.5x_1 + 4x_2 + 3x_3.$$

8–8. Consider a situation of the type discussed in Section 8–10, where a firm has n different projects which it may undertake. A planning horizon of K periods is used. The capital available from outside sources for investment is D_k. Let d_{kj} be the capital required for project j in period k. Suppose now that in period k project j will generate revenue r_{kj} available for investment. This revenue cannot be used, however, until period $k + 1$ or a later period. Let p_j be the present worth of all future profits for project j. Set up the integer linear programming problem whose solution indicates the projects that should be initiated to maximize the present worth of future profits, taking account of the fact that revenues generated from projects can be reinvested.

8–9. Generalize Problem 8–8 to situations where projects need not be initiated at the beginning of the first period, but some can be started in later periods.

8–10. In applying the dual simplex algorithm, show that to delete an inactive cut when forming a new problem, one simply crosses off the row in the simplex tableau where the slack variable appears and deletes the column corresponding to the slack variable.

8–11. Provide an example where LP (8–1) has an optimal solution, but there is no feasible solution to (8–1). Do this for the all-integer case and the mixed integer-continuous variable case.

8–12. Prove that the equivalent of Eq. (8–91) goes through when Eq. (8–105) is used in place of Eq. (8–90).

8–13. Show that by using the algorithm of Section 8–13 it is possible to reduce every element in the simplex tableau to an integral value. [*Hint:* After all components of $\mathbf{p}_0$ have become integers, move to the first $\mathbf{p}_j$. If some component is not an integer, use the corresponding row to form a cut. Note that $f_{u0} = 0$, so that the cut will not influence $\mathbf{p}_0$. Use the lexicographic method of Section 8–13, now treating the first $\mathbf{p}_j$ as though it were $\mathbf{p}_0$. Provide the details of the proof.] This result implies that it is possible to introduce a sufficient number of new variables, so that whenever the nonbasic variables are assigned integer values, the basic variables will also be integer-valued. Furthermore every feasible solution to (8–1) in the all-integer case must be such a solution for some integral values of the nonbasic variables.

8–14. Consider the problem of coloring a map so that no two regions with a common boundary (other than a point) have the same color. It has been conjectured, but never proved, that no more than four colors are needed. Show how integer linear programming can be used to test this hypothesis for any particular case. [*Hint:* Let the subscript j refer to the jth of the regions. Denote the four colors by 0, 1, 2, 3. Then the integer-valued variable ρ_j, $0 \leq \rho_j \leq 3$, will give the color assigned to region j. If regions j and k have a common boundary, we must have $\rho_k \neq \rho_j$. Thus $\rho_k - \rho_j \geq 1$ or $\rho_j - \rho_k \geq 1$. Express these conditions in the integer programming format. How can integer linear programming be used to determine whether or not there is a feasible solution to the problem? This formulation was suggested by Gomory and is presented by Dantzig [5].]

8–15. An assembly line consists of a number of work stations. To assemble the product under consideration, a number of operations (jobs) must be performed subject to certain sequencing requirements concerning the order in which they are performed. Given the desired production rate of the product, management wishes to accomplish two objectives: the jobs are to be assigned to work stations so as to minimize the total number of these stations, and once a piece leaves a station it is not to return. This is called an assembly-line balancing problem. The times required to do each job are specified. Show how the problem can be formulated as an integer linear programming problem. Assume that there are n jobs to be done, and t_j is the length of time to do job j. Let R be the specified production rate. Note that R cannot be greater than the reciprocal of the smallest t_j. If $T = \sum_j t_j$, the number of stations needed will be at least the smallest integer greater than RT. Call this number m. Assume that there need not be more than M stations. Denote by $I(j)$ the set of indices i such that job i must be completed before job j is begun. Assume that the work stations are arranged sequentially on the assembly line, and that it is not possible to have two different stations working on the same unit simultaneously. [*Hint:* Let $\delta_{jk} = 1$ if job j is done at station k and zero otherwise.] What constraint assures us that job j will be done at some station? Note that the total time used at any station cannot exceed $1/R$ and that this time is $\sum_j t_j\delta_{jk}$. Note that if $\delta_{jk} = 1$, then $\sum_{v=1}^{k} \delta_{iv} = 1,\ i \in I(j)$. The number of jobs done at station k is $\sum_j \delta_{jk}$. We would like to maximize the number of stations for which $\sum_j \delta_{jk} = 0$. Write

$$\sum_j \delta_{jk} \leq n(1 - \psi_k), \qquad \psi_k = 0 \quad \text{or} \quad 1.$$

Then we wish to maximize $\sum \psi_k$. Give the complete formulation of the problem.

8–16. Bowman [2] has suggested two different formulations of the assembly-line balancing problem discussed in Problem 8–15, which we shall consider in this and the next problem. Let t_{jk} be the time devoted to job j at station k. Write down the constraints which ensure that each station is not overloaded and that each job is completed. Next it will be required that a job cannot be split among stations. Write $t_{jk} = t_j\delta_{jk}$ where $\delta_{jk} = 0$ or 1. Show that these constraints prevent the splitting of jobs. Finally, the sequencing requirement must be satisfied. Show that constraints of the type shown below will take care of the ordering requirements, since previous constraints require that $t_{jk} = 0$ or t_j.

$$\frac{t_{jk}}{t_j} \leq \sum_{v=1}^{k} \frac{t_{iv}}{t_i}, \qquad i \in I(j).$$

To minimize the number of stations, we can assign progressively larger costs to the use of time in stations $m+1, \ldots, M$, i.e., we can minimize

$$z = \sum_{k=m+1}^{M} (k-m)\left[\sum_{j=1}^{n} t_j\,\delta_{jk}\right],$$

the cost per unit time at station $k(k \geq m+1)$ being simply $k-m$. Develop in detail the formulation of the problem.

8–17. The other formulation suggested for Problem 8–15 by Bowman goes something as follows. Let τ_j be the clock time at which job j is begun. Then the sequencing relations are represented by $\tau_i + t_i \leq \tau_j$, $i \in I(j)$. One must also make sure that two jobs are not being worked on simultaneously. Let $\xi_j = \tau_j + t_j$ be the clock time at which job j is finished. Then we want either $\tau_i - \xi_j \geq 0$ or $\tau_j - \xi_i \geq 0$ for all i and j. We do not need constraints of this sort when the sequencing requirements automatically prevent i and j from being worked on simultaneously. As yet we have said nothing about stations. To do this, we simply assign all jobs whose completion time is $\leq 1/R$ to station 1, and all those completed between $1/R$ and $2/R$ to station 2, etc. Thus let δ_j be an integer-valued variable which can take on the values $0, 1, \ldots, n-1$. If $\delta_j = k$, then job j is performed at station k. Thus we use $\xi_j \leq (1/R)(\delta_j + 1)$, $\tau_j \geq \delta_j/R$. Set up the problem in detail and determine the objective function. Can you provide an alternative formulation for assigning the jobs to the stations?

8–18. The simplest form of a machine-shop scheduling problem assumes that n jobs are to be done and that there are m different machines in the shop. Job i requires a time t_{ij} on machine j, and furthermore, before job i can be placed on machine j, work must have been completed on machines j', $j' \in J(j)$. It is desired to determine the sequencing of jobs on machines which minimizes the total time required to finish all n jobs. Bowman [1] has suggested the following type of integer programming formulation of the problem. First subdivide time into periods sufficiently small so that changes will occur only at the beginning of periods. We shall then imagine that t_{ij} is the number of time periods that job i requires on machine j. Let δ_{ijk} be an integer-valued variable such that $\delta_{ijk} = 1$ if job i is being worked on by machine j in period k, and is 0 otherwise. Write down the requirements that t_{ij} units of time must be devoted to job i on machine j. Similarly, write down the requirements that in each period, a given machine can only work on a single job. Next the sequencing requirements must be accounted for. Show that these can be represented by

$$\delta_{ijk} \leq \frac{1}{t_{ij'}} - \sum_{v=1}^{k-1} \delta_{ij'v}, \qquad j' \in J(j).$$

This formulation does not guarantee that the completion of job i on machine j will not be interrupted. How can one achieve this guarantee? What is the objective function which one desires to minimize? Set up the problem in detail.

8–19. Another formulation of the machine-shop scheduling problem studied in Problem 8–18 is possible. For each machine j, we wish to determine a sequence of tasks to be performed. Let $\delta_{ijk} = 1$ if job i is the kth task to be done on machine j and $\delta_{ijk} = 0$ otherwise. Let τ_{jk} be the time at which task k is begun on machine j and ξ_{jk} the time at which it is finished. Suppose that when work on i is begun on machine j, it will be finished without interruption. Then

$$\xi_{jk} - \tau_{jk} = \sum_i t_{ij}\, \delta_{ijk}.$$

Furthermore, $\xi_{jk} \leq \tau_{j,k+1}$, and if work on i must be done on machine j, $\sum_k \delta_{ijk} = 1$. Consider next the sequencing constraints. We wish that if $j' \in J(j)$, the time when work on i is finished on machine j', shall not be later than the time when work on i is begun on machine j. Thus we want $\xi_{j'k'} \leq \tau_{jk}$ if $\delta_{ij'k'} = \delta_{ijk} = 1$, with no such restriction applying otherwise. To do this, introduce the variables $\psi_{ijj'kk'}$ which can take on only the values 0 or 1. Then write

$$\psi_{ijj'kk'} + 1 \geq \delta_{ij'k'} + \delta_{ijk}, \qquad \psi_{ijj'kk'} \leq \delta_{ij'k'}, \qquad \psi_{ijj'kk'} \leq \delta_{ijk}.$$

The sequencing restrictions can then be written

$$\xi_{j'k'} - \tau_{jk} \leq M(1 - \psi_{ijj'kk'}), \qquad j' \in J(j),$$

where M is a large positive number. Develop any other constraints that are needed, obtain the objective function, and fill in the details in the above arguments.

8–20. Note that in the formulation of the fixed-charge problem given in Eq. (8–6) it is allowable to have $x_j = 0$ and $\delta_j = 1$. Why is it unnecessary to impose the requirement that if $\delta_j = 1$, $x_j > 0$?

8–21. Attempt to solve the example of Section 8–16 as an all-integer problem by converting it to the following form:

$$\begin{aligned} 2x_1 + 4x_2 &\leq 7, \\ 10x_1 + 3x_2 &\leq 15, \\ x_1, x_2 \geq 0; &\quad x_1, x_2 \text{ integers}, \\ \max z &= x_1 + 4x_2. \end{aligned}$$

8–22. In solving an all-integer problem, it may happen at some step that the cutting plane determined is parallel to hyperplanes representing the objective function. Thus, when the resulting problem is solved, there will be alternative optima. In such cases, it will frequently be true that as additional cutting planes are introduced, the optimal value of z will not change for a number of iterations. Explain this behavior in terms of the convergence proof of Section 8–13. Illustrate graphically this sort of behavior. How might one select cutting planes so as to avoid having them parallel to planes representing the objective function?

8–23. A firm has contracted to produce a number of small high-tolerance machined parts in relatively small lots for a major missile manufacturer. The contract is for two years, and no more of the parts will be made after that time. The manufacture requires special machines which the firm must purchase. Assume that d_j units of part j must be produced per week. There are several different processes of production by which some of the parts may be made. Process j requires a_{ij} units of factor of production i. Imagine that there are m different types of machines that will have to be bought and used. If desired, two shifts can be worked on any or all machines. The firm wants to have a rate of return of 20 percent. Set up as an integer linear programming problem, the problem of determining how many of each type of machine to purchase, what processes of production to use, whether or not overtime is desirable and where, so as to maximize the discounted profit over the two-year period.

CHAPTER 9

GRADIENT METHODS

We, we have chosen our path—
Path to a clear-purposed goal,
Path of Advance!—but it leads
A long, steep journey, through sunk
Gorges, o'er mountains in snow.

Matthew Arnold, *Rugby Chapel*

9–1 Introduction. Every method that we have considered thus far for solving nonlinear programming problems numerically, with the exception of the material on classical optimization methods studied in Chapter 3, has been in some sense or other an "adjacent extreme point" method which employed the simplex algorithm as the fundamental computational tool. We would now like to turn our attention to a different iterative approach which is not, in general, an adjacent extreme point method. It is classical in its origin and is based on the fact proved in Section 3–9 that if we move in the direction of the gradient of $f(\mathbf{x})$, we are moving in the direction of the maximum rate of increase in $f(\mathbf{x})$.

We wish to study in this chapter the way in which this principle can be applied to the solution of constrained optimization problems. Its application in the presence of constraints can assume a variety of forms depending on the type of problem to be solved, and on the manner in which it is modified to account for the constraints. We shall study some of these. *Gradient methods*, as the approaches of this chapter will be referred to, will normally converge at best to a local optimum, and perhaps not even a local optimum. It is only when the problem possesses the appropriate convexity or concavity properties that we can be sure that the process will converge to the global optimum. Generally, an infinite number of iterations may be required for convergence, although for certain special cases, such as linear programming problems, convergence can always be made to take place in a finite number of steps. We shall see that even though gradient methods are not adjacent extreme point methods, the simplex algorithm will again appear frequently as a computational tool to aid us in deciding in what direction to move when one or more constraints and/or nonnegativity restrictions prevent us from moving in the direction of the gradient vector.

9-2 Case of linear constraints. We shall begin by restricting our attention to nonlinear programming problems with linear constraints. Let us study problems of the following sort:

$$\sum_{j=1}^{n} a_{ij}x_j \leq b_i, \qquad i \in I_1,$$

$$\sum_{j=1}^{n} a_{ij}x_j = b_i, \qquad i \in I_2, \tag{9-1}$$

$$x_j \geq 0, \qquad j \in J,$$

$$\max z = f(x_1, \ldots, x_n),$$

where I_1, I_2 or both may be empty. All constraint inequalities will be converted to a form involving a $\leq$ sign. We can do this, since for the methods to be discussed, b_i can have any sign. It will not be desirable here to convert inequalities to equations by adding slack variables. We shall say that $\mathbf{x}$ is a feasible solution to (9-1) if it satisfies the constraints and $x_j \geq 0, j \in J$. The function $f(\mathbf{x})$ will be assumed to possess continuous first partial derivatives at every point in the set of feasible solutions.

Let us now imagine that we have feasible solution $\mathbf{x}_0$ to the problem (9-1). One great advantage of the gradient methods is that any feasible solution can be used to initiate the computations, and it is not necessary to have some special form of a feasible solution, such as a basic feasible solution. We shall discuss later how to obtain an initial feasible solution if one is not available. For many practical problems, however, a feasible solution will be available. Assume that we have computed $\nabla f(\mathbf{x}_0)$, the gradient vector for $f(\mathbf{x})$ at $\mathbf{x}_0$, and that $\nabla f(\mathbf{x}_0) \neq \mathbf{0}$. We shall develop an iterative procedure for generating a sequence of feasible solutions $\mathbf{x}_v$ such that $f(\mathbf{x}_{v+1}) > f(\mathbf{x}_v)$. At iteration v, the feasible solution $\mathbf{x}_v$ will be determined.

We must distinguish two possible cases with reference to the initial solution $\mathbf{x}_0$. These are:

(1) There exists an $\epsilon > 0$ such that $\mathbf{x}_1 = \mathbf{x}_0 + \lambda\mathbf{d}_0$, $\mathbf{d}_0' = \nabla f(\mathbf{x}_0)$ (recall that ∇f is a row vector) is a feasible solution for all λ, $0 \leq \lambda \leq \epsilon$. Generally, this implies that I_2 is empty, but this is not necessary.

(2) There exists no $\lambda > 0$ such that $\mathbf{x}_1 = \mathbf{x}_0 + \lambda\mathbf{d}_0$ is a feasible solution.

Case (1) will be examined first, since it involves a direct application of the result obtained in Section 3-9. Inasmuch as $\nabla f(\mathbf{x}_0) \neq \mathbf{0}$, we know from what was proved in Section 3-9 that if we move from $\mathbf{x}_0$ in the direction of $\nabla f(\mathbf{x}_0)$, we are moving in the direction of the maximum rate of increase in z. Furthermore, we shall now show that there exists a $\lambda > 0$ such that if

$$\mathbf{x}_1 = \mathbf{x}_0 + \lambda \mathbf{d}_0, \qquad \mathbf{d}_0' = \nabla f(\mathbf{x}_0), \tag{9-2}$$

then $\mathbf{x}_1$ is a feasible solution, and $f(\mathbf{x}_1) > f(\mathbf{x}_0)$. Note first that by the nature of case (1), $\mathbf{x} = \mathbf{x}_0 + \lambda \mathbf{d}_0$ is a feasible solution for all λ, $0 < \lambda < \epsilon$. Secondly, by Taylor's theorem, for any λ,

$$\begin{aligned} f(\mathbf{x}_0 + \lambda \mathbf{d}_0) &= f(\mathbf{x}_0) + \lambda \nabla f(\boldsymbol{\xi}) \mathbf{d}_0, \\ \boldsymbol{\xi} &= \mathbf{x}_0 + \theta \lambda \mathbf{d}_0, \quad 0 \leq \theta \leq 1. \end{aligned} \tag{9-3}$$

But each $\partial f/\partial x_j$ is a continuous function of $\mathbf{x}$. Thus $\nabla f(\mathbf{x})\mathbf{d}_0$ is a continuous function of $\mathbf{x}$, and since $\mathbf{d}_0'\mathbf{d}_0 > 0$, there exists a $\delta > 0$ such that $\nabla f(\mathbf{x})\mathbf{d}_0 > 0$ for all $\mathbf{x}$, $|\mathbf{x} - \mathbf{x}_0| < \delta$. Therefore, for any λ, $0 < \lambda < \min(\epsilon, \delta)$, it follows that $\mathbf{x} = \mathbf{x}_0 + \lambda \mathbf{d}_0$ is a feasible solution and $f(\mathbf{x}) > f(\mathbf{x}_0)$, so that the λ referred to above does exist.

The question now becomes, What value should be assigned to λ to obtain the new feasible solution $\mathbf{x}$? We would like to obtain the greatest increase possible in $f(\mathbf{x})$ while still maintaining a feasible solution. We first, then, determine the largest value of λ, call it ϵ, for which $\mathbf{x} = \mathbf{x}_0 + \lambda \mathbf{d}_0$ is feasible. To do this we note that it must be true that

$$\mathbf{a}^i(\mathbf{x}_0 + \lambda \mathbf{d}_0) \leq b_i, \quad i \in I_1; \qquad \mathbf{a}^i(\mathbf{x}_0 + \lambda \mathbf{d}_0) = b_i, \quad i \in I_2;$$
$$x_{j0} + \lambda d_{j0} \geq 0, \quad j \in J,$$

where $\mathbf{a}^i = (a_{i1}, \ldots, a_{in})$. Denote by $I_1(0)$, $J(0)$ the subsets of I_1 and J for which constraint $i \in I_1(0)$ is active at $\mathbf{x}_0$ and for which $x_{j0} = 0$, $j \in J(0)$, respectively. Since we originally assumed that we could move a finite distance in the direction of $\mathbf{d}_0$ without violating the constraints, it must be true that for any $\lambda > 0$,

$$\mathbf{a}^i(\mathbf{x}_0 + \lambda \mathbf{d}_0) \leq b_i, \quad i \in I_1(0); \qquad \mathbf{a}^i(\mathbf{x}_0 + \lambda \mathbf{d}_0) = b_i, \quad i \in I_2;$$
$$x_{j0} + \lambda\, d_{j0} \geq 0, \quad j \in J(0).$$

What limits the value of λ, then, is the fact that when λ is made sufficiently large, some constraint inactive at $\mathbf{x}_0$ will usually become active or some component x_j, $j \in J$, of $\mathbf{x}$ which was positive at $\mathbf{x}_0$ will become zero. Thus to determine the largest value of λ for which $\mathbf{x} = \mathbf{x}_0 + \lambda \mathbf{d}_0$ is feasible, we compute

$$\rho = \begin{cases} \min\limits_j \left[-\dfrac{x_{j0}}{d_{j0}} \right], & d_{j0} < 0, \quad j \in J, \quad j \notin J(0), \\ \infty \quad \text{if no } d_{j0} < 0, \quad j \in J, \quad j \notin J(0); \end{cases} \tag{9-4}$$

and

$$\gamma = \begin{cases} \min_i \left[\dfrac{b_i - \mathbf{a}^i\mathbf{x}_0}{\mathbf{a}^i\mathbf{d}_0}\right], & \mathbf{a}^i\mathbf{d}_0 > 0, \quad i \in I_1, \quad i \notin I_1(0), \\ \infty \quad \text{if no } \mathbf{a}^i\mathbf{d}_0 > 0, \quad i \in I_1, \quad i \notin I_1(0). \end{cases} \tag{9–5}$$

If ρ is finite, then some component of $\mathbf{x}$ will be negative when $\lambda > \rho$, and if γ is finite, then some constraint will be violated when $\lambda > \gamma$.

Let $\epsilon = \min(\rho, \gamma)$. Then we know that λ must satisfy $0 < \lambda \leq \epsilon$ if $\mathbf{x}$ is to be feasible. However, it does not follow that we wish to set $\lambda = \epsilon$, because, in general, $\nabla f(\mathbf{x})$ changes with $\mathbf{x}$. Thus, even though $f(\mathbf{x}_0 + \lambda\mathbf{d}_0) > f(\mathbf{x}_0)$ if λ is small enough, it does not follow that this will be the case if λ is too large, since $\nabla f(\boldsymbol{\xi})\mathbf{d}_0$ in (9–3) may become negative when λ is large enough. The logical thing to do, then, is to try to determine that value of λ, $0 < \lambda \leq \epsilon$, which maximizes $f(\mathbf{x}_0 + \lambda\mathbf{d}_0)$. We might try to do this by setting $df/d\lambda = 0$ and solving for λ. For simple cases, this can be done. In general, however, it may be very difficult to solve this equation, and indeed, it may not have a unique solution. Thus when solving the problem on a computer, we would normally use some sort of numerical search procedure to determine the optimal value of λ. A very simple method would be to subdivide the interval $0 < \lambda \leq \epsilon$ by a number of equally spaced mesh points $\lambda_k = k\,\Delta\lambda$ and to evaluate $f(\mathbf{x}_0 + \lambda_k\mathbf{d}_0)$ for each k. Then the largest $f(\mathbf{x}_0 + \lambda_k\mathbf{d}_0)$ would be selected, and the λ_k yielding this value would be used for λ. In carrying out the process, we might find it desirable to check the largest $f(\mathbf{x}_0 + \lambda_k\mathbf{d}_0)$ against $f(\mathbf{x}_0)$ to be certain that $f(\mathbf{x})$ has increased. If $\Delta\lambda$ chosen is too large, $f(\mathbf{x}_0 + \lambda_k\mathbf{d}_0)$ may be less than $f(\mathbf{x}_0)$ for each λ_k. We shall not discuss now in any more detail the best way of performing the search. This subject is considered in the next chapter. Usually, for this problem, one would not attempt to use an elaborate search procedure to determine very precisely the best λ. In most cases, it would be sufficient to make a rough determination of the best λ. There is, of course, a trade-off between the accuracy with which λ is determined at each iteration and the total number of iterations that will be required to solve the problem.

We might point out that if $\nabla f(\mathbf{x})$ is independent of $\mathbf{x}$ so that z is a linear function of $\mathbf{x}$, then $\lambda = \epsilon$, since from (9–3) we see that $f(\mathbf{x}_0 + \lambda\mathbf{d}_0)$ increases linearly with λ. For a linear objective function, we always move as far as we can. In this case, no search is needed to determine λ.

Once we have found $\mathbf{x}_1$, we are reduced to the same situation that we faced when we began with $\mathbf{x}_0$. We compute $\mathbf{d}_1' = \nabla f(\mathbf{x}_1)$. Either case (1) or case (2) will apply if $\nabla f(\mathbf{x}_1) \neq \mathbf{0}$. We shall see later that the process termniates if $\nabla f(\mathbf{x}_1) = \mathbf{0}$. If case (1) applies again, we repeat the procedure just described and replace $\mathbf{x}_0$ and $\mathbf{d}_0$ in (9–4) and (9–5) by $\mathbf{x}_1$ and $\mathbf{d}_1$. Then we determine a new ϵ and λ, and thus $\mathbf{x}_2$.

Let us now turn our attention to case (2). When we encounter this alternative (this may happen at the outset or at a later iteration), the current feasible solution is on the boundary of the set of feasible solutions, and either one or more constraints and/or non-negativity restrictions will be violated if we attempt to move in the direction of the gradient vector; i.e., we shall move out of the set of feasible solutions if we attempt to move in the direction of the gradient vector. We must now modify the principle which tells us the direction in which to move so that no constraint or non-negativity restriction will be violated.

Let us imagine that after having determined $\mathbf{x}_v$ and $\mathbf{d}'_v = \nabla f(\mathbf{x}_v)$, we encounter case (2). Let us denote by $J(v)$ the subset of indices $j \in J$ for which $x_{jv} = 0$, and by $I(v)$ the set of indices i for which the ith constraint holds as a strict equality. We need not, at the moment, concern ourselves with any $j \notin J(v)$ or $i \notin I(v)$, since for all $\mathbf{x}$ in some neighborhood of $\mathbf{x}_v$, these non-negativity restrictions and constraints will not be violated. We showed in Section 2–10 that if $\mathbf{r}$ is any vector of unit length, then, if we move from $\mathbf{x}$ in the direction $\mathbf{r}$, the rate of change of $f(\mathbf{x})$ is $\nabla f(\mathbf{x})\mathbf{r}$. Let us suppose that we consider points $\mathbf{x} = \mathbf{x}_v + \lambda\mathbf{r}$ for any $\mathbf{r}$, $|\mathbf{r}| = 1$, and any $\lambda > 0$. Then, if $\mathbf{x}$ is to be a feasible solution, it must be true that

$$x_j = x_{jv} + \lambda r_j \geq 0, \quad j \in J(v),$$

or

$$r_j \geq 0, \quad j \in J(v), \tag{9–6}$$

since

$$x_{jv} = 0, \quad j \in J(v) \quad \text{and} \quad \lambda > 0.$$

Also

$$\begin{aligned} \mathbf{a}^i\mathbf{x} = \mathbf{a}^i(\mathbf{x}_v + \lambda\mathbf{r}) &\leq b_i, \quad i \in I(v), \quad i \notin I_2, \\ \mathbf{a}^i\mathbf{x} &= b_i, \quad i \in I_2; \end{aligned}$$

or if

$$I_1(v) = \{i | i \in I(v), i \notin I_2\},$$

then

$$\mathbf{a}^i\mathbf{r} \leq 0, \quad i \in I_1(v); \qquad \mathbf{a}^i\mathbf{r} = 0, \quad i \in I_2, \tag{9–7}$$

since

$$\mathbf{a}^i\mathbf{x}_v = b_i, \quad i \in I(v).$$

If $\mathbf{r}$ satisfies (9–6) and (9–7), then we know that if $\lambda > 0$ is sufficiently small, $\mathbf{x} = \mathbf{x}_v + \lambda\mathbf{r}$ will be a feasible solution. We can now determine the direction in which to move to obtain the maximum rate of increase in $f(\mathbf{x})$ without violating any of the constraints or non-negativity restrictions, by finding the solution $\mathbf{r}$ to the following nonlinear programming problem:

$$\begin{aligned} \mathbf{a}^i\mathbf{r} &\le 0, \quad i \in I_1(v), \\ \mathbf{a}^i\mathbf{r} &= 0, \quad i \in I_2, \\ r_j &\ge 0, \quad j \in J(v), \\ \mathbf{r}'\mathbf{r} &= 1, \\ \max D_{\mathbf{r}}f(\mathbf{x}_v) &= \nabla f(\mathbf{x}_v)\mathbf{r}. \end{aligned} \tag{9–8}$$

The solution to (9–8) will be referred to as the locally best direction in which to move. Note that $\nabla f(\mathbf{x}_v)\mathbf{r}/|\nabla f(\mathbf{x}_v)|$ is simply the cosine of the angle between $\mathbf{r}$ and $\nabla f(\mathbf{x}_v)$. Thus, in solving (9–8), we are attempting to determine that $\mathbf{r}$ satisfying the constraints of (9–8) which makes the smallest angle with $\nabla f(\mathbf{x}_v)$.

It is actually possible to solve this problem at each iteration where it is necessary to do so, and we shall show how this can be done in a later section. However, to avoid solving a problem such as (9–8), we might be willing to use a simpler procedure which yielded an $\mathbf{r}$ satisfying (9–6) and (9–7), with

$$D_{\mathbf{r}}f(\mathbf{x}_v) = \nabla f(\mathbf{x}_v)\mathbf{r} > 0 \tag{9–9}$$

but not necessarily $D_{\mathbf{r}}f(\mathbf{x}_v)$ being a maximum subject to the constraints. It is because of the fact that there are various ways of obtaining an $\mathbf{r}$ satisfying the constraints and (9–9) that it is possible to develop a variety of gradient algorithms. They differ in the approach used to determine the direction in which to move when case (2) is encountered.

Let us now suppose that, perhaps by solving (9–8), we have found some $\mathbf{r}$, call it $\mathbf{r}_v$, satisfying (9–9) and the constraints (9–6) and (9–7). We shall then move from $\mathbf{x}_v$ in the direction of $\mathbf{r}_v$, so that $\mathbf{x}_{v+1} = \mathbf{x}_v + \lambda\mathbf{r}_v$. We still need to decide how far we can or should move, i.e., λ must be determined. Note that $\mathbf{x}_{v+1}$ will satisfy the constraints for $i \in I(v)$ and the non-negativity restrictions for $j \in J(v)$ for any $\lambda > 0$ (proof?). This need not be true, however, for $i \notin I(v)$, $j \notin J(v)$. Thus we perform a computation like (9–4) for $j \in J$, $j \notin J(v)$, and a computation like (9–5) for $i \notin I(v)$. The result of these computations yields a value $\epsilon > 0$ which is the largest value that λ can assume without violating some new non-negativity restriction or constraint. Then, as before, we determine λ by searching over the interval $0 < \lambda \le \epsilon$ to find that value of λ where $f(\mathbf{x}_v + \lambda\mathbf{r}_v)$ assumes its maximum value. After determining $\mathbf{x}_v$, we are again reduced to either case (1) or case (2).

We might now note that if we agree at each iteration to solve (9–8) it is unnecessary to distinguish between cases (1) and (2). Both are included in (9–8). If $\mathbf{d}_v/|\mathbf{d}_v|$ satisfies the constraints in (9–8), then $\mathbf{d}_v/|\mathbf{d}_v|$ is a feasible solution to (9–8) and also an optimal solution, since we know from

Section 3–9 that this would be the optimal solution in the absence of constraints. Thus the solution to (9–8) will tell us to move in the direction $\mathbf{d}_v$, which is what we do in case (1). Under these conditions the iterative procedure can be described as follows: We begin with an initial feasible solution $\mathbf{x}_0$ with $\nabla f(\mathbf{x}_0) \neq \mathbf{0}$. At each iteration we first solve (9–8) to determine the direction $\mathbf{r}_v$ in which to move from $\mathbf{x}_v$ to obtain $\mathbf{x}_{v+1}$. Next we determine the maximum value of λ, call it ϵ, for which $\mathbf{x} = \mathbf{x}_v + \lambda \mathbf{r}_v$ is a feasible solution. The value of ϵ is determined by first computing

$$\rho = \begin{cases} \min_j \left[-\frac{x_{jv}}{r_{jv}} \right], & r_{jv} < 0, \quad j \in J, \quad j \notin J(v), \\ \infty \text{ if no } r_{jv} < 0, \quad j \in J, \quad j \notin J(v), \end{cases} \tag{9–10}$$

$$\gamma = \begin{cases} \min_i \left[\frac{b_i - \mathbf{a}^i \mathbf{x}_v}{\mathbf{a}^i \mathbf{r}_v} \right], & \mathbf{a}^i \mathbf{r}_v > 0, \quad i \notin I(v), \\ \infty \text{ if no } \mathbf{a}^i \mathbf{r}_v > 0, \quad i \notin I(v). \end{cases} \tag{9–11}$$

Then $\epsilon = \min(\rho, \gamma)$. To determine λ, that is, how far to move, we perform a search in the interval $0 < \lambda \leq \epsilon$ to locate the maximum value of $f(\mathbf{x}_v + \lambda \mathbf{r}_v)$. Finally we set $\mathbf{x}_{v+1} = \mathbf{x}_v + \lambda \mathbf{r}_v$ and repeat the entire procedure.

If at some step in the iterative process we obtain a feasible solution $\mathbf{x}_v = \bar{\mathbf{x}}$ for which an optimal solution $\bar{\mathbf{r}}$ to (9–8) has the property that $\nabla f(\bar{\mathbf{x}})\bar{\mathbf{r}} \leq 0$, then the iterative process terminates, since there is no allowable direction $\mathbf{r}$ in which we can move such that $D_{\mathbf{r}} f(\bar{\mathbf{x}}) > 0$. A feasible solution $\bar{\mathbf{x}}$ will be called a constrained stationary point of $f(\mathbf{x})$ if $D_{\mathbf{r}} f(\bar{\mathbf{x}}) \leq 0$ for every direction $\mathbf{r}$ which does not immediately lead us out of the set of feasible solutions. The point $\bar{\mathbf{x}}$ is a constrained stationary point of $f(\mathbf{x})$ if and only if the optimal solution to (9–8) for $\bar{\mathbf{x}}$ has the property that the objective function is nonpositive. When no specific assumptions are made about $f(\mathbf{x})$, it is not necessarily true that a constrained stationary point of $f(\mathbf{x})$ will yield the global optimum to (9–1). It may not even yield a local maximum. More will be said about this in the next section.

The iterative procedure will also terminate if we reach a feasible solution $\mathbf{x}_v$ for which the solution to (9–8) yields a direction $\mathbf{r}_v$ with the property that $\mathbf{x} = \mathbf{x}_v + \lambda \mathbf{r}_v$ is a feasible solution for any $\lambda > 0$ and $f(\mathbf{x}_v + \lambda \mathbf{r}_v) > f(\mathbf{x}_v)$ for all $\lambda > 0$. Then it is desirable to allow λ to become infinite, so that $|\mathbf{x}| \to \infty$. This normally implies that there is an unbounded solution. It is conceivable, however, that $f(\mathbf{x}_v + \lambda \mathbf{r}_v)$ approaches a finite limit as $\lambda \to \infty$.

The iterative process will automatically terminate only in one of the two ways just considered. Otherwise, from any feasible solution $\mathbf{x}_v$ we can move to a feasible solution $\mathbf{x}_{v+1}$ such that $f(\mathbf{x}_{v+1}) > f(\mathbf{x}_v)$. It is not necessarily true that one of the terminating conditions will ever be reached in a finite number of steps. We shall consider below the nature of the sequence $\mathbf{x}_v$ when the process does not terminate in a finite number of steps.

We must initiate the iterative procedure with a point $\mathbf{x}_0$ for which $\nabla f(\mathbf{x}_0) \neq \mathbf{0}$, for otherwise we cannot determine a direction in which to move, i.e., the iterative process terminates immediately because we have begun with a stationary point of $f(\mathbf{x})$ as an initial feasible solution. It is rather unlikely that one would ever happen to obtain an initial feasible solution with $\nabla f(\mathbf{x}_0) = \mathbf{0}$. However, if such a feasible solution were obtained, one would attempt to find a nearby feasible solution with $\nabla f(\mathbf{x}) \neq \mathbf{0}$ and initiate the iterative procedure from this point.

9-3 Convergence of the iterative procedure. We shall now examine the properties of the sequence of feasible solutions $\mathbf{x}_v$ obtained by the iterative procedure developed in the previous section for cases where the terminating conditions are not met in a finite number of iterations. Then $\mathbf{x}_v$ is an infinite sequence which may or may not have at least one point of accumulation. If it has no point of accumulation, then $|\mathbf{x}_v| \to \infty$. Usually, in such a case, $f(\mathbf{x}_v) \to \infty$, and problem (9-1) has an unbounded solution. Conceivably, however, $f(\mathbf{x}_v)$ could approach a finite limit.

Consider now the case where $\mathbf{x}_v$ has at least one point of accumulation which will be denoted by $\bar{\mathbf{x}}$. We shall now show that $\bar{\mathbf{x}}$ is a constrained stationary point of $f(\mathbf{x})$. Note first that $\bar{\mathbf{x}}$ must be a feasible solution. Assume, however, that $\bar{\mathbf{x}}$ is not a constrained stationary point of $f(\mathbf{x})$. This implies that an optimal solution $\bar{\mathbf{r}}$ to (9-8) for $\bar{\mathbf{x}}$ has the property that $f(\bar{\mathbf{x}})\bar{\mathbf{r}} > 0$. We shall show that this leads to a contradiction.

At $\bar{\mathbf{x}}$, denote by $\bar{I}_1$ the subset of $i \in I_1$ for which constraint i is inactive. Also let $\bar{J}$ be the subset of $j \in J$ for which $\bar{x}_j > 0$. Then there exists a $\delta_1 > 0$ such that for all $\mathbf{x}$, $|\mathbf{x} - \bar{\mathbf{x}}| < \delta_1$, the constraints i, $i \in \bar{I}_1$ remain inactive and variables x_j, $j \in J$, are positive. Consequently, for any feasible solution $\mathbf{x}$ in this δ_1-neighborhood of $\bar{\mathbf{x}}$, the only constraints which can be active and the only components $j \in J$ of $\mathbf{x}$ which can be zero correspond to those appearing in problem (9-8) for $\bar{\mathbf{x}}$. For a particular $\mathbf{x}$ in this δ_1-neighborhood, some of the constraints or non-negativity restrictions appearing in (9-8) for $\bar{\mathbf{x}}$ may not be active.

Inasmuch as the first partial derivatives of f have been assumed to be continuous, there exists a δ_2 such that $\nabla f(\mathbf{x})\bar{\mathbf{r}} \geq \mu > 0$ for all $\mathbf{x}$, $|\mathbf{x} - \bar{\mathbf{x}}| < \delta_2$. Let $\delta_3 = \min(\delta_1, \delta_2)$. Consider a $\delta_3/2$ neighborhood of $\bar{\mathbf{x}}$. This neighborhood contains an infinite number of $\mathbf{x}_v$, since $\bar{\mathbf{x}}$ has been assumed to be a point of accumulation of the $\mathbf{x}_v$. Consider problem (9-8) for any such $\mathbf{x}_v$ in the $\delta_3/2$-neighborhood of $\bar{\mathbf{x}}$. From what was noted above and from the manner in which δ_3 was chosen, it follows that $\bar{\mathbf{r}}$ is a feasible solution to the problem for $\mathbf{x}_v$ and $f(\mathbf{x}_v)\bar{\mathbf{r}} \geq \mu > 0$. Also for any $\mathbf{x} =$

$\mathbf{x}_v + \lambda \bar{\mathbf{r}}$, we have by Taylor's theorem,

$$f(\mathbf{x}) = f(\mathbf{x}_v) + \lambda \nabla f(\boldsymbol{\xi})\bar{\mathbf{r}}, \qquad \boldsymbol{\xi} = \theta \mathbf{x}_v + (1 - \theta)\mathbf{x}, \qquad 0 \leq \theta \leq 1.$$

Therefore we see that in the move from $\mathbf{x}_v$ to $\mathbf{x}_{v+1}$, $f(\mathbf{x})$ can be increased by at least $\delta_3\mu/2$. But there is an infinite number of such $\mathbf{x}_v$. This leads to a contradiction, because if this were true, $f(\bar{\mathbf{x}}) = \infty$. However, $f(\bar{\mathbf{x}}) = \infty$ cannot occur, for then $\nabla f(\bar{\mathbf{x}})$ would not exist. Thus we must conclude that at $\bar{\mathbf{x}}$, $\nabla f(\bar{\mathbf{x}})\mathbf{r} \leq 0$ for every feasible solution $\mathbf{r}$ to (9–8) and $\bar{\mathbf{x}}$ is a constrained stationary point of $f(\mathbf{x})$.

Whenever the sequence $\mathbf{x}_v$ has a point of accumulation $\bar{\mathbf{x}}$, it will normally have only one, so that $\bar{\mathbf{x}}$ is a limit point of the sequence $\mathbf{x}_v$, i.e, all but a finite number of $\mathbf{x}_v$ lie in every δ-neighborhood of $\bar{\mathbf{x}}$. In theory, however, it might be possible to have more than one point of accumulation, but if this happened, $f(\mathbf{x})$ would have to have the same value at each of these points. We ask the reader to prove this in Problem 9–22. However, in practice, one will rarely encounter more than one point of accumulation.

From a computational point of view, the proof given in this section is only of passing interest, since for the procedure to be practically useful, convergence of the iterative scheme must be sufficiently fast not to require excessive amounts of computer time. The mere fact that the process converges does not guarantee that it converges sufficiently rapidly to be of any value. It is very difficult, in general, to determine the rapidity of convergence. Computational experience does indicate that convergence is sufficiently rapid that the procedure can be used. More will be said later about the computational efficiency of gradient methods.

We have already noted that a constrained stationary point need not correspond to a global maximum of $f(\mathbf{x})$ or even a constrained relative maximum. Any constrained stationary point reached by the iterative procedure described in the previous section cannot correspond to a relative minimum of $f(\mathbf{x})$, but it could correspond to a point at which there is a relative maximum in certain directions and a relative minimum in others, such as a saddle point for a function of two variables or, in general, to a much more complicated type of stationary point. In practice, it would be an extremely difficult task to characterize any terminal stationary point completely, or merely to determine whether or not it corresponded to a relative maximum. We noted in Chapter 3 the difficulties that are involved in trying to determine whether or not stationary points of a function involving a large number of variables correspond to relative maxima of the function. About the best that could be done in practice would be to try to find several feasible solutions in the neighborhood of $\bar{\mathbf{x}}$ different from any of the $\mathbf{x}_v$, and use each of these to initiate the iterative procedure. If the iterative procedure converged to $\bar{\mathbf{x}}$ from each of these, one might reasonably (but not rigorously) conclude that a constrained relative maximum of $f(\mathbf{x})$ occurs at $\bar{\mathbf{x}}$.

Let us note that if at a constrained stationary point $\bar{\mathbf{x}}$ of $f(\mathbf{x})$, $\hat{\mathbf{d}}' = \nabla f(\bar{\mathbf{x}})$ satisfies the constraints and non-negativity restrictions of problem (9–8) appropriate to $\bar{\mathbf{x}}$, then from the fact that $\nabla f(\bar{\mathbf{x}})\mathbf{r} \leq 0$ for any feasible solution $\mathbf{r}$ to (9–8), we can conclude that $\nabla f(\bar{\mathbf{x}}) = \mathbf{0}$, since in this case an optimal solution is $\mathbf{r} = \hat{\mathbf{d}}/|\hat{\mathbf{d}}|$. Thus $|\nabla f(\bar{\mathbf{x}})|^2 \leq 0$. This can be true only if $\nabla f(\bar{\mathbf{x}}) = \mathbf{0}$. Therefore, in this instance, $\bar{\mathbf{x}}$ also is an unconstrained stationary point of $f(\mathbf{x})$.

We might also note that if $f(\mathbf{x})$ is a concave function of $\mathbf{x}$, then the iterative procedure will converge to the global maximum of $f(\mathbf{x})$ over the convex set of feasible solutions, or will indicate that there is an unbounded solution. To see this, consider first the case where either the iterative procedure terminates in a finite number of iterations at a constrained stationary point $\bar{\mathbf{x}}$ of $f(\mathbf{x})$, or the sequence $\mathbf{x}_v$ has a point of accumulation $\bar{\mathbf{x}}$. Then, from what we have shown above, we know that for any $\mathbf{r}$, not necessarily having $\mathbf{r}'\mathbf{r} = 1$, satisfying (9–6) and (9–7), and corresponding to $\bar{\mathbf{x}}$, it must be true that $\nabla f(\bar{\mathbf{x}})\mathbf{r} \leq 0$. It is immediately evident that the global optimum of $f(\mathbf{x})$ over the convex set of feasible solutions must be taken on at $\bar{\mathbf{x}}$ if we apply (3–65) in the form

$$f(\bar{\mathbf{x}} + \mathbf{r}) \leq f(\bar{\mathbf{x}}) + \nabla f(\bar{\mathbf{x}})\mathbf{r}, \tag{9–12}$$

since if we restrict our attention to $\bar{\mathbf{x}} + \mathbf{r}$ lying in the δ_1-neighborhood of $\bar{\mathbf{x}}$, then $\bar{\mathbf{x}} + \mathbf{r}$ will be feasible if it satisfies (9–6) and (9–7). But for any such $\mathbf{r}$, we have seen that $\nabla f(\bar{\mathbf{x}})\mathbf{r} \leq 0$ and from (9–12), $f(\bar{\mathbf{x}} + \mathbf{r}) \leq f(\bar{\mathbf{x}})$ for all feasible solutions in the δ_1-neighborhood of $\bar{\mathbf{x}}$. Thus $f(\mathbf{x})$ takes on a constrained relative maximum at $\bar{\mathbf{x}}$, and since any relative maximum is a global maximum, it also takes on its global maximum at $\bar{\mathbf{x}}$. Clearly, if $f(\mathbf{x})$ can be made arbitrarily large at some iteration or the sequence $f(\mathbf{x}_v)$ is unbounded, then the problem has an unbounded solution. The only two remaining cases are those where at some iteration, λ can be increased without bound and $f(\mathbf{x})$ increases with λ but approaches a finite limit, or where $|\mathbf{x}_v| \to \infty$ and $f(\mathbf{x}_v)$ approaches a finite limit as $v \to \infty$. In this case, the limiting value of $f(\mathbf{x})$ is the global optimum of $f(\mathbf{x})$. Problem 9–24 asks the reader to fill in the details of the proof for this case.

In the proofs developed in this section we assumed that problem (9–8) was solved at each iteration and the distance to move was determined by finding the λ which maximized $f(\mathbf{x}_v + \lambda\mathbf{r}_v)$, $0 < \lambda \leq \epsilon$.

If one does not actually obtain the biggest possible increase in z at each iteration in the sense used above, but uses some simplified procedure for determining $\mathbf{r}_v$ and/or λ, then one must investigate the convergence of these schemes individually, because convergence cannot be guaranteed by the above proof.

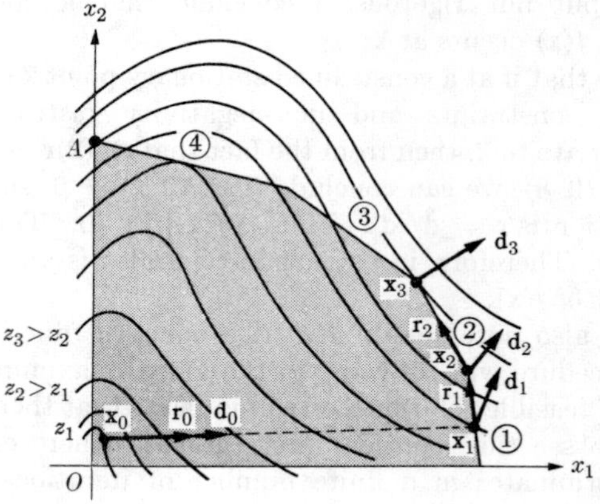

FIGURE 9–1

9–4 Geometrical interpretation. Before going on to discuss any more of the theory it might be helpful to illustrate geometrically with problems involving two variables how the iterative procedure discussed in the previous section might behave. Consider a problem for which the convex set of feasible solutions is that shown in Fig. 9–1. The level curves for the nonlinear objective function are also illustrated, with z increasing as indicated. Assume that we begin with the feasible solution $\mathbf{x}_0$. The gradient vector $\nabla f(\mathbf{x}_0)$, or equivalently $\mathbf{d}_0$, is simply a normal vector for the tangent hyperplane to $f(\mathbf{x}) = z_0$ at $\mathbf{x}_0$ which points in the direction of increasing z. Initially no constraints are active so that $\mathbf{r}_0 = \mathbf{d}_0/|\mathbf{d}_0|$. We could move from $\mathbf{x}_0$ in the direction of $\mathbf{r}_0$ until the boundary of the set of feasible solutions was reached. In general, it might not be desirable to move all the way because the maximum of $f(\mathbf{x}_0 + \lambda\mathbf{r}_0)$ might be reached before the boundary was. In this case, however, $f(\mathbf{x}_0 + \lambda\mathbf{r}_0)$ continues to increase as λ is increased. Thus $\mathbf{x}_1$ is the point shown. Also shown is $\mathbf{d}_1$. We cannot move in the direction of $\mathbf{d}_1$ because we would move out of the convex set of feasible solutions. Problem (9–8) would then have one constraint and no non-negativity restrictions. The solution to this problem would yield the $\mathbf{r}_1$ shown, since this vector makes the smallest angle with $\mathbf{d}_1$ of any vector emanating from $\mathbf{x}_1$ and lying in the convex set of feasible solutions. Thus at the next iteration we would move along constraint 1. Again we would move as far as possible, and $\mathbf{x}_2$ would be the point shown. The values of $\mathbf{d}_2$ and $\mathbf{r}_2$ are also sketched. At the third iteration we move along constraint 2, and again we move as far as possible, obtaining $\mathbf{x}_3$. At this point the process terminates because on solving (9–8), we find that the maximum value is < 0. Geometrically, $\mathbf{d}_3$ does not make a nonobtuse angle with any vector in the set of feasible solutions emanating from $\mathbf{x}_3$. Here we have an example where the process terminated in a finite number (three) of

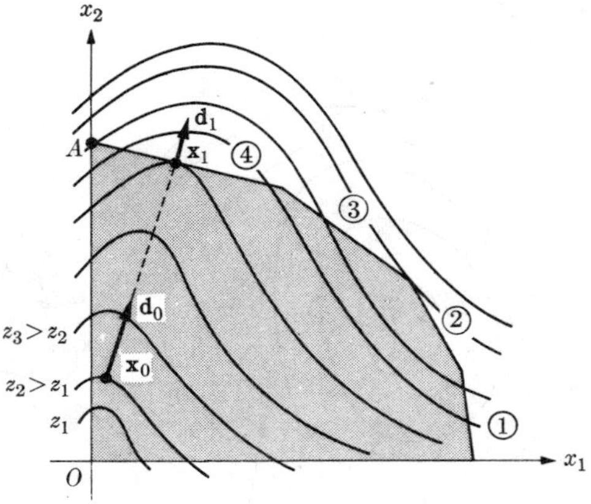

FIGURE 9–2

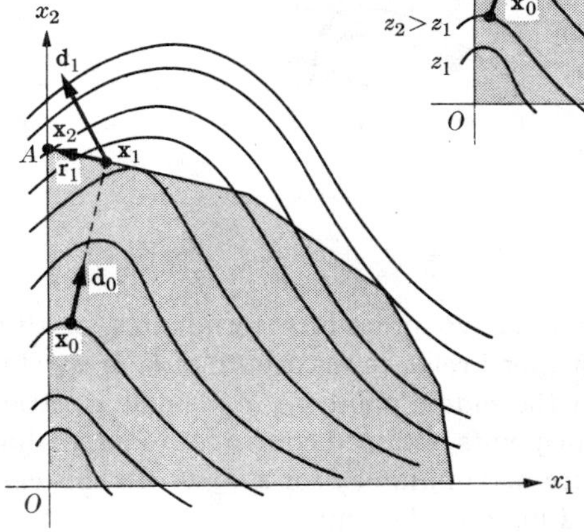

FIGURE 9–3

iterations. Note that $f(\mathbf{x})$ does take on a constrained relative maximum at $\mathbf{x}_3$. Furthermore, $f(\mathbf{x})$ also assumes its global optimum over the convex set at $\mathbf{x}_3$.

Suppose that we are attempting to solve the same problem studied above, but now the initial feasible solution is the point $\mathbf{x}_0$ shown in Fig. 9–2. In this case the process terminates in a single iteration and yields the point $\mathbf{x}_1$. The function $f(\mathbf{x})$ does not, however, take on a constrained relative maximum at $\mathbf{x}_1$. Instead $\mathbf{x}_1$ corresponds to what is a constrained saddle point, since if we move from $\mathbf{x}_2$ in either direction along constraint 4, $f(\mathbf{x})$ increases, whereas if we move from $\mathbf{x}_1$ back toward $\mathbf{x}_0$, $f(\mathbf{x})$ decreases.

Consider once again the same problem and imagine that the initial feasible solution $\mathbf{x}_0$ is that shown in Fig. 9–3. In this case, it is clear that the iterative procedure converges in two iterations to a local optimum A.

As a final example, consider a case where there are no constraints—only non-negativity restrictions. Assume that the level curves for $z = f(\mathbf{x})$ look like those shown in Fig. 9–4. If we start at the point $\mathbf{x}_{0a}$, we obtain the sequence of points shown. Note that at the first iteration, we do not

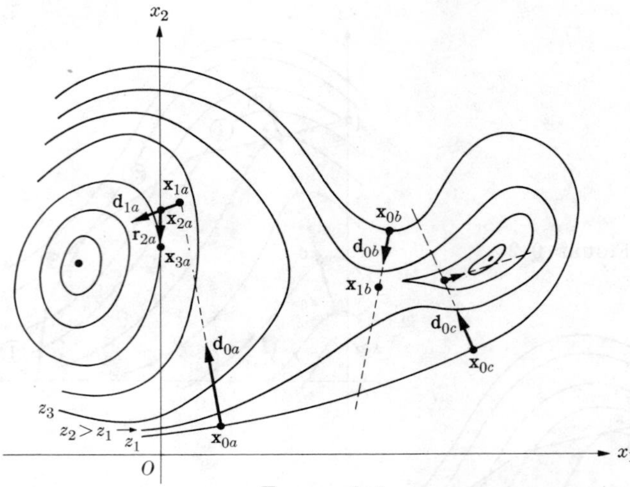

FIGURE 9–4

move as far as possible. The iterative procedure terminates in three iterations at $\mathbf{x}_{3a}$, which is a constrained relative maximum of f. If we start at the point $\mathbf{x}_{0b}$, we terminate at the saddle point $\mathbf{x}_{1b}$ in a single iteration. If we start at $\mathbf{x}_{0c}$, the sequence of points obtained converges to an $\mathbf{x}$ which we shall assume to be the absolute maximum of f for $\mathbf{x} \geq \mathbf{0}$. In this case, the number of iterations required may not be finite.

9–5 The numerical determination of r. We noted in Section 9–2 that if at any iteration, the constraints or non-negativity restrictions prevent us from moving in the direction of the gradient vector, then we must study the problem of (9–8) in order to determine the direction $\mathbf{r}$ in which to move so as to obtain the maximum rate of increase in $f(\mathbf{x})$ without violating any of the constraints or non-negativity restrictions. Problem (9–8) is itself a nonlinear programming problem. In Section 9–2 we did not consider the manner in which this problem can be solved. This will be examined now. We begin by showing that (9–8) is equivalent to a quadratic programming problem.

In particular, consider the following quadratic programming problem:

$$\begin{aligned} \mathbf{a}^i\mathbf{u} &\leq 0, \quad i \in I_1(v), \\ \mathbf{a}^i\mathbf{u} &= 0, \quad i \in I_2, \\ u_j &\geq 0, \quad j \in J(v), \\ \nabla f(\mathbf{x}_v)\mathbf{u} &= 1, \\ \min Z &= \mathbf{u}'\mathbf{u}. \end{aligned} \tag{9–13}$$

Let us first note that there is a one-to-one correspondence between the feasible solutions to (9–8) having $\nabla f(\mathbf{x}_v)\mathbf{r} > 0$ and the feasible solutions to (9–13). If $\mathbf{u}$ is a feasible solution to (9–13), then $\mathbf{r} = \mathbf{u}/|\mathbf{u}|$ is a feasible solution to (9–8), and if $\mathbf{r}$ is a feasible solution to (9–8), $\mathbf{r}/\eta$ is a feasible solution to (9–13) when $\eta = \nabla f(\mathbf{x}_v)\mathbf{r} > 0$. We shall next show that if $\mathbf{r}_v$ is an optimal solution to (9–8), then $\mathbf{u}_v = \mathbf{r}_v/\eta_v$, $\eta_v = \nabla f(\mathbf{x}_v)\mathbf{r}_v$, is an optimal solution to (9–13), provided that $\eta_v > 0$, and if $\mathbf{u}_v$ is an optimal solution to (9–13), $\mathbf{r}_v = \mathbf{u}_v/|\mathbf{u}_v|$ is an optimal solution to (9–8). To prove this, assume that $\mathbf{u}_v = \mathbf{r}_v/\eta_v$, $\mathbf{r}_v$ being an optimal solution to (9–8) with $\eta_v > 0$, and imagine that there exists a feasible solution $\mathbf{u}_-$ to (9–13) such that $\mathbf{u}'_-\mathbf{u}_- < \mathbf{u}'_v\mathbf{u}_v$, so that $|\mathbf{u}_-| < |\mathbf{u}_v|$. If we write $\mathbf{r}_- = \mathbf{u}_-/|\mathbf{u}_-|$, then $\mathbf{r}_-$ is a feasible solution to (9–8) and

$$\nabla f(\mathbf{x}_v)\mathbf{r}_- = \frac{1}{|\mathbf{u}_-|}\,\nabla f(\mathbf{x}_v)\mathbf{u}_- = \frac{1}{|\mathbf{u}_-|} > \nabla f(\mathbf{x}_v)\mathbf{r}_v = \frac{1}{|\mathbf{u}_v|}\cdot \tag{9–14}$$

Equation (9–14) follows because

$$\nabla f(\mathbf{x}_v)\mathbf{u}_- = \nabla f(\mathbf{x}_v)\mathbf{u}_v = 1.$$

Thus a contradiction is obtained and $\mathbf{u}_v = \mathbf{r}_v/\eta_v$ must be an optimal solution to (9–13) if $\mathbf{r}_v$ is an optimal solution to (9–8). Next imagine that $\mathbf{u}_v$ is an optimal solution to (9–13). Then $\mathbf{r}_v = \mathbf{u}_v/|\mathbf{u}_v|$ must be an optimal solution to (9–8), for suppose that there is an $\mathbf{r}_+$ such that $\nabla f(\mathbf{x}_v)\mathbf{r}_+ = \eta_+ > \nabla f(\mathbf{x}_v)\mathbf{r}_v = \eta_v$. Then $\mathbf{u}_+ = \mathbf{r}_+/\eta_+$ is a feasible solution to (9–13), and since $\mathbf{r}'_+\mathbf{r}_+ = \mathbf{r}'_v\mathbf{r}_v = 1$,

$$\mathbf{u}'_+\mathbf{u}_+ = \frac{1}{\eta_+^2} < \mathbf{u}'_v\mathbf{u}_v = \frac{1}{\eta_v^2},$$

which contradicts the fact that $\mathbf{u}_v$ is an optimal solution to (9–13). Thus we can use an optimal solution $\mathbf{u}_v$ to (9–13) to give us the direction in which to move at iteration $v + 1$, that is, we can use $\mathbf{u}_v$ as $\mathbf{r}_v$ (we need not bother to normalize $\mathbf{u}_v$ by dividing by $|\mathbf{u}_v|$). We ask the reader in Problem 9–2 to provide a geometrical interpretation of the equivalence of problems (9–8) and (9–13).

Consider now how we might solve the quadratic programming problem (9–13). Note that the objective function is convex. We could therefore attempt to apply directly one of the methods studied in Chapter 7, e.g. Wolfe's method. However, to do so we would have to apply the simplex method to a problem containing at least n constraints, and possibly as many as $2m + n$. If n were large, the amount of work would be prohibitive, even for the largest computer, especially since the gradient method requires that the problem be re-solved at each iteration. The other methods of Chapter 7 could also lead to prohibitively large problems.

Zoutendijk [8, 9] has suggested an alternative approach which will often require much less computational effort. Let us return to the original form of problem (9–8) and note that if $\mathbf{r}'\mathbf{r} = 1$ is replaced by $\mathbf{r}'\mathbf{r} \leq 1$, the set of optimal solutions is unchanged when the optimal value of the objective function is positive, because an optimal solution will always have the property that $\mathbf{r}'\mathbf{r} = 1$ (for otherwise the objective function could be increased). With this modification, the set of feasible solutions becomes a convex set. Let us include the non-negativity restrictions as part of the constraints, and write the problem equivalent to (9–8) as*

$$\begin{aligned} \mathbf{M}_v\mathbf{r} &\leq \mathbf{0}, \\ \mathbf{r}'\mathbf{r} &\leq 1, \\ \max D_\mathbf{r}f(\mathbf{x}_v) &= \nabla f(\mathbf{x}_v)\mathbf{r}, \end{aligned} \tag{9–15}$$

where in the constraints $\mathbf{M}_v\mathbf{r} \leq \mathbf{0}$, the strict equality holds for $i \in I_2$. Note that in this form the r_j are unrestricted.

We can then apply the theory of Chapter 6 and conclude that a necessary and sufficient condition for $\mathbf{r}$ to be an optimal solution to (9–15) is that there exist a $[\boldsymbol{\phi}, \phi_r]$, and $\mathbf{r}_s \geq \mathbf{0}$, such that

$$\mathbf{M}_v\mathbf{r} + \mathbf{r}_s = \mathbf{0}, \qquad \boldsymbol{\phi}'\mathbf{M}_v + 2\phi_r\mathbf{r}' = \nabla f(\mathbf{x}_v), \qquad \boldsymbol{\phi}'\mathbf{r}_s = 0, \tag{9–16}$$

where in addition all components of $[\boldsymbol{\phi}, \phi_r]$ are non-negative except for $i \in I_2$ which are unrestricted in sign. Also, it must be true that $r_{si} = 0$, $i \in I_2$. We can take the transpose of the second relation in (9–16), multiply by $\mathbf{M}_v$, and obtain

$$\mathbf{M}_v\mathbf{M}_v'\boldsymbol{\phi} + 2\mathbf{M}_v\mathbf{r}\phi_r = \mathbf{M}_v\mathbf{d}_v. \tag{9–17}$$

However, $\mathbf{M}_v\mathbf{r} = -\mathbf{r}_s$, and, since $\phi_r \geq 0$, we can write (9–17) as

$$\mathbf{M}_v\mathbf{M}_v'\boldsymbol{\phi} - \mathbf{w} = \mathbf{M}_v\mathbf{d}_v, \tag{9–18}$$

where $\mathbf{w} = 2\mathbf{r}_s\phi_r \geq \mathbf{0}$. The condition $\boldsymbol{\phi}'\mathbf{r}_s = 0$ can then be replaced by $\boldsymbol{\phi}'\mathbf{w} = 0$, $w_i = 0$, $i \in I_2$.

From Chapter 7, we know that the $[\boldsymbol{\phi}, \mathbf{w}]$ satisfying (9–18) and $\boldsymbol{\phi}'\mathbf{w} = 0$ with $\phi_i \geq 0$; $w_i \geq 0$, $i \notin I_2$; $w_i = 0$, $i \in I_2$, must be a basic solution to (9–18). A basic solution with $\phi_i \geq 0$; $w_i \geq 0$, $i \notin I_2$; $w_i = 0$, $i \in I_2$ will be called feasible. Once a basic feasible solution to (9–18) with $\boldsymbol{\phi}'\mathbf{w} = 0$ has been found, then it is clear from (9–16) that $\mathbf{r} = (\mathbf{d}_v - \mathbf{M}_v'\boldsymbol{\phi})/|\mathbf{d}_v - \mathbf{M}_v'\boldsymbol{\phi}|$ is an optimal solution to (9–15) if $\mathbf{d}_v - \mathbf{M}_v'\boldsymbol{\phi} \neq \mathbf{0}$. If $\mathbf{d}_v - \mathbf{M}_v'\boldsymbol{\phi} = \mathbf{0}$, then $\nabla f(\mathbf{x}_v)$ is a linear combination of the rows of $\mathbf{M}_v$ with each $\phi_i \geq 0$,

---

* Note that if in (9–8), $r_j \geq 0$, the row of $\mathbf{M}_v$ corresponding to this requirement is $-\mathbf{e}_j'$.

$i \notin I_2$, and we see immediately that for any $\mathbf{r}$ satisfying the constraints, the objective function cannot be positive. Thus there is no allowable direction in which to move so as to increase $f(\mathbf{x})$, and a stationary point has been reached. The iterative procedure then terminates. Note that when $\mathbf{d}_v - \mathbf{M}_v\boldsymbol{\phi} \neq \mathbf{0}$, it is not necessary to compute $\mathbf{r}$; one can simply use $\mathbf{d}_v - \mathbf{M}_v'\boldsymbol{\phi}$ as giving the direction in which to move.

Let us now consider how we may obtain a basic feasible solution to (9–18) with $\boldsymbol{\phi}'\mathbf{w} = 0$. Note first that we can immediately obtain a basic (but not necessarily feasible) solution with $\boldsymbol{\phi}'\mathbf{w} = 0$ by taking $\boldsymbol{\phi} = \mathbf{0}$ and $\mathbf{w} = -\mathbf{M}_v\mathbf{d}_v$. We then proceed to obtain a new basic solution with $w_i = 0$, $i \in I_2$. To do this we simply replace w_i by ϕ_i, $i \in I_2$, changing only one basic variable at a time by means of the usual transformation formulas of the simplex method (it is convenient to transform $\mathbf{d}_v - \mathbf{M}_v'\boldsymbol{\phi}$ simultaneously). After this is done, we still have $\boldsymbol{\phi}'\mathbf{w} = 0$ satisfied. If the resulting basic solution is feasible, it is the desired solution. If it is not, we must continue the iterative procedure. Problem 9–3 asks the reader to explain what to do if the above substitution cannot be carried out successfully.

Consider any basic, but not necessarily feasible, solution to (9–18), with the properties that (a) if ϕ_i is a basic variable, then w_i is not, and conversely, and (b) $w_i = 0$, $i \in I_2$. Thus $\boldsymbol{\phi}'\mathbf{w} = 0$. If this solution is not the one we are searching for, at least one of the basic variables which is a ϕ_i or w_i, $i \notin I_2$, must be negative. Consider any such negative basic variable. If the basic variable is ϕ_i, then, if we obtain a new basic solution by removing ϕ_i from the basic solution and replacing it by w_i, $w_i \geq 0$ in the new solution. We ask the reader to prove this in Problem 9–3. Of course, as a result of this change, a basic variable which was originally positive may become negative. Similarly, if a negative basic variable is w_i and we obtain a new basic solution by replacing w_i by ϕ_i, $\phi_i \geq 0$ in the new solution. Zoutendijk was the first to prove these facts. Note that if we change bases in this manner, we always maintain $\boldsymbol{\phi}'\mathbf{w} = 0$. Zoutendijk simply suggested that we proceed by selecting any negative basic variable ($i \notin I_2$); if this variable is ϕ_i, we obtain a new basic solution by replacing ϕ_i by w_i, and if it is w_i, we obtain a new basic solution by replacing w_i by ϕ_i. This iterative procedure is continued until a basic feasible solution is obtained. With what has been outlined above, we have no guarantee that cycling will not occur. It is possible to select the variable to be removed in such a way that one can guarantee that cycling will not occur. Zoutendijk [9] discusses how this may be done. For practical purposes, it is probably best to simply select the most negative basic variable ($i \notin I_2$) for replacement. In carrying out this process we never consider the ϕ_i, $i \in I_2$, for removal, since these variables are unrestricted in sign.

The order of $\mathbf{M}_v\mathbf{M}_v'$ is always less than $m + n$, but is greater than the number of constraints in (9–8) if more than a single non-negativity restriction must be included. Lemke [4] has described a slightly different way to solve (9–13) and (9–8). However, his method involves the manipulation of basis matrices of order n at every iteration, whereas Zoutendijk's procedure may involve basis matrices of order considerably less than n for some, or conceivably even all, iterations of the gradient method.

Let us now consider a different technique of solving (9–13). Note that the objective function is separable and convex. Furthermore, the constraints are linear, and therefore any local optimum is also a global optimum. We can thus use the methods of Chapter 4 to determine an approximate global optimum. Furthermore, we can use the δ-formulation and the especially efficient computational algorithm based on the decomposition principle discussed in Section 4–7. Using this algorithm, we would never need to work with basis matrices of order greater than $m + 1$, and a basis matrix of this size would occur only if all the constraints in the original problem appeared in (9–13). There is one difficulty in using this method, namely the question of determining the allowable range of variation for each u_j. One could attempt to decide ahead of time what range to use for each u_j. For example, in most cases, it would probably be satisfactory to assume that

$$\frac{-2}{|\partial f(\mathbf{x}_v)/\partial x_j|} \le u_j \le \frac{2}{|\partial f(\mathbf{x}_v)/\partial x_j|}, \qquad j \notin J(v),$$

$$0 \le u_j \le \frac{2}{|\partial f(\mathbf{x}_v)/\partial x_j|}, \qquad j \in J(v).$$

However, this assumption requires that a different range of variation be considered for the variables each time the problem is solved.

Thus it would be more convenient if we could, with reasonable assurance, restrict the range of variation of the u_j to some specified interval, say $-1 \le u_j \le 1$, $u_j \notin J(v)$; $0 \le u_j \le 1$, $u_j \in J(v)$. This can be done, because if in (9–13), $\nabla f(\mathbf{x}_v)\mathbf{u} = 1$ is replaced by $\nabla f(\mathbf{x}_v)\mathbf{u} = \rho$ for any $\rho > 0$, an optimal solution to the new problem will be a scalar multiple of the corresponding optimal solution to (9–13), and hence can be used for the locally best direction in which to move. If one selects

$$\rho = \tfrac{1}{2} \min_j \left| \frac{\partial f(\mathbf{x}_v)}{\partial x_j} \right|,$$

then one might reasonably expect that all $|u_j| \le 1$. We have no guarantee that this will be the case, but usually it should. Thus, when u_j is unrestricted in sign, one might represent u_j^2 by the dashed curve shown in Fig. 9–5. For $u_j > 1$ or < -1, we simply write $u_j^2 \doteq 1 + e|u_j|$, where the slope e might be chosen in the range 3 to 5, perhaps. In this manner, one can solve the problem even if u_j is not in the range $|u_j| < 1$; however, the accuracy of the approximation deteriorates rapidly as $|u_j|$ increases above 1. Of course, with the above scaling, $|u_j|$ should not often become greater than unity. For the δ-form of the approximating problem, one would simply replace an unrestricted u_j by (see Problem 4–47)

$$u_j = \sum_{k=1}^{t-1} (\Delta u_{kj})\,\delta_{kj} + \delta_{tj} - \sum_{k=1}^{t-1} (\Delta u_{kj})\,\delta_{-kj} - \delta_{-tj},$$

where the variables δ_{kj}, δ_{-kj} are non-negative and have upper bounds of unity, except δ_{tj} and $-\delta_{tj}$ which have no upper bounds. If u_j is required to be non-negative, the same representation is used; however, the variables δ_{-kj} would not appear.

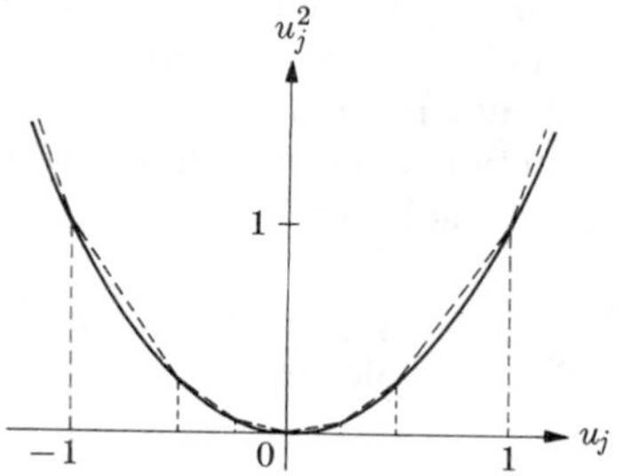

FIGURE 9–5

It should be noted that an optimal solution to the approximating problem satisfies the constraints of (9–13) and indeed yields a feasible direction in which to move. How close the solution comes to the locally best direction in which to move depends on how fine the subdivisions are made in setting up the approximating problem. With the scaling procedure outlined above, it should be possible to obtain very good approximations to the solution to (9–13). Note that only a single positive artificial variable is needed in the computation. Thus no long Phase I computation should be required.

Zoutendijk suggested that instead of trying to solve (9–8) or equivalently (9–13) to find the locally best direction in which to move, we might solve the following problem which yields a feasible direction but not necessarily the locally best one:

$$\begin{aligned} \mathbf{a}^i\mathbf{r} &\le 0, & i &\in I_1(v), \\ \mathbf{a}^i\mathbf{r} &= 0, & i &\in I_2, \\ 0 \le r_j &\le 1, & j &\in J(v), \\ -1 \le r_j &\le 1, & j &\notin J(v), \\ \max Z_1 &= \nabla f(\mathbf{x}_v)\mathbf{r}. \end{aligned} \tag{9–19}$$

The criterion $\mathbf{r}'\mathbf{r} = 1$ has been replaced by the less restrictive one requiring only that each r_j be less than or equal to unity. Note that every feasible solution to (9–8) also is a feasible solution to (9–19). Thus, if there is a direction in which to move such that $f(\mathbf{x})$ can be increased, the solution to (9–19) will yield one such direction. Note that an optimal solution to (9–8) is, in fact, a feasible solution to (9–19) so that the optimal value of the objective function for (9–19) will be at least as great as it is for (9–8). However, the solution to (9–19) does not necessarily yield the locally best direction in which to move because, after we normalize the solution obtained to (9–19) so that $|\mathbf{r}| = 1$, $\nabla f(\mathbf{x}_v)\mathbf{r}$ may be less than that for the optimal solution to (9–8). When some special algorithm is used to handle the upper bounds (the lower bounds are taken care of by introducing new variables $s_j = r_j + 1$), the solution to (9–19) should require less effort than solving the quadratic programming problem (9–13) and about the same amount of effort as solving the δ-form of the approximating problem discussed above. Nonetheless, it would seem that the δ-form of the approximating problem would be preferred, since it determines approximately the locally best direction in which to move, whereas in solving (9–19) we are not sure how close the solution will come to giving this locally best direction.

Instead of using $0 \le r_j \le 1$, $j \in J(v)$; $-1 \le r_j \le 1$, $j \notin J(v)$ in place of $\mathbf{r}'\mathbf{r} \le 1$ in (9–20), we could use

$$\sum_{j=1}^{n} |r_j| \le 1. \tag{9–20}$$

To represent this constraint we would write for $j \notin J(v)$:

$$r_j = r'_j - r''_j, \qquad r'_j, r''_j \ge 0, \qquad r'_j r''_j = 0.$$

Then

$$|r_j| = \begin{cases} r_j, & j \in J(v), \\ r'_j + r''_j, & j \notin J(v). \end{cases}$$

Consequently (9–21) can be written

$$\sum_{j \in J(v)} r_j + \sum_{j \notin J(v)} (r'_j + r''_j) \le 1, \qquad r'_j r''_j = 0, \qquad j \in J(v). \tag{9–21}$$

When (9–21) is used, we introduce only one extra constraint rather than a large number of upper and lower bounds. Note now that the set of feasible solutions is convex, since $|r_j|$ is a convex function. Thus the problem can be solved as a linear programming problem without the use of restricted basis entry. This is to be proved in Problem 9–44.

The use of (9–21) instead of $\mathbf{r}'\mathbf{r} \le 1$ or the use of upper and lower bounds as in (9–19) would probably require fewer computations than would be needed to solve (9–13) by the δ-form of the approximating problem, or (9–19) by an upper-bounds algorithm. Solving (9–13) by the δ-form of the approximation method nonetheless remains the preferred method, because there is no guarantee that (9–21) will yield the locally best direction in which to move. We shall see later, however, that (9–21) will be especially useful for a procedure to be introduced for handling nonlinear constraints.

9–6 The gradient projection method. In the previous section we discussed how we might determine the locally best direction in which to move from the current feasible solution $\mathbf{x}_v$ to (9–1) to obtain a new feasible solution $\mathbf{x}_{v+1}$ with $f(\mathbf{x}_{v+1}) > f(\mathbf{x}_v)$. This involved the solution of a quadratic programming problem. A linear programming problem (9–21) which may, hopefully, yield approximately the locally best direction was also considered. Suppose now that instead of concerning ourselves with the determination of the locally best or approximately locally best direction in which to move, we simply try to determine some feasible direction in which it will be possible to move while increasing $f(\mathbf{x})$. The method we are about to discuss was developed by Rosen [5] and is called the gradient projection method. It does not require that we solve an optimization problem in order to determine the direction in which to move.

Let us begin the exposition of the gradient projection method by attempting to find an $\mathbf{r}$ such that $D_{\mathbf{r}}f(\mathbf{x}_v) > 0$ and all inequalities of (9–6) and (9–7) hold as strict equalities. If this is to be the case, $\mathbf{r}$ must satisfy

$$\mathbf{a}^i\mathbf{r} = 0, \quad i \in I(v); \quad r_j = 0, \quad j \in J(v). \tag{9–22}$$

The constraints (9–22) can be written $\mathbf{M}_v\mathbf{r} = \mathbf{0}$, $\mathbf{M}_v$ being defined as in (9–15). Intuitively, what we are going to do is find the projection of $\nabla f(\mathbf{x}_v)$ on the subspace of E^n which is the orthogonal complement of that generated by the rows of $\mathbf{M}_v$. Let the rank of $\mathbf{M}_v$ be h, and let the matrix $\mathbf{Q}_v = (\mathbf{q}_1, \ldots, \mathbf{q}_h)$ contain as its columns a set of h linearly independent columns of $\mathbf{M}_v'$. Then the subspace S generated by the columns of $\mathbf{Q}_v$ will be the same as that generated by the rows of $\mathbf{M}_v$. Now

$$E^n = S + O(S),$$

where $O(S)$ is the subspace which is the orthogonal complement of S. Consequently, any vector in E^n can be written uniquely as the sum of a vector in S and a vector in $O(S)$. The vector $\mathbf{d}_v$ can then be written

$$\mathbf{d}_v = \mathbf{r}_v + \mathbf{s}_v; \quad \mathbf{r}_v \in O(S), \quad \mathbf{s}_v \in S. \tag{9–23}$$

But since S is generated by the columns of $\mathbf{Q}_v$, we can write

$$\mathbf{s}_v = \sum_i \alpha_{iv}\mathbf{q}_i = \mathbf{Q}_v\boldsymbol{\alpha}_v. \tag{9–24}$$

Thus

$$\mathbf{d}_v = \mathbf{r}_v + \mathbf{Q}_v\boldsymbol{\alpha}_v. \tag{9–25}$$

However, since $\mathbf{r}_v \in O(S)$, $\mathbf{q}_j'\mathbf{r}_v = 0$, $j = 1, \ldots, h$. Therefore, multiplying (9–25) on the left by $\mathbf{Q}_v'$, we obtain

$$\mathbf{Q}_v'\mathbf{d}_v = \mathbf{Q}_v'\mathbf{Q}_v\boldsymbol{\alpha}_v. \tag{9–26}$$

Next let us note that $\mathbf{Q}_v'\mathbf{Q}_v$ is nonsingular. To see this we use the expansion of $|\mathbf{Q}_v'\mathbf{Q}_v|$ developed in {LA 3–17} to see that $|\mathbf{Q}_v'\mathbf{Q}_v|$ is the sum of the squares of all minors of order h in $\mathbf{Q}_v$. Since $r(\mathbf{Q}_v) = h$, there is at least one minor of order h which does not vanish, so that $|\mathbf{Q}_v'\mathbf{Q}_v| \neq 0$. Consequently

$$\boldsymbol{\alpha}_v = (\mathbf{Q}_v'\mathbf{Q}_v)^{-1}\mathbf{Q}_v'\mathbf{d}_v, \tag{9–27}$$

and from (9–24)

$$\mathbf{s}_v = \mathbf{Q}_v(\mathbf{Q}_v'\mathbf{Q}_v)^{-1}\mathbf{Q}_v'\mathbf{d}_v. \tag{9–28}$$

Finally, from (9–23),

$$\mathbf{r}_v = \mathbf{d}_v - \mathbf{s}_v = [\mathbf{I} - \mathbf{Q}_v(\mathbf{Q}_v'\mathbf{Q}_v)^{-1}\mathbf{Q}_v']\mathbf{d}_v = \mathbf{P}_v\mathbf{d}_v, \tag{9–29}$$

where

$$\mathbf{P}_v = \mathbf{I} - \mathbf{Q}_v(\mathbf{Q}_v'\mathbf{Q}_v)^{-1}\mathbf{Q}_v'. \tag{9–30}$$

Since $\mathbf{r}_v \in O(S)$, $\mathbf{r}_v$ is orthogonal to all vectors in S. Consequently, $\mathbf{r}_v$ satisfies $\mathbf{M}_v\mathbf{r}_v = \mathbf{0}$. The matrix $\mathbf{P}_v$ is sometimes referred to as a projection matrix. It "projects" $\mathbf{d}_v$ into the orthogonal complement of the subspace generated by the columns of $\mathbf{M}_v'$.

If $\mathbf{r}_v \neq \mathbf{0}$, then, since $\mathbf{s}_v'\mathbf{r}_v = 0$,

$$\nabla f(\mathbf{x}_v)\mathbf{r}_v = \mathbf{d}_v'\mathbf{r}_v = \mathbf{r}_v'\mathbf{r}_v > 0 \tag{9–31}$$

by (9–23). Consequently, if the $\mathbf{r}_v$ computed from (9–29) is not a null vector, we have found a feasible direction in which to move while increasing $f(\mathbf{x})$. Note that no optimization problem had to be solved in order to determine $\mathbf{r}_v$.

Let us suppose then that at each iteration we determine the direction in which to move by computing $\mathbf{r}_v$ from (9–29). We have left unanswered what happens when $\mathbf{r}_v = \mathbf{0}$. Let us now examine this case. As we shall see, we have not necessarily reached a stationary point when $\mathbf{r}_v = \mathbf{0}$. If $\mathbf{r}_v = \mathbf{0}$, then from (9–23) and (9–24)

$$\mathbf{d}_v = \mathbf{Q}_v\boldsymbol{\alpha}_v, \tag{9–32}$$

that is, $\mathbf{d}_v$ lies in the subspace spanned by the columns of $\mathbf{M}_v'$.

There are two cases which must be distinguished. First, suppose that the $\boldsymbol{\alpha}_v$ of (9–32) satisfies $\alpha_{iv} \geq 0$, $i \notin I_2$. Note that $\alpha_{iv} \geq 0$, $i \notin I_2$, implies $\alpha_{iv} \geq 0$, $i \in I_1(v)$, and $\alpha_{iv} \geq 0$ for the rows of $\mathbf{M}_v$ corresponding to the requirements $-r_j \leq 0, j \in J(v)$ in (9-8). We can then write

$$\nabla f(\mathbf{x}_v) = \sum_{i=1}^{h} \alpha_{iv}\mathbf{q}_i'; \qquad \alpha_{iv} \geq 0, \qquad i \notin I_2.$$

Recall that each $\mathbf{q}_i'$ is some row of $\mathbf{M}_v$. Let us now return to problem (9-8). For any feasible $\mathbf{r}$,

$$\nabla f(\mathbf{x}_v)\mathbf{r} = \sum_{i=1}^{h} \alpha_{iv}\mathbf{q}_i'\mathbf{r}.$$

But $\mathbf{q}_i'\mathbf{r} \leq 0, i \notin I_2$, and $\mathbf{q}_i'\mathbf{r} = 0, i \in I_2$, since $\mathbf{r}$ is a feasible solution and $\mathbf{q}_i'$ is some row of $\mathbf{M}_v$. Thus, because each $\alpha_{iv} \geq 0, i \notin I_2$, we must conclude that

$$\nabla f(\mathbf{x}_v)\mathbf{r} \leq 0$$

for any feasible solution $\mathbf{r}$ to (9-8), and consequently we have reached a constrained stationary point of $f(\mathbf{x})$, so that the iteration process terminates. We have shown, therefore, that if at some iteration, we reach a state where $\mathbf{r}_v = \mathbf{0}$ and $\alpha_{iv} \geq 0, i \notin I_2$, in (9-32) then we have reached a constrained stationary point of $f(\mathbf{x})$.

We still must consider the problem where $\mathbf{r}_v = \mathbf{0}$ and at least one α_{iv}, $i \notin I_2$, is negative. It will be assumed for the present that at $\mathbf{x}_v$, the rank of $\mathbf{M}_v$ is equal to the number of rows in $\mathbf{M}_v$, so that for every row in $\mathbf{M}_v$ there will be one column in $\mathbf{Q}_v$. This means that the normals to the hyperplanes of (9-22) are linearly independent. We shall now show that in this case, if we relax the requirement that every inequality of (9-6) and (9-7) must hold as a strict equality and instead allow one inequality corresponding to a negative α_{iv}, $i \notin I_2$, to hold as a strict inequality, then we can determine a feasible direction in which we can move while increasing $f(\mathbf{x})$. To be specific assume that $\alpha_{hv} < 0$, and $h \notin I_2$. Consider the subspace S' generated by $\mathbf{q}_1, \ldots, \mathbf{q}_{h-1}$. Denote by $O(S')$ the subspace which is the orthogonal complement of S', and let $\mathbf{p}_1, \ldots, \mathbf{p}_{n-h+1}$ be an orthonormal basis for $O(S')$. Then, since the $\mathbf{q}_i$ and $\mathbf{p}_j$ span E^n, we must be able to write

$$\mathbf{q}_h = \sum_{j=1}^{n-h+1} \beta_j\mathbf{p}_j + \sum_{i=1}^{h-1} \gamma_i\mathbf{q}_i. \tag{9-33}$$

Furthermore, since $\mathbf{q}_h$ is linearly independent of $\mathbf{q}_1, \ldots, \mathbf{q}_{n-1}$, at least one $\beta_j \neq 0$. Substitution of (9-33) into (9-32) yields

$$\mathbf{d}_v = \alpha_{hv} \sum_{j=1}^{n-h+1} \beta_j\mathbf{p}_j + \sum_{i=1}^{h-1} (\alpha_{iv} + \alpha_{hv}\gamma_i)\mathbf{q}_i = \hat{\mathbf{r}}_v + \hat{\mathbf{s}}_v$$

and

$$\hat{\mathbf{r}}_v = \alpha_{hv} \sum_{j=1}^{n-h+1} \beta_j\mathbf{p}_j \neq \mathbf{0},$$

so that $\mathbf{d}_v$ does have a non-null projection on $O(S')$. Furthermore, on using (9–33), we have

$$\mathbf{q}_h'\hat{\mathbf{r}}_v = \alpha_{hv} \sum_{j=1}^{n-h+1} \beta_j^2 < 0. \tag{9–34}$$

Consequently, $\hat{\mathbf{r}}_v$ satisfies (9–6) and (9–7), since $\mathbf{q}_i'\hat{\mathbf{r}}_v = 0, i = 1, \ldots, h - 1$, and $\mathbf{q}_h'\hat{\mathbf{r}}_v < 0$ by (9–34). But by our previous assumption this accounts for all the constraints (9–6) and (9–7). Furthermore, from (9–31),

$$\nabla f(\mathbf{x}_v)\hat{\mathbf{r}}_v = \hat{\mathbf{r}}_v'\hat{\mathbf{r}}_v > 0,$$

so that by moving in the direction of $\hat{\mathbf{r}}_v$ we can indeed increase $f(\mathbf{x})$. We have thus proved that if $\mathbf{P}_v\mathbf{d}_v = \mathbf{0}$ and at least one $\alpha_{iv} < 0, i \notin I_2$, then, if the rank of $\mathbf{M}_v$ is equal to the number of rows in $\mathbf{M}_v$, we can find a feasible direction in which to move such that $f(\mathbf{x})$ can be increased. This is done as follows: We remove from $\mathbf{Q}_v$ any single column i corresponding to an $\alpha_{iv} < 0, i \notin I_2$, to yield a new matrix $\hat{\mathbf{Q}}_v$ of order $h - 1$. We next determine from (9–30) the projection matrix $\hat{\mathbf{P}}_v$ appropriate to the matrix $\hat{\mathbf{Q}}_v$. Then $\hat{\mathbf{r}}_v = \hat{\mathbf{P}}_v\mathbf{d}_v$ provides the desired direction. When more than one $\alpha_{iv} < 0, i \notin I_2$, one could choose for removal any of the q_i corresponding to an $\alpha_{iv} < 0, i \notin I_2$. In practice, one might use some rule such as choosing the i corresponding to the most negative α_{iv}.

When the rank of $\mathbf{M}_v$ is less than the number of rows of $\mathbf{M}_v$, we run into a little difficulty. In this case, there will not be one column of $\mathbf{Q}_v$ corresponding to each row of $\mathbf{M}_v$, i.e., to each of the restrictions (9–6) and (9–7). Denote by $\mathbf{m}^k$, $k \in K$, the rows of $\mathbf{M}_v$ not appearing as columns of $\mathbf{Q}_v$. Then we know that

$$(\mathbf{m}^k)' = \sum_{i=1}^{h} \rho_i\mathbf{q}_i, \qquad k \in K.$$

Suppose now that we proceed just as above and remove $\mathbf{q}_h$ from $\mathbf{Q}_v$ so that $\mathbf{q}_h'\hat{\mathbf{r}}_v < 0$. We have shown above that $\mathbf{q}_i'\hat{\mathbf{r}}_v = 0, i \neq h$. However,

$$\mathbf{m}^k\hat{\mathbf{r}}_v = \rho_h\alpha_{hv} \sum_{j=1}^{n-h+1} \beta_j^2, \qquad k \in K,$$

and it does not necessarily follow that

$$\mathbf{m}^k\hat{\mathbf{r}}_v \le 0, \qquad k \in K \cap I_1(v) \quad \text{or} \quad k \in K \cap J(v);$$
$$\mathbf{m}^k\hat{\mathbf{r}}_v = 0, \qquad k \in K \cap I_2.$$

This depends on ρ_h. If all the restrictions (9–6) and (9–7) are satisfied, there is no problem. We proceed just as in the case where the rank of $\mathbf{M}_v$ is equal to the number of rows in $\mathbf{M}_v$. When the restrictions are not satisfied, we can resort to a perturbation technique. For $k \in K$, let us replace b_k in (9–1) by $b_k + \delta^k$, where δ is a very small positive number. After this is done, none of the constraints $k \in K$ is active at $\mathbf{x}_v$, and we are reduced to the case studied above. It can be shown that there exists a $\delta_0 > 0$ such that for all δ, $0 < \delta \leq \delta_0$, no more than h (h being the number of columns in $\mathbf{Q}_v$) of the constraints from $I(v)$ can be active simultaneously after the b_i are perturbed as indicated above. This is to be proved in Problem 9–41. Thus on continuing with the gradient method, we shall never encounter a situation where more than h of the constraints from $I(v)$ are active. The problem just discussed is similar to the degeneracy problem in linear programming. In practice, it is not necessary to actually make a perturbation. In Problem 9–42 we ask the reader to discuss how one might proceed.

In this section we have developed a procedure for selecting the direction in which to move from $\mathbf{x}_v$ in a way which does not require the solution of an optimization problem. We can always find a direction in which to move such that $f(\mathbf{x})$ can be increased unless $\mathbf{P}_v\mathbf{d}_v = \mathbf{0}$ and the $\boldsymbol{\alpha}_v$ of (9–27) satisfies $\alpha_{iv} \geq 0$, $i \notin I_2$. In this case, we have shown that $\mathbf{x}_v$ is a constrained stationary point of $f(\mathbf{x})$ and the iterative procedure terminates. If $\mathbf{r}_v = \mathbf{P}_v\mathbf{d}_v \neq \mathbf{0}$, then $\mathbf{r}_v$ provides the direction in which to move. When $\mathbf{r}_v = \mathbf{0}$ but at least one $\alpha_{iv} < 0$, $i \notin I_2$, we remove from $\mathbf{Q}_v$ a column $\mathbf{q}_i$ corresponding to an $\alpha_{iv} < 0$, $i \notin I_2$, to yield $\hat{\mathbf{Q}}_v$. Then $\hat{\mathbf{P}}_v$ corresponding to $\hat{\mathbf{Q}}$ is determined, and finally $\hat{\mathbf{r}}_v = \hat{\mathbf{P}}_v\mathbf{d}_v$ provides the direction in which to move. In this latter case, a perturbation may be required to ensure that the rank of $\mathbf{M}_v$ is equal to the number of rows in $\mathbf{M}_v$.

Note that if $\mathbf{r}_v = \mathbf{P}_v\mathbf{d}_v \neq \mathbf{0}$, then $\mathbf{x}_{v+1} = \mathbf{x}_v + \lambda\mathbf{r}_v$ and $\mathbf{M}_v\mathbf{r}_v = \mathbf{0}$, so that all the constraints and non-negativity restrictions that were active at $\mathbf{x}_v$ will be active at $\mathbf{x}_{v+1} = \mathbf{x}_v + \lambda\mathbf{r}_v$. If $\lambda = \epsilon$, one (or conceivably more than one) constraint or non-negativity restriction that was inactive at $\mathbf{x}_v$ will become active at $\mathbf{x}_{v+1}$, and to obtain $\mathbf{M}_{v+1}$ we simply annex one (or perhaps more than one) row to $\mathbf{M}_v$. If $\lambda < \epsilon$, then $\mathbf{M}_{v+1} = \mathbf{M}_v$. When $\mathbf{r}_v = \mathbf{0}$, we use $\hat{\mathbf{r}}_v = \hat{\mathbf{P}}_v\mathbf{d}_v$, and in this case, one constraint or non-negativity restriction which was active at $\mathbf{x}_v$ will be inactive at $\mathbf{x}_{v+1}$. Thus, if $\lambda = \epsilon$, we must remove one row from $\mathbf{M}_v$ and add one (or perhaps more than one) to obtain $\mathbf{M}_{v+1}$. If $\lambda < \epsilon$, $\mathbf{M}_{v+1}$ is obtained from $\mathbf{M}_v$ simply by removing the appropriate row.

Let us now see how to obtain $\mathbf{Q}_{v+1}$ when $\mathbf{x}_{v+1} = \mathbf{x}_v + \lambda\mathbf{r}_v$. If $\lambda < \epsilon$, $\mathbf{Q}_{v+1} = \mathbf{Q}_v$. When $\lambda = \epsilon$, assume that $\mathbf{m}$ is the transpose of the new row to appear in $\mathbf{M}_{v+1}$. Then $\mathbf{Q}_{v+1} = (\mathbf{Q}_v, \mathbf{m})$ if $\mathbf{m}$ is linearly independent of the columns of $\mathbf{Q}_v$, and $\mathbf{Q}_{v+1} = \mathbf{Q}_v$ if $\mathbf{m}$ is linearly dependent on the columns of $\mathbf{Q}_v$. Fortunately, it is rather simple to determine whether or not $\mathbf{m}$ is linearly dependent on the columns of $\mathbf{Q}_v$. We compute $\mathbf{P}_v\mathbf{m}$, and if this vector is not null, $\mathbf{m}$ has a non-null projection on the orthogonal complement of the subspace generated by the columns of $\mathbf{Q}_v$ and hence (why?) is linearly independent of the columns of $\mathbf{Q}_v$. If $\mathbf{P}_v\mathbf{m} = \mathbf{0}$, then $\mathbf{m}$ is linearly dependent on the columns of $\mathbf{Q}_v$. When $\mathbf{x}_{v+1} = \mathbf{x}_v + \lambda\hat{\mathbf{r}}_v$ and $\lambda < \epsilon$, $\mathbf{Q}_{v+1} = \hat{\mathbf{Q}}_v$, where $\hat{\mathbf{Q}}_v$ is obtained from $\mathbf{Q}_v$ by removing the column corresponding to the constraint which becomes inactive. If $\lambda = \epsilon$ and $\mathbf{m}$ is defined as above, $\mathbf{Q}_{v+1} = (\hat{\mathbf{Q}}_v, \mathbf{m})$ if $\mathbf{m}$ is linearly independent of the columns of $\hat{\mathbf{Q}}_v$, or $\mathbf{Q}_{v+1} = \hat{\mathbf{Q}}_v$ if $\mathbf{m}$ is linearly dependent on the columns of $\hat{\mathbf{Q}}_v$. To determine whether or not $\mathbf{m}$ is linearly independent of the columns of $\hat{\mathbf{Q}}_v$, we compute $\hat{\mathbf{P}}_v\mathbf{m}$, and if this vector is non-null, $\mathbf{m}$ is linearly independent of the columns of $\hat{\mathbf{Q}}_v$. If more than a single constraint or non-negativity restriction becomes active when $\lambda = \epsilon$, we proceed as above, adding the constraints one at a time.

At each iteration one must compute a new $\mathbf{P}_v$ and $\boldsymbol{\alpha}_v$. It would be extremely laborious if $(\mathbf{Q}_v'\mathbf{Q}_v)^{-1}$ had to be recomputed from its definition at each iteration. We can easily develop a procedure for computing the new inverse when a column is added or moved from $\mathbf{Q}_v$, by means of formulas similar to those of Section 2–1 for the partitioned form of the inverse. In Problems 9–4 and 9–5 the reader is asked to develop an efficient procedure for determining $\mathbf{P}_{v+1}$ and $\boldsymbol{\alpha}_{v+1}$ from $\mathbf{P}_v$ and $\boldsymbol{\alpha}_v$.

In actually attempting to use the gradient projection method just outlined on a digital computer, one would have to make provisions for certain numerical difficulties that could arise. For example, even though $\mathbf{P}_v\mathbf{d}_v = \mathbf{0}$, because of roundoff errors, etc., the vector $\mathbf{P}_v\mathbf{d}_v$ determined by the computer may not be precisely a null vector. One must, therefore, use a different rule for switching over from using $\mathbf{P}_v\mathbf{d}_v$ as the direction in which to move to removing one column of $\mathbf{Q}_v$ and using $\hat{\mathbf{P}}_v\mathbf{d}_v$ instead. One rule would be always to compute $\nabla f(\mathbf{x}_v)\mathbf{r}_v/|\mathbf{r}_v|$, $\mathbf{r}_v = \mathbf{P}_v\mathbf{d}_v$, and $\nabla f(\mathbf{x}_v)\hat{\mathbf{r}}_v/|\hat{\mathbf{r}}_v|$, $\hat{\mathbf{r}}_v = \hat{\mathbf{P}}_v\mathbf{d}_v$, where $\hat{\mathbf{Q}}_v$ was obtained from $\mathbf{Q}_v$ by removing the column corresponding to the most negative α_{iv} if there was at least one negative α_{iv}. Then one would select the direction corresponding to the larger of these two numbers. Although this procedure seems to be a reasonable one, it may involve an unnecessarily extensive computational effort. A better alternative might be to compute $\nabla f(\mathbf{x}_v)\mathbf{r}_v/|\mathbf{r}_v|$, and if the result turned out to be too small, one could also compute $\nabla f(\mathbf{x}_v)\hat{\mathbf{r}}_v/|\hat{\mathbf{r}}_v|$. Then one would select the direction which corresponded to the largest of these numbers, or conversely, he might also consider $\hat{\mathbf{r}}_v$ if there was some sufficiently negative α_{iv}. What is to be considered "too small" or "sufficiently negative" would depend on the problem and on the physical dimensions used for the various variables and parameters appearing in the problem. Conceivably, one might also want these criteria to change as the solution of the problem progressed. We might also encounter similar problems in deciding when to terminate the iterative procedure, since the computer may not yield $\mathbf{P}_v\mathbf{d}_v = \mathbf{0}$ even if $\mathbf{P}_v\mathbf{d}_v = \mathbf{0}$. One would have to introduce some alternative procedure for terminating the iterative procedure other than requiring that $\mathbf{P}_v\mathbf{d}_v = \mathbf{0}$ and $\alpha_{iv} \geq 0,\ i \notin I_2$.

There is one case in which we can be sure that $\mathbf{P}_v\,\mathbf{d}_v = \mathbf{0}$, and thus we do not need to compute $\mathbf{P}_v\mathbf{d}_v$ explicitly. This is when $\mathbf{Q}_v$ is an nth-order matrix. Then the columns of $\mathbf{Q}_v$ span all of E^n, and $O(S)$ contains only $\mathbf{0}$, so that $\mathbf{P}_v\mathbf{d}_v$ must be $\mathbf{0}$. It would be quite convenient to have the computer make use of this fact because, as a result, it may become simpler to determine when to use $\hat{\mathbf{r}}$ instead of $\mathbf{r}$, and when to terminate the iterative process.

Since with the gradient projection method we do not necessarily choose the locally best direction in which to move, a proof is needed that the sequence $\mathbf{x}_v$ when not finite will converge to a constrained stationary point of $f(\mathbf{x})$ or $|\mathbf{x}_v| \to \infty$. It can be proved that if at each iteration one chooses either $\mathbf{r}_v$ or $\hat{\mathbf{r}}_v$ depending on which gives the larger directional derivative of $f(\mathbf{x}_v)$, then the iterative procedure does have these properties. We ask the reader to prove this in Problem 9-6.

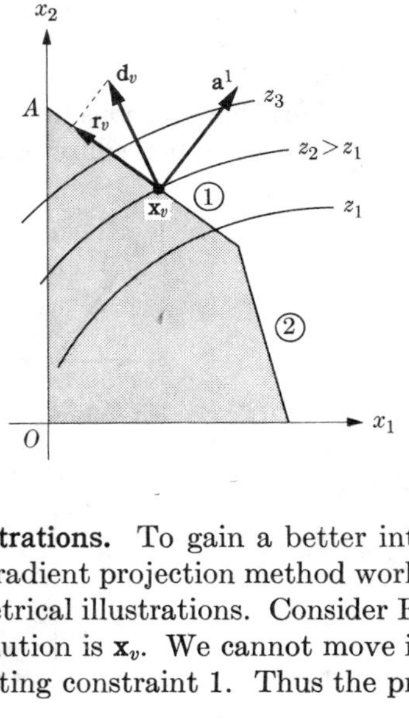

FIGURE 9-6

9-7 Geometric illustrations. To gain a better intuitive feeling for the manner in which the gradient projection method works, it might be helpful to provide some geometrical illustrations. Consider Fig. 9-6. Assume that the current feasible solution is $\mathbf{x}_v$. We cannot move in the direction of the gradient without violating constraint 1. Thus the problem (9-8) becomes

$$\mathbf{a}^1\mathbf{r} \leq 0, \qquad \mathbf{r}'\mathbf{r} = 1, \qquad \max D_{\mathbf{r}}f(\mathbf{x}_v) = \nabla f(\mathbf{x}_v)\mathbf{r}.$$

The matrix $\mathbf{Q}_v$ to be used in the gradient projection method is simply $\mathbf{Q}_v' = \mathbf{a}^1$, and

$$\mathbf{r}_v = \mathbf{P}_v\mathbf{d}_v = \left[\mathbf{d}_v - \left(\frac{\mathbf{a}^1\mathbf{d}_v}{|\mathbf{a}^1|^2}\right)(\mathbf{a}^1)'\right].$$

The vector $\mathbf{r}_v$ obtained by the gradient projection method is nothing but the perpendicular projection of $\mathbf{d}_v$ onto the boundary of the set of feasible solutions, as shown. Thus at the next step one would move along the boundary until extreme point A is reached, at which point the iterative procedure terminates.

Consider next the situation illustrated in Fig. 9–7. In this instance both constraints will be violated if we move in the direction of the gradient vector. Now problem (9–8) becomes

$$\mathbf{a}^i\mathbf{r} \le 0, \qquad i = 1, 2; \qquad \mathbf{r}'\mathbf{r} = 1, \qquad \max D_{\mathbf{r}} f(\mathbf{x}_v) \;=\; \nabla f(\mathbf{x}_v)\mathbf{r},$$

and the matrix $\mathbf{Q}_v$ to be used in the gradient projection method is $\mathbf{Q}_v' = [\mathbf{a}^1, \mathbf{a}^2]$. In this case, the columns of $\mathbf{Q}_v$ span E^2 so that $\mathbf{P}_v\mathbf{d}_v = \mathbf{r}_v = \mathbf{0}$. Intuitively, only one point $\mathbf{0}$ satisfies $\mathbf{a}^i\mathbf{r} = 0$, $i = 1, 2$, so that it is not possible to move from $\mathbf{x}_v$ in any direction such that both constraints hold as strict equalities. Note that when $\mathbf{d}_v'$ is expressed as a linear combination of $\mathbf{a}^1$ and $\mathbf{a}^2$, then $\alpha_{2v} < 0$ and $\alpha_{1v} > 0$. Thus we can find a feasible direction in which to move if we allow $\mathbf{a}^2\mathbf{r} \le 0$ to hold as a strict inequality. We remove $(\mathbf{a}^2)'$ from $\mathbf{Q}_v$ to yield $\hat{\mathbf{Q}}_v$. Then we are reduced to the previous case studied, and $\hat{\mathbf{r}}_v = \hat{\mathbf{P}}_v\mathbf{d}_v$ is the vector shown. At the next step we move up side 1 of the set of feasible solutions until the extreme point A is reached, at which point the iterative procedure terminates.

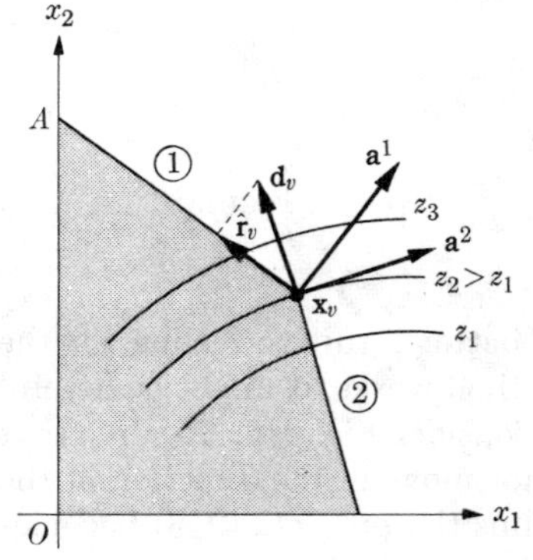

FIGURE 9–7

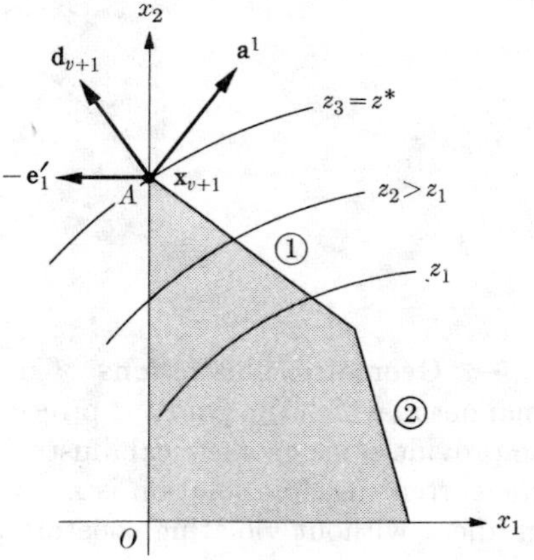

FIGURE 9–8

In the above two illustrations, we have made the statement that the iterative procedure terminates when we reach the extreme point A. It should then be true that $\mathbf{P}_{v+1}\mathbf{d}_{v+1} = \mathbf{0}$ and $\boldsymbol{\alpha}_{v+1} \ge \mathbf{0}$ at $\mathbf{x}_{v+1}$. Let us see that this is indeed true. The situation is illustrated in Fig. 9–8. Problem (9-8) for this case becomes

$$\mathbf{a}^1\mathbf{r} \leq 0, \qquad -r_1 \leq 0, \qquad \mathbf{r}'\mathbf{r} = 1, \qquad \max D_{\mathbf{r}}f(\mathbf{x}_{v+1}) = \nabla f(\mathbf{x}_{v+1})\mathbf{r}.$$

Now $\mathbf{Q}_{v+1}$ contains as columns $-\mathbf{e}_1$ and $(\mathbf{a}^1)'$. Thus $\mathbf{P}_{v+1}\mathbf{d}_{v+1} = \mathbf{0}$. Furthermore, $\mathbf{d}_{v+1}$ lies in the cone spanned by $-\mathbf{e}_1$ and $(\mathbf{a}^1)'$, and hence $\boldsymbol{\alpha}_{v+1} > \mathbf{0}$. Thus the criteria for terminating the iterative procedure are satisfied. In this instance, $f(\mathbf{x})$ takes on its global optimum over the set of feasible solutions at $\mathbf{x}_{v+1}$.

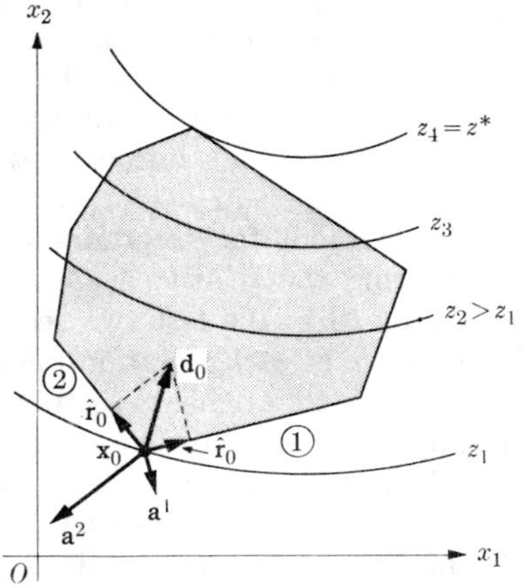

FIGURE 9-9

Suppose that the initial solution $\mathbf{x}_0$ for the problem represented in Fig. 9-9 is the one shown. For $\mathbf{x}_0$, $\mathbf{Q}_0' = [\mathbf{a}^1, \mathbf{a}^2]$ and $\mathbf{P}_0\mathbf{d}_0 = \mathbf{0}$. However, $\alpha_{10} < 0$ and $\alpha_{20} < 0$. Thus we can remove either column from $\mathbf{Q}_0$ to obtain $\hat{\mathbf{Q}}_0$ such that $\hat{\mathbf{r}}_0 = \hat{\mathbf{P}}_0\mathbf{d}_0 \neq \mathbf{0}$, $\nabla f(\mathbf{x}_0)\hat{\mathbf{r}}_0 > 0$, that is, $\mathbf{d}_0$ can be projected as shown on $\mathbf{a}^2\mathbf{x} = b_1$ or on $\mathbf{a}^2\mathbf{x} = b_2$, and we can move along either one of these sides of the set of feasible solutions while increasing $f(\mathbf{x})$. If we apply the gradient method described in the previous section, we shall move along side 1 or side 2, and if we pick the most negative α_{i0}, we shall move along side 2.

Note, however, that moving along either of these sides will ultimately require more iterations than are really necessary, since we can actually move in the direction of $\mathbf{d}_0$ and, in a single iteration, cut completely across the convex set of feasible solutions. The gradient projection method as described in the previous section does not take advantage of moving in the direction of $\mathbf{d}_v$ when it is possible to do so, since only a single constraint is deactivated at a time. It might therefore seem desirable to modify the gradient projection method, at least for the early iterations, so that after computing $\mathbf{d}_v$, we check to see whether $\mathbf{d}_v$ satisfies (9-6) and (9-7). If it does, we move in the direction of $\mathbf{d}_v$ and do not apply the gradient projection method. This procedure leads to one difficulty: after we have moved in the direction of $\mathbf{d}_v$, we shall, in general, be unable to determine $(\mathbf{Q}_{v+1}'\mathbf{Q}_{v+1})^{-1}$ from $(\mathbf{Q}_v'\mathbf{Q}_v)^{-1}$, since the set of i in $\mathbf{M}_{v+1}$ may be completely different from that in $\mathbf{M}_v$. Thus $(\mathbf{Q}_{v+1}'\mathbf{Q}_{v+1})^{-1}$ will have to be computed directly, which may require a greater computational effort than would be called for if we had applied the gradient projection method at each step. It depends on how many iterations (if any) are saved by moving in the direction of $\mathbf{d}_v$. Thus, although at first glance it might seem desirable to make provisions for moving in the direction of the gradient vector when possible, a more detailed analysis makes it appear doubtful that there would really be a saving in computational effort. The desirability of making this modification would no doubt depend on the types of problems being solved and on the nature of the initial solutions available.

9–8 Comparison of the methods for determining *r*. No numerical results are available comparing the relative computational efficiencies of the various methods (discussed in the last two sections) for determining the direction in which to move at each iteration. For this reason it is not possible to make any conclusive statements as to which method is to be preferred. However, there definitely are considerable differences in the amount of computational effort required by the various methods for determining $\mathbf{r}_v$. Those which attempt to solve exactly the quadratic programming problem (9–13) may involve manipulations of matrices of order greater than m, possibly all the way up to $m + n$. On the other hand, the use of the δ-form of the approximation method for solving (9–13) should be quite efficient and will never involve more than $m + 1$ constraints. However, this technique requires the solution of a linear programming problem at each iteration. The gradient projection method does not call for the solution of an optimization problem, but may involve manipulation of matrices of order greater than m, since non-negativity restrictions must be included. Probably, either the δ-form of the approximation method for solving (9–13) or the gradient projection method would be the most suitable one to use.

Normally, when using a gradient method, one would hope to start out with a feasible solution in which only a small number of constraints were active. Thus, for the initial iterations, the size of the matrices involved in determining the directions in which to move would be relatively small. Only toward the end of the iterative procedure would a large number of constraints and/or non-negativity restrictions appear in (9–13). This is the sort of situation where the gradient method would be most efficient. If for all iterations, essentially all m constraints of (9–1) appeared in (9–13), the procedure might easily become impossibly laborious.

As a final observation, we wish to note that it is difficult to compare the various methods of determining $\mathbf{r}$, because it is not necessarily true that the smallest number of iterations will be required if at each step we move in a direction such that the constrained directional derivative of $f(\mathbf{x})$ is maximized. Indeed, just as with linear programming problems, it might sometimes be preferable to move in a direction such that $f(\mathbf{x})$ is decreased for a while. Of course, there is no way of knowing this during the actual process of computation.

9–9 Solution of linear programming problems using gradient methods. Linear programming problems can be solved by the gradient methods we have been discussing. Certain simplifications are introduced when $f(\mathbf{x}) = \mathbf{cx}$, since $\nabla f(\mathbf{x}) = \mathbf{c}$ and is independent of $\mathbf{x}$. We have already noted that for a linear objective function, when we move from $\mathbf{x}_v$ in the direction of $\mathbf{r}_v$ to obtain $\mathbf{x}_{v+1}$, we always move as far as possible, i.e., we move until an inactive constraint or non-negativity restriction becomes active. This feature makes it unnecessary to search for the value of λ for which $f(\mathbf{x}_v + \lambda \mathbf{r}_v)$ is maximized. Further, since ∇f does not change, in going from one iteration to the next, we merely add another constraint (or in exceptional circumstances, more than one) to the old problem (9–15) to obtain the new one and, perhaps, remove one or more of the constraints that were active for the old problem. This feature enables us to use the old solution as an aid in solving the new problem. In Problem 9–7, we ask the reader to discuss the procedure in more detail. In some cases, this approach can considerably reduce the computational effort required when (9–13) is solved at each iteration to determine $\mathbf{r}$. The gradient projection method is also somewhat simplified due to the fact that ∇f never changes. We ask the reader to consider these simplifications in Problem 9–8.

For linear programming problems, we can prove that if (9–8) is solved at each step to determine the direction in which to move, then the gradient method will converge to an optimal solution in a finite number of steps, or provide an indication that there is an unbounded solution. To see this consider problem (9–8) which is to be solved at each iteration. Let $\mathbf{r}_v$ be the optimal solution. Suppose that $\mathbf{a}^i\mathbf{r}_v < 0$, $i \in I_<(v)$, and $r_{jv} > 0$, $j \in J_>(v)$. Then precisely the same solution $\mathbf{r}_v$ would be obtained to (9–8) if the constraints $i \in I_<(v)$ and non-negativity restrictions $j \in J_>(v)$ were omitted. Furthermore, it will be the constraints $i \in I_<(v)$ and non-negativity restrictions $j \in J_>(v)$ which will be dropped, and one (or perhaps more) new constraints or non-negativity restrictions will be added to obtain the new problem appropriate to $\mathbf{x}_{v+1}$. Note then that any feasible solution to the new problem for $\mathbf{x}_{v+1}$ must be a feasible solution to the previous problem for $\mathbf{x}_v$ if the constraints $i \in I_<(k)$ and non-negativity restrictions for $j \in J_>(k)$ are omitted. Consequently, since the solution to (9–8) is unique, and since $\mathbf{r}_v$ does not satisfy the new constraint (or constraints) added to form the new problem, it must be true that the optimal solution $\mathbf{r}_{v+1}$ to the new problem satisfies $\mathbf{cr}_{v+1} < \mathbf{cr}_v$. Therefore, we cannot, at two different iterations, encounter the same problem (9–8) to be solved. Since the number of such problems is finite, the iterative procedure must terminate in a finite number of iterations. The gradient projection method also converges in a finite number of iterations, but the above method of proof cannot be used, since it need not be true that the directional derivative decrease at each iteration. Instead, one shows that there cannot be an infinite number of $\mathbf{x}_v$ in every ϵ-neighborhood of an optimal solution. The general convergence proof which demonstrates that the method will converge to a stationary point of $f(\mathbf{x})$ shows that in a finite number of iterations, the method will yield a solution arbitrarily close to an optimal solution to the linear programming problem. All that remains is to prove that starting from any point in a sufficiently small neighborhood of an optimal solution, we shall reach this optimal solution in a finite number of steps. Problem 9–9 is concerned with the details of this proof.

The very limited computational experience available with the various versions of the gradient method suggests that all require more computational effort per iteration but fewer iterations than would be required if the simplex method were applied. The reduction in the number of iterations holds even if a feasible solution is not available to initiate the gradient method. The reason for this is that with the gradient methods there exists the possibility of cutting through the convex set and cutting across faces, which the simplex method cannot do, since it moves from one extreme point to an adjacent one. When a feasible solution is not available to initiate the gradient method, then on a given type of computer, the simplex method seems to produce an optimal solution in a little less time than the gradient method does. However, if a good starting solution is available, the gradient method should show up much more favorably.

As might be expected, there are interesting connections between the manner of selecting $\mathbf{r}_v$ in the gradient method and the corresponding procedures in the various simplex type algorithms. In particular, there is an interesting connection between the gradient projection method and the dual simplex algorithm for those cases where the initial solution used in the gradient projection method is a basic feasible solution to (9–1). We shall examine the relationships for problems where all the variables in (9–1) must be non-negative and all constraints must hold as strict equalities (I_2 contains all i), that is, (9–1) has been converted to the standard form for a linear programming problem:

$$\mathbf{Ax} = \mathbf{b}, \quad \mathbf{x} \geq \mathbf{0}, \quad \max z = \mathbf{cx}, \quad r(\mathbf{A}) = m. \tag{9–35}$$

The dual of (9-35) is then

$$\mathbf{A}'\mathbf{w} + \mathbf{D}\mathbf{w}_s = \mathbf{c}'; \qquad \mathbf{w}_s \geq \mathbf{0}, \qquad \mathbf{D} = -\mathbf{I}_n, \qquad \min Z = \mathbf{b}'\mathbf{w}. \tag{9-36}$$

Let us now apply the dual simplex algorithm to (9-36), i.e., to the dual of (9-35), and not to (9-35) itself.

Let $\mathbf{x}_0$ denote the initial basic feasible solution to (9-35). Let us assume that it is not degenerate. Note that every $\mathbf{Q}_v$-matrix used in the gradient projection method consists of a linearly independent subset of columns from $(\mathbf{A}', \mathbf{D})$. Since $r(\mathbf{A}) = m$, every $\mathbf{Q}_v$ contains $\mathbf{A}'$. Furthermore, since we are starting with a basic solution to (9-35), $\mathbf{Q}_0$ also contains $n - m$ columns from $\mathbf{D}$. These plus the m columns of $\mathbf{A}'$ are indeed linearly independent, as desired. This is proved in {LP 8-8}. Thus, $\mathbf{Q}_0$ spans E^n and $\mathbf{P}_0\mathbf{c}' = \mathbf{0}$. Therefore $\mathbf{Q}_0$ is a basis matrix for (9-36), and $\boldsymbol{\alpha}_0$ is a basic, but not necessarily feasible, solution to (9-36). If $\alpha_{i0} \geq 0$, $i \notin I_2$,* so that $\boldsymbol{\alpha}_0$ is a basic feasible solution to (9-36), then by the theory developed in {LP 8-8} we know that $\mathbf{x}_0$ is an optimal solution to (9-35) and $\boldsymbol{\alpha}_0$ an optimal solution to (9-36). For this statement to hold it must be true that $\mathbf{x}_0\mathbf{w}_s = 0$. But this will be true, since a column from $\mathbf{D}$ will be included in $\mathbf{Q}_0$ only if the corresponding $x_j = 0$. This, of course, is also the criterion which terminates the iteration scheme in gradient projection method.

Now suppose that at least one $\alpha_{i0} < 0$, $i \notin I_2$. In the gradient projection method we choose the most negative α_{i0}, that is, the most negative basic variable for the basic solution to (9-36), to determine the vector to be dropped from $\mathbf{Q}_0$ to yield $\hat{\mathbf{Q}}_0$. This is also the criterion used in the dual simplex method to determine the column to be removed from the basis. Let α_{r0} be the most negative α_{i0}, $i \notin I_2$. Then for either method, column r of $\mathbf{Q}_0$ is to be removed.

Denote the costs for the problem (9-36) by ρ_i. Then $\rho_i = b_i$ if i refers to a w_i and $\rho_i = 0$ if i refers to a w_{si}. Imagine that $\mathbf{Q}_0$ is arranged so that the columns from $\mathbf{A}'$ come first, to be followed by those from $\mathbf{D}$. Consider then a column $-\mathbf{e}_j$ of $\mathbf{D}$ not in $\mathbf{Q}_0$. For this column,

$$Z_j - \rho_j = Z_j = (\mathbf{b}, \mathbf{0})\mathbf{Q}_0^{-1}(-\mathbf{e}_j) = -x_{j0} < 0, \tag{9-37}$$

where x_{j0} is the jth component of $\mathbf{x}_0$. Since $-\mathbf{e}_j$ is not in $\mathbf{Q}_0$, $x_{j0} > 0$.

When applying the dual simplex algorithm to (9-36), we determine the vector to enter the basis from

$$\min_{j \notin J(0)} \left\{ \frac{Z_j - \rho_j}{y_r^j}, \quad y_r^j < 0 \right\}, \tag{9-38}$$

---

* Note that I_2 contains all the constraints in (9-35), so that the only i, $i \notin I_2$, refer to the conditions $-r_j \leq 0$ if $x_{j0} = 0$.

where y_r^j is the negative of the jth component of the rth row of $\mathbf{Q}_0^{-1}$. This follows, since $\mathbf{y}^j = \mathbf{Q}_0^{-1}(-\mathbf{e}_j)$. Denote the jth component of the rth row of $\mathbf{Q}_0^{-1}$ by q_r^j. Then (9–38) is equivalent to

$$\min_{j \notin J(0)} \left\{ \frac{x_{j0}}{q_r^j}, \quad q_r^j > 0 \right\}. \tag{9–39}$$

The condition (9–39) looks very much like the condition for determining ϵ in the gradient method, i.e., for determining how far we move from $\mathbf{x}_0$. Let us now investigate this point. When the gradient projection method is used, then to determine $\mathbf{r}_0$, the direction in which to move from $\mathbf{x}_0$, column r is dropped from $\mathbf{Q}_0$ to yield $\hat{\mathbf{Q}}_0$, so that $O(S')$, S' being the subspace generated by the columns of $\hat{\mathbf{Q}}_0$, has the dimension one. Therefore, in moving from an extreme point of (9–35), we shall (using the gradient projection method) move along an edge of the convex set to another extreme point. When the new extreme point is reached, one more column will be added to $\hat{\mathbf{Q}}_0$ to obtain $\mathbf{Q}_1$. All that remains is to show that the column is precisely the one determined from (9–39). To do this, consider $\mathbf{Q}_0^{-1}$. The rth row of $\mathbf{Q}_0^{-1}$ is orthogonal to every column of $\mathbf{Q}_0$ except column r. Thus the columns of $\hat{\mathbf{Q}}_0$ and the rth row of $\mathbf{Q}_0^{-1}$ span E^n, and the rth row of $\mathbf{Q}_0^{-1}$ can be used to generate the subspace $O(S')$. Consequently, the projection $\hat{\mathbf{r}}_0$ of $\mathbf{c}$ onto $O(S')$ must be proportional to the rth row of $\mathbf{Q}_0^{-1}$. Now in the gradient method, the new solution will have the form $\mathbf{x} = \mathbf{x}_0 + \lambda\hat{\mathbf{r}}_0$, where λ is chosen such that $x_{j0} + \lambda\hat{r}_{j0} \geq 0$, $j \notin J(0)$. With λ determined in this manner, at least one non-negativity restriction associated with columns not appearing in $\mathbf{Q}_0$ will become active when we move as far as possible, and because of the proportionality between $\hat{\mathbf{r}}_0$ and the rth row of $\mathbf{Q}_0^{-1}$, this restriction will be precisely the one determined by (9–39). Therefore, we see that the gradient projection method yields precisely the same set of basic feasible solutions to (9–35) that would be obtained if we solved (9–36) by the dual simplex algorithm. This demonstrates the equivalence which we set out to show.

9–10 Problems with nonlinear constraints. Let us now examine how the gradient methods we have been studying can be generalized to handle problems involving nonlinear constraints. As might be expected, nonlinear constraints considerably complicate the computational scheme. We shall study problems of the form

$$\begin{aligned} g_i(\mathbf{x}) &\leq b_i, \quad & i \in I_1,\\ g_i(\mathbf{x}) &= b_i, \quad & i \in I_2,\\ x_j &\geq 0, \quad & j \in J,\\ \max z &= f(\mathbf{x}), & \end{aligned} \tag{9–40}$$

where it will be assumed that $f(\mathbf{x})$ and all the $g_i(\mathbf{x})$ have continuous first partial derivatives wherever these are needed.

Let us begin by restricting our attention to the case where I_2 is empty or contains only linear equations, and $g_i(\mathbf{x})$ is convex for $i \in I_1$. Then, if there is a feasible solution, the set of feasible solutions is convex. Consider some feasible solution $\mathbf{x}_v$, and denote by $I_1(v)$ the set of active constraints and by $J(v)$ the set of variables from J which are zero. The plane tangent to each surface $g_i(\mathbf{x}) = b_i$, $i \in I_1(v)$, at $\mathbf{x}_v$ will be a supporting hyperplane to the convex set of feasible solutions at $\mathbf{x}_v$. The equation for such a supporting hyperplane is

$$\nabla g_i(\mathbf{x}_v)\mathbf{x} = \nabla g_i(\mathbf{x}_v)\mathbf{x}_v.$$

Suppose now that we wish to determine a new feasible solution $\mathbf{x} = \mathbf{x}_v + \lambda\mathbf{r}$ for which $f(\mathbf{x}) > f(\mathbf{x}_v)$. If $\mathbf{x} = \mathbf{x}_v + \lambda\mathbf{r}$ is to satisfy $g_i(\mathbf{x}) \le b_i$, $i \in I_1(v)$, it is necessary (but not sufficient) that $\nabla g_i(\mathbf{x}_v)\mathbf{r} \le 0$. This follows from (3-64). Zoutendijk [8, 9] has then suggested the following procedure for determining $\mathbf{r}$. We determine the $\mathbf{r}$ and σ which solve the problem

$$\begin{aligned} \nabla g_i(\mathbf{x}_v)\mathbf{r} + \sigma &\le 0, \qquad i \in I_1(v),\\ \mathbf{a}^i\mathbf{r} &= 0, \qquad i \in I_2,\\ -\nabla f(\mathbf{x}_v)\mathbf{r} + \sigma &\le 0,\\ \mathbf{r}'\mathbf{r} &= 1,\\ \max Z &= \sigma, \end{aligned} \tag{9-41}$$

where if $g_i(\mathbf{x})$ is linear, a σ is not included in the corresponding constraint of (9-41). This procedure selects a direction which will take us back into the interior of the set (with respect to the nonlinear boundaries, anyway) while still maintaining $\nabla f(\mathbf{x}_v)\mathbf{r} > 0$. The $\mathbf{r}$, call it $\mathbf{r}_v$, which is the solution to this problem might then be quite similar to that shown in Fig. 9-10. Once $\mathbf{r}_v$ has been found, we determine ϵ to be the largest λ for which $g_i(\mathbf{x}_v + \lambda\mathbf{r}_v) \le b_i$, $i \in I_1$ and $x_{jv} + \epsilon r_{jv} \ge 0$, $j \in J$. Note that we must now consider all $i \in I_1$, not merely $i \notin I_1(v)$, since moving in the direction $\mathbf{r}_v$, we can strike one of the constraints $i \in I_1(v)$. To determine how far to move, we find the λ, $0 < \lambda < \epsilon$, which maximizes $f(\mathbf{x}_v + \lambda\mathbf{r}_v)$. Problem 9-14 asks the reader to show how (9-41) may be solved numerically.

Rosen [6] has generalized the gradient projection method considered earlier to the maximization of a concave function over a convex set. He proceeds by first converting the problem to one of maximizing the linear objective function $z = x_{n+1}$ by adding an additional constraint $x_{n+1} - f(\mathbf{x}) \le 0$. The new set of feasible solutions is still convex. Consider then a feasible solution $\mathbf{x}_v$ lying on the boundary of the convex set. For the constraints and non-negativity restrictions which are active at this point, we determine the hyperplanes tangent to these surfaces at $\mathbf{x}_v$. Then the

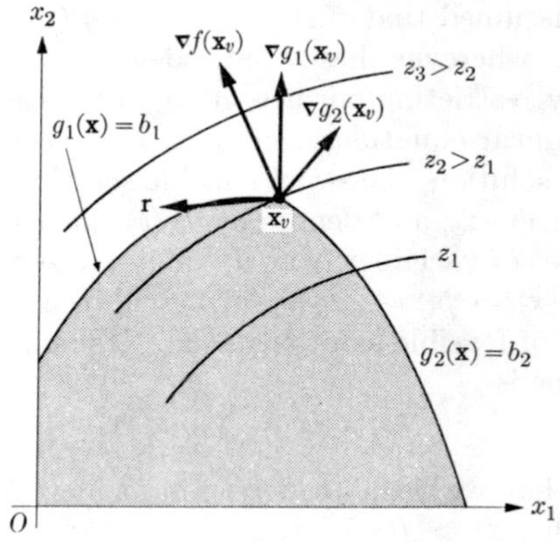

FIGURE 9–10

gradient projection method is applied just as described earlier, to project the gradient vector into the orthogonal complement of the subspace S generated by the normals to the tangent hyperplanes. Next a step is taken in the direction of the gradient projection. In making this step, we move in the intersection of the tangent hyperplanes, and hence the new point so obtained is not feasible. Now a correction procedure is necessary to return to a feasible solution. This requires an iterative procedure ensuring that we always move in a direction contained in S. All these operations are performed in such a way that when a new feasible point $\mathbf{x}_{v+1}$ is obtained, it is true that $f(\mathbf{x}_{v+1}) > f(\mathbf{x}_v)$. We shall not discuss in detail these generalizations of the gradient projection method, but consider a different method which would seem to be at least as efficient, and hopefully more so.

It should be pointed out that for nonlinear constraints, the gradient projection method is not nearly so efficient as it is for linear ones, one important reason being that in the move from $\mathbf{x}_v$ to $\mathbf{x}_{v+1}$, all the gradient vectors for the $g_i(\mathbf{x})$ may change, even though the set of active constraints for $\mathbf{x}_v$ may differ only by one constraint from that for $\mathbf{x}_{v+1}$. Therefore it is not in general possible to compute $(\mathbf{Q}'_{v+1}\mathbf{Q}_{v+1})^{-1}$ from $(\mathbf{Q}'_v\mathbf{Q}_v)^{-1}$, and hence the new inverse matrix must be computed directly. Since $\mathbf{Q}'_{v+1}\mathbf{Q}_{v+1}$ could easily be a matrix of order considerably greater than the total number of constraints (columns for the non-negativity restrictions appear), the computational effort required to recompute the inverse at each iteration can be very sizable. In addition, there is the problem of moving back to the constraint set after one has moved in the intersection of the tangent hyperplanes. This cannot, in general, be done in a single step, but requires an iterative procedure. Furthermore, the method does not guarantee that the new solution will be feasible, but only that it lies within a δ-neighborhood of the boundary of the set of feasible solutions (where δ can be chosen arbitrarily).

Let us consider now the situation where the set of feasible solutions is not required to be convex. Zoutendijk's method cannot be applied if there are any nonlinear constraints which must hold as strict equalities, since his technique provides no way of guaranteeing that these equations will always be satisfied. His method can be used, however, if I_2 is empty or contains only linear equations. Now, of course, one could not guarantee that the sequence of solutions would converge to anything more than a constrained stationary point of $f(\mathbf{x})$. Since no computational experience is available, it is not clear how suitable (9–41) is for determining the direction in which to move. There exists the possibility that only very small steps would be taken.

The gradient projection method could be used for nonconvex regions and even if I_2 contained nonlinear equations. Some of the difficulties in using the gradient projection method have already been indicated. There is also the question, of course, as to whether the steps taken would be so small as to require an impractical number of iterations.

9–11 A gradient method for problems with separable constraints. We would now like to consider a different approach for applying a gradient method to (9–40) which may have some advantages over the two methods just discussed. We shall make the (not very restrictive) assumption that the constraints of (9–40) are separable so that we may write

$$g_i(\mathbf{x}) = \sum_{j=1}^{n} g_{ij}(x_j).$$

Then we shall proceed as in Chapter 4 and replace each $g_{ij}(x_j)$ by its polygonal approximation $\hat{g}_{ij}(x_j)$. In particular, when

$$x_{k_j,j} \le x_j \le x_{k_j+1,j}, \qquad j = 1, \ldots, n, \tag{9–42}$$

we can represent $\hat{g}_{ij}(x_j)$ as

$$\hat{g}_{ij}(x_j) = g_{k_j,ij} + s_{k_j,ij}(x_j - x_{k_j,j}) \tag{9–43}$$

or

$$\hat{g}_{ij}(x_j) = g_{k_j+1,ij} - s_{k_j,ij}(x_{k_j+1,j} - x_j), \tag{9–44}$$

where $s_{k_j,ij}$ is defined by (4–74). Let $\hat{g}_i(\mathbf{x}) = \sum_j \hat{g}_{ij}(x_j)$.

What the procedure of Chapter 4 really does is subdivide the region of E^n over which $\mathbf{x}$ may range into a number of "rectangular" cells specified by (9–42). The function $g_i(\mathbf{x})$ for any given cell is approximated by the linear function $\hat{g}_i(\mathbf{x})$. However, the linear representation of $g_i(\mathbf{x})$ changes as we move from one cell to another. Consider a given cell and let $\hat{g}_i(\mathbf{x})$ be the representation of $g_i(\mathbf{x})$ for this cell. Then, if there are any points in the cell satisfying $\hat{g}_i(\mathbf{x}) = b_i$, the hyperplane $\hat{g}_i(\mathbf{x}) = b_i$ is the approximate representation of the surface $g_i(\mathbf{x}) = b_i$ for the cell under consideration.

We shall then replace the problem (9–40) by the approximating problem

$$\begin{aligned} \hat{g}_i(\mathbf{x}) &\leq b_i, \quad i \in I_1, \\ \hat{g}_i(\mathbf{x}) &= b_i, \quad i \in I_2, \\ x_j &\geq 0, \quad j \in J, \\ \max z &= f(\mathbf{x}). \end{aligned} \tag{9–45}$$

Note that we are not approximating $f(\mathbf{x})$, and indeed, we need not assume that $f(\mathbf{x})$ is separable.

The method we are about to discuss will converge to a constrained stationary point of $f(\mathbf{x})$, which will usually correspond to a constrained relative maximum of $f(\mathbf{x})$. In general, there is no way in which we can guarantee that the process will converge to a point where $f(\mathbf{x})$ takes on its global optimum over the set of feasible solutions. Let us consider then the iterative procedure for generating a set of feasible solutions $\mathbf{x}_v$ to (9–45) with the property that $f(\mathbf{x}_{v+1}) > f(\mathbf{x}_v)$.

Assume that after v iterations, we have obtained the feasible solution $\mathbf{x}_v$. We then determine $\nabla f(\mathbf{x}_v)$. We now wish to determine a direction $\mathbf{r}$ in which to move at the next step such that $\nabla f(\mathbf{x}_v)\mathbf{r} > 0$. The point $\mathbf{x}_v$ may lie in the interior of one of the cells referred to above or it may lie on the boundaries of two or more such cells. Suppose that for $j \in J_e(v)$, the jth component of $\mathbf{x}_v$ lies at one or the other end point of (9–42). We shall not include in this count cases where a component of $\mathbf{x}_v$ vanishes, i.e., $j \in J(v)$. If there are p such components, $\mathbf{x}_v$ lies on the boundaries of 2^p cells.

We are going to consider new feasible solutions of the form $\mathbf{x} = \mathbf{x}_v + \lambda\mathbf{r}$. Denote by $I(v)$ the set of constraints from (9–45) which are active at $\mathbf{x}_v$. We must determine the constraints which $\mathbf{r}$ must satisfy. For $j \notin J_e(v) \cup J(v)$ the jth component of $\mathbf{x}_v$ is in the interior of the interval (9–42), and hence, whether r_j is positive, negative, or zero, if λ is small enough for x_j to remain in the interval, then $g_{ij}(x_j)$ will be represented by (9–43). However, for $j \in J_e(v)$, the representation of $g_{ij}(x_j)$ will differ, depending on whether r_j is positive or negative. To account for this fact, write $r_j = r_j' - r_j''$, where $r_j', r_j'' \geq 0$. Then $x_j = x_{jv} + \lambda r_j' - \lambda r_j''$. By assumption, $x_{jv} = x_{k_j,j}$. If $r_j' > 0$, $r_j'' = 0$, we could use (9–43) to write

$$\hat{g}_{ij}(x_j) = g_{k_j,ij} + \lambda s_{k_j,ij} r'_j, \tag{9–46}$$

and if $r_j' = 0$, $r_j'' > 0$, we could use (9–44) to write

$$\hat{g}_{ij}(x_j) = g_{k_j,ij} - \lambda s_{k_j-1,ij} r''_j. \tag{9–47}$$

Consequently, for r_j having either sign, we can write

$$\hat{g}_{ij}(x_j) = g_{k_j,ij} + \lambda s_{k_j,ij}r'_j - \lambda s_{k_j-1,ij}r''_j, \tag{9–48}$$

provided that we impose the additional restriction that $r'_jr''_j = 0$. In this manner, we have the proper representation of $\hat{g}_{ij}(x_j)$, whether or not x_j increases or decreases at the next step.

Since the constraints for $i \in I(v)$ were active at $\mathbf{x}_v$, we conclude that $\mathbf{r}$ must satisfy

$$\begin{aligned} &\sum_{j\in J_e(v)} (s_{k_j,ij}r'_j - s_{k_j-1,ij}r''_j) + \sum_{j\notin J_e(v)} s_{k_j,ij}r_j \leq 0, \quad i \in I_1(v), \\ &\sum_{j\in J_e(v)} (s_{k_j,ij}r'_j - s_{k_j-1,ij}r''_j) + \sum_{j\notin J_e(v)} s_{k_j,ij}r_j = 0, \quad i \in I_2, \\ &\qquad r_j \geq 0, \quad j \in J(v), \end{aligned} \tag{9–49}$$

where in addition it must be true that

$$r'_j, r''_j \geq 0, \qquad r'_jr''_j = 0, \qquad j \in J_e(v).$$

We would like to specify that $\mathbf{r}'\mathbf{r} = 1$, or $\mathbf{r}'\mathbf{r} \leq 1$, so that the locally best direction in which to move would be determined. However, because of the restrictions $r'_jr''_j = 0$, we cannot proceed to convert the problem to a quadratic programming problem and use the efficient algorithm for the δ-form of the approximating problem to solve it. There seems to be no easy way of incorporating the requirement that $\mathbf{r}'\mathbf{r} \leq 1$. Instead we might use an upper-bounds approach like that indicated in (9–19). However, the simplest approach to use here is to require that $\sum_j |r_j| \leq 1$, since we already have requirements that for some j, $r'_jr''_j = 0$. Consequently, we shall assume that $\mathbf{r}$ satisfies

$$\sum_{j\in J(v)} r_j + \sum_{j\notin J(v)} (r'_j + r''_j) \leq 1, \tag{9–50}$$

where

$$r_j = r'_j - r''_j, \qquad r'_j, r''_j \geq 0, \qquad r'_jr''_j = 0, \qquad j \notin J(v). \tag{9–51}$$

Now (9–51) replaces the previous requirement that r'_j, $r''_j \geq 0$, $r'_jr''_j = 0$, $j \in J_e(v)$.

We wish to determine the $\mathbf{r}$ satisfying (9–49), (9–50), and (9–51) which maximizes

$$Z = \nabla f(\mathbf{x}_v)\mathbf{r}. \tag{9–52}$$

This problem can be solved by means of the restricted basis entry procedure introduced in Chapter 4. From Chapter 4, we know that the solution so obtained will yield a local maximum of the objective function, but there is no guarantee that it is the global optimum. However, so long as the objective function is positive for the solution obtained, $f(\mathbf{x})$ can be increased at the next step.

The iterative procedure will terminate when the solution obtained to (9–49) through (9–56) is $\mathbf{r} = \mathbf{0}$. If we know that this is the global optimum, then the current feasible solution is a constrained stationary point of $f(\mathbf{x})$. Now because of the special nature of the constraints (9–49), one can show that if $\mathbf{r} = \mathbf{0}$ (note that this is always a feasible solution) is obtained by applying the simplex method with restricted basis entry so that it corresponds to a local maximum of the objective function, then it is the global optimum. We ask the reader to prove this in Problem 9–15. Thus there does not exist the possibility that a solution $\mathbf{r} = \mathbf{0}$ is obtained to the problem when there actually exists a direction in which we can move to increase $f(\mathbf{x})$. If I_2 is empty or contains only linear equations and the $g_{ij}(x_j)$ are convex so that the set of feasible solutions is convex, then the set of $\mathbf{r}$ satisfying (9–49) will be a convex set. (Problem 9–16 requires the proof.) Under these circumstances, a local optimum is also a global optimum so that for such problems there do not exist any local optima different from the global optimum of the objective function (9–52).

Once $\mathbf{r}_v$ has been obtained, we must determine how far to move from $\mathbf{x}_v$ in the direction of $\mathbf{r}_v$. It is at this point convenient to study separately problems where I_2 contains nonlinear equations and those where I_2 is empty or contains only linear equations. Consider first the case where I_2 contains nonlinear equations. Given $\mathbf{r}_v$, we know the cell into which we are going to move from $\mathbf{x}_v$. We then determine the half-spaces which, in this cell, represent the constraints that were inactive at $\mathbf{x}_v$. Denote these representations of the constraints by $\mathbf{a}^i\mathbf{x} \leq b_i$. We also determine the limits (9–42) to the range of variation of the x_j in this cell. We then compute the largest value of λ, call it ϵ, such that

$$\begin{aligned} \mathbf{a}^i(\mathbf{x}_v + \lambda\mathbf{r}_v) &\leq b_i \qquad i \notin I_1(v), \qquad i \in I_1; \\ x_{k_j,j} \leq x_{jv} + \lambda r_{jv} &\leq x_{k_j+1,j}, \qquad j = 1, \ldots, n. \end{aligned} \tag{9–53}$$

Finally, we determine that value of λ, $0 < \lambda \leq \epsilon$, which maximizes $f(\mathbf{x}_v + \lambda\mathbf{r}_v)$. The new feasible solution is $\mathbf{x}_{v+1} = \mathbf{x}_v + \lambda\mathbf{r}_v$.

Now let us examine the case where I_2 is empty or contains only linear constraints. We begin by substituting $\mathbf{r}_v$ into the constraints (9–49) for $i \in I_1(v)$. If $\mathbf{r}_v$ satisfies one or more of these as a strict equality, we proceed exactly as in the case studied above. Suppose, however, that $\mathbf{r}_v$ satisfies all of these as a strict inequality. In this event, we go back to the original constraints and determine ϵ to be the largest number λ for which

$$g_i(\mathbf{x}_v + \lambda\mathbf{r}_v) \leq b_i, \qquad i \in I_1, \qquad x_{jv} + \lambda r_{jv} \geq 0, \qquad j \in J. \tag{9–54}$$

To determine the λ which yields $g_i(\mathbf{x}_v + \lambda \mathbf{r}_v) = b_i$, we must, in general, use some numerical technique such as Newton's method to solve this equation (see Problem 9–18). Once ϵ has been determined, we find that value of λ, $0 < \lambda \leq \epsilon$, which maximizes $f(\mathbf{x}_v + \lambda \mathbf{r}_v)$. If $\lambda < \epsilon$, we consider the point $\mathbf{x} = \mathbf{x}_v + \lambda \mathbf{r}_v$. For the cell containing $\mathbf{x}$ (or for any one of the cells containing $\mathbf{x}$ when $\mathbf{x}$ lies on the boundaries of two or more cells), we compute the half-spaces $\mathbf{a}^i\mathbf{x} \leq b_i$, $i \in I_1$, which are the approximations to the constraints $g_i(\mathbf{x}) \leq b_i$ for this cell. If $\mathbf{x}$ satisfies all these, we set $\mathbf{x}_{v+1} = \mathbf{x}_v + \lambda \mathbf{r}_v$ and proceed. When λ is close to ϵ, it may turn out that even though $\mathbf{x}$ is a feasible solution to (9–40), it is not a feasible solution to (9–45). In this event, we must reduce λ until it is. To do this we determine the largest value of λ, call it $\hat{\lambda}$, such that $\hat{\mathbf{x}} = \mathbf{x}_v + \hat{\lambda} \mathbf{r}_v$ satisfies $\mathbf{a}^i\mathbf{x} \leq b_i$, $i \in I_1$. If $\hat{\mathbf{x}}$ is in the same cell $\mathbf{x}$ was in, we set $\mathbf{x}_{v+1} = \hat{\mathbf{x}}$. It may happen, however, that $\hat{\mathbf{x}}$ is in a different cell so that $\mathbf{a}^i\mathbf{x} \leq b_i$ is not the proper representation of $g_i(\mathbf{x}) \leq b_i$ for the cell appropriate to $\hat{\mathbf{x}}$. If this is the case, we determine the cell to move into as λ is reduced from the value which yielded $\hat{\mathbf{x}}$. We then find the representations of the constraints appropriate to this cell and repeat the process. In this way, λ is progressively reduced until we have found a feasible solution to (9–45).

Now, if the λ which maximizes $f(\mathbf{x}_v + \lambda \mathbf{r}_v)$ is ϵ, but must be reduced below ϵ, we proceed as above. If, however, $\mathbf{x}_v + \epsilon \mathbf{r}_v$ satisfies each constraint $\mathbf{a}^i\mathbf{x} \leq b_i$, $i \in I_1$, as a strict inequality, λ can be increased above ϵ before we reach the boundary of the set of feasible solutions to (9–45). In this case, we can reverse the above procedure and increase λ until we reach the boundary. Then we compute $f(\mathbf{x}_v + \lambda \mathbf{r}_v)$. If this is greater than, or equal to, $f(\mathbf{x}_v + \epsilon \mathbf{r}_v)$, we set $\mathbf{x}_{v+1} = \mathbf{x}_v + \lambda \mathbf{r}_v$, and if it is less, we set $\mathbf{x}_{v+1} = \mathbf{x}_v + \epsilon \mathbf{r}_v$.

The reason for adopting a special procedure when $\mathbf{r}_v$ satisfies all the constraints $i \in I_1(v)$ as strict inequalities at any iteration is that it allows us to move through the interior of the set of feasible solutions (interior with respect to the inequality constraints) without always encountering the cell boundaries and changing the representation of the $g_i(\mathbf{x})$, thus solving a new direction-finding problem, even though all the inequality constraints are inactive. The modified procedure enables us to take a big step if this is possible. However, its usefulness is probably limited to the early stages of the iterative process.

To take the best advantage of being able to move across the interior of the set of feasible solutions when such a move is possible, it would seem desirable, in cases where I_2 is empty, to determine whether $\mathbf{d}_v$ satisfies (9–49) even before attempting to compute $\mathbf{r}_v$. If it does, we immediately proceed to move in the direction of $\mathbf{d}_v$.

The procedure we have just presented may have some additional advantages over the other gradient methods besides those already discussed.

With the above technique, the $g_i(\mathbf{x})$ do not need to possess partial derivatives everywhere on the boundaries of the set of feasible solutions. Indeed, if we do not use the special procedure for cutting across the interior of the set when possible, we do not even need an analytic representation for the $g_{ij}(x_j)$. They may simply be curves plotted from experimental data. Furthermore, if we wish, we can easily approximate $f(\mathbf{x})$ in the same manner. As a final point concerning our method, consider Fig. 9–11 and the feasible solution $\mathbf{x}_v$. The projection of the gradient vector on the tangent hyperplane is $\mathbf{0}$, and indeed, $\nabla f(\mathbf{x}_v)$ is a scalar multiple of $\nabla g_1(\mathbf{x}_v)$ with $\alpha > 0$. Thus Zoutendijk's procedure and Rosen's would terminate at this point, which is indeed a constrained stationary point of $f(\mathbf{x})$ but not a relative maximum. However, the approximation method would not terminate, if the constraint were approximated as indicated.

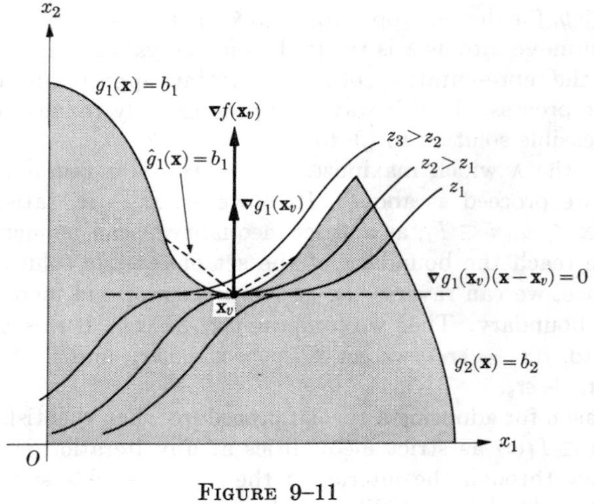

FIGURE 9–11

In employing the method just described it would be desirable initially to use very rough approximations to the $g_{ij}(x_j)$ so that large steps could be taken and one could rapidly reach the neighborhood of a stationary point. In the neighborhood of the point so obtained, one could then introduce better approximations, using interval halfing, and thus increase the accuracy of the computation. Note that although the final solution will be a feasible solution to the approximating problem (9–45), there is no guarantee that it will be a feasible solution to (9–40) (see Chapter 4). However, if the set of feasible solutions is convex, then we know from the arguments of Chapter 4 that any feasible solution to (9–45) will also be a feasible solution to (9–40).

The reader might wonder why anybody would ever think of resorting to a gradient method of the type discussed here where a problem (9–49) through (9–52) must be solved at each iteration, instead of using the methods of Chapter 4 which permit one to solve the same sort of problem only once. The important thing to note is that the computational effort involved in the solution of a linear programming problem by the simplex method increases roughly as the cube of the number of constraints. Frequently, many of the constraints are inactive for an optimal solution. If one can initiate the gradient method with a feasible solution having the property that only few of the constraints are active, and then build up the number of active constraints slowly, so that only in the last iterations all appropriate constraints will be active, less computational effort may be required than would be necessitated by the direct application of the methods of Chapter 4. For example, if the original problem had 100 constraints, one might be able to go through 500 iterations of the gradient method with 10 constraints active per iteration before the computational effort reaches the proportions encountered when the original problem is solved by the methods of Chapter 4. Another possible advantage is that problems too large to be treated by the methods of Chapter 4 might be handled by the gradient method, because constraints of the form $\sum_k \lambda_{kj} = 1$ are not needed, and because only a relatively small number of constraints may turn out to be active.

9–12 Determination of a feasible solution. One of the great advantages of the gradient methods is that any feasible solution can serve as the initial solution for the iterative process and that a basic feasible solution is not required. It seems likely that in the absence of an initial feasible solution, the gradient method would be considerably less useful, because of the additional labor required to obtain an initial solution. However, it is possible to obtain an initial solution by the introduction of artificial variables in a manner quite similar to that used for the simplex calculations. Assume that no feasible solution to (9–40) is available. This implies that $\mathbf{x} = \mathbf{0}$ is not feasible. Let I_1^- and I_2^- be the subsets of i from I_1 and I_2, respectively, for which $g_i(\mathbf{0}) > b_i$. Then to find an initial feasible solution, we replace (9–40) by the problem

$$\begin{aligned}
g_i(\mathbf{x}) &\le b_i, \qquad i \notin I_1^-, \qquad i \in I_1,\\
g_i(\mathbf{x}) - \xi &\le b_i, \qquad i \in I_1^-,\\
g_i(\mathbf{x}) - \xi_i &= b_i, \qquad i \in I_2^-,\\
g_i(\mathbf{x}) + \xi_i &= b_i, \qquad i \notin I_2^-, \qquad i \in I_2,\\
x_j \ge 0, \quad j \in J; &\quad \xi \ge 0; \quad \xi_i \ge 0, \quad i \in I_2,\\
\max \hat{z} &= -\xi - \sum_{i \in I_2} \xi_i.
\end{aligned} \tag{9–55}$$

An initial feasible solution to this problem is

$$\mathbf{x} = \mathbf{0}; \qquad \xi = \max_{i \in I_1^-} (g_i(\mathbf{0}) - b_i); \qquad \xi_i = |g_i(\mathbf{0}) - b_i|, \qquad i \in I_2. \tag{9-56}$$

When $\hat{z} = 0$, a feasible solution to (9–40) has been found. It is desirable to introduce as few new variables as possible, especially if the gradient projection method is being used, since these variables increase the size of the matrices which must be handled. This is the reason that only one variable ξ was introduced for the inequality constraints.

Note that if the set of feasible solutions to (9–40) is convex, so will be the set of feasible solutions to (9–55). In such a case, since $\hat{z}$ is linear, we know that if the terminating conditions are satisfied for any of the gradient methods, the global optimum of $\hat{z}$ has been found. There will be no problems with local optima. In general, however, the terminal conditions may be satisfied by $\hat{z} < 0$ when in reality the problem has a feasible solution. There seems to be no way of avoiding this possibility. We noted in Chapter 4 that it could also occur with the methods discussed there.

9–13 Example. Let us use the theory developed in Section 9–11 to obtain an approximate global optimum for the example studied in Section 4–3. We shall approximate $g_1(x_1)$ and $g_2(x_2)$ in precisely the same way as was done there. The origin is a feasible solution, and hence we shall use $\mathbf{x} = \mathbf{0}$ as the initial feasible solution. Note that

$$\nabla f(\mathbf{x}) = (2 - 2x_1, 1),$$

so that $\nabla f(\mathbf{0}) = (2, 1)$. The problem (9–49) through (9–52) for $\mathbf{x} = \mathbf{0}$ becomes

$$\begin{gathered} r_1 \geq 0, \qquad r_2 \geq 0, \\ r_1 + r_2 \leq 1, \\ \max Z = 2r_1 + r_2. \end{gathered} \tag{9-57}$$

The constraints corresponding to (9–49) are simply $\mathbf{r} \geq \mathbf{0}$. Note that $\mathbf{r}' = \nabla f(\mathbf{0}) \geq \mathbf{0}$. Here we have encountered the special case where we can immediately move in the direction of $\nabla f(\mathbf{0})$, and hence we do not need to solve (9–57). It might be noted, however, that the solution to (9–57) would not yield the locally best direction in which to move, since the solution is $r_1 = 1$, $r_2 = 0$.

The non-negativity restrictions will never be violated when we move in the direction of the gradient vector. Thus the constraint will limit how far we can move. We wish to determine ϵ, the largest value of λ, such that

$\mathbf{x} = [2\lambda, \lambda]$ is a feasible solution. Thus ϵ must satisfy

$$2(2\epsilon)^2 + 3\epsilon^2 = 6, \qquad \text{or} \quad 11\epsilon^2 = 6, \qquad \text{or} \quad \epsilon^2 = 0.546;$$

so

$$\epsilon = 0.739.$$

Next we wish to determine that value of λ, $0 < \lambda \leq 0.739$, such that $f(\mathbf{x})$, $\mathbf{x} = \lambda[2, 1]$ is maximized, i.e., we wish to maximize

$$4\lambda - 4\lambda^2 + \lambda = 5\lambda - 4\lambda^2$$

with respect to λ. This yields $\lambda = \frac{5}{8} = 0.625$, and we do not move all the way to the boundary. Thus

$$\mathbf{x}_1 = 0.625\,[2, 1] = [1.250, 0.625].$$

Clearly $\mathbf{x}_1$ satisfies $\mathcal{g}(\mathbf{x}_1) < 6$.

We now compute

$$\nabla f(\mathbf{x}_1) = (-0.50, 1).$$

Again it is clear that we should move in the direction of the gradient vector. We must then determine ϵ, the largest λ, such that $\mathbf{x} = \mathbf{x}_1 + \lambda\,[-0.50, 1]$ is a feasible solution. Now the extent of our move may be limited by two causes: the constraint may become active or x_1 may become negative. Clearly the constraint becomes active first, and hence ϵ must satisfy

$$2(1.250 - 0.50\epsilon)^2 + 3(0.625 + \epsilon)^2 = 6 \ \text{ or } \ 3.50\epsilon^2 + 1.25\epsilon - 1.71 = 0;$$

so

$$\epsilon = 0.542.$$

Here we have solved for ϵ directly instead of using an iterative numerical procedure as was suggested in Section 9–11. Next we must find the λ, $0 < \lambda \leq 0.542$, which maximizes $f(\mathbf{x}_1 + \lambda\mathbf{d}_1)$, that is, which maximizes

$$2(1.250 - 0.50\lambda) - (1.250 - 0.50\lambda)^2 + 0.625 + \lambda.$$

Thus

$$-1 + 1.250 - 0.50\lambda + 1 = 0, \qquad \text{or} \qquad \lambda = 2.50,$$

which is outside the allowable interval. Thus we move all the way to the boundary. If $\mathbf{x} = \mathbf{x}_1 + \epsilon\mathbf{d}_1$, then

$$\mathbf{x} = [1.250, 0.625] + 0.542[-0.50, 1] = [0.979, 1.167].$$

We next determine the half-space which is the approximation to the constraint in the cell containing $\mathbf{x}$, that is, in the cell $0.75 \leq x_1 \leq 1.0$,

$1.0 \leq x_2 \leq 1.25$. It follows from Table 4–1 that this half-space is

$$1.1250 + \left(\frac{2.0000 - 1.1250}{0.2500}\right)(x_1 - 0.7500) + 3.0000 + \left(\frac{4.6875 - 3.0000}{0.2500}\right)(x_2 - 1) \leq 6,$$

or

$$3.50\, x_1 + 6.75\, x_2 \leq 11.25. \tag{9–58}$$

Now we must determine the point which is the intersection of the boundary of (9–58) and $\mathbf{x} = [1.250 - 0.50\lambda, 0.625 + \lambda]$. Thus λ is determined from

$$3.50(1.250 - 0.50\lambda) + 6.75(0.625 + \lambda) = 11.25, \quad \text{or} \quad \lambda = 0.530,$$

so that in moving in the direction of $\mathbf{d}_1$, we encounter the boundary of (9–58) before the boundary of the actual constraint. Thus

$$\mathbf{x}_2 = [1.250, 0.625] + 0.530\,[-0.50, 1] = [0.985, 1.155],$$

since this point does indeed lie in the cell where (9–58) is the approximation to the constraint. Note that $z_2 = f(\mathbf{x}_2) = 2.156$.

To initiate the new iteration, we compute

$$\nabla f(\mathbf{x}_2) = (0.030, 1);$$

the direction in which to move is determined by solving

$$\begin{gathered} 3.50(r_1' - r_1'') + 6.75(r_2' - r_2'') \leq 0, \\ r_1' + r_1'' + r_2' + r_2'' \leq 1, \\ r_1', r_1'', r_2', r_2'' \geq 0; \qquad r_1' r_1'' = 0, \qquad r_2' r_2'' = 0, \\ \max Z = 0.030(r_1' - r_1'') + (r_2' - r_2''). \end{gathered}$$

This problem is illustrated graphically in Fig. 9–12. The solution occurs where

$$r_1'' + r_2' = 1, \qquad -3.50\, r_1'' + 6.75\, r_2' = 0;$$

so $r_1 = -r_1'' = -0.659$, and $r_2 = r_2' = 0.341$. When we move in the direction $\mathbf{r}_2 = [-0.659, 0.341]$, Eq. (9–58) will always be satisfied. However, (9–58) is the approximate representation of the constraint only when $0.75 \leq x_1 \leq 1.0$ and $1.0 \leq x_2 \leq 1.25$. We cannot move beyond these cell boundaries. It will be one of these latter restrictions which will limit the extent of our move, rather than the non-negativity restriction on x_1. Thus we wish to determine ϵ, the largest λ, such that

$$0.985 - 0.659\,\lambda \geq 0.750, \qquad 1.155 + 0.341\,\lambda \leq 1.250.$$

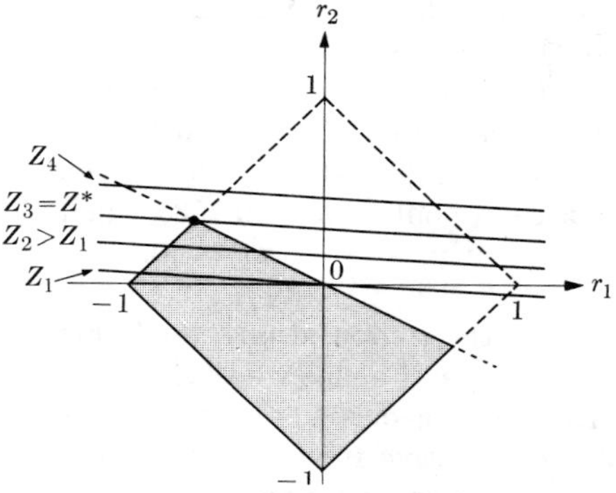

FIGURE 9-12

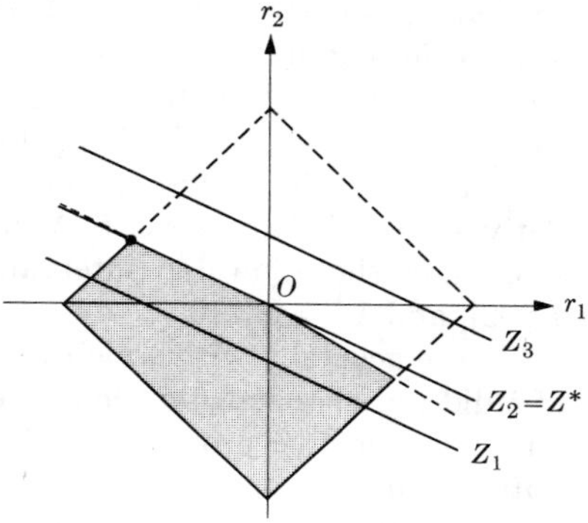

FIGURE 9-13

This yields $\epsilon = 0.279$. To determine how far to move, we wish to find the λ, $0 < \lambda \leq 0.279$, which maximizes $f(\mathbf{x}_2 + \lambda\mathbf{r}_2)$. On setting the derivative of f with respect to λ equal to zero, we obtain $\lambda = 1.111$, which is outside the allowable interval. Hence $\lambda = \epsilon$, and we move as far as possible, so that $\mathbf{x}_3 = [0.801, 1.250]$ and $z_3 = 2.210$.

The value of $\nabla f(\mathbf{x}_3)$ is

$$\nabla f(\mathbf{x}_3) = (0.398, 1).$$

We have reached a feasible solution $\mathbf{x}_3$ which lies on the boundaries of two cells, since $x_2 = 1.250$ is the end point of the two intervals $1.00 \leq x_2 \leq 1.25$ and $1.25 \leq x_2 \leq 1.50$. We must then compute the slope of the line approximating $g_2(x_2)$ in the interval $1.25 \leq x_2 \leq 1.50$. From Table 4-1 we see that it is

$$\frac{6.7500 - 4.6875}{0.2500} = 8.24.$$

The problem which must now be solved to determine the new direction in which to move is

$$3.50(r_1' - r_1'') + 8.24\,r_2' - 6.75\,r_2'' \leq 0,$$
$$r_1' + r_1'' + r_2' + r_2'' \leq 1,$$
$$r_1', r_1'', r_2', r_2'' \geq 0, \qquad r_1'r_1'' = 0, \qquad r_2'r_2'' = 0,$$
$$\max Z = 0.398(r_1' - r_1'') + r_2' - r_2''.$$

This is illustrated geometrically in Fig. 9-13. The optimal solution is $\mathbf{r}_3 = [-0.702, 0.298]$. The new feasible solution will have the form

$$\mathbf{x} = [0.801, 1.250] + \lambda[-0.702, 0.298],$$

so that x_1 is decreased and x_2 is increased. We thus move along the line approximating $g(\mathbf{x}) = 6$ in the cell $0.75 \leq x_1 \leq 1.0$, $1.25 \leq x_2 \leq 1.50$. Clearly, it is the limitation $x_1 \geq 0.75$ which determines how far we can move. Thus $\epsilon = 0.0727$. To determine how far to move, we wish to find the value of λ, $0 < \lambda \leq \epsilon$, which maximizes $f(\mathbf{x}_3 + \lambda\mathbf{r}_3)$. On setting the derivative of f with respect to λ equal to zero, we obtain $\lambda = 0.733$, which is outside the allowable interval. Consequently, $\lambda = \epsilon$, $\mathbf{x}_4 = [0.7500, 1.272]$, and $z_4 = 2.210$.

To the accuracy with which we have made the computations, the value of z did not change from the previous iteration, and hence we shall terminate the iterative procedure. The solution obtained is the same as that obtained in Section 4–3. The value of the objective function could be a little different here, since we have not used any approximate relations to represent the objective function. One can actually continue the iterative procedure, since, if one formulates the problem to determine the direction in which to move from $\mathbf{x}_4$, a direction will be found. However, there is nothing to be gained from making additional iterations. To illustrate this point, we ask the reader in Problem 9–17 to carry out one more iteration.

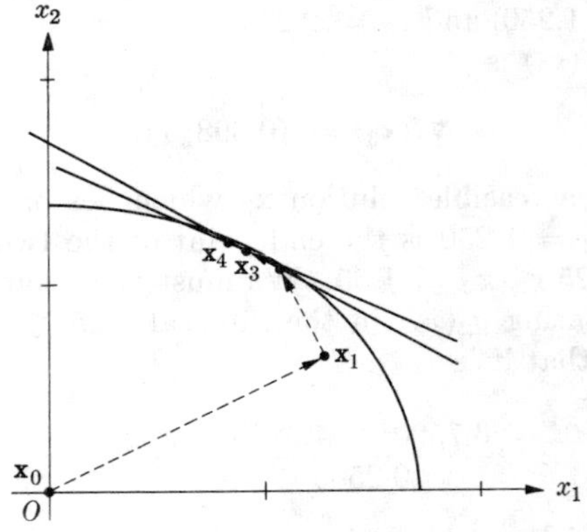

FIGURE 9–14

The amount of numerical work required here is roughly the same as that encountered in Section 4–3. However, if we had used some numerical technique to determine the locally best direction at each iteration, the computational effort would have been increased. The sequence of solutions obtained from the gradient method is shown in Fig. 9–14, as are the approximating hyperplanes which entered into the computation.

9–14 Some additional comments on convergence. For each of the variants of the gradient method discussed, conditions have been provided which, if satisfied, guarantee that we have reached a constrained stationary point of $f(\mathbf{x})$. In general, however, an infinite number of iterations may be required before these conditions will be satisfied. Consequently, other conditions must usually be provided to terminate the iterative procedure if the conditions guaranteeing that a stationary value of $f(\mathbf{x})$ is reached are not met first. These alternative conditions will usually be based on the change in $f(\mathbf{x})$ from one iteration to the next. If the percentage change in $f(\mathbf{x})$ is less than some prespecified number for some prespecified number of iterations, then the process will be terminated.

Quite frequently, when one approaches a stationary point of $f(\mathbf{x})$, the size of the steps taken will get small, and the convergence will be very slow. This will be especially true if the process is converging to an interior point of the set of feasible solutions, so that $\partial f/\partial x_j$ is very close to zero for all j. If, in this case, one encounters numerical problems in computing accurately the $\partial f/\partial x_j$, the process may not even converge; instead the sequence of points $\mathbf{x}_v$ may vary in a random way about the stationary point. We can then sometimes improve the convergence by making use of the second partial derivatives of f and approximating f by the sum of a linear and a quadratic form, rather than merely a linear form. Assume that we have the feasible solution $\mathbf{x}_v$ and would like to determine the stationary point where $\nabla f = \mathbf{0}$. Let us use the approximation

$$f(\mathbf{x}) = f(\mathbf{x}_v) + \nabla f(\mathbf{x}_v)\mathbf{x} + \tfrac{1}{2}\mathbf{x}'\mathbf{H}_f(\mathbf{x}_v)\mathbf{x}, \tag{9-59}$$

where $\mathbf{H}_f(\mathbf{x}_v) = ||\partial^2 f/\partial x_i \partial x_j||$ is the Hessian matrix of f when the partial derivatives are evaluated at $\mathbf{x}_v$. We then set $\nabla f(\mathbf{x}) = \mathbf{0}$ in (9-59) and solve the resulting set of linear equations for $\mathbf{x}$. This yields

$$\mathbf{x}' = -\nabla f(\mathbf{x}_v)\mathbf{H}_f^{-1}(\mathbf{x}_v) \tag{9-60}$$

as the estimate of the stationary point. Since, to compute $\mathbf{x}'$, we must solve a set of n linear equations (we would not actually invert $\mathbf{H}_f$ to do so), one would not want to use this approach except perhaps for the last one or two iterations.

9-15 The Arrow-Hurwicz gradient method for concave programming. The gradient techniques discussed in this chapter are sometimes referred to as large-step gradient methods, because at each iteration $f(\mathbf{x})$ is increased by a finite and, hopefully, large amount. Arrow and Hurwicz [1] have developed what might be referred to as a differential gradient method for solving problems involving the maximization of a concave function $f(\mathbf{x})$ over the convex set of solutions to $g_i(\mathbf{x}) \leq b_i$, $i = 1, \ldots, m$, $\mathbf{x} \geq \mathbf{0}$, where the $g_i(\mathbf{x})$ are convex. The method is differential in the intuitive sense, in that only an infinitesimal step is taken at each iteration, or more precisely, one finds the limiting solution to a set of differential equations to determine the solution to the given problem.

They proceed by first forming the Lagrangian function

$$F(\mathbf{x}, \boldsymbol{\lambda}) = f(\mathbf{x}) + \sum_{i=1}^{m} \lambda_i[b_i - g_i(\mathbf{x})].$$

Then from Chapter 6, we know that if $\mathbf{x}^*$ is an optimal solution to the given problem, there exists a $\boldsymbol{\lambda}^* \geq \mathbf{0}$ such that $[\mathbf{x}^*, \boldsymbol{\lambda}^*]$ is a global saddle point of $F(\mathbf{x}, \boldsymbol{\lambda})$ for $[\mathbf{x}^*, \boldsymbol{\lambda}^*] \geq \mathbf{0}$. Thus, to reach $[\mathbf{x}^*, \boldsymbol{\lambda}^*]$, one wants to move "uphill" with respect to $\mathbf{x}$ and "downhill" with respect to $\boldsymbol{\lambda}$.

Arrow and Hurwicz then proceed by introducing a parameter t and considering the set of ordinary differential equations

$$\begin{aligned} \frac{dx_j}{dt} &= 0 \quad \text{if} \quad \frac{\partial F}{\partial x_j} < 0 \quad \text{and} \quad x_j = 0, \\ \frac{dx_j}{dt} &= \frac{\partial F}{\partial x_j} \quad \text{otherwise}; \\ \frac{d\lambda_i}{dt} &= 0 \quad \text{if} \quad \frac{\partial F}{\partial \lambda_i} > 0 \quad \text{and} \quad \lambda_i = 0, \\ \frac{\partial \lambda_i}{dt} &= -\frac{\partial F}{\partial \lambda_i} \quad \text{otherwise.} \end{aligned} \tag{9–61}$$

They showed that if one starts with an initial feasible solution sufficiently close to $[\mathbf{x}^*, \boldsymbol{\lambda}^*] \geq \mathbf{0}$ and if the matrix $||\partial F/\partial x_i \partial x_j||$ is negative definite, then $\mathbf{x}(t)$, the solution to the above set of differential equations for the given initial conditions, has the property that $\lim_{t\to\infty} \mathbf{x}(t) = \mathbf{x}^*$. Uzawa [1] generalized the results to show that if F is strictly concave with continuous second partial derivatives, then for any initial feasible solution, the resulting solution to the above differential equations has the property that $\lim_{t\to\infty} \mathbf{x}(t) = \mathbf{x}^*$.

We shall not attempt to consider this differential gradient procedure in any detail, since it does not seem to yield a feasible computational procedure for digital computers. (It can be noted, however, that the technique might be mechanized for an analog computer.) The method also suffers from the severe restrictions which must be placed on the character of the original problem in order to ensure convergence.

References

1. Arrow, K. J., L. Hurwicz, and H. Uzawa, *Studies in Linear and Non-Linear Programming*. Stanford, California: Stanford University Press, 1958.

2. Dennis, J. B., *Mathematical Programming and Electrical Networks*. Cambridge, Massachusetts: M.I.T. Press, 1959.

3. Dorn, W. S., "Non-Linear Programming—A Survey," *Management Science*, **9**, 1963, pp. 171–208.

4. Lemke, C. E., "The Constrained Gradient Method of Linear Programming," *Journal of the Society for Industrial and Applied Mathematics*, **9**, 1961, pp. 1–17.

5. Rosen, J. B., "The Gradient Projection Method for Nonlinear Programming, Part I. Linear Constraints," *Journal of the Society for Industrial and Applied Mathematics*, **8**, 1960, pp. 181–217.

6. Rosen, J. B., "The Gradient Projection Method for Nonlinear Programming, Part II. Nonlinear Constraints," *Journal of the Society for Industrial and Applied Mathematics*, **9**, 1961, pp. 514–532.

7. Spang, H. A., "A Review of Minimization Techniques for Nonlinear Functions," *Journal of the Society for Industrial and Applied Mathematics*, **4**, 1962, pp. 343–365.

8. Zoutendijk, G., "Maximizing a Function in a Convex Region," *Journal of the Royal Statistical Society (B)*, **21**, 1959, pp. 338–355.

9. Zoutendijk, G., *Methods of Feasible Directions*. Amsterdam: Elsevier, 1960.

Problems

9–1. Consider the function

$$z = 36 - 9(x_1 - 6)^2 - 4(x_2 - 6)^2.$$

Start at the point $x_1 = 7$, $x_2 = 6 + \sqrt{\frac{27}{4}}$ and use the gradient method to determine the point where z assumes its maximum value. At the last iteration, use the method described in Section 9–14 to locate the maximizing point as accurately as possible.

9–2. For the two-variable case, provide a geometrical interpretation of the equivalence of the problems described by Eqs. (9–8) and (9–13).

9–3. Consider the problem of finding a basic feasible solution to Eq. (9–18) with $\boldsymbol{\phi}'\mathbf{w} = \mathbf{0}$. First prove that the quadratic form $\mathbf{y}'\mathbf{M}\mathbf{M}'\mathbf{y}$ is positive semidefinite, and is positive definite if the columns of $\mathbf{M}'$ are linearly independent. [*Hint:* Let $\boldsymbol{\mu} = \mathbf{M}'\mathbf{y}$.] If the form is positive definite, the elements on the main diagonal of $\mathbf{M}\mathbf{M}'$ are positive. If it is positive semidefinite, these elements are non-negative. Consider now any basic solution to Eq. (9–18) with $\boldsymbol{\phi}'\mathbf{w} = 0$. Denote the basis matrix by $\mathbf{B}$, and imagine that $\mathbf{B}$ is partitioned so that the columns containing the φ_i come first, to be followed by those containing the w_i; hence $\mathbf{B}$ may be written

$$\mathbf{B} = \begin{bmatrix} \mathbf{P} & \mathbf{0} \\ \mathbf{Q} & -\mathbf{I} \end{bmatrix}.$$

Compute the inverse of $\mathbf{B}$ and show that $\mathbf{v}'\mathbf{P}^{-1}\mathbf{v}$ is a positive definite quadratic form. Let the matrix of the coefficients of Eq. (9–18) be written

$$\begin{bmatrix} \mathbf{P} & \mathbf{T} & -\mathbf{I} & \mathbf{0} \\ \mathbf{Q} & \mathbf{R} & \mathbf{0} & -\mathbf{I} \end{bmatrix}.$$

Compute $\mathbf{B}^{-1}$ times this matrix and show that $\mathbf{r}'(-\mathbf{Q}\mathbf{P}^{-1}\mathbf{T} + \mathbf{R})\mathbf{r}$ is positive semidefinite. Then show that if for this basic solution some $\varphi_i < 0$, a new basic solution can be obtained with w_i replacing φ_i, and it will turn out that $w_i > 0$. Similarly, if some $w_i < 0$, a new basic solution can be obtained by replacing w_i by φ_i and in the new solution, $\varphi_i > 0$. [*Hint:* Use the procedure described in Section 2–1 for computing the new inverse when only a single column of a matrix is changed.] Under what conditions will it be impossible to make the replacement? How does one proceed in such cases?

9–4. For the gradient projection method discussed in Section 9–6, assume that we know $(\mathbf{Q}_v'\mathbf{Q}_v)^{-1}$ and would like to compute $(\mathbf{Q}_{v+1}'\mathbf{Q}_{v+1})^{-1}$ when $\mathbf{Q}_{v+1}$ differs from $\mathbf{Q}_v$ in that only a single column has been removed from, or added to, $\mathbf{Q}_v$ to obtain $\mathbf{Q}_{v+1}$. Develop an efficient procedure for computing the new inverse from the old one. [*Hint:* Consider first the case where a column is to be added to $\mathbf{Q}_v$ to obtain $\mathbf{Q}_{v+1}$ so that $\mathbf{Q}_{v+1} = (\mathbf{Q}_v, \mathbf{q})$. Compute $\mathbf{Q}_{v+1}'\mathbf{Q}_{v+1}$, using the partitioned form for $\mathbf{Q}_{v+1}$. Then, using the method of computing the inverse of a partitioned matrix, compute $(\mathbf{Q}_{v+1}'\mathbf{Q}_{v+1})^{-1}$. Next consider the case where $\mathbf{Q}_v = (\mathbf{Q}_{v+1}, \mathbf{q})$ so that a column is being removed from $\mathbf{Q}_v$. Generalize this so that any column can be removed from $\mathbf{Q}_v$. See Section 2–1.]

9–5. Make use of the results obtained in Problem 9–4 to show how one transforms the projection matrix $\mathbf{P}_v$ in going from one iteration to the next of the gradient projection method. Also show how to transform $\boldsymbol{\alpha}_v$.

9–6. Prove that the gradient projection method will converge to a stationary point of $f(\mathbf{x})$ or $|\mathbf{x}_v| \to \infty$ as $v \to \infty$, when at each step either $\mathbf{r}_v$ or $\hat{\mathbf{r}}_v$ is chosen, depending on which yields the larger directional derivative.

9–7. For linear programming problems, show that in going from one iteration to the next in a gradient method which solves Eq. (9–13) at each iteration, one can use the previous solution to get started on the new problem. [*Hint:* See {LP 11–5} concerning the addition of a new constraint after a problem has been solved.]

9–8. For linear programming problems where ∇f does not change from one iteration to the next, generalize the results of Problem 9–5 to show how $\mathbf{Pc}'$ can be transformed directly in going from one iteration to the next.

9–9. Show that the gradient projection method will solve a linear programming problem in a finite number of steps. [*Hint:* First let $\mathbf{x}^*$ be an optimal extreme point and assume that the optimal solution is unique. Consider an ϵ-neighborhood about $\mathbf{x}^*$ so small that no other extreme points are included. Show that once we reach this neighborhood, only a finite number of iterations are required before we reach an edge of the convex set. However, when an edge is reached, the next iteration will take us to $\mathbf{x}^*$.] What happens when the optimal solution is not unique?

9–10. Solve the linear programming problem of Eq. (1–14), beginning with the initial feasible solution $x_1 = 3$, $x_2 = 2$, by solving the problem of Eq. (9–8) or Eq. (9–13) at each iteration.

9–11. Use the gradient projection method to solve the linear programming problem of Eq. (1–14), beginning with the initial feasible solution $x_1 = 3$, $x_2 = 2$.

9–12. Solve the linear programming problem of Eq. (1–14), beginning with the initial feasible solution $x_1 = 3$, $x_2 = 2$, by using the gradient projection method modified to allow moves in the direction of the gradient vector if it is possible to do so.

9–13. Solve the linear programming problem of Eq. (1–14), using one of the gradient methods and the technique introduced in Section 9–12 for determining an initial feasible solution.

9–14. Show how to transform Eq. (9–41) into a form which can be solved readily.

9–15. Show that if $\mathbf{r} = \mathbf{0}$ is a local maximum to Eqs. (9–49) through (9–52), it is also a global optimum.

9–16. Prove that when the $g_{ij}(x_j)$ are convex and I_2 is empty or contains only linear equations, the set of $\mathbf{r}$ satisfying Eq. (9–49) forms a convex set.

9–17. Carry out one more iteration of the example of Section 9–13.

9–18. Consider the problem of determining the value of λ which satisfies the equation $f(\mathbf{x} + \lambda\mathbf{r}) = 0$. Assume that λ_0 is our estimate of the root. Then write

$$f(\mathbf{x} + \lambda\mathbf{r}) = 0 \doteq f(\mathbf{x} + \lambda_0\mathbf{r}) + \left(\sum_{j=1}^{n} \frac{\partial f}{\partial x_j} r_j\right)(\lambda - \lambda_0).$$

Use this relation to determine an iterative method for computing λ. This technique is called Newton's method.

9–19. Discuss the application of gradient methods to the solution of quadratic programming problems.

9–20. Solve the example of Section 9–13 by the gradient projection method.

9–21. Solve the problem represented in Fig. 1–2 by one of the gradient methods.

9–22. With reference to Section 9–3, prove that if the sequence has more than one point of accumulation, $f(\mathbf{x})$ must have the same value at each one of these points.

9–23. Try to construct a simple graphical example illustrating a case where the sequence referred to in Section 9–3 has more than one point of accumulation.

9–24. Consider the situation of Section 9–3 given that $f(\mathbf{x})$ is concave and λ can be increased without bound at some iteration with either $f(\mathbf{x})$ always increasing and approaching a finite limit, or $|\mathbf{x}_v| \to \infty$ and $f(\mathbf{x}_v)$ approaching a finite limit. Show that the limiting value of $f(\mathbf{x})$ is the global optimum of $f(\mathbf{x})$.

9–25. Solve the example of Section 9–13, assuming that we move initially in the direction given by the optimal solution to Eq. (9–57), and at each succeeding step, in the direction of the solution to Eqs. (9–49), (9–51), and (9–52).

9–26. Modify the development of Section 9–11 to take account of the case where $f(\mathbf{x})$ is separable, and it is desired to approximate $f(\mathbf{x})$ also.

9–27. For a problem involving two variables, illustrate geometrically the following situation: at some step in applying the gradient method of Section 9–11, we cut through the interior of the set of feasible solutions, and the point where we strike the approximation to the boundary lies in a different cell than the point where we strike the true boundary.

9–28. Solve the example of Section 9–13 by not making use of the procedure permitting us to cut through the interior of the set of feasible solutions without stopping each time we hit a cell boundary. Actually determine a new direction in which to move each time a cell boundary is reached.

9–29. Show the connection between each of the termination conditions for the various forms of the gradient method and the Kuhn-Tucker conditions.

9–30. Show that Eq. (9–18), along with $\boldsymbol{\phi}'\mathbf{w} = 0$ and $\boldsymbol{\phi} \geq \mathbf{0}$, $\mathbf{w} \geq \mathbf{0}$, are the Kuhn-Tucker conditions for the quadratic programming problem

$$z = \boldsymbol{\phi}'\mathbf{M}_v\mathbf{d}_v - \tfrac{1}{2}\boldsymbol{\phi}'\mathbf{M}_v\mathbf{M}_v'\boldsymbol{\phi}, \qquad \boldsymbol{\phi} \geq \mathbf{0}.$$

This was first noted by Dennis [2].

9–31. Use one of the gradient methods to find a stationary point for Problem 1–1. Illustrate graphically.

9–32. Use one of the gradient methods to find a stationary point for Problem 1–2. Illustrate graphically.

9–33. Apply one of the gradient methods to Problem 1–3 and illustrate graphically.

9–34. Apply Zoutendijk's method discussed in Section 9–10 to find an optimal solution to Problem 1–5.

9–35. Apply the method of Section 9–11 to find an approximate solution to Problem 1–5, and compare the computational effort required with that needed for Problem 9–34.

9–36. Apply the gradient method of Section 9–11 to Problem 1–7 and illustrate graphically.

9–37. Solve the example of Section 9–13, using Zoutendijk's method discussed in Section 9–10.

9–38. Show that there is always a feasible solution to Eq. (9–8) if the convex set of feasible solutions to (9–1) contains more than a single point.

9–39. Problem 9–4 dealt with the process of changing $(\mathbf{Q}_v'\mathbf{Q}_v)^{-1}$ from one iteration to the next in the gradient projection method. How does one obtain this matrix for the initial feasible solution? Are there any special cases where this task is particularly easy?

9–40. What is a good numerical procedure for solving the set of equations in Eq. (9–60)?

9–41. Consider a set of u constraints $\mathbf{a}^i\mathbf{x}\{\leq, =\}b_i$. Assume that the rank of the matrix whose rows are the $\mathbf{a}^i$ is h, and that the first h of the $\mathbf{a}^i$ are linearly independent. Now replace b_i by $b_i + \delta^i$ for $i = h + 1, \ldots, u$. Show that after this replacement is made, there exists a $\delta_0 > 0$ such that for all δ, $0 < \delta < \delta_0$, there is no $\mathbf{x}$ for which more than h of the constraints are simultaneously active. Show that making perturbations in this manner eliminates the danger of difficulties arising from the case where the rank of $\mathbf{M}_v$ in the gradient projection method is less than the number of rows in $\mathbf{M}_v$.

9–42. In practical applications of the gradient projection method, how can one handle cases where the rank of $\mathbf{M}_v$ is less than the number of rows in $\mathbf{M}_v$? [*Hint*. Just as with degeneracy in the simplex method, $f(\mathbf{x})$ may remain unchanged for several iterations.]

9–43. Provide a geometric example of a case where the rank of $\mathbf{M}_v$ in equation (9–15) is less than the number of rows in $\mathbf{M}_v$, and $\mathbf{P}_v\mathbf{d}_v = \mathbf{0}$. Illustrate what happens when the perturbation method discussed in Section 9–6 is applied.

9–44. Show that when the set of feasible solutions to Eq. (9–40) is convex, then one can obtain an optimal solution to Eqs. (9–49) through (9–52) by solving the problem as a strict linear programming problem without the use of restricted entry.

9–45. Solve the problem corresponding to Fig. 9–12, using the simplex method both with and without restricted basis entry.

9–46. Assume that we have solved a problem using the method of Section 9–11 and a rather coarse grid. Suppose that we would like to improve the accuracy by using finer subdivisions. Discuss how one can proceed to find a solution to the new problem. Note that here the solution for the coarse-grid problem can be used to initiate the procedure when a finer grid is used (this was not possible in Chapter 4).

CHAPTER 10

DYNAMIC PROGRAMMING I

Repetition is the only form of permanence that nature can achieve.

Santayana, *Soliloquies in England*

10–1 Introduction. As was pointed out in Chapter 1, dynamic programming as we shall use the term refers to a computational technique rather than to a particular type of nonlinear programming problem. It developed initially, however, as the result of studying certain types of sequential decision problems, especially the sequential decision stochastic programming problems which arise in inventory theory. The name that became associated with the computational technique really referred to the types of problems to which it was applied originally. The basic idea which led to the computational technique was developed by Richard Bellman in the early 1950's. He also suggested that it be called dynamic programming. A very large part of the work which has been carried out since then to develop the technique has been done by Bellman and his associates at the RAND Corporation.

In this chapter and the next we wish to study the computational technique called dynamic programming, examine the sorts of problems that can be solved by it, and also point out the limitations of the method. We shall, in addition, study briefly how we can use the same approach analytically to gain information about the nature of the optimal solution to a problem without actually solving it numerically.

10–2 The nature of the computational method. Consider the following nonlinear programming problem:

$$\sum_{j=1}^{n} a_j x_j \le b; \qquad a_j > 0, \qquad j = 1, \ldots, n,$$

$$x_j \ge 0, \qquad j = 1, \ldots, n; \qquad \text{all } x_j \text{ integers,} \tag{10–1}$$

$$\max z = \sum_{j=1}^{n} f_j(x_j).$$

Note that this problem involves only one constraint and has a separable objective function. Note also that we are requiring that the variables assume only integral values. Problems of this type occur fairly frequently in practice. A typical example is the one concerned with stocking an atomic submarine with spare parts (presented in Section 5–2). For that example,

$$f_j(x_j) = -\pi_j \sum_{v_j=x_j}^{\infty} (v_j - x_j)p_j(v_j).$$

The minus sign appears because in (10–1), z is being maximized, whereas in (5–3), z is being minimized. If the x_j were allowed to be continuous and the $f_j(x_j)$ were concave functions, the methods of Chapter 4 could be used to yield an approximate optimal solution to this problem. If the $f_j(x_j)$ were concave and differentiable everywhere, it might also be feasible to use the Lagrange multiplier technique to solve the problem. However, if z has a number of local maxima, the methods of Chapter 4 can do no better than yield an approximate local optimum, and it becomes extremely difficult to use the Lagrange multiplier approach. We thus have no straightforward method of finding a global optimum in such cases. When, in addition, we require that the x_j be integers, none of the methods described previously can be used to yield an exact optimal solution. The best that could be done would be to treat the x_j as continuous, and then round off the values so obtained to integers. When the optimal x_j are large, this is usually quite satisfactory. However, in general, this procedure cannot be used unless the $f_j(x_j)$ are concave, since otherwise there could be a number of local maxima. Moreover, when the optimal x_j are small, it is usually not satisfactory to treat the x_j as continuous and then round off the solution to the nearest integers satisfying the constraint. In summary, then, the techniques that have been studied thus far will not, in general, provide us with an optimal solution to (10–1), and may not be of any assistance at all in solving the problem.

We shall now consider a computational method which yields an optimal solution to (10–1), and indeed yields all alternative optimal solutions, if the optimal solution is not unique. Before proceeding, let us assume that the a_j and b in (10–1) are integers. This is not really any restriction, because to an arbitrary degree of accuracy this can always be made to be the case. The restriction only limits the selection of the physical dimensions used to measure the a_j and b. For example, if b is a volume, then we may have to measure b in cubic centimeters rather than cubic feet, and the a_j in cubic centimeters per unit rather than cubic feet per unit, in order that all these coefficients become integers. The reason for doing this will become clear below.

In developing a computational method for solving (10–1) it is important to note that we can carry out the maximization of z in any way we like, provided that the method makes it possible to examine every set of feasible

x_j if it is desirable to do so. Before proceeding, it will be helpful to make one comment about notation. Consider a function $h(\mathbf{x})$ of n variables $\mathbf{x} = [x_1, \ldots, x_n]$. Then by

$$\max_{x_i, x_j, \ldots, x_r} h(\mathbf{x})$$

we mean the absolute maximum of $h(\mathbf{x})$ with respect to allowable variations in $x_i, x_j, \ldots, x_r$ for specified fixed values of the remaining variables not included in the set $x_i, x_j, \ldots, x_r$.

Denote by z^* the absolute maximum of z in (10–1). Then

$$z^* = \max_{x_1, \ldots, x_n} \left\{ \sum_{j=1}^{n} f_j(x_j) \right\}, \tag{10–2}$$

the maximization being made over non-negative integers x_j satisfying

$$\sum_{j=1}^{n} a_j x_j \leq b. \tag{10–3}$$

Suppose that we proceed as follows: We select a value of x_n and, holding x_n fixed, maximize z over the remaining variables, i.e., over $x_1, \ldots, x_{n-1}$. The values of $x_1, \ldots, x_{n-1}$ which maximize z under these conditions will, of course, depend on the value of x_n selected. Imagine that we do this for every allowable value of x_n. Then z^* will be the largest of all the z values so obtained, and we thus find a set of x_j which maximize z. Let us now indicate the above steps in equation form. We first select a value of x_n and compute

$$\max_{x_1, \ldots, x_{n-1}} \left\{ \sum_{j=1}^{n} f_j(x_j) \right\} = f_n(x_n) + \max_{x_1, \ldots, x_{n-1}} \sum_{j=1}^{n-1} f_j(x_j). \tag{10–4}$$

The term $f_n(x_n)$ can be factored out, since it is independent of $x_1, \ldots, x_{n-1}$. Once x_n has been selected, $x_1, \ldots, x_{n-1}$ must be restricted to non-negative integers which satisfy

$$\sum_{j=1}^{n-1} a_j x_j \leq b - a_n x_n. \tag{10–5}$$

Now

$$\max_{x_1, \ldots, x_{n-1}} \sum_{j=1}^{n-1} f_j(x_j)$$

for non-negative integers satisfying (10–5) depends on x_n, or more specifically, on $b - a_n x_n$. Let us therefore write

$$\Lambda_{n-1}(b - a_n x_n) = \max_{x_1, \ldots, x_{n-1}} \sum_{j=1}^{n-1} f_j(x_j), \tag{10–6}$$

where the maximization is carried out for non-negative integers $x_1, \ldots, x_{n-1}$ satisfying (10–5). Suppose that we compute $\Lambda_{n-1}(b - a_n x_n)$ for every allowable value of x_n. Then it is clear that

$$z^* = \max_{x_n} [f_n(x_n) + \Lambda_{n-1}(b - a_n x_n)], \tag{10–7}$$

and x_n can take on the values 0, 1, . . . , $[b/a_n]$, where $[b/a_n]$ is the largest integer less than, or equal to, b/a_n. To evaluate the maximum in (10–7), we simply evaluate

$$\Omega_n(x_n) = f_n(x_n) + \Lambda_{n-1}(b - a_n x_n) \tag{10–8}$$

for each possible x_n and select the largest Ω_n. We then simultaneously determine x_n^*, an optimal value of x_n. Thus, if we had available the function $\Lambda_{n-1}(b - a_n x_n)$, we could reduce the problem of finding z^* to a maximization over just a single variable.

Let us then consider how to compute $\Lambda_{n-1}(b - a_n x_n)$. Recall that $\Lambda_{n-1}(b - a_n x_n)$ is defined by (10–6), where maximization is carried out for non-negative integers satisfying (10–5). For any arbitrary non-negative integer ξ, let

$$\Lambda_{n-1}(\xi) = \max_{x_1, \ldots, x_{n-1}} \sum_{j=1}^{n-1} f_j(x_j), \tag{10–9}$$

where the maximization is taken over non-negative integers satisfying

$$\sum_{j=1}^{n-1} a_j x_j \le \xi. \tag{10–10}$$

However, if we now proceed just as above, then

$$\Lambda_{n-1}(\xi) = \max_{x_{n-1}} [f_{n-1}(x_{n-1}) + \Lambda_{n-2}(\xi - a_{n-1} x_{n-1})], \tag{10–11}$$

where

$$\Lambda_{n-2}(\zeta) = \max_{x_1, \ldots, x_{n-2}} \sum_{j=1}^{n-2} f_j(x_j), \tag{10–12}$$

and the maximization is carried out for non-negative integers $x_1, \ldots, x_{n-2}$ satisfying

$$\sum_{j=1}^{n-2} a_j x_j \le \zeta. \tag{10–13}$$

In (10–11), x_{n-1} can take on the values 0, 1, . . . , $[\xi/a_{n-1}]$. Consequently, if we know the function $\Lambda_{n-2}(\zeta)$, we can evaluate $\Lambda_{n-1}(\xi)$ by carrying out a maximization over a single variable x_{n-1}. Note that for each different value of ξ for which we wish to evaluate $\Lambda_{n-1}(\xi)$, we must repeat the maximization computation in (10–11).

The process used above can be extended to yield a method for evaluating $\Lambda_{n-2}(\zeta)$. This same approach is continued until finally at the last step we are reduced to evaluating

$$\Lambda_1(\rho) = \max_{x_1} f_1(x_1), \tag{10–14}$$

where in the course of maximization, x_1 can take on the values 0, 1, . . . , $[\rho/a_1]$. To actually solve the problem, we would begin by determining $\Lambda_1(\rho)$, and then work our way up to computing the function $\Lambda_{n-1}(\xi)$ and finally z^*.

The computational procedure can be systematized as follows: Let us define the sequence of functions

$$\Lambda_k(\xi) = \max_{x_1,\ldots,x_k} \sum_{j=1}^{k} f_j(x_j), \qquad k = 1, \ldots, n, \tag{10–15}$$

where the maximization is carried out for non-negative integers satisfying

$$\sum_{j=1}^{k} a_j x_j \leq \xi. \tag{10–16}$$

Once $\Lambda_1(\xi)$ has been determined directly, the remaining $\Lambda_k(\xi)$ can be computed recursively, since

$$\Lambda_k(\xi) = \max_{x_k}\left[f_k(x_k) + \max_{x_1,\ldots,x_{k-1}} \sum_{j=1}^{k-1} f_j(x_j)\right], \tag{10–17}$$

where in computing

$$\max_{x_1,\ldots,x_{k-1}} \sum_{j=1}^{k-1} f_j(x_j) \tag{10–18}$$

the maximization is taken over non-negative integers $x_1, \ldots, x_{k-1}$ satisfying

$$\sum_{j=1}^{k-1} a_j x_j \leq \xi - a_k x_k.$$

But under these conditions, (10–18) is simply $\Lambda_{k-1}(\xi - a_k x_k)$. Thus

$$\Lambda_k(\xi) = \max_{x_k} [f_k(x_k) + \Lambda_{k-1}(\xi - a_k x_k)], \qquad k = 2, \ldots, n, \tag{10–19}$$

and x_k varies over the values 0, 1, . . . , $[\xi/a_k]$. Finally

$$z^* = \Lambda_n(b). \tag{10–20}$$

We have sketched a numerical procedure for determining z^*. We have not yet indicated how one determines an optimal set of x_j while making the computation. Let us now review the computational procedure, and simultaneously show how an optimal set of x_j (or all alternative optimal solutions) is obtained. We begin by computing

$$\Lambda_1(\xi) = \max_{0 \le x_1 \le [\xi/a_1]} f_1(x_1), \tag{10–21}$$

where in computing $\Lambda_1(\xi)$ for a given ξ, we can have x_1 range over integers in the interval indicated. We compute $\Lambda_1(\xi)$ for each $\xi = 0, 1, \ldots, b$. Denote by $\hat{x}_1(\xi)$ the value(s) of x_1 for which

$$\Lambda_1(\xi) = f_1[\hat{x}_1(\xi)], \tag{10–22}$$

that is, $\hat{x}_1(\xi)$ is a value of x_1 which maximizes $f_1(x_1)$ when x_1 can assume the values $0, 1, \ldots, [\xi/a_1]$. The value of $\hat{x}_1(\xi)$ may not be unique; there may be more than one $\hat{x}_1(\xi)$ for which (10–22) holds. Imagine then that we construct a table such as Table 10–1. If $\hat{x}_1(\xi)$ is not unique, and if we are only interested in finding an optimal solution, we need tabulate only one of the values. However, if we ultimately wish to find all alternative

TABLE 10–1

ξ	$\Lambda_1(\xi)$	$\hat{x}_1(\xi)$
0	$\Lambda_1(0)$	$\hat{x}_1(0)$
1	$\Lambda_1(1)$	$\hat{x}_1(1)$
⋮	⋮	⋮
b	$\Lambda_1(b)$	$\hat{x}_1(b)$

optimal solutions, then for each ξ, we should tabulate every x_1 for which (10–22) holds.

Having obtained $\Lambda_1(\xi)$, we proceed to compute $\Lambda_2(\xi)$ for every $\xi = 0, 1, \ldots, b$, using

$$\Lambda_2(\xi) = \max_{0 \le x_2 \le [\xi/a_2]} [f_2(x_2) + \Lambda_1(\xi - a_2 x_2)]. \tag{10–23}$$

In carrying out the maximization, we can let x_2 range over integers in the interval indicated. To compute $\Lambda_2(\xi)$ for a given ξ, we simply compute

$$\begin{aligned} \Omega_2(0; \xi) &= f_2(0) + \Lambda_1(\xi), \\ \Omega_2(1; \xi) &= f_2(1) + \Lambda_1(\xi - a_2), \\ &\vdots \\ \Omega_2\left(\left[\frac{\xi}{a_2}\right]; \xi\right) &= f_2\left(\left[\frac{\xi}{a_2}\right]\right) + \Lambda_1\left(\xi - a_2\left[\frac{\xi}{a_2}\right]\right), \end{aligned} \tag{10–24}$$

and $\Lambda_2(\xi)$ is the largest of these values. Simultaneously, we determine the value, or values, $\hat{x}_2(\xi)$ for which $\Lambda_2(\xi) = \Omega_2(\hat{x}_2; \xi)$. Note that to determine $\Lambda_2(\xi)$, we need to know $\Lambda_1(\xi - a_2x_2)$ for all integers x_2, $0 \leq x_2 \leq [\xi/a_2]$. Note also that $\xi - a_2x_2$ is a non-negative integer for any such x_2, since we originally assumed that a_2 was an integer. Because we evaluated $\Lambda_1(\xi)$ for every integer $\xi = 0, 1, \ldots, b$, we can determine $\Lambda_1(\xi - a_2x_2)$ from Table 10–1 simply by finding the number in the Λ_1-column corresponding to the number $\xi - a_2x_2$ in the ξ-column. We then construct a table of the same form as Table 10–1 for $\Lambda_2(\xi)$ and $\hat{x}_2(\xi)$.

Next we compute a table of $\Lambda_3(\xi)$ and $\hat{x}_3(\xi)$ for each $\xi = 0, 1, \ldots, b$, using (10–19) and the table for $\Lambda_2(\xi)$. This procedure is repeated until we are finally ready to determine $\Lambda_n(\xi)$. At this point, we need to compute only $\Lambda_n(b) = z^*$. We do not need a table of $\Lambda_n(\xi)$-values. The value(s) $\hat{x}_n(b) = x_n^*$, that is, the value(s) of x_n which yields $\Lambda_n(b)$ is simply x_n^*, as we noted in our discussion of (10–7). Then we have found x_n^* (which may not be unique). To obtain $x_1^*, \ldots, x_{n-1}^*$ we must use the tables $\hat{x}_k(\xi)$ which we have computed. Once we know x_n^*, then we know that the remaining $n - 1$ variables must satisfy

$$\sum_{j=1}^{n-1} a_jx_j \leq b - a_nx_n^*. \tag{10–25}$$

Thus $\sum_{j=1}^{n-1} f_j(x_j)$ must be maximized for non-negative integers satisfying (10–25). But this maximum is simply $\Lambda_{n-1}(b - a_nx_n^*)$, and the value(s) of x_{n-1} which yields $\Lambda_{n-1}(b - a_nx_n^*)$ is $\hat{x}_{n-1}(b - a_nx_n^*)$. Therefore

$$x_{n-1}^* = \hat{x}_{n-1}(b - a_nx_n^*), \tag{10–26}$$

and to evaluate x_{n-1}^*, we look in the $\hat{x}_{n-1}(\xi)$-table for $\xi = b - a_nx_n^*$. Next we find in the same way that

$$x_{n-2}^* = \hat{x}_{n-2}(b - a_nx_n^* - a_{n-1}x_{n-1}^*)$$

or, in general,

$$x_{n-i}^* = \hat{x}_{n-i}\left(b - \sum_{u=0}^{i-1} a_{n-u}x_{n-u}^*\right), \qquad i = 1, \ldots, n-1. \tag{10–27}$$

Thus we have provided a numerical procedure for computing exactly z^* and an optimal set of x_j. The computational procedure also makes it possible to determine all alternative optimal solutions. We begin with the value of x_n^* or one of the x_n^*-values. We then find x_{n-1}^*. If x_{n-1}^* is not unique for the given x_n^*, we must trace things back for this given x_n^* and each of the x_{n-1}^*-values. Starting with a given x_n^*, one might then obtain a treelike structure (Fig. 10–1); the final set of x_j^*-values on the terminal branches will correspond to different alternative optimal solutions. It is necessary to go through this procedure for each different x_n^*. Frequently, we are not interested in all alternative optimal solutions and, when tabulating the $\hat{x}_j(\xi)$, we shall therefore tabulate only one of the values which yields $\Lambda_j(\xi)$, so that only one of the alternative optimal solutions will ultimately be obtained.

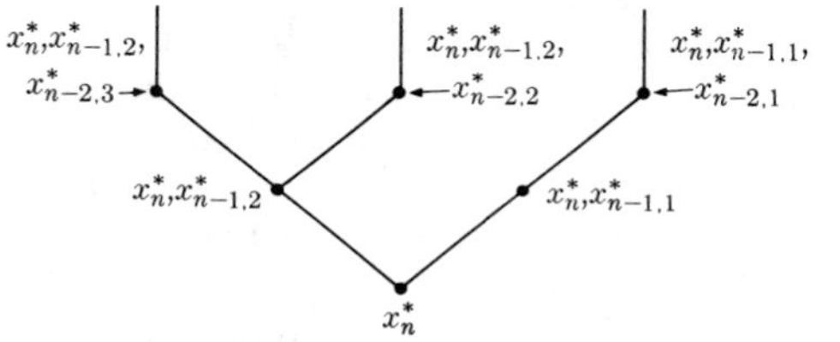

FIGURE 10–1

Let us now explain in more detail precisely why the $\Lambda_k(\xi)$, $k = 1, \ldots, n-1$, were tabulated for all $\xi = 0, 1, \ldots, b$. All we ultimately need is $\Lambda_n(b)$. However, to compute $\Lambda_n(b)$, we must perform a maximization over x_n and compute $\Lambda_{n-1}(b - a_n x_n)$ for all $x_n = 0, 1, \ldots, [b/a_n]$. The values of ξ for which we need $\Lambda_{n-1}(\xi)$ will depend on a_n. If $a_n = 1$, then we need $\Lambda_{n-1}(\xi)$ for all $\xi = 0, 1, \ldots, b$. In other cases we might need $\Lambda_{n-1}(\xi)$ only for even or odd ξ, or for some other particular set of ξ-values. For each ξ for which $\Lambda_{n-1}(\xi)$ is required, we need $\Lambda_{n-2}(\xi - a_{n-1}x_{n-1})$ for all $x_{n-1} = 0, 1, \ldots, [\xi/a_{n-1}]$, etc. It quickly becomes apparent that if we have a large number of variables, it is, in general, exceedingly difficult to trace things back to decide for precisely what values of ξ we will need $\Lambda_k(\xi)$. To avoid making this detailed analysis, it is usually much simpler to compute $\Lambda_k(\xi)$ for each $\xi = 0, 1, \ldots, b$. In this manner, we can be sure that all values needed can be computed. As one works backward, it very often becomes apparent that although $\Lambda_{n-1}(\xi)$ may not be needed for all $\xi = 0, 1, \ldots, b$, the $\Lambda_k(\xi)$ must be known for essentially all values of $\xi = 0, 1, \ldots, b$. The reason for our original requirement that the a_j be integers was to ensure that the arguments of the Λ_k would always be integers. This made it easy to determine the set of values for which Λ_k would need to be evaluated. To make this determination, one would essentially have to make the conversion anyway, and hence it is simplest to do it at the outset.

For hand computation, the procedure just suggested is extremely tedious, and becomes completely impossible unless b and n are quite small. However, it is easily coded for a digital computer. Although not absolutely necessary, it is convenient to have sufficient high-speed storage in the computer to store simultaneously tables for $\Lambda_{k-1}(\xi)$, $\Lambda_k(\xi)$, and $f_k(x_k)$ [the functions $f_k(x_k)$ would frequently be entered into the computer as tables]. Note that once the table for $\Lambda_k(\xi)$ has been computed, the table for $\Lambda_{k-1}(\xi)$ is no longer needed and can be erased from memory. The values $\hat{x}_k(\xi)$ which are determined when $\Lambda_k(\xi)$ is determined can be stored on magnetic tape as computed. They are not needed again until the x_k^* are to be determined. On modern high-speed computers such as the IBM 7090, as many as 10,000 entries in the $\Lambda_k(\xi)$-tables do not present any problem as far as high speed-storage is concerned. Quite large problems involving over 100 variables can be solved in a very few minutes. Although a table involving more than 10,000 entries for $\Lambda_k(\xi)$ may be needed occasionally, this exigency does not seem to occur too frequently if one is careful to choose the proper dimensions for a_j, b, and sometimes also the x_j. As a matter of fact, even as many as 20,000 entries in the $\Lambda_k(\xi)$-table will not present any serious problem for an IBM 7090; a little more tape reading is all that will be required. Of course, the more entries in the table, the longer the time required to solve the problem.

The computational method introduced in this section for solving (10–1) is an illustration of the dynamic programming technique. In Section 10–4 we shall try to characterize more precisely the nature of the dynamic programming approach.

10–3 Computational efficiency of the method. Let us now compare the computational efficiency of the dynamic programming approach to solving (10–1) with that of simply enumerating all possible sets of non-negative integers x_j which satisfy the constraint, evaluating the objective function for each, and then selecting that set or sets of x_j which yield the maximum value of the objective function. It is difficult to make an exact comparison of the computational effort required in the general case. For illustrative purposes, it will suffice to consider the case where each $a_j = 1$. Then the constraint becomes $\sum x_j \leq b$. In both methods it is necessary to evaluate $f_j(x_j)$ at each of the $b + 1$ values which x_j can take on. The difference between the two approaches lies essentially in the number of different combinations of variables for which the objective function must be evaluated. Consider first the direct enumeration. The computation of the number of different sets of integral values of the x_j which satisfy the constraint is also difficult to evaluate. However, a lower bound on this number will suffice. Let us compute the number of different combinations that can be obtained when the constraint holds as a strict equality. This is the number of ways of placing b indistinguishable balls into n cells, that is,

$$\binom{n+b-1}{b} = \frac{(n+b-1)!}{b!(n-1)!}.$$

For $n = 5$ and $b = 20$, this number is

$$\frac{24(23)(22)(21)}{4(3)(2)} = 23(22)(21) = 10{,}626.$$

Thus z must be evaluated for more than 10,626 different sets of x_j.

Consider now the dynamic programming approach outlined above. To evaluate $\Lambda_k(\xi)$ for a given ξ, we must compare $\xi + 1$ values, so that to determine the whole table of $\Lambda_k(\xi)$ we must compute

$$\sum_{\xi=0}^{b} (\xi + 1) = b + 1 + \frac{b(b+1)}{2}$$

numbers; evaluating the first $n - 1$ functions $\Lambda_k(\xi)$ requires $n - 1$ times the above number. Only $\Lambda_n(b)$ is needed and this requires $b + 1$ comparisons. Thus the total number of comparisons is

$$b\left[n + \frac{(n-1)(b+1)}{2}\right] + n,$$

which for $n = 5$, $b = 20$, yields 945. Therefore the number of comparisons which must be made by means of the computational method introduced in the last section requires considerably less than one-tenth the number of comparisons required if one simply evaluated the objective function for all possible combinations of non-negative integers x_j which satisfy the constraint. Furthermore, using the computational technique introduced in the previous section, we need to perform a single addition to compute the numbers to be compared, whereas n additions are required to evaluate z for a given set of x_j.

The computational efficiency of the dynamic programming approach as compared to a direct enumeration becomes more and more impressive as n is increased. The reason for this greater efficiency is that at each step for a given ξ, all unfavorable combinations of variables are eliminated and are not carried over to the next step where they would have to be reconsidered.

10–4 General nature of dynamic programming. Usually, the problem studied in Section 10–2 can be imagined to be an allocation problem in which there is a single limited resource, and x_j is the quantity of resource to be allocated to activity j. Then $f_j(x_j)$ can be thought of as the return from activity j when x_j units of the resource are allocated to it. With this interpretation in mind, $\Lambda_k(\xi)$ is simply the maximum return from the first k activities when a total quantity ξ of the resource is available for allocation to these activities. Similarly $\hat{x}_k(\xi)$ is the optimal value for x_k when there are only k activities and a quantity ξ of the resource is available for allocation to these activities.

The problem of Section 10–2 can be thought of as an n-stage decision problem, where at stage j the decision is made on how much to allocate to activity j, that is, x_j is selected. The basic nature of the problem is unchanged regardless of how many stages there are; in other words, it has the same form regardless of what n happens to be. The dynamic programming approach to solving the problem makes use of this fact and really solves a sequence of problems beginning with a one-stage problem, moving on to a two-stage one, etc., until finally all n stages are included. The solution for k stages is obtained from the solution for $k - 1$ stages by adding the kth stage and making use of the solution for $k - 1$ stages. When only k stages are considered, the optimal values of the x_j, $j = 1, \ldots, k$, depend on ξ, the total quantity of the resource which is available for allocation to the k stages. Once the $f_j(x_j)$ and a_j are specified, the quantity ξ of the resource available for allocation to the k stages is the only parameter which influences the x_j-values, i.e., the quantity which should be allocated to each stage. The dynamic programming approach not only solves the problem for $1, 2, \ldots, n$ stages, but in addition, determines for each $k < n$ an optimal solution for every value of ξ up to the amount b ultimately available for all n stages. We must, in general, know the solution for $k - 1$ stages for every $\zeta = 0, 1, \ldots, \xi$ in order to find the optimal solution when there are k stages with an amount ξ of the resource available for allocation to these k stages. The essence of the dynamic programming approach was, then, that aspect of the procedure which permitted us to solve a given n-stage problem by solving a whole sequence of problems, first for a one-stage, then a two-stage, etc., and finally the n-stage problem. What made this approach feasible was the fact that one stage could be added at a time, and the solution for k stages could be obtained relatively simply if the solution for $k - 1$ stages was known for all possible quantities of the resource ξ which might be available for allocation to the first $k - 1$ stages.

The simple problem studied in Section 10–2 illustrated the main features which will be encountered in the process of solving a problem by dynamic programming. We shall now attempt to discuss in somewhat more general terms precisely what the dynamic programming approach for solving a problem is. To do this, we must first describe the type of problem which can be attacked by the use of this technique. First of all, it must be possible to think of the problem as an n-stage decision problem, where at stage j the decision involves the selection of one or more control variables. Furthermore, the problem must be defined for any number of stages, and must have the same structure regardless of how many stages there are. When considering a problem involving k stages, there must be a certain set of parameters which describe the state of the system, i.e., parameters on which the optimal values of the control variables and the value of the objective function for the k-stage problem will depend. The same set of parameters must describe the state of the system regardless of how many stages there are. There was only a single parameter for the problem studied in Section 10–2, and it was ξ, the quantity of the resource available for allocation to the k stages. Selecting the control variable or variables for stage k in a k-stage problem must, for the remaining $k - 1$ stages have no effect other than that of changing the parameters which describe the state with k stages into the set of parameters which describe the state of the system with $k - 1$ stages.

When the above conditions are fulfilled, one can usually formulate the problem within the framework of dynamic programming, and thus solve a whole sequence of problems, beginning with a one-stage problem, a two-stage problem, etc., until finally the n-stage problem is solved. This is done as follows. Let $\boldsymbol{\xi}$ denote a vector containing the parameters which describe the state of the system when there are k stages. We shall call these the *state parameters.* Then $\Lambda_k(\boldsymbol{\xi})$ will be defined to be the optimal value of the objective function when there are k stages and the state parameters are described by $\boldsymbol{\xi}$. The $\Lambda_k(\boldsymbol{\xi})$ will be referred to as *state functions.* Denote by $\mathbf{x}_k$ a vector containing the variables to be selected at stage k. Assume that once an $\mathbf{x}_k$ and $\boldsymbol{\xi}$ are selected, the vector of the state parameters for the remaining $k - 1$ stages is $\mathbf{T}(\boldsymbol{\xi}, \mathbf{x}_k)$. The essential feature of the dynamic programming approach is the development of a set of recurrence relations such that $\Lambda_k(\boldsymbol{\xi})$ can be determined in a relatively simple way once $\Lambda_{k-1}(\boldsymbol{\zeta})$ is known for all $\boldsymbol{\zeta}$ that might be appropriate for the $(k - 1)$-stage problem. Typically, the recurrence relations will have a form such as

$$\Lambda_k(\boldsymbol{\xi}) = \max_{\mathbf{x}_k} \{f_k(\boldsymbol{\xi}, \mathbf{x}_k) + \Lambda_{k-1}[\mathbf{T}(\boldsymbol{\xi}, \mathbf{x}_k)]\}. \tag{10–28}$$

However, this is by no means the only form which they can take. Many other forms are possible, and some of these will be illustrated later. When $\Lambda_k(\boldsymbol{\xi})$ is obtained for a given $\boldsymbol{\xi}$, then we have also determined $\hat{\mathbf{x}}_k(\boldsymbol{\xi})$, the optimal values of the decision variables for stage k when there are k stages and the state parameters for these stages are described by $\boldsymbol{\xi}$. We shall call the $\hat{\mathbf{x}}_k(\boldsymbol{\xi})$ the *policy functions.* At the nth stage, we obtain

$$z^* = \Lambda_n(\boldsymbol{\xi}_0)$$

and $\mathbf{x}_n^*$, where $\boldsymbol{\xi}_0$ is the set of state parameters appropriate to the given problem.

Note that (10–19) is a special case of (10–28). For the problem of Section 10–2 there was only a single state parameter, and only a single control variable was to be selected at each stage. This will be true of all problems studied in this chapter. We shall defer until the next chapter the study of cases with more than a single state parameter, or more than a single control variable to be selected at each stage. Equation (10–28) can be given an interesting physical interpretation, which is really the basis for the existence of the recurrence relations that are involved in the solution of a problem by dynamic programming. It says that we cannot have an optimal value of the objective function for k stages unless for any $\mathbf{x}_k$ selected for stage k, the value of the objective function for the remaining $k - 1$ stages is optimal, given the $\mathbf{x}_k$ selected for stage k. Bellman [3] refers to this statement as the *principle of optimality*. It can be used to obtain directly the recurrence relations involving the state functions. In general, we shall not obtain the recurrence relations in this manner, but will derive them from the definitions of the state functions.

The general description of the characteristics of dynamic programming and the sorts of problems which can be formulated in the format of dynamic programming must necessarily be very general and somewhat vague, since there exists an immense variety of widely different types of problems which can be formulated as dynamic programming problems. It is only by studying a number of examples that one obtains a better understanding of the structure of dynamic programming. We shall do this in the remainder of the present chapter and in the next chapter. In the course of formulating a problem as a dynamic programming problem, it is usually easy to recognize the n-stage structure. Probably the most subtle task is to select the state parameters. Once this is accomplished, it is usually straightforward to obtain the recurrence relations.

10–5 A numerical example. Let us work out a greatly simplified example of the stocking of a submarine with spare parts. We shall imagine that there are only three parts to be stocked and that these have unit volumes of 1, 2, and 2 ft^3, respectively. A total of 10 ft^3 of storage space is available. The stockout costs π_j are \$800, \$600, and \$1300, respectively. It will be imagined that the demand for each spare part has a Poisson distribution and that the means are 4, 2, and 1, respectively. We wish to determine how many of each spare part should be stocked so as to minimize the expected stockout cost while not exceeding the storage space available.

In mathematical terms, we wish to determine non-negative integers x_1, x_2, x_3 which minimize

$$z = \sum_{j=1}^{3} \left[\pi_j \sum_{v_j=x_j}^{\infty} (v_j - x_j)p(v_j; \mu_j) \right] \tag{10–29}$$

while satisfying

$$x_1 + 2x_2 + 2x_3 \leq 10.$$

In the objective function,

$$p(v_j; \mu_j) = \frac{\mu_j^{v_j}}{v_j!} e^{-\mu_j} \tag{10–30}$$

is the Poisson density function, and μ_j is the expected demand for item j. From (10–30), note that

$$v_j p(v_j; \mu_j) = \mu_j p(v_j - 1; \mu_j), \qquad v_j \geq 1.$$

Thus we can write

$$\sum_{v_j=x_j}^{\infty} (v_j - x_j)p(v_j; \mu_j) = \begin{cases} \mu_j P(x_j - 1; \mu_j) - x_j P(x_j; \mu_j), & x_j \geq 1, \\ \mu_j, \quad x_j = 0, \end{cases} \tag{10–31}$$

where

$$P(x_j; \mu_j) = \sum_{v_j=x_j}^{\infty} p(v_j; \mu_j)$$

is the complementary cumulative function. Equation (10–31) makes it easy to evaluate the expected number of demands for item j occurring when the system is out of stock on j, since the complementary cumulative function for the Poisson distribution is tabulated in tables such as those given in [14]. Let

$$\Lambda_k(\xi) = \min_{x_1, \ldots, x_k} \sum_{j=1}^{k} \pi_j[\mu_j P(x_j - 1; \mu_j) - x_j P(x_j; \mu_j)], \tag{10–32}$$

where the minimization is carried out over non-negative integers satisfying $\sum_{j=1}^{k} a_j x_j \leq \xi$ when a_j is the unit volume of x_j. Then $z^* = \Lambda_3(10)$.

If the suggestion of the text in Section 10–2 were followed, we would tabulate Λ_1, Λ_2 for all $\xi = 0, 1, \ldots, 10$. To save computational effort we have constructed an example where it is only necessary to tabulate Λ_1, Λ_2 for even ξ. To see this, note that x_3 can take on the values 0, $1, \ldots, 5$; thus to compute $\Lambda_3(10)$, we need Λ_2 for $\xi = 10$ ($x_3 = 0$), 8, 6, 4, 2, 0 ($x_3 = 5$). However, to evaluate $\Lambda_2(\xi)$, we need Λ_1 for all $\xi - 2x_2$, $x_2 = 0, 1, \ldots, [\xi/2]$, that is, since $\Lambda_2(\xi)$ is needed only for even ξ, $\Lambda_1(\xi)$ is also needed for even ξ.

To evaluate $\Lambda_1(\xi)$, no minimization needs to be carried out, because the stockout cost for item 1 will be minimized by stocking as many units of item 1 as possible. Thus

$$\Lambda_1(\xi) = 800[4P(\xi - 1; 4) - \xi P(\xi; 4)]; \qquad \hat{x}_1(\xi) = \xi.$$

The values of $\Lambda_1(\xi)$ and $\hat{x}_1(\xi)$ are given in Table 10–2. For example

$$\Lambda_1(6) = 800[4P(5; 4) - 6P(6; 4)] = 800[4(0.3712) - 6(0.2149)]$$
$$= \$156.32.$$

TABLE 10–2

ξ	$\Lambda_1(\xi)$	$\hat{x}_1(\xi)$	$\Lambda_2(\xi)$	$\hat{x}_2(\xi)$
0	3200	0	4400	0
2	1688	2	2888	0
4	625.3	4	1825.3	0
6	156.32	6	1306.5	1
8	26.91	8	837.5	1
10	3.30	10	481.1	2

To compute Λ_2, Λ_3 we use the recurrence relation

$$\Lambda_k(\xi) = \min_{0 \le x_k \le [\xi/a_k]} \{\pi_k[\mu_k P(x_k - 1;\mu_k) - x_k P(x_k;\mu_k)] + \Lambda_{k-1}(\xi - a_k x_k)\}, \quad k = 2, 3. \tag{10–33}$$

Let us illustrate with the computation of $\Lambda_2(8)$. For $\xi = 8$, x_2 can take on the values 0, 1, 2, 3, 4. For each of these values, we compute

$$\Omega_2(x_2;8) = 600[2P(x_2 - 1;2) - x_2P(x_2;2)] + \Lambda_1(8 - 2x_2),$$

and Λ_2 is the smallest of these. Before computing any of the $\Lambda_2(\xi)$, one should compute $600[2P(x_2 - 1;2) - x_2P(x_2;2)]$ for $x_2 = 0, 1, 2, 3, 4, 5$ since all these values will be used in determining the various $\Lambda_2(\xi)$. For the case under consideration, we find that $\Omega_2(0;8) = 1226.9$, $\Omega_2(1;8) = 837.5$, $\Omega_2(2;8) = 950.1$. It is not necessary to evaluate $\Omega_2(3;8)$, $\Omega_2(4;8)$, since they are clearly greater than $\Omega_2(2;8)$. Note that

$$\Omega_2(1;8) = 681.2 + \Lambda_1(6) = 681.2 + 156.3 = 837.5 = \Lambda_2(8).$$

It remains to evaluate $\Lambda_3(10)$. For $\Omega_3(x_3;10)$, we find $\Omega_3(0;10) = 1781.1$, $\Omega_3(1;10) = 1315.8$, $\Omega_3(2;10) = 1441.3$. It is unnecessary to compute $\Omega_3(4;10)$, $\Omega_3(5;10)$, since they are greater than $\Omega_3(2;10)$. Thus $z^* = \Lambda_3(10) = \Omega_3(1;10) = \$1315.8$ and $x_3^* = 1$. To compute x_2^* and x_1^*, we note that

$$x_2^* = \hat{x}_2(10 - 2) = \hat{x}_2(8) = 1; \quad x_1^* = \hat{x}_1(10 - 2 - 2) = \hat{x}_1(6) = 6.$$

The unique optimal solution to the problem is then $x_1^* = 6$, $x_2^* = 1$, $x_3^* = 1$, with the minimum expected stockout cost being $1315.8.

10–6 Some other practical examples. In this section we shall give three other examples of problems of the mathematical form (10–1) which can be encountered in practice.

(1) *Cargo-loading problems.* Let us assume that n different items are available for loading on a vessel of limited volume b. The unit volume and unit value of item j will be denoted by a_j and p_j, respectively. We wish to determine the number of units, x_j, of each product that should be loaded on the vessel in order to maximize the value of the cargo. Mathematically, we wish to determine non-negative integers x_j which satisfy

$$\sum_{j=1}^{n} a_j x_j \leq b$$

and maximize

$$z = \sum_{j=1}^{n} p_j x_j.$$

This is the simplest type of problem of the form (10–1), since the $f_j(x_j) = p_j x_j$ are linear in the x_j. The cargo-loading problem can also be considered an integer linear programming problem.

(2) *Allocation of a procurement to a number of warehouses.* Consider a large inventory system which consists of a number n of warehouses located all over the continental United States. Periodically, a certain item stocked by the warehouses is ordered from its manufacturer. Imagine that the warehouses do not place orders individually, but that ordering is done centrally for all warehouses at the same time. Suppose that a quantity Q has been ordered from the manufacturer on some particular occasion. There will be a lead time between the date at which the order is placed and the date at which it is ready to be shipped to the various warehouses. When the order is ready to be shipped, it is necessary to decide how the Q units will be allocated among the n warehouses. For simplicity, it will be imagined that warehouses will not receive any further shipment of the product under consideration for a time period of length T, i.e., until the next procurement is made. The units are to be allocated to the warehouses in a way that will minimize the sum of transportation costs plus expected stockout costs in the period preceding the next procurement.

Let $C_j(x_j)$ be the cost of transporting x_j units from the factory to warehouse j, y_j the on-hand inventory of the product at warehouse j at the time the allocation is made, π_j the cost incurred for each unit demanded when warehouse j is out of stock, and $p_j(v_j)$ the probability that v_j units will be demanded at warehouse j in a time T. Then, ignoring the transportation time, we find that the cost of transportation to warehouse j plus expected stockout costs at j if x_j units are shipped to j is

$$f_j(x_j) = C_j(x_j) + \pi_j \sum_{v_j=y_j+x_j}^{\infty} (v_j - y_j - x_j) p_j(v_j). \qquad (10\text{–}34)$$

Thus we wish to determine non-negative integers x_j satisfying

$$\sum_{j=1}^{n} x_j = Q,$$

and minimizing

$$z = \sum_{j=1}^{n} f_j(x_j),$$

where $f_j(x_j)$ is given by (10–34). When solving this problem it is at times possible to use various computational shortcuts. For example, it might be known *a priori* that it would not be optimal to ship more than $Q/3$ to any given warehouse. In this case, one would not need to evaluate the $f_j(x_j)$ for $x_j > Q/3$; furthermore, if $\xi > Q/3$, the search over $\Omega_k(x_k;\, \xi)$ to determine $\Lambda_k(\xi)$ would not need to be carried beyond $x_k = Q/3$. Also $\Lambda_1(\xi)$ and $\Lambda_2(\xi)$ must be tabulated only up to $\xi = Q/3$ and $\xi = 2Q/3$, respectively. Moreover, packaging and shipment specifications may simplify matters further. For example, there may be a certain minimum package size, and it may be stipulated that shipments must be made in integral multiples of this size; or there may be some rule stating that up to 25 units, any number can be shipped, whereas from 25 to 100 units only multiples of 5 units and for over 100 units only multiples of 10 units are to be shipped.

(3) *Allocation of tolerances.* Consider some product which is assembled from n pieces. Associated with each of the n pieces is some measurable characteristic which may be a physical dimension, electrical resistance, etc. Denote by x_j the value of the characteristic for piece j. There is also a measurable characteristic associated with the final product, which is perhaps an overall dimension or a voltage. Let y be the value of this characteristic. Then imagine that y is related to the x_j by the function $y = g(x_1, \ldots, x_n)$. If y is measured on a number of different assembled units it will be found that y varies somewhat from one unit to the next, and really behaves like a random variable. The reason for this is that the x_j must themselves be considered to be random variables, for example, the dimension of part j used in the assembly must be considered to be a random variable. Let μ_j be the expected value of x_j. We shall suppose that the deviations of x_j from μ_j are not large.

By Taylor's theorem we can write approximately

$$y = g(x_1, \ldots, x_n) = g(\mu_1, \ldots, \mu_n) + \sum_{j=1}^{n} \left(\frac{\partial g}{\partial x_j}\right)_0 (x_j - \mu_j), \tag{10–35}$$

where $(\partial g/\partial x_j)_0$ is $\partial g/\partial x_j$ evaluated at $\mu_1, \ldots, \mu_n$. Taking the expected value of y, we see from (10–35) that the expected value μ_y satisfies

$$\mu_y \doteq g(\mu_1, \ldots, \mu_n). \tag{10–36}$$

Let us now imagine that the x_j are independent random variables. Then from (10–35) we see that σ_y^2, the variance of y, is

$$\sigma_y^2 \doteq \sum_{j=1}^{n} \left(\frac{\partial g}{\partial x_j}\right)_0^2 \sigma_j^2, \tag{10–37}$$

where σ_j^2 is the variance of x_j.

Assume that for an assembled unit to pass inspection, y must lie in the interval $y_1 \leq y \leq y_2$. Assume also that y is essentially normally distributed with its mean given by (10–36). The probability that y lies outside the interval $y_1 \leq y \leq y_2$ will then be the long-run fraction of the assembled units that will be classified as defective and will not pass inspection. Once μ_y and the long-run fraction defective are specified, σ_y^2 is determined. The value of σ_y^2 is, of course, determined in turn by the values of the σ_j^2. Now assume that the μ_j are chosen so that $\mu_y = (y_1 + y_2)/2$. Then for any given σ_y^2, the long-run fraction defective is minimized. However, the long-run fraction defective will depend on σ_y^2 and will decrease as σ_y^2 is decreased. Let us suppose that within limits, we can make σ_j^2 as low as desired, but that the installed cost of part j increases as σ_j^2 is decreased. We shall imagine that the σ_j^2 can be assigned only discrete values (say, 1 or 5 per cent resistors), and, if x_j has a variance of σ_j^2, the installed cost of part j is $f_j(\sigma_j^2)$. There may not be any combination of σ_j^2 which yields σ_y^2 exactly when σ_y^2 is specified so as to yield a given long-run fraction defective. Suppose, however, that we would like to determine the minimum cost of the assembled unit as a function of the long-run fraction defective. Specification of the fraction defective f determines σ_y^2, and for this σ_y^2, the σ_j^2 which minimize the cost are the $\sigma_j^2 \geq 0$ satisfying

$$\begin{gathered} \sum_{j=1}^{n} \left(\frac{\partial g}{\partial x_j}\right)_0^2 \sigma_j^2 \leq \sigma_y^2, \\ \min z = \sum_{j=1}^{n} f_j(\sigma_j^2), \end{gathered} \tag{10–38}$$

which is of the form (10–1) in the variables σ_j^2.

The computational scheme introduced in Section 10–2 makes it very easy to trace out a sequence of optimal solutions as b is changed. All that is required is that at the last stage, $\Lambda_n(\xi)$ is evaluated for all the b-values of interest, not merely a single b-value. Hence very little additional computational effort is needed to study how z^* and the x_j^* change as b is changed. Of course, in making the computation, one would evaluate all the $\Lambda_k(\xi)$, $k = 1, \ldots, n - 1$, for all integers ξ up to the largest b that was of interest. Consequently, it would be quite easy to generate the curve giving the minimum cost of the assembled unit as a function of the long-run fraction defective. This is the curve we wanted.

10–7 Case where variables are continuous. Unlike the other computational methods we have studied, dynamic programming lends itself better to problems whose variables are restricted to being discrete than to those whose variables are allowed to be continuous. Let us consider the problems involved in solving (10–1) when we no longer require that the x_j be integral. We shall then also drop the restriction that the a_j, b be integers.

Formally, we can proceed precisely as in Section 10–2. Let us define the sequence of state functions

$$\Lambda_k(\xi) = \max_{x_1,\ldots,x_k} \sum_{j=1}^{k} f_j(x_j), \qquad k = 1, \ldots, n, \tag{10–39}$$

where in carrying out the maximization we consider only non-negative x_j which satisfy

$$\sum_{j=1}^{k} a_j x_j \leq b. \tag{10–40}$$

Then, precisely as before,

$$\Lambda_1(\xi) = \max_{0 \leq x_1 \leq b/a_1} f_1(x_1). \tag{10–41}$$

Note that x_1 varies up to b/a_1, not $[b/a_1]$. The same recurrence relations follow that applied to the case where the x_j were to be integers, that is,

$$\Lambda_k(\xi) = \max_{0 \leq x_k \leq b/a_k} [f_k(x_k) + \Lambda_{k-1}(\xi - a_k x_k)], \qquad k = 2, \ldots, n, \tag{10–42}$$

and $z^* = \Lambda_n(b)$.

The differences between the present problem and that of Section 10–2 arise in the course of maximizing over x_k, and in the manner of determining the tables of $\Lambda_k(\xi)$. Let us first examine the problem of determining $\Lambda_k(\xi)$ for a fixed ξ. Then

$$\Lambda_k(\xi) = \max_{0 \leq x_k \leq b/a_k} \Omega_k(x_k; \xi), \tag{10–43}$$

where

$$\Omega_k(x_k; \xi) = f_k(x_k) + \Lambda_{k-1}(\xi - a_k x_k). \tag{10–44}$$

Assume that the function $\Lambda_{k-1}(\xi)$ is known. Now $\Omega_k(x_k; \xi)$ is defined over a continuum of values x_k in the interval $0 \leq x_k \leq b/a_k$. If $\Omega_k(x_k; \xi)$ is plotted, it might look like the curve shown in Fig. 10–2. We would like to determine the value $\hat{x}_k(\xi)$ at which $\Omega_k(x_k; \xi)$ assumes its maximum value.

When it is not known whether Ω_k will have a unique maximum, one has little choice but to search for all the relative maxima and then select the one (or those) x_k which maximizes Ω_k. To reduce as much as possible the

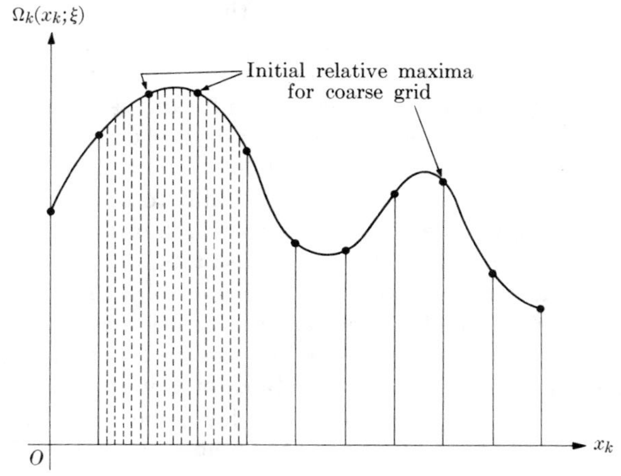

FIGURE 10-2

computational effort required, one might do a rough initial search using a coarse grid; that is, $\Omega_k(x_k;\ \xi)$ would be evaluated at the widely spaced mesh points (solid lines) shown in Fig. 10-2, and thus the approximate location of the maximum would be found. Then a finer grid (dashed lines in Fig. 10-2) would be used in the neighborhood of the maximum to determine $\hat{x}_k(\xi)$ more accurately. The procedure of using a finer grid might be repeated several times to obtain the desired accuracy in $\hat{x}_k(\xi)$. During the coarse search, one would not necessarily make a finer search only in the neighborhood of the largest value obtained. Instead, each relative maximum on the coarse grid would be determined, and if several of these relative maxima were close enough to the largest value of $\Omega_k(x_k;\ \xi)$ obtained, a finer search would be made in the neighborhood of each to make sure that the actual maximum did not lie in the neighborhood of one of the relative maxima which did not yield the absolute maximum with respect to the coarse grid. One would have to develop some criterion indicating precisely which relative maxima should be included. It will be observed that the search procedure is not completely foolproof. It is possible that our original grid was so coarse that it completely missed the point where $\Omega_k(x_k;\xi)$ took on its maximum. In theory, one cannot guarantee that this will not happen, no matter how fine the initial grid is. We have now presented a procedure by which $\hat{x}_k(\xi)$ and $\Lambda_k(\xi)$ can usually be found to any accuracy desired. Of course, the greater the accuracy required, the greater will be the computational effort needed. In the next section, we shall show that the search procedure required to determine $\hat{x}_k(\xi)$ and $\Lambda_k(\xi)$ can be considerably simplified if the $f_j(x_j)$ happen to be concave or convex functions. However, if they are not, one has little choice but to go through a search procedure of the type described above.

Consider next the problems which arise in the tabulation of the $\Lambda_k(\xi)$. A difficulty is encountered here because $\Lambda_k(\xi)$ is defined for all ξ, $0 \leq \xi \leq b$. Furthermore, examination of the search procedure introduced above shows that $\Lambda_k(\xi)$ may actually be needed for any ξ in this interval, due to the fact that when finer and finer grids are used to determine $\Lambda_k(\xi)$ for a given ξ, Λ_{k-1} may be required for a very large number of different arguments. It would usually be impossible to tabulate the $\Lambda_k(\xi)$ for all possible ξ that might be required with the search procedure described above. Clearly, if this cannot be done, we must tabulate the $\Lambda_k(\xi)$ for a smaller number of ξ and then interpolate in these tables to obtain the Λ_k for the other arguments needed. However, interpolation cannot be safely used unless we know that the $\Lambda_k(\xi)$ are continuous functions of ξ. In general, they need not be continuous functions of ξ if the $f_j(x_j)$ are not continuous functions of x_j. Unfortunately, for some applications, we would like to allow the $f_j(x_j)$ to have a finite number of jumps. However, this complicates matters considerably, when the variables are to be treated as continuous. We shall say something below about how the case of discontinuous $f_j(x_j)$ may be treated. For the present, let us assume that each $f_j(x_j)$ is a continuous function of x_j. We shall then prove that all the $\Lambda_k(\xi)$ are continuous functions of ξ.

The proof that the $\Lambda_k(\xi)$ are continuous if the $f_j(x_j)$ are is made by induction. Consider first

$$\Lambda_1(\xi) = \max_{0 \leq x_1 \leq \xi/a_1} f_1(x_1).$$

To show that $\Lambda_1(\xi)$ is continuous, we must show that for every ξ, there exists a $\delta(\epsilon, \xi) > 0$ such that for all ζ, $|\zeta - \xi| < \delta$, $|\Lambda_1(\zeta) - \Lambda_1(\xi)| < \epsilon$ for any $\epsilon > 0$. Now it follows from the definition of $\Lambda_1(\zeta)$ and $\Lambda_1(\xi)$ that both are determined by finding the largest value of $f_1(x_1)$ over some interval. Furthermore, the interval over which the search is made differs only at the right end by an interval of length $|\zeta - \xi|$. Consequently, $|\Lambda_1(\zeta) - \Lambda_1(\xi)|$ is less than or equal to, the difference of the maximum value of $f_1(x_1)$ and the minimum value of $f_1(x_1)$ over the interval of length $|\zeta - \xi|$. However, by the continuity of $f_1(x_1)$, this variation can be made arbitrarily small by choosing $|\zeta - \xi|$ small enough. Therefore $|\Lambda_1(\zeta) - \Lambda_1(\xi)|$ can be made arbitrarily small if $|\zeta - \xi|$ is made small enough, and $\Lambda_1(\xi)$ is continuous.

To carry out the inductive step, assume that $\Lambda_{k-1}(\xi)$ is continuous. We shall then show that in this case, $\Lambda_k(\xi)$ is also continuous. Let

$$\Omega_k(x_k; \xi) = f_k(x_k) + \Lambda_{k-1}(\xi - a_k x_k). \tag{10–45}$$

Then $\Omega_k(x_k; \xi)$ is a continuous function of x_k and ξ, since Λ_{k-1} and f_k are continuous. Consequently, $\Lambda_k(\zeta)$ and $\Lambda_k(\xi)$ cannot differ by more than the greater of (illustrate graphically)

$$\gamma_1 = \max_{x_k} |\Omega_k(x_k;\, \xi) - \Omega_k(x_k;\, \zeta)|, \qquad 0 \le x_k \le \min(\xi, \zeta) = \epsilon,$$

and

$$\gamma_2 = \max_{x_k} \Omega_k(x_k; \psi) - \min_{x_k} \Omega_k(x_k; \psi) + |\Omega_k(\epsilon;\, \zeta) - \Omega_k(\epsilon;\, \xi)|,$$

$$\epsilon \le x_k \le \epsilon + |\zeta - \xi|, \qquad \psi = \max(\xi, \zeta).$$

However, because of the continuity of $\Omega_k(x_k;\, \xi)$, γ_1, γ_2, as well as $|\Lambda_k(\zeta) - \Lambda_k(\xi)|$, can be made arbitrarily small by making $|\zeta - \xi|$ small enough. Thus $\Lambda_k(\xi)$ is continuous if $\Lambda_{k-1}(\xi)$ is. Consequently, all the $\Lambda_k(\xi)$ are continuous if the $f_j(x_j)$ are continuous.

The above arguments show that if the $f_j(x_j)$ are continuous, the $\Lambda_k(\xi)$ will be continuous, and one can usually interpolate safely in the tables of $\Lambda_k(\xi)$. Generally, the procedure would be to tabulate the $\Lambda_k(\xi)$ at points ξ_u, $\xi_u = \xi_{u-1} + \Delta\xi$ and to use linear interpolation to obtain $\Lambda_k(\xi)$ for ξ other than the ξ_u. Fortunately, the $\Lambda_k(\xi)$ are frequently very smooth functions which do not change rapidly with ξ. Thus $\Delta\xi$ can be chosen to be fairly large in such cases and the number of entries in the $\Lambda_k(\xi)$-tables does not need to be excessively great. The ultimate accuracy of the computation will, of course, depend in part on the value of $\Delta\xi$ chosen.

Even though the $\Lambda_k(\xi)$ are continuous, it need not be true at all that the $\hat{x}_k(\xi)$ are continuous. The fact that the $\hat{x}_k(\xi)$ can be discontinuous causes difficulties if we attempt to tabulate the $\hat{x}_k(\xi)$ only at the same values ξ_u for which the $\Lambda_k(\xi)$ are tabulated, and then later use these tables to determine the x_k^*. The reason is that to compute

$$x_{n-i}^* = \hat{x}_{n-i}\left(b - \sum_{u=0}^{i-1} a_{n-u} x_{n-u}^*\right),$$

it may be necessary to evaluate $\hat{x}_{n-1}(\xi)$ for a value of ξ different from one of the tabulated values; thus interpolation may be required. However, if $\hat{x}_{n-i}(\xi)$ happens to be discontinuous in the interval of interpolation, the value obtained may be far from the true x_{n-i}^*. This is illustrated in Fig. 10–3, where the true $\hat{x}_k(\xi)$-curve is represented by the solid curve, and the tabulated points by the dots. If one had to interpolate between ξ_u and ξ_{u+1}, one would estimate x_k^* to be at B, whereas the correct value is at A.

It is possible to avoid the problems discussed by simply omitting the tabulation of the $\hat{x}_k(\xi)$, and, instead, computing the values of $\hat{x}_k(\xi)$ directly for the values needed. Imagine then that we proceed as before, but tabulate only the $\Lambda_k(\xi)$. At the last stage we determine $\Lambda_n(b)$ and x_n^*. To obtain

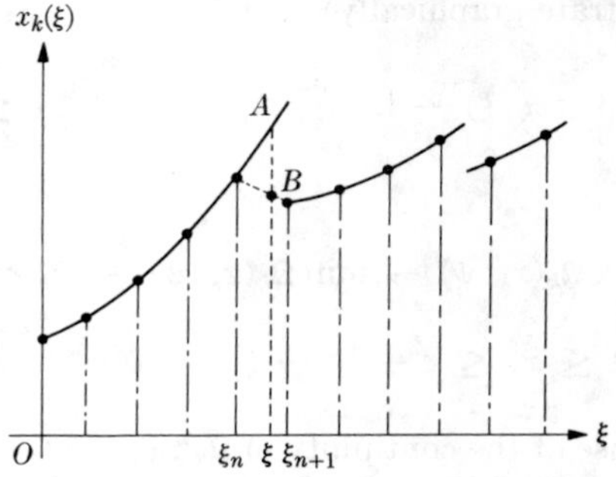

FIGURE 10–3

$x_{n-1}^* = \hat{x}_{n-1}(b - a_n x_n^*)$, we actually determine $\Lambda_{n-1}(b - a_n x_n^*)$ by direct computation:

$$\Lambda_{n-1}(b - a_n x_n^*) = \max_{x_{n-1}} [f_{n-1}(x_{n-1}) + \Lambda_{n-2}(b - a_n x_n^* - a_{n-1}x_{n-1})].$$

In doing so we obtain directly $x_{n-1}^* = \hat{x}_n(b - a_n x_n^*)$. The same procedure is then used to compute x_{n-2}^* directly, etc. This method is the only one which guarantees that the x_k^* are determined accurately. Note that all $\Lambda_k(\xi)$-tables must be retained in order to perform these computations.

It was indicated earlier that great difficulties are encountered when one attempts to treat the variables as continuous and the $f_j(x_j)$ as discontinuous. If the $f_j(x_j)$ are discontinuous, it is best to convert the problem into a discrete one by imagining that the variables can only take on values $x_j = m\,\Delta x$, $m = 0, 1, 2, \ldots, M_j$. If one introduces a new set of variables y_j which take on only the values $0, 1, \ldots, M_j$, so that $x_j = (\Delta x)y_j$, the problem becomes

$$\sum_{j=1}^{n} (a_j\,\Delta x)y_j \leq b,$$

$$y_j \geq 0, \qquad y_j \text{ integers}, \tag{10–46}$$

$$\max z = \sum_{j=1}^{n} f_j(y_j\,\Delta x),$$

and assumes the form (10–1).

Fortunately, for many practical problems, the x_j are naturally discrete variables, or it is very easy to treat them as discrete. For this reason, many of the above-mentioned difficulties which arise when the x_j must be treated as continuous do not cause as many difficulties in practice as might be at first imagined. Indeed, strictly speaking, one will usually find that treating the variables as continuous, rather than treating them as discrete, is what requires the making of approximations.

10–8 Case where the $f_j(x_j)$ are convex or concave. Let us again consider a problem of the type (10–1) when the variables x_j are assumed to be continuous, that is, are not restricted to being integers. We shall now see what simplifications can be introduced into the computational procedure suggested in the previous section when the $f_j(x_j)$ are convex or concave functions.

Consider first the case where the $f_j(x_j)$ are convex functions. We shall then show that the $\Lambda_k(\xi)$ are convex functions of ξ. This will be done by induction. For notational simplicity (and without loss of generality) we shall assume in the following that each $a_j = 1$.

$$\Lambda_1(\lambda\xi_1 + (1 - \lambda)\xi_2) = \max_{0 \le x_1 \le \lambda\xi_1 + (1-\lambda)\xi_2} f_1(x_1). \tag{10–47}$$

Now write $x_1 = \lambda x_1' + (1 - \lambda)x_1''$. Then having x_1 vary between 0 and $\lambda\xi_1 + (1 - \lambda)\xi_2$ is equivalent to having x_1' vary between 0 and ξ_1 and x_2'' vary between 0 and ξ_2 when x_1' and x_2'' can be varied independently. Thus (10–47) is equivalent to

$$\Lambda_1(\lambda\xi_1 + (1 - \lambda)\xi_2) = \max_{\substack{0 \le x_1' \le \xi_1 \\ 0 \le x_1'' \le \xi_2}} f_1(\lambda x_1' + (1 - \lambda)x_1''). \tag{10–48}$$

However, since $f_1(x_1)$ is a convex function,

$$\begin{aligned}\Lambda_1(\lambda\xi_1 + (1 - \lambda)\xi_2) &\le \max_{\substack{0 \le x_1' \le \xi_1 \\ 0 \le x_1'' \le \xi_2}} [\lambda f_1(x_1') + (1 - \lambda)f_1(x_1'')] \\ &\le \lambda \max_{0 \le x_1' \le \xi_1} f_1(x_1') + (1 - \lambda) \max_{0 \le x_1'' \le \xi_2} f_1(x_1'') \\ &\le \lambda\Lambda_1(\xi_1) + (1 - \lambda)\Lambda_1(\xi_2).\end{aligned} \tag{10–49}$$

Therefore, $\Lambda_1(\xi)$ is a convex function.

Assume next that $\Lambda_{k-1}(\xi)$ is a convex function. We shall then prove that $\Lambda_k(\xi)$ is convex also. Define $\Omega_k(x_k; \xi)$ by (10–45). Note that since $\Lambda_{k-1}(\xi)$ is assumed to be a convex function, $\Lambda_{k-1}(\xi - a_k x_k)$ is a convex function of x_k and ξ, and since $f_k(x_k)$ is a convex function, it is a convex function of x_k and ξ [adding ξ does not matter, because $f_k(x_k)$ is independent of ξ]. Thus $\Omega_k(x_k; \xi)$ is a convex function of x_k and ξ. Now

$$\Lambda_k(\lambda\xi_1 + (1 - \lambda)\xi_2) = \max_{0 \le x_k \le \lambda\xi_1 + (1-\lambda)\xi_2} \Omega_k(x_k; \lambda\xi_1 + (1 - \lambda)\xi_2). \tag{10–50}$$

We then use the same trick as above and write $x_k = \lambda x_k' + (1 - \lambda)x_k''$.

Therefore

$$\Lambda_k(\lambda\xi_1 + (1-\lambda)\xi_2) = \max_{\substack{0\le x_k'\le\xi_1 \\ 0\le x_k''\le\xi_2}} \Omega_k(\lambda x_k' + (1-\lambda)x_k''; \lambda\xi_1 + (1-\lambda)\xi_2), \tag{10–51}$$

and, since $\Omega_k(x_k; \xi)$ is a convex function,

$$\begin{aligned}\Lambda_k(\lambda\xi_1 + (1-\lambda)\xi_2) &\le \lambda \max_{0\le x_k'\le\xi_1} \Omega_k(x_k'; \xi_1) \\ &\quad + (1-\lambda) \max_{0\le x_k''\le\xi_2} \Omega_k(x_k''; \xi_2) \\ &\le \lambda\Lambda_k(\xi_1) + (1-\lambda)\Lambda_k(\xi_2),\end{aligned} \tag{10–52}$$

and $\Lambda_k(\xi)$ is a convex function if $\Lambda_{k-1}(\xi)$ and $f_k(x_k)$ are. Thus, by induction, all the $\Lambda_k(\xi)$ are convex functions if the $f_j(x_j)$ are. Precisely the same sort of proof shows that if the $f_j(x_j)$ are concave functions, then so are the $\Lambda_k(\xi)$. Bellman [3] attributes the proof just given to Glicksberg and Fleming.

When the $f_j(x_j)$ are convex functions, the task of searching $\Omega_k(x_k; \xi)$ over x_k to determine $\Lambda_k(\xi)$ is tremendously simplified. We have shown above that $\Lambda_{k-1}(\xi)$ is a convex function of ξ, and hence $\Lambda_{k-1}(\xi - a_k x_k)$ is a convex function of x_k alone, since

$$\begin{aligned}\Lambda_{k-1}(\xi - a_k[\lambda x_k' + (1-\lambda)x_k'']) &= \Lambda_{k-1}[\lambda(\xi - a_k x_k') + (1-\lambda)(\xi - a_k x_k'')] \le \lambda\Lambda_{k-1}(\xi - a_k x_k') \\ &\quad + (1-\lambda)\Lambda_{k-1}(\xi - a_k x_k'').\end{aligned}$$

Therefore $\Omega_k(x_k; \xi)$ is a convex function of x_k for a fixed ξ, since it is the sum of two convex functions of x_k. Now

$$\Lambda_k(\xi) = \max_{0\le x_k\le\xi} \Omega(x_k; \xi).$$

However, the maximum of a convex function over a closed convex set will be assumed at one of the extreme points (Section 3–12). The convex set in this case is $0 \le x_k \le \xi$. Therefore

$$\Lambda_k(\xi) = \Omega_k(0; \xi) \quad \text{or} \quad \Omega_k(\xi; \xi). \tag{10–53}$$

No search needs to be performed at all. It is only necessary to compute Ω_k at $x_k = 0$ and ξ; $\Lambda_k(\xi)$ is the largest of these two values. In certain cases, both end points may yield $\Lambda_k(\xi)$. An interior point can yield $\Lambda_k(\xi)$

only if $\Omega_k(x_k; \xi)$ is independent of x_k. The above results show that when the $f_j(x_j)$ are convex, the task of solving the problem is considerably simplified, since no search over x_k must be made to determine $\Lambda_k(\xi)$; only the points $x_k = 0$ and ξ need to be examined.

When the $f_j(x_j)$ are concave functions, the reduction in computational effort is not so drastic as in the case where they are convex, but it can be considerable nonetheless. When the $f_j(x_j)$ are concave functions, then $\Omega_k(x_k; \xi)$ is a concave function of x_k for a fixed ξ, and hence (Section 3-12) any relative maximum is also a global maximum. One might again start with a relatively coarse grid. If the value of $\Omega_k(x_k; \xi)$ begins to decrease as x_k is increased above zero, it is immediately clear that $\Lambda_k(\xi) = \Omega_k(0; \xi)$, and no more searching is needed. If $\Omega_k(x_k; \xi)$ begins to increase, the change in Ω_k is determined each time, and when one passes through a relative maximum with respect to the coarse grid (change in Ω_k becoming negative), searching the remaining part of the interval becomes unnecessary. One can immediately use the fine grid in the neighborhood of the relative maximum. There cannot be two isolated strict relative maxima. When the Ω_k are strictly concave functions of x_k or when they are concave but one is not interested in finding all alternative optima, the search procedure can be made even much more efficient than that just described. Problem 10-30 deals with the more efficient approach.

We have noted previously that even though the $\Lambda_k(\xi)$ are continuous, the $\hat{x}_k(\xi)$-functions need not be continuous. However, when the $f_j(x_j)$ and hence $\Omega_k(x_k; \xi)$, are concave, then the $\hat{x}_k(\xi)$ are continuous. We ask the reader to prove this in Problem 10-13. If the $\hat{x}_k(\xi)$ are continuous, then we can tabulate these functions for the same ξ-values as the $\Lambda_k(\xi)$, and interpolate to estimate $\hat{x}_k(\xi)$ for values of ξ other than those tabulated. This means that we can work our way back to determine the x_k^* by interpolation in the $\hat{x}_k(\xi)$-tables, and it is unnecessary to compute the x_k^* directly as in the case where they may be discontinuous. There is yet another advantage to having the $\hat{x}_k(\xi)$ continuous. Once $\Lambda_k(\xi)$ and $\hat{x}_k(\xi)$ are determined, then in computing $\Lambda_k(\xi + \Delta\xi)$, we know that if $\Delta\xi$ is small, $\hat{x}_k(\xi + \Delta\xi)$ should be close to $\hat{x}_k(\xi)$. Thus to determine $\hat{x}_k(\xi + \Delta\xi)$ and $\Lambda_k(\xi + \Delta\xi)$, we need to search $\Omega_k(x_k; \xi + \Delta\xi)$ only in a neighborhood of $\hat{x}_k(\xi)$. This can often considerably reduce the computational effort required for searching.

10-9 Deterministic sequential decision problems. The various forms of the simple allocation problem which we have been discussing in this chapter had the property that it made absolutely no difference how we named the variables. In solving the problem, we could have considered any stage to be the first stage. There was no special time sequence that had to be observed in making the allocations to the various activities. All x_j could be selected simultaneously, or in any sequence, and it would have no influence on the optimal values of the x_j. Many problems, however, have a structure which requires that the decisions be made in some specified time sequence. Such problems can also be imagined to be multistage decision problems, and for these, there is a definite sequence in which the dynamic programming solution of the problem must be carried out, and cannot name the variables arbitrarily.

In general, for deterministic sequential decision problems, one is able to use either what will be called a *forward solution* or a *backward solution*, and one has the option of selecting one or the other. A forward solution works forward in time, with the first stage in the dynamic programming problem being that corresponding to the first decision to be made. The backward solution works backward in time so that the first stage of the dynamic programming corresponds to the last decision (in time) to be made. The criterion that determines whether a forward or backward solution is to be preferred often depends on whether some parameter in the problem is specified to be a given value at the start of the process or at the end of the process (or both at the end and the beginning). In the next section we shall use an example to clarify further the notion of forward and backward solutions.

10–10 A simple manpower loading problem. Let us imagine that a manufacturer is attempting to determine the optimal size of his work force in each of the coming n months. Production requirements have already been determined for this time period. Assume that in month j, m_j men would be the ideal number required to get out the jobs. If the manufacturer could lay off and hire workers without any cost, then he would simply use m_j men in month j. However, there are sizable layoff and hiring costs, and therefore it may not be optimal to use precisely m_j men in month j. We shall assume that the work must be done in month j but that it can be done with less than m_j men if those working put in overtime. Let x_j be the optimal number of men to use in month j. The cost of laying off or hiring men in month j will be written $f_j(x_j - x_{j-1})$; this is the cost of changing the size of the work force from month $j - 1$ to j. If $x_j - x_{j-1} > 0$, it is a hiring cost, and if $x_j - x_{j-1} < 0$, it is a layoff cost. There is no cost if there is no change in the work force so that $f_j(0) = 0$. There will be another cost $g_j(x_j - m_j)$ in month j, which is the cost incurred by not having the ideal number of men on the job. If $x_j > m_j$, it is the cost of having men idle, and if $m_j > x_j$, it is the cost of overtime. If $x_j = m_j$, it will be assumed that there is no cost so that $g_j(0) = 0$. Let us suppose that at the moment (month 0) the size of the work force is m_0.

To determine a set of optimal x_j, we must find a set of non-negative integers which minimize

$$z = \sum_{j=1}^{n} [f_j(x_j - x_{j-1}) + g_j(x_j - m_j)], \tag{10–54}$$

where $x_0 = m_0$. As the problem has been formulated, no requirements are placed on the size of the work force in month $n + 1$. The important thing to note here is that the size of the work force is specified in month 0 but not in month $n + 1$.

Let us proceed to develop the recurrence relations that can be used to solve the problem. Note that we can write

$$z = \min_{x_1} \{f_1(x_1 - m_0) + g_1(x_1 - m_1) + \min_{x_2,\ldots,x_n} \sum_{j=2}^{n} [f_j(x_j - x_{j-1}) + g_j(x_j - m_j)]\}$$

and

$$\min_{x_2,\ldots,x_n} \sum_{j=2}^{n} [f_j(x_j - x_{j-1}) + g_j(x_j - m_j)] = \min_{x_2} \{f_2(x_2 - x_1) + g_2(x_2 - m_2) + \min_{x_3,\ldots,x_n} \sum_{j=3}^{n} [f_j(x_j - x_{j-1}) + g_j(x_j - m_j)]\}.$$

This procedure can be continued in an obvious way, and it suggests that we define the sequence of functions

$$\Lambda_k(\xi) = \min_{x_k,\ldots,x_n} \sum_{j=k}^{n} [f_j(x_j - x_{j-1}) + g_j(x_j - m_j)], \quad k = 1, \ldots, n, \tag{10–55}$$

where $x_{k-1} = \xi$; in carrying out the minimization, note that the x_j are restricted to being non-negative integers. Then $z^* = \Lambda_1(m_0)$, and

$$\Lambda_n(\xi) = \min_{x_n} [f_n(x_n - \xi) + g_n(x_n - m_n)], \tag{10–56}$$

$$\Lambda_k(\xi) = \min_{x_k} [f_k(x_k - \xi) + g_k(x_k - m_k) + \Lambda_{k+1}(x_k)], \quad k = 1, \ldots, n - 1. \tag{10–57}$$

In making the computations, we would also tabulate the value(s) $\hat{x}_k(\xi)$ which yielded $\Lambda_k(\xi)$. At the last stage, x_1^* is determined. The other x_k^* are found from

$$x_k^* = \hat{x}_k(x_{k-1}^*). \tag{10–58}$$

For this problem, the state function $\Lambda_k(\xi)$ is the minimum cost for months k through n when the size of the work force in month $k - 1$ is ξ. The state parameter ξ is simply the size of the work force in period $k - 1$. Note that in this problem one works backward in time. We begin by finding the optimal work force for month n for every possible work force in month $n - 1$. Then we do the same thing for month $n - 1$. At the last step, we determine the optimal work force for month 1, given that the work force in month 0 is m_0. Here we have an example of a backward solution. It was convenient to work backward in time, since nothing was specified about what should be the work force in month $n + 1$, while on the other hand, the work force in month 0 was specified.

Next, let us suppose that it is specified that the size of the work force in month $n + 1$ is m_{n+1} (the ideal value for that month) and that in month 0 is m_0. In this case, we wish to find non-negative integers x_j which minimize

$$z = \sum_{j=1}^{n} [f_j(x_j - x_{j-1}) + g_j(x_j - m_j)] + f_{n+1}(m_{n+1} - x_n), \tag{10–59}$$

where $x_0 = m_0$. Now we can write

$$z = \min_{x_n} \Big\{ f_{n+1}(m_{n+1} - x_n) + \min_{x_1,\ldots,x_{n-1}} \sum_{j=1}^{n} \Big[f_j(x_j - x_{j-1}) + g_j(x_j - m_j) \Big] \Big\} . \tag{10–60}$$

This suggests that we define the sequence of functions

$$\Lambda_k(\xi) = \min_{x_1,\ldots,x_k} \Big\{ f_{k+1}(\xi - x_k) + g_{k+1}(\xi - m_{k+1}) + \sum_{j=1}^{k} [f_j(x_j - x_{j-1}) + g_j(x_j - m_j)] \Big\} , \quad k = 1, \ldots, n, \tag{10–61}$$

where $x_0 = m_0$ and the minimization is carried out over non-negative integers $x_1, \ldots, x_k$. Then

$$\Lambda_1(\xi) = \min_{x_1} \{ f_2(\xi - x_1) + g_2(\xi - m_2) + f_1(x_1 - m_0) + g_1(x_1 - m_1) \} , \tag{10–62}$$

and

$$\Lambda_k(\xi) = \min_{x_k} \{ f_{k+1}(\xi - x_k) + g_{k+1}(\xi - m_{k+1}) + \Lambda_{k-1}(x_k) \} , \quad k = 2, \ldots, n. \tag{10–63}$$

Finally, $z^* = \Lambda_n(m_{n+1})$.

Here we have developed a forward solution for the problem. For this solution, the state function $\Lambda_k(\xi)$ is the minimum cost for the first $k + 1$ periods when the size of the work force in period $k + 1$ is specified to be ξ. Thus the state variable ξ is the size of the work force in period $k + 1$.

It may now be observed that we could use a forward solution even if the size of the work force were not specified for month $n + 1$. We would simply determine the minimum cost for each possible work force in period $n + 1$ and the optimal work force would be the one which yielded the smallest of all these minimum costs, or to make the solution strictly comparable to the backward solution introduced earlier, we would compute $\Lambda_{n-1}(\xi)$ for each ξ, and x_n^* would be that value of ξ which minimized $\Lambda_{n-1}(\xi)$.

There can be certain advantages to selecting either a forward or a backward solution in preference to the other. For example, if one wanted to make a sensitivity study to see how the size of the work force in month 0, that is m_0, influenced the solution, then one would clearly want to use the backward solution, since at the last step, one computes $\Lambda_1(m_0)$, and the problem for a whole range of m_0-values can be solved with only a slight increase in effort. This would not be true for the forward solution (why?). On the other hand, if one wanted to study how the size of the work force in period $n + 1$ influenced the solution, then he would want to use a forward rather than a backward solution. Conceivably, one might be interested in knowing how the length of the planning horizon, i.e., the number of months n included in the computation, influenced the decision on the size of the work force for the first couple of months. To do this, it is very convenient to use the forward solution, since in this way additional months are added on as the solution progresses. After solving the problem for the maximum number of months in the planning horizon, one automatically generates the information needed to obtain the optimal x_j for the first couple of months, using any number of months in the planning horizon.

10-11 Deterministic inventory problems. Consider a manufacturer which produces a certain item in lots. This manufacturer is a subcontractor to a major appliance producer, and usually receives firm orders on a monthly basis eight or nine months before a particular month's order must be shipped. The manufacturer could, if desired, always manufacture the order to be shipped at the end of a given month in the month it is to be shipped. However, the order quantities vary quite a bit from month to month, and hence in some months considerable overtime would be required to produce the order, while in other months, the number to be produced might not justify the cost of a setup. At certain times it is better to produce the demand for several months on a single production run and then inventory the output until demanded.

Let us suppose that the manufacturer is attempting to schedule production runs over the next n months. If desired, a production run can be made in each month, but no more than one production run per month is scheduled. Let d_j be the number of units which must be shipped at the end of month j, x_j the number of units produced in month j, and y_j the inventory at the beginning of month j (this does not include any units produced in month j). The cost of making x_j units in a production run in month j will be written $A_j + C_j(x_j)$, where A_j is the setup cost for a production run and $C_j(0) = 0$. The inventory holding cost in month j will be a function of $y_j + x_j$ and will be written $g_j(y_j + x_j)$. At the moment we need not be concerned with the precise form of the g_j. Then write

$$f_j(x_j, y_j) = \alpha_j[A_j\delta_j + C_j(x_j) + g_j(y_j + x_j)], \tag{10–64}$$

where α_j can be interpreted as a discount factor which is needed if one wishes to discount the costs, and $\delta_j = 0$ if $x_j = 0$, $\delta_j = 1$ if $x_j > 0$.

With the above definitions, the (discounted) cost over the planning horizon for a given set of x_j is

$$z = \sum_{j=1}^{n} f_j(x_j, y_j). \tag{10–65}$$

We shall assume that y_1 is specified. The value of y_{n+1} may or may not be specified. The y_j and x_j are related by the following material-balance equation

$$y_j + x_j - d_j = y_{j+1}, \qquad \text{all } j. \tag{10–66}$$

It is being assumed, of course, that the demand in each month must be met in the month scheduled. We then wish to determine non-negative integers x_j which satisfy (10–66) and minimize (10–65). This can be thought of as an n-stage decision problem where the decision at stage j involves the selection of the value of x_j. The state parameter for each stage will be either the initial inventory for the month y_j or the ending inventory for the month y_{j+1}.

This problem can be solved by means of dynamic programming. The backward solution will be illustrated first. To be specific, assume that the ending invetory for month n is not specified. Let us define the sequence of state functions

$$\Lambda_k(\xi) = \min_{x_k,\ldots,x_n} \sum_{j=k}^{n} f_j(x_j, y_j), \qquad k = 1, \ldots, n, \tag{10–67}$$

where the minimization is carried out over non-negative integers x_j. The parameters y_j must satisfy equations (10–66) and $y_k = \xi$. Thus the state function $\Lambda_k(\xi)$ is the minimum cost for months $k, \ldots, n$ when the on-hand inventory at the beginning of month k is ξ, and the state parameter ξ is the on-hand inventory at the beginning of period k. We note that

$$\Lambda_k(\xi) = \min_{x_k}\left[f_k(x_k, \xi) + \min_{x_{k+1},\ldots,x_n} \sum_{j=k+1}^{n} f_j(x_j, y_j)\right], \quad k \neq n. \tag{10–68}$$

The inventory at the beginning of period $k + 1$ will be $\xi + x_k - d_k$. Thus

$$\Lambda_k(\xi) = \min_{x_k} [f_k(x_k, \xi) + \Lambda_{k+1}(\xi + x_k - d_k)],$$
$$k = 1, \ldots, n - 1. \tag{10–69}$$

Finally

$$\Lambda_n(\xi) = \min_{x_n} f_n(x_n, \xi), \tag{10–70}$$

and $z^* = \Lambda_1(y_1)$. In addition to tabulating the $\Lambda_n(\xi)$, we also tabulate the $\hat{x}_k(\xi)$ which yield $\Lambda_k(\xi)$. At the last step, we obtain x_1^*. The other x_k^* are then found from

$$x_k^* = \hat{x}_k\left[y_1 + \sum_{j=1}^{k-1} (x_j^* - d_j)\right], \qquad k = 2, \ldots, n. \tag{10–71}$$

The argument of $\hat{x}_k$ is the on-hand inventory at the beginning of period k. In actually solving a problem of this sort on a computer, we would have to decide ahead of time over what range of ξ each table of $\Lambda_k(\xi)$ should be tabulated. For each month k, we would decide on the maximum reasonable inventory that we might have at the beginning of the month, and this value would be the largest ξ for which $\Lambda_k(\xi)$ would be tabulated. The size of the $\Lambda_k(\xi)$-tables would tend to become smaller or remain unchanged in size as one moved toward the end of the planning horizon.

The forward solution will now be obtained in the case where the inventory y_{n+1} at the end of month n is specified as well as y_1. The state parameter appearing in the $\Lambda_k(\xi)$ will now be the inventory on hand at the end of month k. Let us define the sequence of functions

$$\Lambda_k(\xi) = \min_{x_1,\ldots,x_k} \sum_{j=1}^{k} f_j(x_j, y_j), \qquad k = 1, \ldots, n, \tag{10–72}$$

the minimization being made over non-negative integers x_j, and under the condition that $y_{k+1} = \xi$, that is, $y_k + x_k - d_k = \xi$, with the other y_j being related by (10–66). Then

$$\Lambda_k(\xi) = \min_{x_k}\left[f_k(x_k, y_k) + \min_{x_1,\ldots,x_{k-1}} \sum_{j=1}^{k-1} f_j(x_j, y_j)\right].$$

If the inventory level is ξ at the end of month k, it is $\xi + d_k - x_k$ at the end of month $k - 1$. Thus

$$\Lambda_k(\xi) = \min_{x_k} [f_k(x_k, \xi + d_k - x_k) + \Lambda_{k-1}(\xi + d_k - x_k)], \quad k = 2, \ldots, n, \tag{10-73}$$

and

$$\Lambda_1(\xi) = \min_{x_1} f_1(x_1, y_1), \qquad y_1 + x_1 - d_1 = \xi.$$

Only one value of x_1 satisfies the constraint and hence

$$\Lambda_1(\xi) = f_1(\xi + d_1 - y_1, y_1). \tag{10-74}$$

At the last step, x_n^* is determined; the other x_k^* are found from

$$x_k^* = x_k\left[y_{n+1} + \sum_{j=k+1}^{n} (d_j - x_j^*)\right], \qquad k = 1, \ldots, n-1. \tag{10-75}$$

We have now shown how the problem can be formulated for both forward and backward solutions. When the costs involved in problems of this sort have an especially simple form, it is possible to develop a much more efficient computational procedure for solving the problem than that considered above. We shall discuss this in the next section.

10–12 Case where the $f_j(x_j, y_j)$ are concave functions. We shall now study the simplifications which can be introduced into the computational method of the previous section when the variables x_j and y_j are assumed to be continuous and the $f_j(x_j, y_j)$ are concave functions of x_j, y_j. At the outset it will be desirable to specify in a little more detail the form of the $f_j(x_j, y_j)$. We have already assumed that the f_j can be written as in (10–64) where $C_j(0) = 0$. Note that $A_j\delta_j$ is a concave function of x_j. We shall now assume that $C_j(x_j)$ is a concave function of x_j so that the average cost per unit decreases or remains unchanged as x_j increases.

Consider now the inventory-carrying cost for period j, which was denoted in (10–64) by $g_j(y_j + x_j)$. To obtain an explicit form for this term we shall introduce several additional assumptions. First of all, the time required to manufacture a lot of x_j units will be ignored. It will be imagined that if x_j units are to be produced in month j, they are produced at the beginning of the period, and because the time required to produce them is being ignored, they will be imagined to come into inventory as a batch at the beginning of the period. Although we are going to imagine that production runs enter inventory as a batch at the beginning of a period, we shall allow demands to occur for the units throughout the period according to some deterministic demand law which may have the property that the rate of demand can vary with time even within a period. We shall suppose that the rate of incurring carrying costs at any time t in period j is proportional to the on-hand inventory at that time. Suppose, to be specific that the rate of incurring carrying costs is measured in the units of dollars per year, and let K_j be the constant of proportionality (with dimensions of dollars per year per unit in inventory). The rate at which units are demanded at any time t will be written $\lambda(t)$. Then the on-hand inventory at any time t in period j is

$$x_j + y_j - \int_0^t \lambda(t)\,dt$$

when the time origin is the start of period j and the demand is treated as continuous. The carrying cost for period j thus becomes

$$g_j(x_j + y_j) = K_j \int_0^{T_j} \left[x_j + y_j - \int_0^{\zeta} \lambda(t)\,dt\right] d\zeta, \qquad (10\text{–}76)$$

where T_j is the length of period j in years. To simplify (10–76) it is convenient to introduce $y_{j+1} = x_j + y_j - d_j$, the inventory on hand at the end of period j. Then (10–76) becomes

$$\begin{aligned} g_j(x_j + y_j) &= K_j \int_0^{T_j} \left[y_{j+1} + d_j - \int_0^{\zeta} \lambda(t)\,dt\right] d\zeta \\ &= K_j T_j y_{j+1} + K_j \int_0^{T_j} \left[d_j - \int_0^{\zeta} \lambda(t)\,dt\right] d\zeta. \qquad (10\text{–}77) \end{aligned}$$

However,

$$K_j \int_0^{T_j} \left[d_j - \int_0^{\zeta} \lambda(t)\,dt\right] d\zeta \qquad (10\text{–}78)$$

is simply the carrying cost in period j for the units demanded in period j. This cost is unavoidable, and is independent of the x_j. Thus, this cost need not be included in the objective function, i.e., a set of optimal x_j can be found without including the costs (10–78). On the other hand, $K_j T_j y_{j+1}$ is simply the cost incurred in period j on the units which are carried into period $j + 1$. This is the only inventory carrying cost that we need to consider in period j. The variable costs for period j are then

$$f_j(x_j, y_{j+1}) = \alpha_j[A_j \delta_j + C_j(x_j) + K_j T_j y_{j+1}], \qquad (10\text{–}79)$$

where we have now made f_j a function of x_j and y_{j+1}. It will be observed that the f_j will be concave functions of x_j and y_{j+1} if $C_j(x_j)$ is a concave function, since $\alpha_j > 0$. If this is true, then

$$z = \sum_j f_j(x_j, y_{j+1}) \tag{10–80}$$

is a concave function of all the variables. We wish to find non-negative x_j, y_j which minimize (10–80) subject to the constraints

$$x_1 - y_2 = d_1 - y_1; \quad y_j + x_j - y_{j+1} = d_j,$$
$$j = 2, \ldots, n-1; \quad y_n + x_n = d_n + y_{n+1}. \tag{10–81}$$

We shall suppose that y_1 and y_{n+1} are specified.

Before considering the simplified solution procedure, it might be well to point out that with the assumptions made at the beginning of the section, the model we are studying can be given other interpretations than the one provided in the previous section. More generally, we can imagine that an inventory system is trying to determine an optimal operating doctrine for the next n periods. Procurements or production lots can be scheduled to be delivered only at the beginning of periods. It is assumed that the demand rate $\lambda(t)$ is known with certainty as a function of time. All demands in a given period must be met from stock. It is desired to determine the timing and size of procurements so as to minimize the (discounted) costs of holding and procuring the units. We are now ready to consider the solution procedure.

We are minimizing a concave function over a convex set. Hence we know that at least one extreme point of the convex set of feasible solutions will be optimal. Note that there are n constraints. Thus we know that there will be an optimal solution with no more than n of the variables from the set x_j, $j = 1, \ldots, n$; y_j, $j = 2, \ldots, n$, which are positive. However, in each period either y_j or x_j must be positive (if the demand in the period is positive), since we are assuming that all demands are met from stock. Let us now imagine that $y_1 = 0$, that is, when the first order arrives, no stock is on hand. Given that this is the case, there is no period in which $x_j > 0$ and $y_j > 0$, because if this were true, then, in general, more than n positive variables would be required. Thus there will be an optimal solution with the property that either $x_j > 0$ or $y_j > 0$, but not both. This property can also be expressed by saying $x_j y_j = 0$, $j = 1, \ldots, n$. Intuitively, this feature of an optimal solution says that an order will never arrive at the beginning of a period when there is inventory on hand, or equivalently, that there will never be inventory on hand at the beginning of a period when an order is to arrive. The reader will observe that the argument appears to break down if in some period k the demand is zero, for then x_k and y_k could both be zero and this would make it possible for both x_j and y_j to be positive in some other period. If it was optimal to have $x_k = y_k = 0$, we could then break the problem down into two separate problems, one containing the periods before k and one the periods after k (a total of $n - 1$ periods) and repeat our arguments on these two problems, and thus conclude that $x_j y_j = 0$, $j \neq k$. Therefore, in every case, it must be true that $x_j y_j = 0$.

Once we know that $x_j y_j = 0$, it follows immediately that if

$$d_j = \int_0^{T_j} \lambda(t)\, dt$$

is the demand in period j, then

$$x_j = 0 \quad \text{or} \quad d_j \quad \text{or} \quad d_j + d_{j+1} \quad \text{or} \cdots \text{or} \quad d_j + \cdots + d_n + y_{n+1},$$

so that the quantity delivered will be for the demands of an integral number of periods. Furthermore, of course, if the order arriving at the beginning of period j satisfies the demands of periods j through k, the next order will not arrive until the beginning of period k.

Consider now the forward solution method of dynamic programming, and let $\Lambda_k(\xi)$ be the minimum cost for the first k periods when the on-hand inventory at the end of period k is ξ. When the inventory on hand at the end of period k is ξ, an optimal policy for operating the system for the first k periods will have the property that the procurement which satisfies the demand of period k will arrive at the beginning of period i ($i \leq k$) and meet the demands for periods $i, i + 1, \ldots, k$. Furthermore the on-hand inventory y_i at the beginning of period i (before arrival of the procurement) will be zero. The policy will also have the feature that the x_j, $j = 1, \ldots, i - 1$, will be those which are optimal when there are only $i - 1$ periods, and the on-hand inventory at the end of period $i - 1$ is zero. This follows directly from the recurrence relations. By (10–73)

$$\Lambda_k(\xi) = \min_{x_k} [f_k(x_k, \xi) + \Lambda_{k-1}(\xi + d_k - x_k)]. \tag{10–82}$$

However, since $x_k y_k = 0$,

$$\Lambda_k(\xi) = \min \begin{cases} f_k(\xi + d_k, \xi) + \Lambda_{k-1}(0), \\ f_k(0, \xi) + \Lambda_{k-1}(\xi + d_k). \end{cases} \tag{10–83}$$

But

$$\Lambda_{k-1}(\xi + d_k) = \min \begin{cases} f_{k-1}(\xi + d_k + d_{k-1}, \xi + d_k) + \Lambda_{k-2}(0), \\ f_{k-1}(0, \xi + d_k) + \Lambda_{k-2}(\xi + d_k + d_{k-1}), \end{cases} \tag{10–84}$$

and so on. Thus the optimal policy has the form stated, and

$$\Lambda_k(\xi) = \min_i Y_k(i), \tag{10–85}$$

where i assumes the values $1, \ldots, k$, and

$$Y_k(i) = \sum_{j=i+1}^{k} f_j\left(0, \xi + \sum_{u=j+1}^{k} d_u\right) + f_i\left(\xi + \sum_{u=i}^{k} d_u, \xi + \sum_{u=i+1}^{k} d_u\right) + \Lambda_{i-1}(0), \tag{10–86}$$

provided we use the definition $\Lambda_0(0) = 0$. Note that to compute $\Lambda_k(\xi)$ we only need the $\Lambda_j(0), j = 1, \ldots, k - 1$. Thus we never need to evaluate the Λ_k for ξ other than $\xi = 0$, except possibly at the last stage, where we need $\Lambda_n(y_{n+1})$. Thus at each stage, only one Λ_k is needed, rather than a whole table. The task of solving the problem has thus been reduced to a form which requires considerably less effort than the direct application of the dynamic programming method studied in the previous section.

A special case that is of particular interest arises when the unit cost of the item is a constant C independent of the period or the quantity ordered, so that $C_j(x_j) = Cx_j$, and where no discounting is used, that is, $\alpha_j = 1$. Then the total cost of the units procured is

$$C\left(y_{n+1} + \sum_{j=1}^{n} d_j\right),$$

and is independent of the variables x_j. Thus, in this case, it is unnecessary to include the costs of the units themselves. With these simplifications, the problem reduces to that of finding non-negative x_j which minimize

$$z = \sum_{j=1}^{n} (A_j\delta_j + H_jy_{j+1}) \tag{10–87}$$

subject to (10–81), with $y_1 = 0$. In (10–87), $H_j = K_jT_j$. When $\xi = 0$, $Y_k(i)$ of (10–86) becomes

$$Y_k(i) = A_i + \sum_{j=i}^{k-1}\left[H_j \sum_{w=j+1}^{k} d_w\right] + \Lambda_{i-1}(0). \tag{10–88}$$

There is one additional computational simplification which can be made in this case. We can show that if for $\Lambda_{k-1}(0)$, the order which satisfied the demand in period $k - 1$ arrives at the beginning of period v, then in computing $\Lambda_k(0)$, we know that the order which satisfies the demand in period k will arrive at the beginning of period v or a later period. This means that in computing $\Lambda_k(0)$ we do not need to consider $i < v$ in carrying out the minimization in (10–85). We shall prove this by contradiction. Assume that

$$\Lambda_k(0) = Y_k(u) = A_u + \sum_{j=u}^{k-1}\left[H_j \sum_{w=j+1}^{k} d_w\right] + \Lambda_{u-1}(0) < Y_k(v) \quad (10\text{–}89)$$

when

$$\Lambda_{k-1}(0) = Y_{k-1}(v) = A_v + \sum_{j=v}^{k-2}\left[H_j \sum_{w=j+1}^{k-1} d_w\right] + \Lambda_{v-1}(0) \quad (10\text{–}90)$$

and $v > u$. However, if the carrying costs for the items carried from period u through k to satisfy the demand in period k are factored out in $\Lambda_k(0)$, we have

$$\Lambda_k(0) = d_k \sum_{j=u}^{k-1} H_j + Y_{k-1}(u) = Y_k(u). \quad (10\text{–}91)$$

But

$$Y_k(v) = d_k \sum_{j=v}^{k-1} H_j + Y_{k-1}(v). \quad (10\text{–}92)$$

On subtracting $Y_k(v)$ from $\Lambda_k(0)$, we obtain

$$\Lambda_k(0) - Y_k(v) = d_k \sum_{j=u}^{v-1} H_j + Y_{k-1}(u) - Y_{k-1}(v) \geq 0,$$

since by assumption

$$Y_{k-1}(u) \geq Y_{k-1}(v) = \Lambda_{k-1}(0)$$

and $d_k \sum_{j=u}^{v-1} H_j \geq 0$. But this is a contradiction.

The computational procedure for the model where $C_j(x_j) = C(x_j)$ and no discounting is used was first developed by Wagner and Whitin [17]. A convenient tabular format for making the computations in this case is shown in Table 10–3. In the last line, the optimal x_j are indicated by enclosing in parentheses all periods for which the demands are met by the order arriving at the beginning of the period whose number appears first in the parentheses. Table 10–3 indicates the results which might be obtained in a typical case. The asterisks on the $Y_k(i)$ indicate the minima over i, that is, $\Lambda_k(0)$. This model is often referred to as a dynamic lot size model, since it can be imagined to be a dynamic version of the simple lot size model of inventory theory.

10–13 Example. In Section 4–11 we studied a simple fixed-charge linear programming problem which was really nothing but an example of the type of problem we studied in the previous section. The problem was

TABLE 10–3

TABLEAU FORMAT FOR SOLVING DYNAMIC LOT SIZE MODEL

Periods		1	2	3	4		$n-1$	n
Demands		d_1	d_2	d_3	d_4	$\cdots$	d_{n-1}	d_n
$Y_k(i)$	i							
	1	$Y_1^*(1)$	$Y_2(1)$			$\cdots$		
	2		$Y_2^*(2)$	$Y_3^*(2)$	$Y_4^*(2)$	$\cdots$		
	3			$Y_3(3)$	$Y_4(3)$	$\cdots$		
	4				$Y_4(4)$	$\cdots$		
	$\vdots$					$\vdots$		
	$n-1$						$Y_{n-1}^*(n-1)$	$Y_n^*(n-1)$
$\Lambda_k(0)$		$\Lambda_1(0) = Y_1(1)$	$\Lambda_2(0) = Y_2(1)$	$\Lambda_3(0) = Y_3(2)$	$\Lambda_4(0) = Y_4(2)$		$\Lambda_{n-1}(0) = Y_{n-1}(n-1)$	$\Lambda_n(0) = Y_n(n-1)$
x_k^*		(1)	(1)(2)	(1)(2, 3)	(1)(2, 3, 4)		$(1)(2, 3, 4)(5 \ldots) \ldots (n-1)$	$(1)(2, 3, 4)(5 \ldots) \ldots (n-1, n)$

to find $x_j > 0$ which minimize

$$z = 300 \sum_{j=1}^{7} \delta_j + 2 \sum_{j=2}^{7} y_j$$

subject to

$$x_1 - y_2 = d_1 = 90; \qquad y_j + x_j - y_{j+1} = d_j, \qquad j = 2, \ldots, 6; \qquad y_7 + x_7 = d_7 = 130,$$

where $d_2 = 125$, $d_3 = 140$, $d_4 = 100$, $d_5 = 45$, and $d_6 = 60$. We found in Chapter 4 that this problem had many local minima, and the methods of Chapter 4 did not yield the absolute minimum. We shall now solve the problem and show how the optimal solution given in Chapter 4 was obtained.

We first note that

$$\Lambda_1(0) = 300,$$

$$\Lambda_2(0) = \min \begin{Bmatrix} 300 + \Lambda_1(0) = 600 \\ 300 + 2(125) = 550 \end{Bmatrix} = 550$$

from (10-85) and (10-88). Thus when there are only two periods and nothing is on hand at the end of the second period, it is optimal to have the procurement arriving at the beginning of period 1 satisfy the demand for both periods. Next

$$\Lambda_3(0) = \min \begin{Bmatrix} 300 + \Lambda_2(0) = 850 \\ 300 + 2(140) + \Lambda_1(0) = 880 \\ 300 + 2(140) + 2(140 + 125) = 1110 \end{Bmatrix} = 850.$$

The remainder of the computation is shown in Table 10-4. It is seen that the unique optimal solution is $z^* = 1770$, $x_1^* = 215$, $x_2^* = 0$, $x_3^* = 240$, $x_4^* = 0$, $x_5^* = 105$, $x_6^* = 0$, $x_7^* = 130$. This is the solution which was quoted in Chapter 4.

10-14 Functional equations for systems with an infinite number of stages. In the past two sections we have been considering a simple deterministic inventory system in which the rate of demand for the item stocked could vary with time. We were interested in determining an optimal operating doctrine for the inventory system over a total of n periods when it was specified that procurements could arrive only at the beginning of a period. Let us now study a somewhat different deterministic inventory problem. We shall imagine that the demand rate is a constant λ

TABLE 10–4

COMPUTATIONS FOR EXAMPLE

Periods		1	2	3	4	5	6	7
Demands		90	125	140	100	45	60	130
$Y_k(i)$	i = 1	300*	550*	1110				
	2		600	880				
	3			850*	1050*	1230*	1590	
	4				1150	1240	1480	
	5					1350	1470*	1990
	6						1530	1790
	7							1770*
$\Lambda_k(0)$		300	550	850	1050	1230	1470	1770
x_k^*		(1)	(1, 2)	(1, 2)(3)	(1, 2) (3, 4)	(1, 2) (3, 4, 5)	(1, 2) (3, 4) (5, 6)	(1, 2) (3, 4) (5, 6) (7)

which is independent of time. We shall also assume that units are demanded one at a time. Thus the time between the occurrences of demands is $\Delta t = 1/\lambda$. It will be imagined that this inventory system will continue to operate for all future time and that it is possible to decide whether or not to place an order after the occurrence of every demand. The restriction will be imposed that the system is never out of stock when a demand occurs. This restriction can be legitimately made because the times of occurrence of the demands are assumed to be deterministic. Denote by A the fixed cost of placing an order, and by C the unit cost of the item. The unit cost will be assumed to be independent of the number of units ordered so that the cost of x units will be Cx. The rate of incurring inventory carrying costs will be taken to be proportional to the on-hand inventory, and the constant of proportionality will be written K. The procurement lead time, i.e., the time elapsed between the placing of an order and its arrival will be imagined to be a constant τ. Note that A, C, K, and τ are assumed to be independent of time.

Suppose that a demand occurs at time t. After the occurrence of the demand one must decide whether or not to place an order for replenishment stock, and if so, what the quantity ordered should be. Let us assume that the times at which orders are placed and the order quantities are chosen so as to minimize the discounted cost of ordering and carrying inventory over all future time. Note first of all that the inventory carrying costs incurred between t and $t + \tau$ are independent of the decision made at time t and all future decisions, since any order placed at time t will not arrive until time $t + \tau$. Thus, these costs need not be included in the cost expression. Inventory carrying costs will be included only beginning at time $t + \tau$. Next note that the inventory on hand at time $t + \tau$ can be computed directly, if we know how much is on hand and on order at time t. Let ξ be the number of units on hand plus on order at time t after the demand occurs but before any decision is made, and let $x \geq 0$ be the number of units ordered, so that $\xi + x$ units are on hand plus on order after the decision is made. Since all demands are met from inventory (none are lost), and since everything on order at time t will arrive by time $t + \tau$, we conclude that the number of units on hand at time $t + \tau$ (after any order placed at time t has arrived) is $\xi + x - m$, where m is the largest integer less than, or equal to, $\lambda\tau$. In other words, m units will be demanded in the lead time. The next unit after m will be demanded at time $(m + 1)\,\Delta t$, which occurs at a time $(m + 1)\,\Delta t - \tau$ after any units ordered at time t arrive in the system. Thus in the time interval $t + \tau$ to $t + \tau + \Delta t$, we shall have on hand $\xi + x - m$ units for a time period of length $(m + 1)\,\Delta t - \tau$ and $\xi + x - m - 1$ units for a period of length $\tau + \Delta t - (m + 1)\,\Delta t = \tau - m\,\Delta t$. The inventory carrying costs $f(\xi + x)$ for the time interval $t + \tau$ to $t + \tau + \Delta t$ are then

$$\begin{aligned} f(\xi + x) &= K\{(\xi + x - m)[(m + 1)\,\Delta t - \tau] \\ &\qquad\qquad + (\xi + x - m - 1)(\tau - m\,\Delta t)\} \\ &= K(\xi + x - m)(\Delta t) - K(\tau - m\,\Delta t). \end{aligned} \tag{10–93}$$

Since we are requiring that the system never be out of stock when a demand occurs, it is clear that we must require that $\xi + x \geq m + 1$. To have this requirement automatically satisfied, we shall set $f(\xi + x) = \infty$, $\xi + x < m + 1$. The various quantities introduced above are illustrated in Fig. 10–4. Note that the inventory carrying costs incurred between $t + \tau$ and $t + \tau + \Delta t$ depend only on $\xi + x$.

Let β be a discount factor which discounts the carrying costs incurred between $t + \tau$ and $t + \tau + \Delta t$ to time t, and α a discount factor which discounts costs known at time $t + \Delta t$ to time t. Then let $\Lambda_t(\xi)$ be the present worth at time t of all future costs when an optimal ordering decision is made at time t and all future times, and when inventory carrying

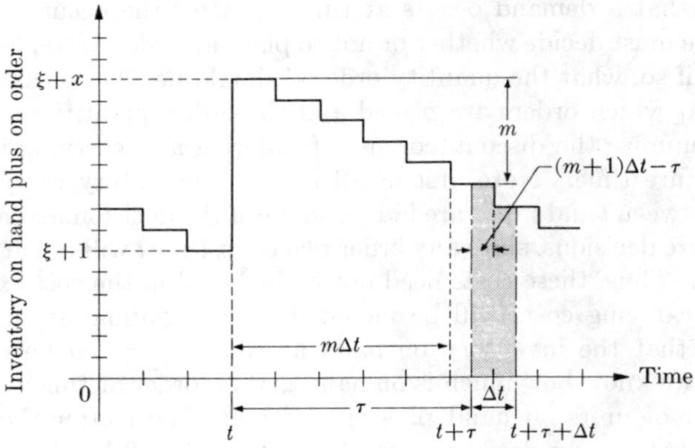

FIGURE 10–4

costs incurred between times t and $t + \tau$ are not included. Similarly, let $\Lambda_{t+\Delta t}(\xi)$ be the present worth at time $t + \Delta t$ of all future costs when an optimal ordering decision is made at time $t + \Delta t$ and when inventory carrying costs incurred between times $t + \Delta t$ and $t + \Delta t + \tau$ are not included. If y_j is the quantity on hand at time $t + j\,\Delta t$ after the demand has occurred but before an order is placed, x_j is the quantity ordered, $y_0 = \xi$, $x_0 = x$, and $f(y_j + x_j)$ is the inventory carrying charge incurred between $t + j\Delta t + \tau$ and $t + (j + 1)\,\Delta t + \tau$ and discounted to time t, then

$$\Lambda_t(\xi) = \min_{x, x_1, x_2, \ldots} \sum_{j=0}^{\infty} \alpha^j [A\,\delta_j + Cx_j + f(y_j + x_j)], \qquad (10\text{–}94)$$

$$\Lambda_{t+\Delta t}(\xi) = \min_{x_1, x_2 \ldots} \sum_{j=1}^{\infty} \alpha^{j-1} [A\,\delta_j + Cx_j + f(y_j + x_j)]. \qquad (10\text{–}95)$$

Consequently,

$$\Lambda_t(\xi) = \min_x \Big\{ A\,\delta + Cx + f(\xi + x) + \alpha \min_{x_1, x_2, \ldots} \sum_{j=1}^{\infty} \alpha^{j-1} [A\,\delta_j + Cx_j + f_j(y_j + x_j)] \Big\},$$

where the quantity on hand plus on order at time $t + \Delta t$ before any decision is made is $\xi + x - 1$. Thus using the definition of $\Lambda_{t+\Delta t}(\xi)$, we have

$$\Lambda_t(\xi) = \min_x \{A\,\delta + Cx + f(\xi + x) + \alpha\Lambda_{t+\Delta t}(\xi + x - 1)\}. \qquad (10\text{–}96)$$

We note, however, that if in (10–95) we let $u = j - 1$, we obtain (10–94), that is,

$$\Lambda_t(\xi) = \Lambda_{t+\Delta t}(\xi), \tag{10–97}$$

or more generally,

$$\Lambda_t(\xi) = \Lambda_{t+j\Delta t}(\xi), \qquad j = 1, 2, \ldots \tag{10–98}$$

This simply says that when the quantity on hand plus on order is ξ and optimal decisions are made at the current time and all future times, then the present worth of all future costs at the time a demand occurs is independent of the time at which the demand occurs. The reason for this, of course, is the fact that we are here considering an infinite time horizon.

Because of (10–98), we can drop the subscript t on $\Lambda_t(\xi)$, and (10–96) becomes

$$\Lambda(\xi) = \min_x \{A\delta + Cx + f(\xi + x) + \alpha\Lambda(\xi + x - 1)\}. \tag{10–99}$$

Observe that the same function (evaluated for different arguments) appears in two places in (10–99), so that (10–99) can be thought of as an equation whose solution yields the function $\Lambda(\xi)$. An equation of this type involving an unknown function is called a *functional equation.*

Although it is seldom easy to solve directly a functional equation such as (10–99), it can be done in certain special cases. We shall say more about this below. However, functional equations such as (10–99) are often valuable in that they provide information concerning the structure of the optimal operating doctrine. Let us see how such information can be obtained for the simple inventory problem being studied. The term $C\xi$ is added to, and subtracted from, the right-hand side of (10–99), and we write

$$F(\xi + x) = C(x + \xi) + f(\xi + x) + \alpha\Lambda(\xi + x - 1). \tag{10–100}$$

Then (10–99) becomes

$$\begin{aligned}\Lambda(\xi) &= -C\xi + \min_x [A\delta + F(\xi + x)] \\ &= -C\xi + \min \begin{cases} F(\xi) \\ A + \min_x F(\xi + x), \end{cases}\end{aligned} \tag{10–101}$$

where the minimization is carried out over non-negative integers x. Let the absolute minimum of $F(y)$ be taken on at $y = R$ (if this minimum is not unique, R will denote the smallest y where it is taken on). Also, let

$r(r < R)$ be the largest integer for which $F(r) \geq A + F(R)$. Then, it follows from (10–101) that if ξ lies between R and r, an optimal way of operating the system would be not to place any order until the on-hand plus on-order inventory level reaches r; at this point one places an order for a quantity $R - r$. Thus the quantity on hand plus on order would never get above R or below r. We have not said what to do if the initial on-hand plus on-order inventory level ξ is less than r or greater than R. We shall see below that ξ cannot be less than r. The case of $\xi > R$ would require a more detailed discussion of the nature of $F(y)$. Note, however, that once the value of ξ reaches the interval $r \leq \xi \leq R$, it will never again get out of this interval, provided the system is operated optimally thereafter. Furthermore, ξ never has the value r for a finite length of time, since an order is immediately placed when a demand reduces the inventory level to r. The system is said to be in a steady-state mode of operation when the on-hand plus on-order inventory level continually fluctuates between $r + 1$ and R in the manner discussed above. If the system is started out with ξ between r and R, then it is optimal to have the on-hand plus on-order inventory always between R and r, with orders being placed for a quantity $R - r$ only when the on-hand plus on-order inventory level reaches r. In inventory theory such an optimal operating doctine is referred to as an Rr-doctrine. We have proved that such a doctrine is optimal for the model being considered. Note, though, that the above analysis provided no procedure for computing R and r. However, for the problem being considered, we can immediately determine r. Recall that since $f(\xi + x) = \infty$, $\xi + x < m + 1$, r cannot be less than m. This follows from an examination of the case of $\xi = r + 1$, where no order is placed. If $r < m$, $f(r + 1) = \infty$ so that $\Lambda(r + 1) = \infty$, or looked at differently, if $r < m$, there will be one or more backorders on the books when the order placed at time t arrives. On the other hand, r cannot be greater than m, because costs could be reduced by having $r = m$, the reason being that if $r > m$, then $r - m$ units are on hand when the order arrives that was placed when $\xi = r$. These $r - m$ units are always on hand and are never used. Costs could be reduced by not carrying them. Thus we conclude that $r = m$. An order should be placed when the on-hand plus on-order inventory drops to m immediately after a demand occurs. The remaining problem involves the computation of R, or, equivalently $R - r$, which is the optimal order quantity. In the following section we shall see how this can be done.

10–15 Explicit solution of the functional equation. If the numbers r, R discussed in the last section are known, we shall show that it is possible to solve explicitly the functional equation (10–99) for $\Lambda(\xi)$, $r \leq \xi \leq$

$R - 1$. By the definition of r and R, it must be true that

$$\Lambda(R-1) = f(R-1) + \alpha\Lambda(R-2), \tag{10–102}$$

$$\Lambda(R-2) = f(R-2) + \alpha\Lambda(R-3), \tag{10–103}$$

$$\vdots$$

$$\Lambda(r) \quad = A + C(R-r) + f(R) + \alpha\Lambda(R-1). \tag{10–104}$$

Thus

$$\begin{aligned}\Lambda(R-1) &= f(R-1) + \alpha f(R-2) + \alpha^2\Lambda(R-3)\\ &= f(R-1) + \alpha f(R-2) + \alpha^2 f(R-3) + \alpha^3\Lambda(R-4)\\ &= \sum_{j=1}^{R-r-1} \alpha^{j-1} f(R-j) + \alpha^{R-r-1}[A + C(R-r) + f(R)]\\ &\quad + \alpha^{R-r}\Lambda(R-1),\end{aligned} \tag{10–105}$$

or

$$\Lambda(R-1) = \frac{1}{1-\alpha^{R-r}}\Big\{\alpha^{R-r-1}[A + C(R-r)] + \sum_{j=1}^{R-r-1} \alpha^{j-1} f(R-j) + \alpha^{R-r-1} f(R)\Big\}. \tag{10–106}$$

It is also possible to solve for the other $\Lambda(\xi)$, $r \leq \xi \leq R - 1$, beginning with (10–104) and working backward. We ask the reader to do this in Problem 10–18. An interesting physical interpretation can be given to (10–106). Note that the inventory system repeats itself every $(R - r)\,\Delta t$ units of time. We shall say that the system goes through one cycle in a time period of length $(R - r)\,\Delta t$. Consider the situation when we imagine the cycle to begin at a time Δt after an order is placed, i.e., immediately after the demand occurs which reduces the on-hand plus on-order inventory level to $R - 1$. Then the next order will be placed at a time $(R - r - 1)\,\Delta t$ after the beginning of the cycle, and the cycle will end with R units on hand plus on order for the last Δt units of time. With this definition of a cycle, the expression in brackets in (10–106) is simply the cost for a cycle discounted to the beginning of a cycle, and $\Lambda(R - 1)$ is the discounted sum of the costs over all such cycles. Observe that if H is the cost per cycle discounted to the beginning of a cycle, then the discounted cost over all time is

$$H + \alpha^{R-r}H + \alpha^{2(R-r)}H + \cdots = \frac{1}{1-\alpha^{R-r}}\,H,$$

which is precisely the form of the expression for $\Lambda(R-1)$. The other $\Lambda(\xi)$ differ from $\Lambda(R-1)$ only in that the point in time chosen to be the initial point in the cycle changes.

There are several ways in which one might compute $R-r$. Thus, for example, one might approximate the infinite stage system by a finite number of stages, and as each stage is added, the minimum in (10–96) is computed directly. After a sufficient number of stages have been included, $\hat{x}(\xi)$ will cease to change as additional stages are added. Then $R-r$ is simply the magnitude of the jump when $\hat{x}(\xi)$ changes from zero to a finite value. Another procedure is to use (10–106). An exact way of determining $R-r$ is to substitute (10–106) into (10–100) with $\xi=r$, and then carry out the minimization over $x=R-r$ in (10–101) for $\xi=r$. Still another approximate procedure for determining $R-r$ would be to minimize the average annual cost rather than the discounted cost over all future time. For interest rates of practical significance, the $R-r$ so obtained will be negligibly different from the values obtained by the above methods, provided that the time between the placements of orders is not exceedingly long, say greater than one year. There is indeed a close connection between the $\Lambda(\xi)$ and the average annual cost. It is approximately true that the average annual cost is $i\Lambda(\xi)$, where i is the annual interest rate. This relation is approximate for positive interest rates. However, when the interest rate is zero, the average annual cost is given exactly by

$$\lim_{i\to 0} i\Lambda(R-1).$$

Problem 10–19 requires the reader to verify this result. Problem 10–20 asks the reader to show that

$$\lim_{i\to 0} i\Lambda(\xi)$$

is the same for every $\xi=r, r+1, \ldots, R-1$, so that the average annual cost is $\lim_{i\to 0} i\Lambda(\xi)$ for any one of these ξ-values. As suggested above, the average annual cost can be used to determine $R-r$ even if i is sizable, and the value so obtained will be very close to that obtained by minimizing $\Lambda(\xi)$. Problem 10–21 asks the reader to determine the average annual cost expression for an arbitrary i and to develop from it a method for obtaining $R-r$.

10–16 Equipment replacement problems. One important problem faced by most industrial concerns is the determination of optimal policies for equipment replacement. The equipment under consideration might be anything from machine tools to trucks to marine tankers. As a piece of equipment grows older, its operating and maintenance cost usually increases while its productivity and salvage value decrease. Often, if enough money is spent on upkeep, a piece of equipment can be kept running indefinitely. However, in any continuing operation, a point is always reached where it is better to buy a new piece of equipment instead of keeping the old one. We would like to consider methods of determining how long to keep a piece of equipment.

The customary criterion used to determine an optimal replacement policy is that of maximizing the discounted expected profit or minimizing the discounted expected cost over some time horizon. From a practical point of view, cost minimization, rather than profit maximization, is used for a variety of reasons. One is that when a product must undergo operations on a number of machines, it is difficult to determine what the contribution of any single machine is to the total profit. Secondly, the output is frequently specified, and therefore the revenue received is a constant so that profit maximization is equivalent to cost minimization. Finally, when known, lost profits from lower productivity can be included as a cost.

We shall imagine that decisions on equipment replacement are made periodically, perhaps once a year. We shall also suppose that the equipment can be kept operating indefinitely if enough is spent on repairs. The decisions on whether or not to replace a machine will be based solely on its age and the costs which will be imagined to be a function of age also. We shall not attempt here to develop a stochastic model with the property that the times between failures of the equipment are random variables, and after each failure we decide whether to repair the equipment or buy a new piece. Models of the latter type are very relevant for certain types of equipment, but we shall imagine that for the type of equipment to be considered here, individual failures are almost always of a relatively minor sort which would not in themselves justify the replacement of the existing piece of equipment with a new piece. The only randomness will then be in the costs incurred for a period when the machine is of a given age. We shall minimize expected discounted costs, and to do this, all that is necessary is to use the expected cost functions. Thus the problem is equivalent to a deterministic one, with the costs being the expected costs referred to above.

Technological improvement is often an important factor which should be considered in equipment replacement problems. Unfortunately, it is also very difficult to take technological improvement into account, since it is essentially impossible to predict just what the results of technological improvement may be. We shall begin by considering a case where there is no technological improvement. It will be imagined that a machine is always replaced by a machine of precisely the same type. We shall frequently (as we have just done) refer to the piece of equipment simply as a machine, although it may not be a machine in the ordinary sense. Denote by I the installed cost of the machine (the installed cost is used since the cost of installation can, in some cases, be a considerable part of the total), $C(j)$ the expected cost of operation and maintenance in the jth period of use, and $S(j)$ the expected salvage value when the machine is j periods old (the salvage value will be taken to be the sale price minus dismantling costs). All of these costs will be assumed to be the same for each new machine purchased. Let α be a discount factor which discounts costs known at the end of a period to the beginning of the period. Thus α^j discounts costs known at the end of period j to the beginning of period 1. For simplicity, we shall imagine that all operating and maintenance costs incurred during a period are treated as though incurred at the end of the period.

For the case being considered, the usual approach to the problem is to note that, since there is no technological improvement, an optimal policy should have the form that a machine is kept for N periods and then replaced. The value of N is then determined by imagining that machines of the type under consideration will be used for all future time, and by minimizing the discounted cost over the infinite planning horizon. The cost of a machine over the N periods it is kept, discounted to the time it is purchased is

$$H = I + \sum_{j=1}^{N} \alpha^j C(j) - \alpha^N S(N), \tag{10–107}$$

and the discounted cost of an infinite sequence of such machines is

$$\begin{aligned} K(N) &= H + \alpha^N H + \alpha^{2N} H + \cdots = \frac{1}{1-\alpha^N} H \\ &= \frac{1}{1-\alpha^N}\left[I + \sum_{j=1}^{N} \alpha^j C(j) - \alpha^N S(N)\right]. \end{aligned} \tag{10–108}$$

An optimal value of N is found simply by computing $K(N)$ for $N = 1, 2, \ldots$, and selecting an N which minimizes $K(N)$.

Consider now the dynamic programming approach to the same problem. It will be imagined that at the beginning of each period a decision is made as to whether or not to replace the machine in use at the present time. At the beginning of any period, let ξ be the age (in periods) of the machine currently used, and $\Lambda(\xi)$ the costs incurred over all future time discounted to the beginning of the period under consideration, when an optimal decision is made for the current and all future periods. Note that because an infinite planning horizon is being used, $\Lambda(\xi)$ has the same value regardless of what period we consider, when the machine in current use has age ξ. This follows by the same reasoning as was used in Section 10–14. Since we either keep the current machine or buy a new one, it must be true that

$$\Lambda(\xi) = \min \begin{cases} I - S(\xi) + \alpha C(1) + \alpha \Lambda(1): & \text{buy new machine,} \\ \alpha C(\xi + 1) + \alpha \Lambda(\xi + 1): & \text{keep current one.} \end{cases} \tag{10–109}$$

Equation (10–109) is the functional equation which determines $\Lambda(\xi)$. We ask the reader to show in Problem 10–22 that there exists a number N such that if $\xi \leq N$, then an optimal policy has the form that a machine is kept until it is N periods old and then a new one is bought. It remains undecided however, what to do if $\xi > N$. One can also solve explicitly for $\Lambda(\xi)$, $\xi = 1, \ldots, N$, as was done in Section 10–15. (See Problem 10–23.) In doing this, one essentially obtains (10–108) for $\Lambda(N)$ except that no discount factor will appear on $S(N)$, due to the fact that in developing (10–108) we imagined that the process was started by buying a new machine without selling an old one, whereas for $\Lambda(N)$ an old machine is sold when the new one is purchased. It is to be expected that the functional equation approach would yield the same result as (10–108), since both methods are solving the same problem.

We shall next consider a case in which technological improvement is taken into account. In this case, a finite planning horizon must be used in the computation. We shall imagine that the total production of a machine is to remain constant over time, so that any increase in productivity due to technological improvement will be reflected in lower operating costs. We shall also imagine that the planning horizon will consist of n one-year periods. Decisions are made only at the beginning of a period. The periods will be named $1, 2, \ldots, n$, so that the first period in time will be called 1. Now the installed cost of a machine may depend on the period in which it was purchased. Similarly, the maintenance and operating costs and the salvage value will depend not only on the age of the machine, but also on the year in which it was purchased. We shall assume that the year of purchase properly describes the state of technological improvement for the machine. The installed cost of a machine purchased in year i will be denoted by I_i. Let $C_i(j)$ be the expected operating and maintenance cost for a machine purchased at the beginning of period i in its jth period of operation; and $S_i(j)$ the salvage value of a machine purchased at the beginning of year i after j periods of use.

Now let $\Lambda_k(\xi)$ be the cost over years k through n discounted to the beginning of year k, when an optimal decision is made at the beginning of year k and in all future periods, and when at the beginning of year k the machine currently in use is ξ years old. Then, since we either keep the present machine or buy a new one, the recurrence relations for the $\Lambda_k(\xi)$ must have the form

$$\Lambda_k(\xi) = \min\begin{cases} I_k - S_{k-\xi}(\xi) + \alpha C_k(1) + \alpha\Lambda_{k+1}(1): & \text{buy new machine;} \\ \alpha C_{k-\xi}(\xi+1) + \alpha\Lambda_{k+1}(\xi+1): & \text{keep old machine.} \end{cases} \tag{10–110}$$

We shall assume that at the end of year n, the machine in use is sold. Thus

$$\Lambda_n(\xi) = \min\begin{cases} I_n - S_{n-\xi}(\xi) + \alpha C_n(1) + \alpha S_n(1), \\ \alpha C_{n-\xi}(\xi+1) + \alpha S_{n-\xi}(\xi+1). \end{cases} \tag{10–111}$$

The problem is solved by means of a backward solution. The solution provides an optimal decision for each year. When there is technological improvement, the length of time which one keeps a machine may vary from one machine to the next. Note that the dynamic programming problem based on (10–110) and (10–111) is especially easy to solve, since to evaluate $\Lambda_k(\xi)$ only two alternatives need be considered. This type of problem represents one of the few cases where it is possible to solve manually a dynamic programming problem of realistic size. Of course, the computation is also very easy to code for a computer, and thus if the computation is to be made frequently, it will be desirable to carry out the computations on a digital computer. Although the above formulation is completely general, and allows for the fact that technological improvement influences the costs arbitrarily, in practice, the method gives rise to difficulties when we try to make predictions concerning the nature of technological improvement. Fortunately, the problem of equipment replacement seems to have a feature common to many economic problems, namely that in the neighborhood of the minimum, the cost surface as a function of the decision variables is quite flat, so that the best time for replacement need be determined only approximately in order to realize almost all savings possible.

The dynamic programming approach to equipment replacement is quite flexible, and it can also be used if each year there are several new machines that might be purchased. It can also be employed to investigate whether it might be better to rebuild the current machine than buy a new one. The formulation of the problem with these latter two generalizations requires the use of some material to be presented in the next chapter. Hence, we shall not give them here, but defer the discussion to Chapter 11.

The reader will note that in this section, the recurrence relations (10–109) and (10–110) were not derived in the usual way, but were written down directly. This was especially easy here. We ask the reader to derive them in the usual way in Problem 10–24, taking account of the fact that the control variable at any stage can be imagined to assume only two values, say 0 and 1, corresponding to the two alternatives of keeping the present machine or buying a new one.

In this section, we have treated the equipment replacement problem as though one could consider one machine independently of the other machines in operation. While in many instances this assumption is valid, there are also important cases where all machines possessed by the firm must be considered simultaneously. Suppose that a firm currently has a number of machines in operation (perhaps of different ages). Management has an estimate of how demand for the product made by these machines will increase over a certain number of years. They also have estimates of the effects of technological improvement on machines that will become available. The problem is to determine an optimal program for replacing machines and/or augmenting the number of machines in current use so as to meet the expected demand while minimizing the discounted costs over the planning horizon. This is a very complicated problem, and we shall not attempt to solve it here.

The application of dynamic programming to the solution of equipment replacement problems was developed by Bellman and Dreyfus [5, 8, 11]. Other approaches to the problem are given in [1, 15].

10–17 Stochastic sequential decision problems. The nature of stochastic sequential decision problems was discussed in Chapter 5. It was noted there that the standard techniques for solving programming problems which merely determine a set of values for the control variables are not satisfactory for solving stochastic sequential decision problems, due to the fact that the control variables should be allowed to be functions of the random parameters which are observed before the decision is made. The dynamic programming technique is ideally suited, however, for solving certain types of stochastic sequential decision problems, since at each stage, the decision variable is automatically determined as a function of the state parameters for the stage. It is by no means true, though, that dynamic programming can be used to solve all stochastic sequential decision problems. Some of the limitations will be pointed out in the next chapter. At present we merely wish to show how inventory problems of the type considered in Chapter 5 can be solved by means of dynamic programming.

It will be recalled that when solving deterministic sequential decision problems by dynamic programming, one may use either a backward or a forward solution. With stochastic sequential decision problems, it is always necessary to use a backward solution, since, due to the stochastic nature of the process, one cannot arbitrarily specify what the state of the system will be at the end of the planning horizon.

10–18 A stochastic dynamic inventory model. Let us consider once again the stochastic inventory problem formulated in Section 5–4. We shall now show how the problem can be solved by dynamic programming. First, however, we shall generalize the formulation slightly. Consider a particular item stocked by an inventory system. The state of the system is reviewed periodically, and at these review times one must decide whether or not to place an order, and if an order is placed, how much should be ordered. In making the decision, one considers a planning horizon of n periods, and the quantity to be ordered, if any, is chosen so as to minimize the expected costs incurred over the planning horizon. The demand in each period over the planning horizon must be treated as a random variable. It will be convenient here to treat the random variable v_j representing the demand in period j as discrete having a probability density function $p_j(v_j)$. The demands in different periods will be assumed to be independent random variables, but the expected demand may vary from one period to another.

It will be imagined that a fixed cost A_j is incurred if an order is placed in period j. The cost of x_j units ordered in period j will be denoted by $C_j(x_j)$; $C_j(x_j)$ can be of arbitrary form. The procurement lead time will be assumed to be a constant τ, so that an order placed at time t will arrive at time $t + \tau$. Just as for the deterministic case studied in Section 10–14, if a decision is to be made at time t, nothing can be done about the inventory carrying costs or stockout costs incurred between t and $t + \tau$, and these costs are independent of the decision to be made at time t or at any future time, and hence need not be included in the cost expression. We shall restrict our attention to the case where all demands that occur when the system is out of stock are backordered, so that all demands must ultimately be filled. Let y_j denote the quantity on hand plus on order minus backorders at the beginning of period j (if there are any backorders on the books, nothing will be on hand, and if anything is on hand, there are no backorders outstanding). The amount on hand plus on order minus backorders will be referred to as the inventory position. Note that y_j may be negative, as well as positive, or zero. The inventory position after the placing of any order will be $y_j + x_j$, where x_j is the quantity ordered. In a lead time everything on order will arrive in the system. If d_τ is the lead-time demand, then immediately after any order placed at the beginning of period j has arrived, the on-hand inventory will be $y_j + x_j - d_\tau$ if this quantity is non-negative, and the number of backorders outstanding will be $d_\tau - y_j - x_j$ if this quantity is positive. If t_j is the time corresponding to the beginning of period j, and Δt_j is the length of period j, then the expected cost of carrying inventory and of stockouts incurred in the time interval $t_j + \tau$ to $t_j + \tau + \Delta t_j$ will normally be a function only of $y_j + x_j$. This was certainly true of the simple case studied in Section 5–4, and it is also true of the models developed in [13]. We shall therefore assume it to be the case here, and will write this expected cost (discounted to time t_j) as $g_j(y_j + x_j)$. One special case of $g_j(y_j + x_j)$ was given in Section 5–4. More realistic situations are considered in [13]. Here, we need not concern ourselves with the specific functional form of the $g_j(y_j + x_j)$.

Let us assume that at the time a decision is made at the beginning of period j, the decision maker knows the inventory position y_j for the product, and would like to determine the optimal quantity that should be ordered at the beginning of period 1. Since the decision affects future periods, we must consider a planning horizon of n periods and take into account the decisions which can be made at future periods. The problem will be resolved each time a decision is made, using a planning horizon of n periods and taking into account the latest demand information available. The optimal decision at the beginning of period 1 is to be made by minimizing the expected discounted cost over the planning horizon. However, this expected cost also depends on the decisions made in periods 2 through n. Thus one cannot determine x_1^* without optimizing with respect to $x_2, \ldots, x_n$. As noted in Section 5–4, in selecting $x_j, j \geq 2$, one should take into account the demands which have occurred in periods 1 through $j - 1$. It was also observed in Section 5–4 that all information of value obtained from a knowledge of the past can be summarized in y_j. Therefore the $x_j, j \geq 2$, should be allowed to be functions of y_j, that is, $x_j(y_j)$. This can be done quite easily by means of dynamic programming.

Let

$$\Lambda_k(\xi) = \min_{x_k,\ldots,x_n} \sum_{\text{all } v_j} \left[\prod_{j=k}^{n} p_j(v_j)\right]\left\{\sum_{j=k}^{n} \alpha^{j-k}[A_j\delta_j + C_j(x_j)] + g_k(\xi + x_k) + \sum_{j=k+1}^{n} \alpha^{j-k} g_j\left(\xi + \sum_{i=k}^{j} x_j - \sum_{i=k}^{j-1} v_j\right)\right\}, \quad k = 1, \ldots, n. \tag{10–112}$$

Then $\Lambda_k(\xi)$ is the minimum expected discounted cost for periods k through n when the inventory position at the beginning of period k, before the placement of any order is ξ. Since we are imagining that in (10–112) we are not determining a set of numbers x_j but a set of functions $x_j(y_j)$, we should try to understand very clearly the precise meaning of (10–112). It means the following. Let us select an arbitrary set of policy functions $x_j(y_j)$. Imagine that we are now given a set of demands v_j, one for each period. Then, beginning with the first period, we can sequentially compute the y_j, and hence the x_j, using our policy functions. Knowing the x_j and v_j, we can compute the discounted cost over the planning horizon for this set of v_j. Let us now repeat the process for every possible set of v_j and compute the discounted cost in each case. Next we weight each of these costs by the probability of obtaining that particular set of v_j. We add all these to obtain the expected cost for the particular set of policy functions. Imagine that we repeat this entire procedure for every conceivable set of policy functions. An optimal set will then be the one yielding the smallest value of all the expected costs. This is the sort of computation that is implied by (10–112). Note that in the above expression, it is legitimate to use for period j the expected cost of carrying inventory and of stockouts given $y_j + x_j$, rather than the actual costs for a specified pattern of demands; i.e., we may perform this average first before averaging over the v_j. The reader is asked to explain this in more detail in Problem 10–25.

Now $\Lambda_k(\xi)$ can be written

$$\Lambda_k(\xi) = \min_{x_k} \left\{ \sum_{\text{all } v_j} \left[\prod_{j=k}^{n} p_j(v_j) \right] [A_k\delta_k + C_k(x_k) + g_k(\xi + x_k)] + \alpha \sum_{v_k=0}^{\infty} p_k(v_k) \left[\min_{x_{k+1},\ldots,x_n} \sum_{\text{all } v_j} \left[\prod_{j=k+1}^{n} p_j(v_j) \right] \times \left\{ \sum_{j=k+1}^{n} \alpha^{j-k-1} \left[A_j\delta_j + C_j(x_j) + g_{k+1}(\xi + x_k + x_{k+1} - v_k) + \sum_{j=k+2}^{n} \alpha^{j-k-1} g_j \left(\xi + x_k - v_k + \sum_{i=k+1}^{j} x_j - \sum_{i=k+1}^{j-1} v_j \right) \right] \right\} \right] \right\},$$

$$k = 1, \ldots, n-1, \qquad (10\text{–}113)$$

or

$$\Lambda_k(\xi) = \min_{x_k} \left[A_k\delta_k + C_k(x_k) + g_k(\xi + x_k) + \alpha \sum_{v_k=0}^{\infty} p_k(v_k)\Lambda_{k+1}(\xi + x_k - v_k) \right],$$

$$k = 1, \ldots, n-1. \qquad (10\text{–}114)$$

To obtain (10–113) we used the fact that

$$\sum_{\text{all } v_j} \left[\prod_{j=k}^{n} p_j(v_j) \right] f(v_k, \ldots, v_n) = \sum_{v_k=0}^{\infty} p_k(v_k) \times \left\{ \sum_{\text{all } v_j} \left[\prod_{j=k+1}^{n} p_j(v_j) \right] f(v_k, \ldots, v_n). \right\}$$

Equation (10–114) followed from the definition of $\Lambda_{k+1}(\xi)$, and from the observation that $A_k\delta_k + C_k(x_k) + g_k(\xi + x_k)$ is independent of $v_k, \ldots, v_n$ and that

$$\sum_{\text{all } v_j} \left[\prod_{j=k}^{n} p_j(v_j) \right] = 1.$$

Note finally that

$$\Lambda_n(\xi) = \min_{x_n} [A_n\delta_n + C_n(x_n) + g_n(\xi + x_n)]. \tag{10–115}$$

When computing $\Lambda_1(y_1)$, where y_1 is the initial inventory position, we obtain x_1^*, the optimal quantity to order for the first period. When we compute $\Lambda_k(\xi)$, for the other periods, we obtain $\hat{x}_k(\xi)$, the optimal quantity to order when the inventory position at the beginning of period k is ξ. Thus for $k \geq 2$, we do obtain functions $x_k(\xi)$ of the type needed (see Section 5–4). Hence, by dynamic programming, we can solve the stochastic sequential decision problem formulated in Section 5–4.

The recurrence relations (10–114) are more complicated than the corresponding ones expressed by (10–69) because $\Lambda_{k+1}(\xi + x_k - v_k)$ must be averaged over the possible values for the demand in period k. In actually solving a problem of this type, the upper limits ∞ on the summation sign in (10–114) would be replaced by some finite d_k such that the probability of having a demand greater than d_k in period k is small enough to be ignored. After making this modification, one can solve problems of this type on a computer in precisely the same manner used to treat the problems considered previously.

In certain cases, the optimal ordering policy for the problem just considered will have the very simple form which says that if at the beginning of period j, the inventory position y_j is less than, or equal to, some number r_j, then one should order a quantity sufficient to bring the inventory position up to the value R_j; however, if $y_j > r_j$, then no order should be placed. The recurrence relations (10–114) can be used to study the conditions under which an optimal policy has the above form. In general, an optimal policy will not have this simple form unless the unit cost of the item is a constant C_j independent of the quantity ordered. Let us assume that this is the case. For the analysis to follow, it is convenient to treat all variables as continuous rather than as discrete. The modification needed in (10–114) is to replace the discrete density $p_k(v_k)$ by a continuous density $\phi_k(v_k)$ and the summation sign by an integral sign. Then the recurrence relations (10–114) become

$$\Lambda_k(\xi) = -C_k\xi + \min_{x_k} [A_k\delta_k + G_k(\xi + x_k)], \tag{10–116}$$

where

$$G_k(\xi + x_k) = (\xi + x_k)C_k + g_k(\xi + x_k) + \alpha \int_0^\infty \Lambda_k(\xi + x_k - v_k)\phi_k(v_k)\, dv_k. \tag{10–117}$$

Suppose that $G_k(u)$ had the shape shown in Fig. 10–5. In this case it is

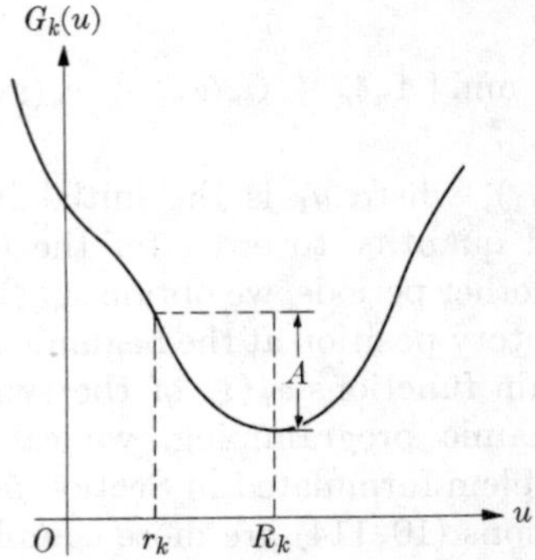

FIGURE 10–5

clear that if $\xi > r_k$, it is optimal not to order, but if $\xi \leq r_k$, then a quantity $R_k - \xi$ should be ordered. Thus, when $G_k(u)$ has the shape shown in Fig. 10–5, the optimal policy for period k has the simple form discussed above. On the other hand, if $G_k(u)$ has the shape shown in Fig. 10–6, an optimal policy has the following form: if $\xi \leq r_1$, order $R_1 - \xi$; if $r_1 < \xi \leq r_2$, do not order; if $r_2 < \xi \leq r_3$, order $R_1 - \xi$; if $r_3 \leq \xi \leq r_4$, do not order; if $r_4 < \xi \leq r_5$, order $R_2 - \xi$; if $\xi > r_5$, do not order.

One would usually expect $G_k(u)$ to look more like the curve shown in Fig. 10–5 than the curve shown in Fig. 10–6. It is surprisingly difficult, however, to determine the most general conditions under which a simple policy of the type discussed above will be optimal at each stage. The most general result available is that proved by Scarf [16]. He showed that if the unit cost of the item is a constant in each period, and if all $g_k(u)$ are convex functions of u, then for each k, an optimal policy has the form that there exist numbers r_k, R_k such that if $y_k \leq r_k$, one should order $R_k - y_k$, whereas if $y_k > r_k$, one should not place an order. In other words, the optimal policy has the simple form considered above. A proof is also presented in [13].

In Chapter 5, it was pointed out that in solving stochastic sequential decision problems, one should allow the control variables to be only functions of the information actually known to the decision maker at the time he makes the decision. In the above formulation, we assumed that the inventory position of the item was known before the quantity to be ordered was decided on at the beginning of period k. Let us now consider a slightly different case in which there is a one-period time lag in reporting the demand, so that at the beginning of period k the decision maker does not know y_k, but only $y_{k-1} + x_{k-1}$, the inventory position at the beginning of period $k - 1$ after any order was placed. Write $w_{k-1} = y_{k-1} + x_{k-1}$.

To solve the present version of the problem, let $\Lambda_k(\xi)$ be the expected cost for periods k through n discounted to the beginning of period k when

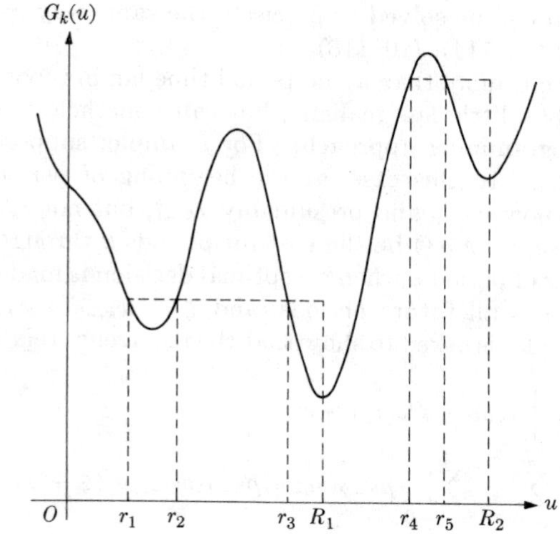

FIGURE 10–6

an optimal decision is made at the beginning of period k and all succeeding periods and $w_{k-1} = \xi$. Then

$$\Lambda_k(\xi) = \min_{x_k,\ldots,x_n} \sum_{\text{all } v_j} \left[\prod_{j=k-1}^{n} p_j(v_j) \right] \times \left\{ \sum_{j=k}^{n} \alpha^{j-k}[A_j\delta_j + C_j(x_j)] + g_k(\xi - v_{k-1} + x_k) + \sum_{j=k+1}^{n} \alpha^{j-k} g_j\left(\xi + \sum_{i=k}^{j} x_j - \sum_{i=k-1}^{j-1} v_j\right)\right\},$$

$$k = 1, \ldots, n. \quad (10\text{–}118)$$

After using the same arguments which led to (10–114) and (10–115), we conclude that

$$\Lambda_k(\xi) = \min_{x_k} \left\{ A_k\delta_k + C_k(x_k) + \sum_{v_{k-1}=0}^{\infty} p_{k-1}(v_{k-1}) \times [g_k(\xi - v_{k-1} + x_k) + \alpha\Lambda_{k+1}(\xi - v_{k-1} + x_k)] \right\},$$

$$k = 1, \ldots, n-1, \quad (10\text{–}119)$$

$$\Lambda_n(\xi) = \min_{x_n} \left\{ A_n\delta_n + C_n(x_n) + \sum_{v_n-1=0}^{\infty} p_{n-1}(v_{n-1}) g_n(\xi - v_{n-1} + x_n) \right\}. \quad (10\text{–}120)$$

This problem can be solved in precisely the same way as the formulation described by (10–114), (10–115).

When there is more than a one-period time lag in reporting demand, the situation gets a little less realistic, but can nonetheless be treated by the dynamic programming approach. For example, suppose that there is a two-period lag. In this case, at the beginning of period k, the decision maker will know w_{k-2} and presumably x_{k-1}, but not v_{k-2} and v_{k-1}. To treat this case, let $\Lambda_k(\xi)$ be the cost for periods k through n discounted to the beginning of period k when an optimal decision is made at the beginning of period k and all future periods, and $\xi = w_{k-2} + x_{k-1}$. In Problem 10–26, the reader is asked to show that the recurrence relations then become

$$\Lambda_k(\xi) = \min_{x_k} \Bigg\{ A_k\delta_k + C_k(x_k) + \sum_{v_{k-2}=0}^{\infty} \sum_{v_{k-1}=0}^{\infty} p_{k-2}(v_{k-2})p_{k-1}(v_{k-1})g_k(\xi + x_k - v_{k-2} - v_{k-1}) + \alpha \sum_{v_{k-2}=0}^{\infty} p_{k-2}(v_{k-2})\Lambda_{k+1}(\xi - v_{k-2} + x_k) \Bigg\},$$
$$k = 1, \ldots, n-1. \qquad (10\text{–}121)$$

Dynamic programming is of no assistance in the solution of the one particular case mentioned in Chapter 5, where no attempt is made to take account of information about the values of the random variables that have been observed; but instead, at the beginning of period 1, we determine a set of numbers $x_1, \ldots, x_n$ which are the quantities to be ordered in each period regardless of what happens. In Problem 10–27 the reader is asked to explain why dynamic programming cannot be used in this case.

As in the deterministic case, we can change the type of model discussed in this section to one where the distribution of demand and the costs do not change from one period to the next and infinite planning horizon is used. Then let $\Lambda(\xi)$ be the cost over all future time discounted to a review time (with the usual convention that one does not include the expected carrying and stockout costs incurred up to the point in time when any order placed at the review time arrives) when an optimal decision is made every review time if the inventory portion at the review time prior to the placing of any order is ξ. Then $\Lambda(\xi)$ is independent of the review time being considered. When all variables are treated as continuous, the functional equation for $\Lambda(\xi)$ then becomes

$$\Lambda(\xi) = \min_{x} \left\{ A\delta + C(x) + g(\xi + x) + \alpha \int_0^{\infty} \Lambda(\xi + x - v)\phi(v)\, dv \right\}. \qquad (10\text{–}122)$$

Problem 10–28 requires the derivation of the functional equation (10–122). It can be proved that if $g(u)$ is a convex function and the unit cost of the item is a constant, then an Rr-policy will be optimal. In this case, there also exists the possibility of finding an explicit solution for the functional equation. However, the task is not nearly so easy as in the deterministic case. The method of carrying out the solution is considered in [13].

10–19 Dynamic programming and the calculus of variations. As previously noted, stochastic sequential decision problems have the property that, in general, their solution requires that one find not simply a set of numbers representing optimal values of the variables, but a set of functions, the arguments of the functions being random variables whose values will be observed by the time the decision is made. Of course, even for deterministic problems, it may be desirable to find a set of functions for the control variables, with the arguments of the functions being certain parameters of the problem, such as the availability of resources. There is, however, a different class of classical deterministic optimization problems which requires the determination of one or more functions, rather than the values of one or more variables. These problems form the subject matter of the calculus of variations.

Perhaps the simplest and best-known problem in the calculus of variations is that of finding the curve lying in the xy-plane which passes through two given points $\mathbf{a} = (\alpha, a)$ and $\mathbf{b} = (\beta, b)$ and has the property that the distance along the curve from **a** to **b** is a minimum. Everyone knows that a straight line gives the shortest distance between two points in a plane. The calculus of variations provides a method of obtaining this result (if one did not know the answer), and also provides a way of *proving* that a straight line does yield the shortest distance. Let us formulate this question as a problem in the calculus of variations. Let $y(x)$ be any curve passing through **a** and **b**. We shall restrict our attention to curves which are continuous and differentiable. Such curves are called *admissible arcs*. The element of distance ds along $y(x)$ is related to dx and dy by

$$ds^2 = dx^2 + dy^2 \qquad \text{or} \qquad \frac{ds}{dx} = \left[1 + \left(\frac{dy}{dx}\right)^2\right]^{1/2}.$$

Now the total distance D along the curve from **a** to **b** is simply

$$D = \int_\alpha^\beta \frac{ds}{dx}\,dx = \int_\alpha^\beta \left[1 + \left(\frac{dy}{dx}\right)^2\right]^{1/2} dx. \tag{10–123}$$

We would like to determine that admissible arc $y(x)$ which minimizes D in (10–123). Finding the function $y(x)$ which minimizes the integral (10–123) is a problem in the calculus of variations.

As another elementary example, suppose that a curve $y(x)$ is passed through the points $\mathbf{a} = (\alpha, a)$, $\mathbf{b} = (\beta, b)$ in the xy-plane, with the properties that $a, b > 0$ and $y(x) \geq 0$, $\alpha \leq x \leq \beta$. This curve is then rotated about the x-axis to yield a surface of revolution. We desire to determine the curve $y(x)$ for which the area of the surface of revolution will be minimized. If ds is the element of length along the curve, then the element of surface area dA is

$$dA = 2\pi y \, ds = 2\pi y \left[1 + \left(\frac{dy}{dx}\right)^2\right]^{1/2} dx,$$

or the area A is

$$A = 2\pi \int_\alpha^\beta y \left[1 + \left(\frac{dy}{dx}\right)^2\right]^{1/2} dx. \tag{10–124}$$

It is desired to determine the function $y(x)$ passing through $\mathbf{a}$ and $\mathbf{b}$ which minimizes A. This is another problem in the calculus of variations.

As a final example, consider an entrepreneur who produces a good having a seasonal demand pattern. The rate of sales q depends not only on the time of year t, but also on the rate of advertising expenditures $s(t)$. The sales response to advertising can be assumed to be instantaneous so that $q = q(s, t)$; this is assumed to be a known function. The good is of a highly perishable nature and cannot be stored. Thus, the production rate will be maintained at a value equal to the known (and predictable) sales rate. There is a requirement that all demands must be met. If q is the production rate, production costs are incurred at a rate of $c(q, \dot{q})$, $\dot{q} = dq/dt$. Production costs depend on the production rate and the rate of change of the production rate. However, since $q = q(s, t)$ we can express the rate of incurring production costs in terms of s, $\dot{s} = ds/dt$, and t, that is, $c(s, \dot{s}, t)$. It is of interest to determine the rate of advertising expenditures $s(t)$ as a function of time over the period t_0 to t_1 which maximizes the profit received from the sale of the good. The unit selling price of the good is assumed to be a constant p. The rate at which revenues are obtained is pq. The rate at which production and advertising costs are incurred is $c + s$. Thus the rate at which profits are obtained is $pq - c - s$. The total profit P received between t_0 and t_1 is

$$P = \int_{t_0}^{t_1} \left[pq(s, t) - c(s, \dot{s}, t) - s\right] dt. \tag{10–125}$$

It is desired to determine the function $s(t)$, the rate of advertising expenditures, which maximizes P. This is also a problem in the calculus of variations.

Each of the examples discussed above is a special case of a general problem which seeks to find a function $y(x)$, called an *extremal curve*, passing through the points $\mathbf{a} = (\alpha, a)$ and $\mathbf{b} = (\beta, b)$ in the xy-plane and minimizing the integral

$$I = \int_{\alpha}^{\beta} F(y, y', x)\, dx, \tag{10–126}$$

where $y' = dy/dx$. Problems of this general type are the simplest ones studied in the calculus of variations. The classical approach to finding a function $y(x)$ which minimizes (10–126) is to determine a second-order nonlinear, ordinary differential equation (called the Euler equation) which the optimizing function must satisfy. For the first two examples considered above it is possible to solve this differential equation analytically and obtain an analytic expression for $y(x)$. In general, however, one must resort to numerical techniques to solve the Euler equation.

We shall not attempt to derive the Euler equation for the above problem or consider in more detail the classical techniques for solving it. Instead, we shall study how the dynamic programming formalism can be used to determine $y(x)$ numerically. This approach does not yield an analytic expression for $y(x)$, but yields the value of $y(x)$ at a finite number of points. To begin, the interval $\alpha \leq x \leq \beta$ is divided by the grid points $x_j \doteq \alpha + j\,\Delta x$, $j = 0, \ldots, n$, into n subintervals of length Δx. For any admissible arc, let $y_j = y(x_j)$. If Δx is small, then $y'(x_j)$ can be approximated by

$$y'(x_j) = y'_j \doteq \frac{y_{j+1} - y_j}{\Delta x}. \tag{10–127}$$

In terms of the points (x_j, y_j), the integral can be represented approximately by the finite sum,

$$I \doteq \sum_{j=0}^{n-1} F\left(y_j, \frac{y_{j+1} - y_j}{\Delta x}, x_j\right) \Delta x. \tag{10–128}$$

The problem of finding the function $y(x)$ which minimizes (10–126) can then be replaced by the approximating problem of finding the $n - 1$ values y_j which minimize (10–128) when y_0 and y_n are specified to have the values a and b, respectively.

Now let

$$\Lambda_k(\xi) = \min_{y_{k+1},\ldots,y_{n-1}} \sum_{j=k}^{n-1} F\left(y_j, \frac{y_{j+1} - y_j}{\Delta x}, x_j\right) \Delta x, \tag{10–129}$$

where $y_k = \xi$. Then

$$\Lambda_k(\xi) = \min_{y_{k+1}} \left[F\left(\xi, \frac{y_{k+1} - \xi}{\Delta x}, x_k\right) \Delta x + \min_{y_{k+2},\ldots,y_{n-1}} \sum_{j=k+1}^{n-1} F\left(y_j, \frac{y_{j+1} - y_j}{\Delta x}, x_j\right) \Delta x \right]$$

or

$$\Lambda_k(\xi) = \min_{y_{k+1}} \left[F\left(\xi, \frac{y_{k+1} - \xi}{\Delta x}, x_k\right) \Delta x + \Lambda_{k+1}(y_{k+1}) \right],$$

$$k = 0, 1, \ldots, n - 2, \qquad (10\text{–}130)$$

and

$$\Lambda_{n-1}(\xi) = F\left(\xi, \frac{b - \xi}{\Delta x}, x_{n-1}\right) \Delta x. \qquad (10\text{–}131)$$

The minimum value of I is then approximately $\Lambda_0(a)$.

In the above formulation, ξ, and hence the y_k, are continuous variables. To solve the problem numerically, we could proceed in two different ways. The first would be to treat both ξ and y_k as discrete, that is, for each k, we would determine a discrete set of values which ξ and also y_k could assume. Then $\Lambda_k(\xi)$ would be tabulated only for these values. To compute $\Lambda_k(\xi)$, y_{k+1} would only be allowed to take on the set of discrete values appropriate to x_{k+1}. In addition to tabulating the $\Lambda_k(\xi)$, one would also tabulate $\hat{y}_{k+1}(\xi)$. At the final stage, one would determine $\Lambda_0(a)$, as well as y_1^*. The optimal values of the other y_k would be obtained by means of

$$y_{k+1}^* = \hat{y}_{k+1}(y_k^*), \qquad k = 1, \ldots, n - 2. \qquad (10\text{–}132)$$

With this approach none of the problems associated with minimizing over continuous variables would be encountered.

The other approach would be to treat ξ and the y_k as continuous variables. Since $F(y_k, (y_{k+1} - y_k)/\Delta x, x_k)$ usually is a continuous function of y_{k+1}, y_k, and x_k, it follows that $\Lambda_k(\xi)$ will be a continuous function of ξ. Furthermore, for this type of problem, this implies that the $\hat{y}_k(\xi)$ are also continuous. Thus it is possible to interpolate in both the $\Lambda_k(\xi)$- and the $\hat{y}_k(\xi)$-tables. These results are to be proved in Problem 10–29. One would then proceed as in the discrete case, tabulating both $\Lambda_k(\xi)$ and $\hat{y}_k(\xi)$ for a discrete set of ξ. However, in carrying out the minimization over y_k, one would treat y_k as a continuous variable, and use some technique such as the one discussed in Section 10–7 to effect the minimization. The task of carrying out the minimization is somewhat simplified here because $y(x)$ is a continuous function of x, and, since $y_k = \xi$, one can begin looking for the optimal value of y_{k+1} in the neighborhood of $y_{k+1} = \xi$. In the backward search, to find the y_k^*, interpolation in the $\hat{y}_k(\xi)$-tables will, in general, be needed.

In solving a problem in the calculus of variations by the numerical method just suggested, one actually determines a whole family of extremal curves as one moves away from the point **b**. At the last step, one determines the particular extremal curve emanating from **b**, which also passes through **a**. This is illustrated geometrically in Fig. 10–7. In obtaining

$\Lambda_k(\xi)$, we determine $y_{k+1}(\xi)$, which tells us which of the extremal curves terminating at x_{k+1} pass through (x_k, ξ).

In this section, we have considered only the simplest class of problems arising in the calculus of variations. We have seen that numerical solutions to these problems can be obtained by means of dynamic programming. In the next chapter, we shall consider somewhat more complicated problems, and examine the effectiveness of dynamic programming for solving these.

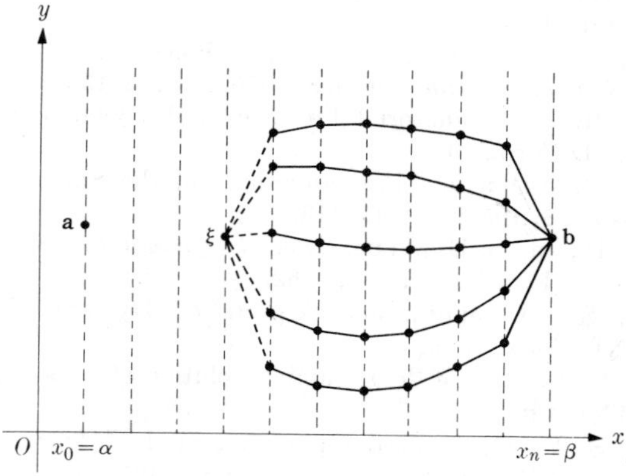

FIGURE 10–7

10–20 Computer codes for solving problems by dynamic programming. The reader examining the recurrence relations used to compute the $\Lambda_k(\xi)$ for the various problems considered in this chapter will note that no two problems yielded precisely the same form of recurrence relations. This is a characteristic of dynamic programming. The recurrence relations obtained to solve the problem are strongly dependent on the particular structure of the problem being solved. For this reason, for example, it is not possible to develop a general computer code for solving all dynamic programming problems, as we were able to do for linear problems. Indeed, it is often difficult to develop a code of sufficient generality to solve even a small subclass of problems by dynamic programming. Usually, for each type of problem to be solved by dynamic programming, it is necessary to develop a special computer code. Fortunately, the task of coding a dynamic programming solution is quite easy, in contrast to linear programming, where the development of an efficient code is a very extensive undertaking.

References

1. ALCHIAN, A., "Economic Replacement Policy," *R-224*, The RAND Corp., 1952.

2. ARIS, R., R. BELLMAN, and R. KALABA, "Some Optimization Problems in Chemical Engineering," *P-1798*, The RAND Corp., 1959.

3. BELLMAN, R., *Dynamic Programming*. Princeton, N. J.: Princeton University Press, 1957.

4. BELLMAN, R., *Adaptive Control Processes: A Guided Tour*. Princeton, N. J.: Princeton University Press, 1961.

5. BELLMAN, R., "Equipment Replacement Policy," *Journal of the Society for Industrial and Applied Mathematics*, **3**, 1955, pp. 133–136.

6. BELLMAN, R., "Combinatorial Processes and Dynamic Programming," *P-1284*, The RAND Corp., 1958.

7. BELLMAN, R., "Dynamic Programming and the Smoothing Problem," *Management Science*, **3**, 1956, pp. 111–113.

8. BELLMAN, R., and S. DREYFUS, *Applied Dynamic Programming*. Princeton, N. J.: Princeton University Press, 1962.

9. DREYFUS, S., "Computational Aspects of Dynamic Programming," *P-924*, The RAND Corp., 1956.

10. DREYFUS, S., "Dynamic Programming Solution of Allocation Problems," *P-1083*, The RAND Corp., 1957.

11. DREYFUS, S., "A Generalized Equipment Study," *Journal of the Society for Industrial and Applied Mathematics*, **8**, 1960, pp. 425–435.

12. DREYFUS, S., "Dynamic Programming and the Calculus of Variations," *Journal of Mathematical Analysis and Applications*, **1**, 1960, pp. 228–239.

13. HADLEY, G., and T. M. WHITIN, *Analysis of Inventory Systems*. Englewood Cliffs, N. J.: Prentice-Hall, 1963.

14. MOLINA, E. C., *Poisson's Exponential Binomial Limit*. Princeton, N. J.: Van Nostrand, 1942.

15. TERBORGH, G., *Dynamic Equipment Policy*. New York: McGraw-Hill, 1949.

16. SCARF, H., "The Optimality of (S,s) Policies in the Dynamic Inventory Problem," in *Mathematical Methods in the Social Sciences*, K. J. Arrow, S. Karlin, and P. Suppes, editors. Stanford, California: Stanford University Press, 1960, pp. 196–202.

17. WAGNER, H. M., and T. M. WHITIN, "Dynamic Version of the Economic Lot Size Model," *Management Science*, **5**, 1958, pp. 89–96.

Problems

10–1. Consider the problem discussed in Section 10–2. What difficulties, if any, are encountered if one or more a_j are negative? How would one solve the problem in this case?

10–2. Suppose that in Eq. (10–1) the constraint must hold as a strict equality. What changes would have to be made in the computational technique to take account of this fact?

10–3. Consider a flyaway kit problem in which there are only three items. The total volume available is 13 ft^3. The unit volume of item A is 2 ft^3, that of item B is 3 ft^3, and that of item C is 2 ft^3. The cost of having a demand occur when the system is out of stock is \$600 for item A, \$1200 for item B, and \$800 for item C. The demand for each item is Poisson distributed with the means being 3, 2, 2 for items A, B, C, respectively. How many of each item should be loaded in order to minimize the expected stockout costs? What would adding 1 ft^3 of storage space be worth?

10–4. For the example solved in Section 10–5, what would adding 1 ft^3 of storage space be worth?

10–5. An overseas naval base is supplied with certain critical spare parts only once every month, when a plane from the main depot arrives to replenish the inventory. There are n parts which are normally resupplied in this way. Just before the time that the plane is to be loaded at the main depot, the base radios in the number of each of the n parts which it has on hand. Let y_j be the number of item j on hand just prior to replenishment. The plane which brings the spares can carry a volume V, and the unit volume of item j is v_j. A cost π_j is incurred each time a demand occurs for item j and the base is out of stock. The monthly demand for item j is Poisson distributed with mean μ_j. Show how you would solve the problem of determining the quantity x_j of each item to be loaded so as to minimize the expected stockout costs for the coming month, using dynamic programming. Solve such a problem when there are only three items and the appropriate parameters are: $V = 14$ ft^3, $v_1 = 4$ ft^3, $v_2 = 3$ ft^3, $v_3 = 2$ ft^3; $y_1 = 1$, $y_2 = 0$, $y_3 = 2$; $\pi_1 = \$5000$; $\pi_2 = \$3000$; $\pi_3 = \$8000$; $\mu_1 = 1.5$; $\mu_2 = 3.4$; $\mu_3 = 5.8$.

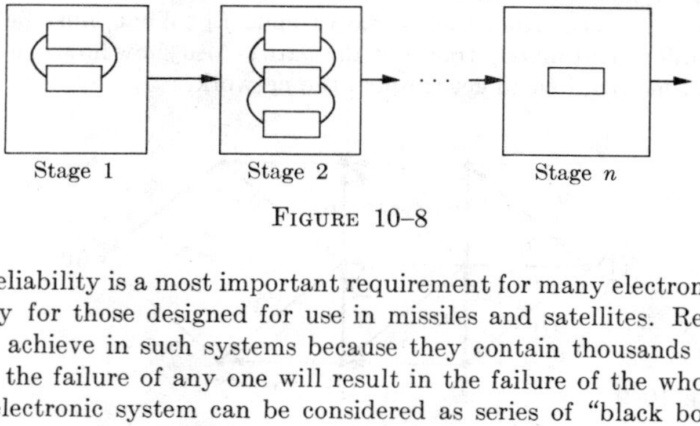

FIGURE 10–8

10–6. Reliability is a most important requirement for many electronic systems —especially for those designed for use in missiles and satellites. Reliability is difficult to achieve in such systems because they contain thousands of components, and the failure of any one will result in the failure of the whole system. Often an electronic system can be considered as series of "black boxes" (Fig. 10–8). These may be amplifiers, transformers, or more complicated subsystems. To increase the reliability of the total system, one might attempt to introduce redundancy into some or all of the subsystems, that is, instead of using just one subsystem at stage j, we use two or more in parallel, along with switching circuits, in such a way that if one of the subsystems fails, one of the redundant systems is automatically switched in to take its place. Suppose that the total sum of money which can be spent in building one of these electronic systems cannot be greater than M. Within this budget, it is desired to build the most reliable system possible. The cost of one subsystem j is C_j. As a quantitative measure of the reliability of the system, we use the probability that it will not fail under operational conditions for some given period of time. Assume that the only way of increasing the reliability is to introduce redundancy. At stage j, we must use at least one subsystem. Let the number actually used be $1 + x_j$, so that the nonnegative integer x_j is the redundancy introduced at stage j. Let $f_j(x_j)$ be the probability that stage j will operate successfully when the redundancy is x_j. Assume that this probability is independent of what is done for the other stages. Thus the reliability of the whole system is the product of the $f_j(x_j)$. Show how to solve the problem of determining an optimal set of x_j by dynamic programming. Determine the precise form of $f_j(x_j)$ if p_j is the probability that a single subsystem j will not fail and if the switching circuits never fail. *Hint:* The recurrence relations have the form

$$\Lambda_k(\xi) = \max_{x_k} [f_k(x_k)\Lambda_{k-1}(\xi - C_k x_k)].$$

This type of problem is discussed in [8].

10–7. Consider a network such as that shown in Fig. 10–9. There is a single node numbered 1, called the source, and a node numbered n, called the sink. Each branch joining two nodes i and j has a sense of direction indicated by the arrowhead, and a number t_{ij} which will be imagined to be the time required to move from i to j along the branch. We wish to find the shortest time required to move through the network from the source to the sink, given that one can move along any branch only in the direction of the arrowhead. Show how this problem can be solved by dynamic programming. [*Hint.* Let Λ_j be the minimum time required to move from the source to node j.] What must be tabulated with Λ_j in order to ultimately trace out the path? Also show how one determines the longest time required to get through the network.

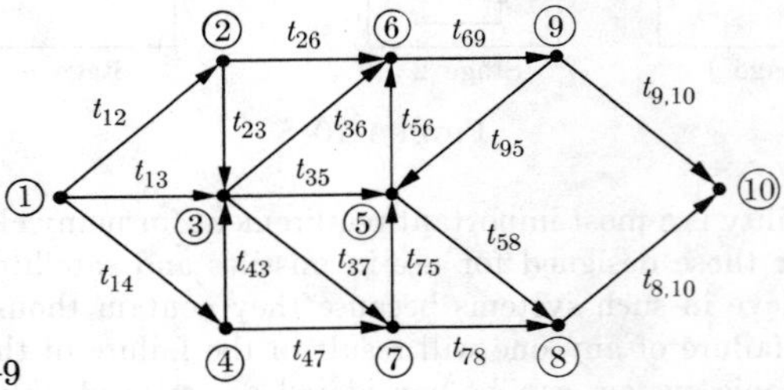

FIGURE 10–9

10–8. Develop a procedure for solving Problem 10–7 by successively labeling nodes until node n is labeled. [*Hint:* Label node j with the minimum time to get to j and the node from which we come to reach j.]

10–9. Consider some complex project, perhaps a large construction project, which has the property that a number of activities must be completed before the project can be completed. However, certain activities cannot be started until others have been completed. To measure the progress of the project, imagine that certain bench marks, called events, can be defined. An event will correspond to the completion of one or more activities. To represent graphically the character of the project, one can construct a network such as Fig. 10–9, where the nodes refer to events and the branches to activities. Now t_{ij} will be the time required to finish activity (i, j). Show that the problem of determining the earliest time at which each event can be completed may be solved by dynamic programming. Thus show how one determines the earliest time at which the whole project can be completed. Also show how one determines the latest time at which an event must be completed if the entire project is to be completed at the earliest time. [*Hint:* To solve the latter problem, start from the end of the project with the earliest completion time and successively determine the latest time that each event can be completed.] The difference between the earliest and latest times for achieving an event is called the slack. What is the physical interpretation of slack? There will be a path through the network such that there is zero slack on every node in the path. This is called the critical path. Why is this path important?

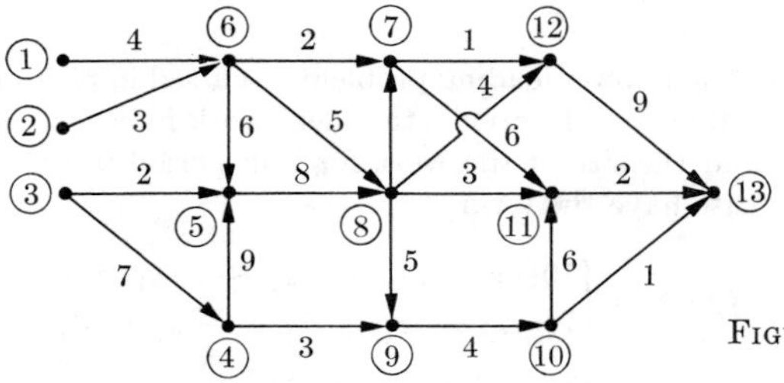

FIGURE 10–10

10–10. For the project represented by the network in Fig. 10–10, find the earliest time that each event and the entire project can be completed. Also determine the latest time at which each event can be achieved, the slack for each, and the critical path. [*Hint:* Refer to Problem 10–9.]

10–11. Consider a large military supply system which stocks a particular item at a number of different depots. Replenishment stock is ordered periodically on a centralized basis and then allocated to the various depots. Occasionally, because of the stochastic nature of demands at the depots, it happens that in the period between replenishments some depot will be in danger of running out of stock, so that it becomes advisable to consider a redistribution of stock from the other depots to the needy depot. Imagine that there are n depots, and at a time T before the next replenishment of stock, the on-hand inventory reaches a level y_n which is considered to be the level that triggers the consideration of a redistribution of stock from the other depots to n. Let y_j be the on-hand inventory at depot $j, j \neq n$, at this time. The cost of shipping x_j units from depot j to depot n will be denoted by $C_j(x_j)$. For each demand which occurs at depo j when the depot is out of stock, a stockout cost π_j is incurred. We shall denote by $p_j(v_j)$ the probability of having v_j units demanded at depot j in time T, that is, the time period preceding the next replenishment. We wish to determine how much each depot j should ship to n so as to minimize transportation costs plus the expected costs of stockouts for all depots in this time interval T. Ignore the time required to make the redistribution. Show that the problem can be solved by dynamic programming. [*Hint:* Let $\Lambda_k(\xi)$ be the expected minimum cost for depots $k, \ldots, n$ if only the depots $k, \ldots, n-1$ are allowed to ship to depot n, and the on-hand inventory at n is ξ before any redistribution is made.]

10–12. Consider the problem of finding $r_j \geq 1, j = 1, \ldots, n$ which minimize

$$z = \sum_{j=1}^{n} r_j^\alpha$$

when the r_j must satisfy

$$r_1 r_2 \ldots r_n = r.$$

Show how to solve this problem by the use of dynamic programming.

10–13. For the problem discussed in Section 10–8, prove that when the $f_j(x_j)$ are concave functions, then the $\hat{x}_k(\xi)$ are continuous functions of ξ. [*Hint:* Use the fact that if the $f_j(x_j)$ are concave, they are also continuous in the interior of any interval.]

10–14. Solve the manpower loading problem discussed in Section 10–10 for the special case where there are 4 periods, the ideal work force size in these periods being 2, 5, 3, 1, and the size of the work force in period 0 is 2. The functions f_j and g_j for this case have the form

$$f_j(x_j) = \begin{cases} 10(x_j - x_{j-1}), & x_j - x_{j-1} > 0, \\ 7(x_{j-1} - x_j), & x_{j-1} - x_j < 0; \end{cases}$$

$$g_j(x_j) = \begin{cases} 7(x_j - m_j), & x_j > m_j, \\ 11(m_j - x_j), & m_j > x_j. \end{cases}$$

10–15. For the model discussed in Section 10–12, is it true that if $C(x_j)$ is independent of j and is concave, and when no discounting is used, then in computing $\Lambda_k(0)$ it is unnecessary to go back farther in time than the beginning of the period when an order arrived which satisfied the demand in period $k-1$ when computing $\Lambda_{k-1}(0)$?

10–16. A manufacturer of table model radios produces its own capacitors in lots. The setup cost for a lot is \$250. The variable production cost per unit is \$0.85. An inventory carrying charge of \$0.02 per capacitor per month is used. The production schedule for radios over the next year calls for the following quantities of capacitors to be used each month: 15,000, 25,000, 20,000, 15,000 11,000, 6000, 5000, 11,000, 13,000, 24,000, 30,000, 8000. The time required to produce the capacitors can be ignored. Assume that setups are considered only at the beginning of a month. Compute the optimal times at which lots should be produced, and the size of each of these lots, if 1000 capacitors are now on hand, and it is desired to have 5000 on hand at the end of the year.

10–17. A manufacturer of pumps for rocket motors is under contract to deliver the following quantities to the producer of the rocket motors on the first of each month for the coming year: 30, 60, 100, 200, 300, 325, 275, 125, 100, 75, 150, 200. The pumps are produced in lots and the setup cost is \$650. Each pump costs \$150 to produce. The manufacturer uses an inventory carrying charge of \$2.00 per pump per month. If setups are considered only at the beginning of a month, and production in one month becomes available for delivery at the beginning of the next month, determine when setups should be made and the size of each setup. As the problem is stated, would there be any advantage to considering setups more frequently than once per month?

10–18. Use Eq. (10–106) to solve explicitly for the other $\Lambda(\xi)$, $\xi = r, \ldots, R - 2$.

10–19. For the model studied in Section 10–15, show that the average annual cost for a zero interest rate is given by

$$\lim_{i \to 0} i\Lambda(R - 1)$$

where i is the interest rate. [*Hint:* The system goes through one cycle's operation in the time between the receipt of two successive orders. Determine the average annual cost directly by computing the expected cost per cycle and then multiplying by the average number of cycles per year.]

10–20. Show that

$$\lim_{i \to 0} i\Lambda(\xi), \ \xi = r, \ldots, R - 2$$

is also the average annual cost for the model of Section 10–15.

10–21. Show how the minimization of the average annual cost can be used as a means to obtain $R - r$ for the model of Section 10–15. Will the $R - r$ obtained in this way be the same as those which satisfy Eqs. (10–102) through (10–104) for all values of the interest rate? [*Hint:* To obtain the average annual cost for an arbitrary interest rate from that for a zero interest rate, replace K by $K + i$. Why?]

10–22. For the functional equation of Eq. (10–109), prove that if we can start with a new machine, then an optimal policy will have the form that we hold the machine for N periods and then buy a new one.

10–23. Solve explicitly the functional equation of Eq. (10–109) as was done in Section 10–15.

10–24. Derive the recurrence relations (10–109), (10–110) in the usual way by defining a sequence of functions $\Lambda_k(\xi)$ and then obtaining from these the recurrence relations.

10–25. In Eq. (10–112), explain why it is permissible to compute the expected value $g_k(\xi + x_k)$ and then average over the v_j. In particular show that if one uses the density function for the times between demands and the quantities demanded when a demand occurs, and if in place of $g_k(\xi + x_k)$, the actual cost incurred between $t + \tau$ and $t + \tau + \Delta t$ is used, then on computing the expected cost directly, Eq. (10–112) will be obtained after averaging in the proper way.

10–26. Derive the recurrence relations of Eq. (10–121).

10–27. Explain why dynamic programming is of no assistance in solving a problem of the type discussed in Section 10–18 if one does not use the information on the values which have been taken on by the random parameters.

10–28. Derive Eq. (10–122).

10–29. For the problems in the calculus of variations studied in Section 10–19, prove that if F is a continuous function of y_k, y_{k+1}, x_k, then $\Lambda_k(\xi)$ and $\hat{y}_k(\xi)$ are continuous functions of ξ.

10–30. We noted in Section 10–7 that when x_k is treated as a continuous variable, it may be difficult to determine

$$\max_{0 \leq x_k \leq b/a_k} \Omega_k(x_k; \xi).$$

Consider, however, the case where Ω_k is a strictly concave function. Then we can use an entirely different type of search procedure. Suppose that we select two values of x_k, say α_1 and α_2 ($\alpha_1 < \alpha_2$), in the interval of interest. We then compute $\Omega_k(0; \xi)$, $\Omega_k(\alpha_1; \xi)$, $\Omega_k(\alpha_2; \xi)$, $\Omega_k(b/a_k; \xi)$. If the largest of these values is either $\Omega_k(0; \xi)$ or $\Omega_k(b/a_k; \xi)$, we know the maximum lies between 0 and α, or α_2 and b/a_k. If the largest value is $\Omega_k(\alpha_1; \xi)$, we know that the absolute maximum lies in the interval $0 \leq x_k \leq \alpha_2$. If $\Omega_k(\alpha_2; \xi)$ is the largest, we know that the maximum lies in the interval $\alpha_1 \leq x_k \leq b/a_k$. Why are these statements true? If, for example, we reduce the interval to $0 \leq x_k \leq \alpha_2$ at the first step, we select a value β of x_k different from α_1 in this interval, compute $\Omega_k(\beta; \xi)$, and repeat the process. In this way, one can very quickly narrow down the interval of interest, and at each step, only one new value of Ω_k needs to be computed. In starting out, one might take α_1, α_2 to be about one-fifth of the way from either end, and then at succeeding steps, if the interior point in the interval is a fraction β ($\beta \neq 0.5$) of the length of the interval from one end, the new point is chosen to be a fraction β from the other end. Why does this procedure seem sound? Illustrate it graphically.

10–31. Derive the functional equation for $\Lambda(\xi, x)$ which replaces Eq. (10–130) when we take the limit as $\Delta x \to 0$. *Hint:* Expand $\Lambda(\xi + \Delta\xi, x + \Delta x)$ by Taylor's theorem, retaining terms through the first derivative, and obtain the partial differential equation (functional equation)

$$-\frac{\partial \Lambda}{\partial x} = \min_{y'} \left[F(y, y', x) + y' \frac{\partial \Lambda}{\partial \xi} \right].$$

10–32. A processor of a condensed vegetable soup does the canning during the vegetable season, that is, during the months of July, August, and September. Chickens are usually contracted for in March. They are delivered in dressed form. The price per chicken varies with the quantity purchased and the delivery date. Chickens are always purchased in multiples of 100. In general, some dressed chickens can be delivered to the plant during each week of the canning season. If chickens are not used in the week in which they were delivered, they must be kept in frozen storage which the company rents. It is of interest to determine how many chickens should be purchased each week so as to minimize the cost of the chickens plus storage, given that the number of chickens to be used in each week is specified. Set up the general form of this problem and show that it can be solved by dynamic programming. Solve the above problem in the special case where there are only five weeks in the season, no chickens are in inventory at the beginning, none are to be in inventory at the end, 300 chickens are used each week, and the cost of procuring x chickens is independent of the week in which they are delivered. The costs of the chickens and of storage are given in the following table. Storage costs are based on the number of chickens which remain in storage for the full week.

Cost of chickens		Storage cost	
x, hundreds	cost, dollars	inventory, hundreds	cost, dollars per week
1	150	1	10
2	280	2	20
3	410	3	30
4	540	4	50
5	660	5	70
6	780	6	100
7	890		
8	1000		
9	1100		

10–33. Suppose that some economy has a given yearly productive capacity M (measured in dollar units perhaps). This productive capacity can be used either for producing consumer goods or capital goods (i.e., more productive capacity). If x units of the productive capacity are allocated for one year to the manufacture of consumer goods, the utility to consumers is $f(x)$. At the end of the year, some of the productive capacity allocated to the production of consumer goods will be worn out, and only a quantity αx, $0 < \alpha < 1$, will be usable in the following year. If y units of productive capacity are allocated to the formation of capital goods, then at the end of the year, we have a productive capacity of βy, $\beta > 1$. We shall assume that there is no technological improvement so that α remains constant over time. We shall also assume that $f(x)$ does not change over time, but consumer goods obtained at a later time are not as valuable as those available immediately. It is of interest to determine how the economy should each year divide its productive capacity between consumer goods and capital goods so as to maximize the present worth of the consumers' utility over a period of N years. Set up the problem and show that it can be solved by dynamic programming.

10–34. Often one can come very close to an optimal solution to a cargo-loading problem by using as much as possible of the item with the highest value per unit volume and then moving to the item with the next highest value per unit volume, etc. Explain why this procedure will not always yield an optimal solution.

10–35. Would it be possible to use dynamic programming to solve dynamic inventory problems in cases where the demands in different periods were not independent random variables? Discuss in detail.

10–36. Consider an inventory system consisting of n depots. At a given point in time, we wish to redistribute the stock of some item among the depots so as to minimize the transportation costs plus the expected stockout costs over some time period. Any depot can ship to any other one, and any given depot may either incur a net gain or a net loss of stock. It is desired to determine how much each depot i should ship to each of the other depots. Can this problem be formulated as a dynamic programming problem? Would the situation be altered if the depots that are exclusively shippers and those that are only receivers of stock were specified?

10–37. Consider once again the inventory model discussed in Section 10–18. Assume that instead of specifying a stockout cost, we stipulate that the probability of having an outage occur in the period $t_j + \tau_j$ to $t_j + \tau_j + \Delta t_j$ must be less than or equal to γ_j. Show how this problem can be solved by dynamic programming. [*Hint:* Review the discussion of this subject in Chapter 5.]

10–38. Develop a version of Eq. (10–107) in which the length of time T during which a machine is kept is treated as a continuous variable. Use continuous discounting. Differentiate the cost with respect to T and set the derivative to zero. Give an economic interpretation of the result.

CHAPTER 11

DYNAMIC PROGRAMMING II

We are indeed in the era and also in the native land of applied science.

Albert Einstein, Address to Students at the California Institute of Technology

11–1 Introduction. In the previous chapter we studied a number of different kinds of problems which could be formulated as dynamic programming problems. Each of these problems had the characteristic that only a single state parameter was needed and only a single control variable was to be determined at each stage. Now we wish to investigate more complicated problems in which there may be two or more state parameters, and where at each stage values for two or more control variables must be determined. When examining these problems, we shall at once encounter one of the greatest limitations to the use of dynamic programming, namely the *dimensionality* restriction. The numerical difficulties involved in solving a problem increase with incredible rapidity as the number of state parameters is increased. This is true even if there is only a single control variable to be determined at each stage. It is equally true that the computational problems can quickly become overwhelming as the number of control variables to be determined at each stage increases, even if only a single state parameter is needed. We shall proceed as in the previous chapter and study a series of particular types of problems.

11–2 An allocation problem with two constraints. Let us begin by studying an allocation problem which differs from that studied in Section 10–2 only in that there are now two constraints rather than a single constraint. The problem which we wish to solve has the form

$$\sum_{j=1}^{n} a_{1j}x_j \leq b_1; \qquad \sum_{j=1}^{n} a_{2j}x_j \leq b_2,$$

$$x_j \geq 0, \qquad j = 1, \ldots, n; \qquad \text{all } x_j \text{ integers}, \tag{11–1}$$

$$\max z = \sum_{j=1}^{n} f_j(x_j),$$

where all the a_{ij}, b_i are assumed to be positive integers. A practical interpretation of a problem of this type might be that of loading a submarine with spare parts when we have both a weight and a volume constraint. This problem can be thought of as an n-stage problem where at stage j we select the value of x_j. When x_j is specified, then $a_{1j}x_j$ units of resource 1 and $a_{2j}x_j$ units of resource 2 will be allocated to the jth activity. For this problem, however, the state of the system is not determined until the availabilities of both resources are specified. Thus there are two state parameters for this problem—one for each resource.

Once we introduce two state parameters, it becomes fairly clear how the problem can be solved by dynamic programming. Let us proceed in a way analogous to that used in Section 10–2 and define the sequence of functions

$$\Lambda_k(\xi_1, \xi_2) = \max_{x_1,\ldots,x_k} \sum_{j=1}^{k} f_j(x_j), \qquad j = 1, \ldots, n, \tag{11–2}$$

where the maximization is taken over non-negative integers satisfying

$$\sum_{j=1}^{k} a_{1j}x_j \le \xi_1, \quad \sum_{j=1}^{k} a_{2j}x_j \le \xi_2. \tag{11–3}$$

Then, just as in Section 10–2, it is clear that

$$\Lambda_1(\xi_1, \xi_2) = \max_{0 \le x_1 \le \delta_1} f_1(x_1), \tag{11–4}$$

$$\Lambda_k(\xi_1, \xi_2) = \max_{0 \le x_k \le \delta_k} [f_k(x_k) + \Lambda_{k-1}(\xi_1 - a_{1k}x_k, \xi_2 - a_{2k}x_k)],$$
$$k = 2, \ldots, n, \tag{11–5}$$

and

$$z^* = \Lambda_n(b_1, b_2), \tag{11–6}$$

where

$$\delta_k = \min\left\{\left[\frac{\xi_1}{a_{1k}}\right], \left[\frac{\xi_2}{a_{2k}}\right]\right\}. \tag{11–7}$$

When $\Lambda_k(\xi_1, \xi_2)$ is determined, we simultaneously determine $\hat{x}_k(\xi_1, \xi_2)$, the value(s) of x_k which yields $\Lambda_k(\xi_1, \xi_2)$. At the nth stage, we determine x_n^* when $\Lambda_n(b_1, b_2)$ is determined. The optimal values of the remaining variables can then be obtained from the $\hat{x}_k(\xi_1, \xi_2)$-tables as follows:

$$x_{n-i}^* = \hat{x}_{n-i}\left(b_1 - \sum_{u=0}^{i-1} a_{1,n-u}x_{n-u}^*, b_2 - \sum_{u=0}^{i-1} a_{2,n-u}x_{n-u}^*\right),$$
$$i = 1, \ldots, n-1. \tag{11–8}$$

Observe that the state functions $\Lambda_k(\xi_1, \xi_2)$ are the maximum return from the first k activities when ξ_1 and ξ_2 units of resources 1 and 2, respectively, are available for allocation to these stages. The policy function $\hat{x}_k(\xi_1, \xi_2)$ is an optimal value for x_k when there are only k stages, and the quantities of resources 1 and 2 available for allocation to these stages are ξ_1 and ξ_2, respectively.

At first glance, it might appear that the difficulties involved in solving the present problem would not be much greater than those encountered in solving the problem studied in Section 10–2. However, this is not at all true. It is much more difficult to solve the present problem than the problem studied in Section 10–2, because the Λ_k and $\hat{x}_k$ are now functions of two arguments. Recall that for the problem in Section 10–2 it was, in general, necessary to compute and tabulate Λ_k and $\hat{x}_k$ for every $\xi = 0, 1, \ldots, b$. Precisely the same reasoning shows that for the present problem, it may be necessary to tabulate $\Lambda_k(\xi_1, \xi_2)$ for every combination of ξ_1 and ξ_2, where ξ_1 ranges over $0, 1, \ldots, b_1$ and ξ_2 ranges over $0, 1, \ldots, b_2$. If both ξ_1 and ξ_2 can take on 100 values, then in general, one may have to tabulate $\Lambda_k(\xi_1, \xi_2)$ for the 10,000 possible combinations of ξ_1 and ξ_2. Just as for the problem studied in Section 10–2, it is very difficult to trace things through to determine at each stage precisely what combinations of ξ_1 and ξ_2 will really be required (this, of course, depends on b_1 and b_2). Thus, except in exceptional circumstances, one must tabulate $\Lambda_k(\xi_1, \xi_2)$ for all possible combinations of ξ_1 and ξ_2. However, to determine each $\Lambda_k(\xi_1, \xi_2)$ for specified values of ξ_1 and ξ_2, a maximization over x_k must be performed. Thus, if it is possible for both ξ_1 and ξ_2 to assume 100 different values, 10,000 maximizations must be carried out at each stage, whereas for the problem of Section 10–2, when ξ takes on 100 different values, only 100 maximizations need to be carried out at each stage. Thus for each stage, the task of computing a table of $\Lambda_k(\xi_1, \xi_2)$ may easily require at least 100 times as great a computational effort as was needed at the kth stage for the problem of Section 10–2.

There is another difficulty which arises due to the fact that tables of $\Lambda_k(\xi_1, \xi_2)$ must be stored in the computer's memory. We have noted that if both ξ_1 and ξ_2 can take on 100 values, the table of $\Lambda_k(\xi_1, \xi_2)$ will have 10,000 values. If ξ_1 and ξ_2 can take on 1000 values, the table of $\Lambda_k(\xi_1, \xi_2)$ will have 10^6 values. Thus the size of the tables to be stored in the computer's memory quickly becomes huge. The high-speed memory of computers that are at the present available has an upper limit of about 32,000 values. Hence just a single table of $\Lambda_k(\xi_1, \xi_2)$ could considerably exceed the high-speed memory capacity of the computer, thus requiring the use of magnetic tapes, which frequently reduces a good deal the speed with which computations can be made.

However, problems involving only two state parameters can usually be solved on a large digital computer. On the other hand, if there were three state parameters, it would often be out of the question to solve a problem directly, even with the largest computer. The reason is that even if each ξ_i could take on only 100 values, the tables of Λ_k would contain 10^6 values, and the computation of each table would require 10,000 times the effort needed in the corresponding case involving only one state parameter. We shall see later that it is sometimes possible to reduce the number of state parameters by one. Thus there are problems involving three state parameters which can currently be solved on large-scale computers. Problems involving four or more state parameters are almost always beyond the computational abilities available at present.

In this section, by studying a simple extension of the problem examined in Section 10–2, we have encountered perhaps the most severe limitation to the use of dynamic programming in solving problems. This is the limitation on the number of state parameters needed in the problem. If more than three are required, it is not possible to use dynamic programming at the present time. When there are three state parameters, it may be possible to solve the problem, but it would be wise to examine alternative methods of solution. Problems involving two state parameters can usually be solved, but may easily require 100 times as much computer time as a corresponding problem with only a single state parameter.

11–3 A problem requiring the selection of two control variables at each stage. The resource allocation problem studied in the previous section had the property that the resources could not be allocated independently to each stage. Instead, the selection of x_j determined the quantities of both resources to be allocated to stage j. We shall now consider a somewhat different type of problem in which there are two resources, which, however, can be allocated independently in discrete quantities to each stage, and the return from a stage will be a function of the quantity of each resource allocated to that stage. Thus the problem which we wish to consider has the following form:

$$\sum_{j=1}^{n} a_{1j}x_j \leq b_1; \qquad \sum_{j=1}^{n} a_{2j}y_j \leq b_2,$$

$$x_j \geq 0, \qquad y_j \geq 0, \qquad j = 1, \ldots, n; \qquad \text{all } x_j, y_j \text{ integers}, \tag{11–9}$$

$$\max z = \sum_{j=1}^{n} f_j(x_j, y_j).$$

The problem of (11–9) is again an n-stage decision problem, but now at stage j it is necessary to select the values of both x_j and y_j. To describe the state of the system when there are k stages, two parameters are required, i.e., the quantity of each resource available for allocation to these stages.

Let us then proceed as usual to define the state functions

$$\Lambda_k(\xi_1, \xi_2) = \max_{\substack{x_1,\ldots,x_k \\ y_1,\ldots,y_k}} \sum_{j=1}^{k} f_j(x_j, y_j), \qquad k = 1, \ldots, n, \tag{11–10}$$

where the maximization is taken over non-negative integers x_j, y_j satisfying

$$\sum_{j=1}^{k} a_{1j}x_j \leq \xi_1; \qquad \sum_{j=1}^{k} a_{2j}y_j \leq \xi_2. \tag{11–11}$$

The recurrence relations then take the form

$$\Lambda_k(\xi_1, \xi_2) = \max_{x_k, y_k} [f_k(x_k, y_k) + \Lambda_{k-1}(\xi_1 - a_{1k}x_k, \xi_2 - a_{2k}y_k)], \qquad k = 2, \ldots, n, \tag{11–12}$$

where x_k can assume the values $0, 1, \ldots, [\xi_1/a_{1k}]$ and y_k can assume the values $0, 1, \ldots, [\xi_2/a_{2k}]$. The maximization over x_k and y_k is performed simply by considering every combination of x_k and y_k. If x_k and y_k each can take on 100 different values, then 10,000 values of

$$\Omega_k(x_k, y_k; \xi_1, \xi_2) = f_k(x_k, y_k) + \Lambda_{k-1}(\xi_1 - a_{1k}x_k, \xi_2 - a_{2k}y_k) \tag{11–13}$$

must be determined before the absolute maximum can be found. Thus the solution of the current problem requires a considerably greater numerical effort than did the problem studied in the previous section, because now the effort required to compute each $\Lambda_k(\xi_1, \xi_2)$ is increased tremendously. Indeed, the labor is even much greater than the one associated with a problem of the type studied in the previous section, which had $2n$ variables (it would then have the same number of variables as the current problem does).

In this section we have seen that if at a given stage values must be assigned to more than a single control variable, the computational effort required to solve a problem is increased tremendously. Problems involving the determination of two control variables at each stage can usually be solved on a large-scale computer. Sometimes, problems involving the determination of three control variables at each stage are within the realm of computational feasibility. It is very rarely the case that problems involving the determination of four or more control variables can be solved numerically at the present time.

11–4 Case where variables are continuous. In Section 10–7, we examined the complications encountered when the variables of the problem studied in Section 10–2 were allowed to vary continuously. Problems of a similar nature are encountered when there are two or more state parameters associated with the problem and/or two or more control variables must be determined at each stage. For the problems studied in Sections 11–2 and 11–3, if the f_j are continuous functions [either $f_j(x_j)$ or $f_j(x_j, y_j)$], then the state functions $\Lambda_k(\xi_1, \xi_2)$ are continuous functions of ξ_1 and ξ_2. The proof is precisely of the same form as that given in Section 10–7, and we ask the reader to provide it in Problem 11–1. If the f_j are not continuous, it is for all practical purposes necessary to treat the variables as discrete. When the $\Lambda_k(\xi_1, \xi_2)$ are continuous, then one can interpolate in the tables with relative safety. Usually, the Λ_k are very smooth functions, and therefore the intervals used for tabulating them do not need to be too small. Now, however, when there are two parameters, it is necessary to interpolate in tables involving two arguments.

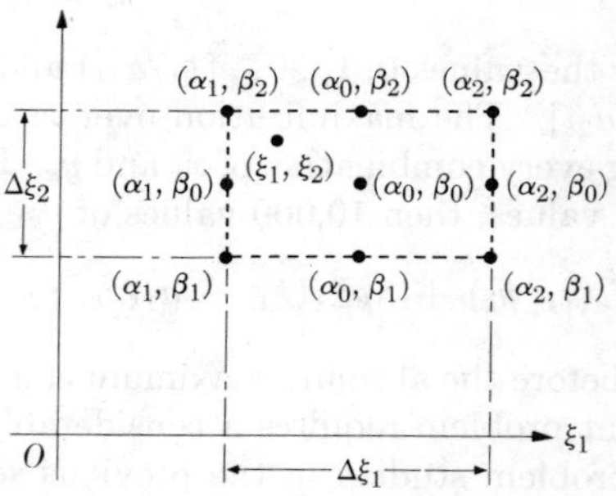

FIGURE 11–1

The first-order interpolation formula in this case is not too well known, and hence we shall develop it. Suppose that we wish to compute $\Lambda_k(\xi_1, \xi_2)$. Denote the tabulated values which surround this point by $\Lambda_k(\alpha_1, \beta_1)$, $\Lambda_k(\alpha_1, \beta_2)$, $\Lambda_k(\alpha_2, \beta_1)$, and $\Lambda_k(\alpha_2, \beta_2)$. All these points are illustrated in Fig. 11–1. Consider the point

$$(\alpha_0, \beta_0) = (\tfrac{1}{2}(\alpha_1 + \alpha_2), \tfrac{1}{2}(\beta_1 + \beta_2)),$$

which is at the center of the rectangle shown in the figure. Then replacing partial derivatives by finite differences in Taylor's formula (Section 2–10), we have the following approximate relation:

$$\Lambda_k(\xi_1, \xi_2) \doteq \Lambda_k(\alpha_0, \beta_0) + \frac{(\xi_1 - \alpha_0)}{\Delta\xi_1}[\Lambda_k(\alpha_2, \beta_0) - \Lambda_k(\alpha_1, \beta_0)] + \frac{(\xi_2 - \beta_0)}{\Delta\xi_2}[\Lambda_k(\alpha_0, \beta_2) - \Lambda_k(\alpha_0, \beta_1)]. \quad (11\text{–}14)$$

However, this cannot be used directly, since we have not tabulated $\Lambda_k(\alpha_0, \beta_0)$, $\Lambda_k(\alpha_2, \beta_0)$, $\Lambda_k(\alpha_1, \beta_0)$, $\Lambda_k(\alpha_0, \beta_2)$, and $\Lambda_k(\alpha_0, \beta_1)$. We can, nonetheless, represent these values in the form needed, using the following approximate relations:

$$\Lambda_k(\alpha_0, \beta_0) \doteq \tfrac{1}{4}[\Lambda_k(\alpha_1, \beta_1) + \Lambda_k(\alpha_2, \beta_1) + \Lambda_k(\alpha_1, \beta_2) + \Lambda_k(\alpha_2, \beta_2)],$$

$$\Lambda_k(\alpha_2, \beta_0) - \Lambda_k(\alpha_1, \beta_0) \doteq \tfrac{1}{2}[\Lambda_k(\alpha_2, \beta_2) + \Lambda_k(\alpha_2, \beta_1) - \Lambda_k(\alpha_1, \beta_2) - \Lambda_k(\alpha_1, \beta_1)],$$

$$\Lambda_k(\alpha_0, \beta_2) - \Lambda_k(\alpha_0, \beta_1) \doteq \tfrac{1}{2}[\Lambda_k(\alpha_2, \beta_2) + \Lambda_k(\alpha_1, \beta_2) - \Lambda_k(\alpha_2, \beta_1) - \Lambda_k(\alpha_1, \beta_1)].$$

Substitution of these relations into (11–14) yields the following interpolation formula,

$$\begin{aligned}\Lambda_k(\xi_1, \xi_2) \doteq\ & \frac{1}{4}\left[1 - \frac{(2\xi_1 - \alpha_1 - \alpha_2)}{\Delta\xi_1} - \frac{(2\xi_2 - \beta_1 - \beta_2)}{\Delta\xi_2}\right]\Lambda_k(\alpha_1, \beta_1) \\ & + \frac{1}{4}\left[1 - \frac{(2\xi_1 - \alpha_1 - \alpha_2)}{\Delta\xi_1} + \frac{(2\xi_2 - \beta_1 - \beta_2)}{\Delta\xi_2}\right]\Lambda_k(\alpha_1, \beta_2) \\ & + \frac{1}{4}\left[1 + \frac{(2\xi_1 - \alpha_1 - \alpha_2)}{\Delta\xi_1} - \frac{(2\xi_2 - \beta_1 - \beta_2)}{\Delta\xi_2}\right]\Lambda_k(\alpha_2, \beta_1) \\ & + \frac{1}{4}\left[1 + \frac{(2\xi_1 - \alpha_1 - \alpha_2)}{\Delta\xi_1} + \frac{(2\xi_2 - \beta_1 - \beta_2)}{\Delta\xi_2}\right]\Lambda_k(\alpha_2, \beta_2),\end{aligned} \quad (11\text{–}15)$$

which is easily programmed for a computer. Note that it makes use of all four tabulated points which are nearest neighbors to (ξ_1, ξ_2).

As for the model studied in Section 10–2, the policy functions $\hat{x}_k(\xi_1, \xi_2)$ will not necessarily be continuous functions of ξ_1 and ξ_2. Hence, if it is not known that these functions are continuous, one would not normally tabulate the policy functions; instead he would determine the x_k^* by direct computation, working backward from x_n^* as was described in Section 10–7.

In cases like that studied in Section 11–2, where only a single control variable is determined at each stage, then the task of maximizing x_k can be handled in precisely the way described in Section 10–7. Furthermore, if the $f_j(x_j)$ are concave functions, then the $\Omega_k(x_k; \xi_1, \xi_2)$, $\Lambda_k(\xi_1, \xi_2)$ are also concave functions. The proofs are carried out in a different way than in Section 10–8, and we ask the reader to provide them in Problem 11–2. In such cases, the simplified computational procedures discussed in Section 10–8 and Problem 10–30 can be applied.

Consider now the problems involved in maximizing over two variables at each stage. If nothing was known about the $\Omega_k(x_k, y_k; \xi_1, \xi_2)$, we would begin by subdividing the region of the $x_k y_k$-plane over which the maximization is to be carried out by a coarse grid, as shown in Fig. 11–2. Then, in a region about the maximum and any other relative maxima which were

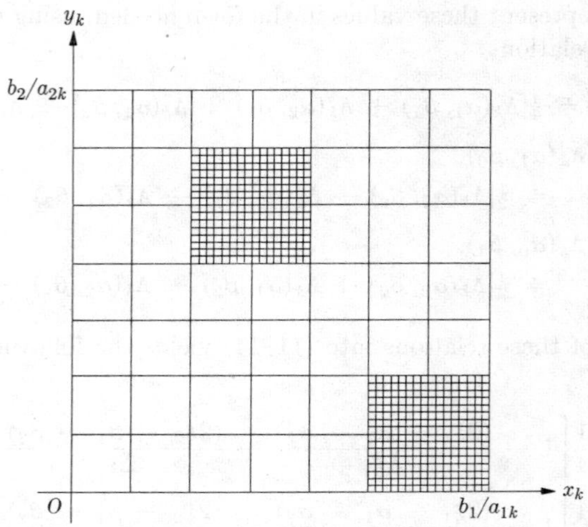

FIGURE 11–2

sufficiently close to the maximum, a finer grid would be used and the procedure would be repeated. This is also illustrated in Fig. 11–2. With the finer grid we would only find the maximum value in the region where the finer grid was applied. Note that the comparisons required to find the absolute maximum are simple, because each time we compute an Ω_k, we compare it with the previous one, and retain only the larger value (also keeping track of the coordinates which yielded it). However, it is more difficult to find all relative maxima, as is necessary when the original coarse grid is used. To determine whether the value of Ω_k at a particular grid point is a relative maximum, it must be compared with the value of Ω_k at the eight nearest neighboring points (on the boundaries, the number of neighbors is either five or three).

When all the $f_j(x_j, y_j)$ in (11–9) are convex (concave) functions, then the $\Omega_k(x_k, y_k; \xi_1, \xi_2)$ and $\Lambda_k(\xi_1, \xi_2)$ will also be convex (concave). We ask the reader to prove this result in Problem 11–3. If the $f_j(x_j, y_j)$ are convex functions, then we know from Section 3–12 that since the maximization is being carried out over a convex set (a rectangle), the maximum of Ω_k will occur at an extreme point of the convex set, i.e., at one of the corners of the rectangle. In this case, then, we need to evaluate Ω_k at only four points to obtain $\Lambda_k(\xi_1, \xi_2)$.

When the $f_j(x_j, y_j)$ are concave functions, simplified search procedures can be used to determine the maximum. Let us assume either that the f_j are strictly concave (so that the Ω_k will be strictly concave) or that we are not interested in obtaining all alternative optima. We shall then show how the method of Problem 10–30 can be generalized. We begin by selecting two values of x_k, say α_1, α_2, perhaps one-third of the distance from either end of the interval over which x_k can range. Using the one-dimensional search procedure discussed in Problem 10–30, we compute

$$h(\alpha_1) = \max_{y_k} \Omega_k(\alpha_1, y_k; \xi_1, \xi_2); \qquad h(\alpha_2) = \max_{y_k} \Omega_k(\alpha_2, y_k; \xi_1, \xi_2).$$

Then, if $h(\alpha_1) > h(\alpha_2)$, the maximizing point must lie in the rectangle $0 \leq x_k \leq \alpha_2$, $0 \leq y_k \leq b_2/a_{2k}$ (see Fig. 11–3). If the maximum of Ω_k was not taken on in this rectangle, we could obtain a result contradicting the fact that Ω_k is concave by considering the line segment connecting the point where the maximum of Ω_k is taken on and the point which yields $h(\alpha_1)$, since this line would not be everywhere on or below the surface Ω_k. When $h(\alpha_2) > h(\alpha_1)$, the maximizing point must be in the rectangle $\alpha_1 \leq x_k \leq b_1/a_{1k}$, $0 \leq y_k \leq b_2/a_{2k}$. If $h(\alpha_2) = h(\alpha_1)$, the maximizing point must lie in the rectangle $\alpha_1 \leq x_k \leq \alpha_2$, $0 \leq y_k \leq b_2/a_{2k}$.

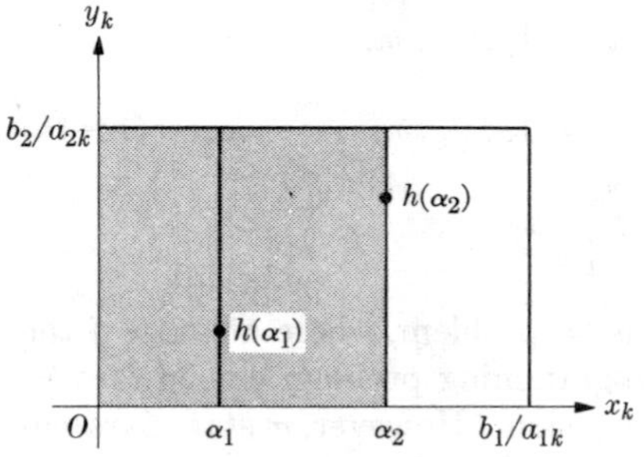

FIGURE 11–3

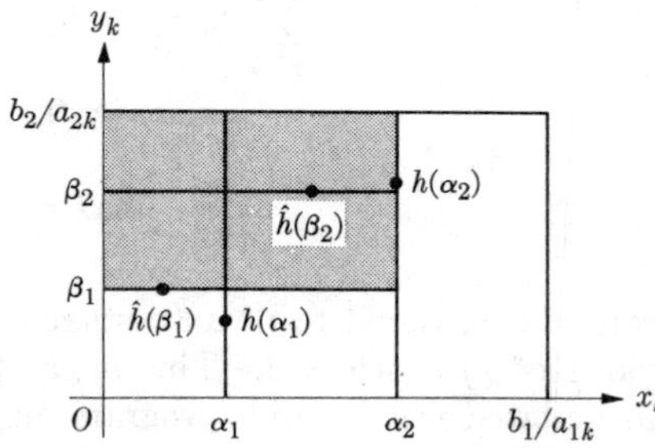

FIGURE 11–4

At the next step, select two values of y_k, call them β_1 and β_2, about one-third of the distance from either end of the interval over which y_k can vary. We compute

$$\hat{h}(\beta_1) = \max_{x_k} \Omega_k(x_k, \beta_1; \xi_1, \xi_2); \qquad \hat{h}(\beta_2) = \max_{x_k} \Omega_k(x_k, \beta_2; \xi_1, \xi_2).$$

Then, if $\hat{h}(\beta_1) > \hat{h}(\beta_2)$, the maximizing point must be in the rectangle $0 \leq x_k \leq \alpha_2$, $0 \leq y_k \leq \beta_2$ [if at the previous step $h(\alpha_1) > h(\alpha_2)$], or if $\hat{h}(\beta_2) > \hat{h}(\beta_1)$, the maximizing point must be in the rectangle $0 \leq x_k \leq \alpha_2$, $\beta_1 \leq y_k \leq b_2/a_{2k}$ (see Fig. 11–4), or if $\hat{h}(\beta_1) = \hat{h}(\beta_2)$, the maximizing point lies in the rectangle $0 \leq x_k \leq \alpha_2$, $\beta_1 \leq y_k \leq \beta_2$, etc., for the other possible ranges for x_k.

Next one selects two new values of x_k, call them α_3 and α_4, about one-third the distance from either end of the remaining interval of variation for x_k (perhaps $0 \leq x_k \leq \alpha_2$), and repeats the maximization over y_k to further reduce the interval of variation over x_k, etc. This procedure has the effect of successively narrowing down the rectangle in which the maximizing point lies. Moreover, two new maxima will usually have to be computed for each variable at each step, because it may no longer be true that a previously computed maximum will be in the remaining rectangle.

This section has illustrated how we can handle numerically situations where the variables are to be treated as continuous when there are two or more state parameters and/or two or more control variables over which a maximization must be carried out. We saw for the problems studied in the previous chapter, that treating the variables as discrete, rather than as continuous, was the more realistic and convenient approach. The same is true for the situations to be studied in this chapter.

11–5 Comparison of linear and dynamic programming. A linear programming problem

$$\sum_{j=1}^{n} a_{ij}x_j = b_i, \qquad i = 1, \ldots, m,$$
$$x_j \geq 0, \qquad j = 1, \ldots, n, \tag{11–16}$$
$$\max z = \sum_{j=1}^{n} c_jx_j$$

can be considered to be an n-stage decision problem, where at stage j the value of x_j is selected. This linear programming problem can in fact be formulated as a dynamic programming problem. However, m state parameters will be needed as arguments in the state functions—one for each constraint. To obtain the dynamic programming formulation, let

$$\Lambda_k(\xi_1, \ldots, \xi_m) = \max_{x_1,\ldots,x_k} \sum_{j=1}^{k} c_jx_j, \quad k = 1, \ldots, n, \tag{11–17}$$

where the maximization is carried out over non-negative x_j which satisfy the constraints

$$\sum_{j=1}^{k} a_{ij}x_j = \xi_i, \qquad i = 1, \ldots, m. \tag{11–18}$$

Then the recurrence relations become

$$\Lambda_k(\xi_1, \ldots, \xi_m) = \max_{x_k} [c_kx_k + \Lambda_{k-1}(\xi_1 - a_{1k}x_k, \ldots, \xi_m - a_{mk}x_k)],$$
$$k = 2, \ldots, n. \tag{11–19}$$

Consider now the interval over which x_k can vary. Denote by I the set of i for which $a_{ij} \geq 0$ for each j. Then for $i \in I$, $\xi_i \geq 0$. For $i \notin I$, the constraint can be satisfied with x_j being arbitrarily large; also ξ_i can be negative. Hence, the maximum value θ_k that x_k can assume is

$$\theta_k = \min_i \left\{\frac{\xi_i}{a_{ik}}\right\}, \quad i \in I \quad \text{or} \quad \infty, \quad \text{if } I \text{ is empty.} \tag{11-20}$$

The difficulty with using the dynamic programming approach lies, of course, in the number of state parameters. If there were 100 constraints, there would be 100 state parameters. If a table of Λ_k were constructed in which each state parameter assumed only 100 values, the table of Λ_k would contain 100^{100} entries. This is an incredibly large number. The reader familiar with computers might wish to calculate how many miles of magnetic tape would be needed to store such a table. If the computer could compute as many as 10^6 values of Λ_k per second, 100^{97} sec, or about 100^{93} years, would be required merely to compute one table of Λ_k. Thus we see that it is totally out of the question to solve a general type of linear programming problem with any sizable number of constraints by dynamic programming. Even for one or two constraints, the simplex method is much more efficient.

In solving linear programming problems by dynamic programming, we might encounter one other difficulty. If some of the a_{ij} are negative, then it is no longer true that b_i is the largest value of ξ_i that will ever be needed. Indeed, if one was not sure whether or not the problem had an unbounded solution, it might be true that the ξ_i could become infinite. In any event, it might be exceptionally difficult to determine precisely what the range of variation on each ξ_i should be for $i \notin I$.

11-6 Dynamic programming formulation of transportation problems with two origins. Consider a transportation problem with two origins and n destinations. Such a problem has the form

$$\sum_{j=1}^{n} x_{1j} = a_1; \qquad \sum_{j=1}^{n} x_{2j} = a_2;$$

$$x_{1j} + x_{2j} = b_j, \qquad j = 1, \ldots, n; \; x_{ij} \geq 0, \;\text{all } i, j, \tag{11-21}$$

$$\min z = \sum_{i,j} c_{ij}x_{ij} = \sum_j (c_{1j}x_{1j} + c_{2j}x_{2j}).$$

Because of its special structure, it is possible to cast this problem into a dynamic programming format involving considerably fewer state parameters than would be needed for a general linear programming problem with the same number of constraints. Indeed, we shall see that only a single state parameter is needed to characterize the state functions for this problem.

To begin, let us imagine (11–21) to be an n-stage decision problem, where at stage j we decide how much origin 1 and how much origin 2 will send to destination j. Since $x_{2j} = b_j - x_{1j}$, it follows that specification of the quantity to be shipped by origin 1 automatically determines how much origin 2 will ship. Consider then a problem of the form (11–21) in which there are k stages and a quantity ξ is available at origin 1 and η at origin 2. However, $\xi + \eta = \sum_{j=1}^{k} b_j$, so that $\eta = \sum_{j=1}^{k} b_j - \xi$. Thus when ξ is specified, η is determined. Therefore ξ is the only state parameter required. We then define the sequence of state functions

$$\Lambda_k(\xi) = \min_{\substack{x_{11},\ldots,x_{1k} \\ x_{21},\ldots,x_{2k}}} \sum_{j=1}^{k} (c_{1j}x_{1j} + c_{2j}x_{2j}), \tag{11–22}$$

where the minimization is carried out over non-negative x_{ij} satisfying

$$\sum_{j=1}^{k} x_{1j} = \xi; \quad \sum_{j=1}^{k} x_{2j} = \sum_{j=1}^{k} b_j - \xi;$$

$$x_{1j} + x_{2j} = b_j, \qquad j = 1, \ldots, k. \tag{11–23}$$

The recurrence relations then assume the form

$$\Lambda_k(\xi) = \min_{x_{1k}} [c_{1k}x_{1k} + c_{2k}(b_k - x_{1k}) + \Lambda_{k-1}(\xi - x_{1k})],$$

$$k = 2, \ldots, n, \tag{11–24}$$

where x_{1k} must satisfy

$$0 \le x_{1k} \le \min \{\xi, b_k\} \tag{11–25}$$

and

$$x_{2k} = b_k - x_{1k} \le \sum_{j=1}^{k} b_k - \xi, \quad \text{that is} \quad x_{1k} \ge \xi - \sum_{j=1}^{k-1} b_j. \tag{11–26}$$

This is equivalent to

$$\theta_k^- = \max \left\{0, \xi - \sum_{j=1}^{k-1} b_j\right\} \le x_{1k} \le \min \{\xi, b_k\} = \theta_k^+. \tag{11–27}$$

In making the computations, $\Lambda_k(\xi)$ would be tabulated for all integers $\xi = 0, 1, \ldots, \sum_{j=1}^{k} b_j$. Note that the size of the tables will increase with k. When tabulating $\Lambda_k(\xi)$, we would also tabulate $\hat{x}_{1k}(\xi)$. At the last stage, x_{1n}^* is determined (and $x_{2n}^* = b_n - x_{1n}^*$). The other x_{1k}^* are found from

$$x_{1,n-i}^* = \hat{x}_{1,n-i}\left(a_1 - \sum_{u=0}^{i-1} x_{1,n-u}^*\right), \qquad i = 1, \ldots, n-1. \tag{11–28}$$

No interpolation in these tables will be needed, because we know that if the a_i, b_j are integers, the x_{ij}^* will be integers. If $\sum b_j$ is large, the tables of $\Lambda_k(\xi)$, $\hat{x}_{1k}(\xi)$ will contain a large number of entries. However, this problem can usually be solved quite easily on a digital computer. Even for this special case, the dynamic programming approach cannot compete with the other techniques which have been developed for solving transportation problems.

Nonetheless, the above formulation could be useful in solving a problem of the type described when the costs are nonlinear. To generalize the above formulation to nonlinear costs, all we need to do is replace $c_{1j}x_{1j}$ by $C_{1j}(x_{1j})$ and $c_{2j}x_{2j}$ by $C_{2j}(x_{2j})$, where $C_{1j}(x_{1j})$ and $C_{2j}(x_{2j})$ are the costs of shipping x_{1j} and x_{2j} units to destination j from origins 1 and 2, respectively. These can be arbitrary functions. The solution could be carried out in precisely the same way except that in obtaining the minimum in (11–24), we might not be able to introduce the simplifications that result from the convexity of the costs. With nonlinear costs one would normally restrict the x_{1j} to integers, and the search in (11–24) could be made directly. Problems with two origins having nonlinear transportation costs could be solved quite readily by dynamic programming, whereas alternative procedures are not, in general, available in this case.

11–7 Reduction in dimensionality by use of a Lagrange multiplier. We have noted previously that when the number of state parameters needed in the state functions exceeds two, it becomes essentially impossible, with current computing machinery, to solve problems by dynamic programming. We shall now show that in some cases, a Lagrange multiplier can be used to reduce the number of state parameters by one.

To illustrate how the procedure works, consider the problem of (11–1) for the case where the x_j are continuous variables. We shall also assume that the $f_j(x_j)$ are nondecreasing functions of x_j. Then it is clear that at least one of the constraints must hold as a strict equality for any optimal solution. Frequently, it is easy to determine before the problem is solved that one of the constraints will hold as a strict equality. Assume that we know that the second constraint will hold as a strict equality for an optimal solution. Let us then solve the following problem for a fixed value of λ:

$$\sum_{j=1}^{n} a_{1j}x_j \leq b_1,$$

$$x_j \geq 0, \qquad j = 1, \ldots, n, \tag{11–29}$$

$$\max z_1 = \sum_{j=1}^{n} f_j(x_j) - \lambda \sum_{j=1}^{n} a_{2j}x_j.$$

This problem is much more easily solved than (11–1), because there is only a single constraint so that only a single state parameter is needed. In fact, the recurrence relations for the state functions are

$$\Lambda_k(\xi) = \max_{x_k} [f_k(x_k) - \lambda a_{2k}x_k + \Lambda_{k-1}(\xi - a_{1k}x_k)], \qquad k = 2, \ldots, n. \tag{11–30}$$

Imagine now that the optimal solution $\mathbf{x}^*$ obtained for (11–29) has the property that

$$\sum_{j=1}^{n} a_{2j}x_j^* = b_2.$$

We shall then prove that $\mathbf{x}^*$ is an optimal solution to (11–1). Note first that $\mathbf{x}^*$ is indeed a feasible solution to (11–1). Now suppose that an optimal solution to (11–1) is $\mathbf{x}^0$ and

$$z(\mathbf{x}^0) = \sum_{j=1}^{n} f_j(x_j^0) > \sum_{j=1}^{n} f_j(x_j^*) = z(\mathbf{x}^*). \tag{11–31}$$

However, since $\mathbf{x}^*$ is an optimal solution to (11–29),

$$z_1(\mathbf{x}^*) = z(\mathbf{x}^*) - \lambda \sum_{j=1}^{n} a_{2j}x_j^* \geq z(\mathbf{x}^0) - \lambda \sum_{j=1}^{n} a_{2j}x_j^0 = z_1(\mathbf{x}^0),$$

or $z(\mathbf{x}^*) \geq z(\mathbf{x}^0)$, because $\sum a_{2j}x_j^* = \sum a_{2j}x_j^0 = b_2$. This contradicts (11–31). Therefore $\mathbf{x}^*$ is an optimal solution to (11–1) when the x_j are treated as continuous.

The above observations then suggest the following computational technique for solving (11–1) when the x_j are continuous variables. We begin by selecting an arbitrary value of λ and solve (11–29). If the solution $\mathbf{x}^*$ is such that $\sum a_{2j}x_j^* = b_2$, we have found an optimal solution to (11–1). If $\sum a_{2j}x_j^* \neq b_2$, we select a new value of λ and repeat the process. We use the two values of λ and the two values of $\sum a_{2j}x_j^*$ so obtained to interpolate or extrapolate linearly to estimate a new value of λ which should yield $\sum a_{2j}x_j = b_2$. We then re-solve the problem (11–29), using this value of λ. One can graph the resulting three points and thus estimate a new value of λ by passing a curve through the points, etc. Usually, one can converge on the correct λ in five or six iterations, and thus solve (11–1). This procedure requires a great deal less work then the procedure suggested in Section 11–2. One could try 100 or more different values of λ before the computational effort would approach that associated with the method of Section 11–2.

What we are really doing in the above procedure is assigning a cost to resource 2 and removing the constraint on the quantity of resource 2 used.

We then vary the cost of this resource in the objective function until the quantity used is precisely b_2. This interpretation points out that if for our initial guess at λ, $\sum a_{2j}x_j^* > b_2$, then we should increase λ for the next trial.

The same procedure can be used when the x_j must be integers. In this case, it is not necessarily true that either constraint must hold as a strict equality. One proceeds by varying λ to make $z[\mathbf{x}(\lambda)]$ as large as possible while not violating either of the constraints. If the eliminated constraint holds as a strict equality when the x_j are not restricted to be integers, this procedure is normally equivalent to that of determining the λ such that the constraint comes as close as possible to holding as a strict equality without having the amount of the resource used exceed the quantity available.

It is by no means true that the Lagrange multiplier procedure suggested above will always work. Problem 11-4 provides an example where there is no λ with the desired properties. We have not provided any sufficient conditions which when satisfied guarantee that the Lagrange multiplier procedure will work. It seems difficult to give sufficient conditions which are general enough to be of practical value. The methods of Chapter 6, however, can be used to prove that if the x_j are assumed to be continuous variables, and the $f_j(x_j)$ are concave, then the Lagrange multiplier technique can be used. The reader is asked to provide the proof in Problem 11-6. From a practical point of view, one determines by trial whether or not the method will work. If one can find a λ such that the eliminated constraint holds as a strict equality, then from what was proved above, we know that the method has indeed provided an optimal solution. The problems will ask the reader to show how the Lagrange multiplier approach could be used to simplify the solution of several types of problems involving two constraints. It is the use of a Lagrange multiplier which enables us to solve problems involving three constraints (three state parameters), by effectively reducing the problem to the solution of a series of problems with only two state parameters.

We shall conclude the discussion of the Lagrange multiplier technique by showing how a transportation problem involving three origins and n destinations can be solved by dynamic programming in such a way that only a single state parameter is needed in the state functions. If we proceeded to formulate the problem in the manner described in the previous section, two state parameters would be needed. Let us first formulate the problem, using the direct approach for the case where the costs may be nonlinear, and then show how one introduces a Lagrange multiplier. We begin by defining the state functions

$$\Lambda_k(\xi_1, \xi_2) = \min_{\text{all } x_{ij}} \sum_{j=1}^{k} [C_{1j}(x_{1j}) + C_{2j}(x_{2j}) + C_{3j}(x_{3j})], \qquad k = 1, \ldots, n, \tag{11-32}$$

where the minimization is taken over non-negative x_{ij} satisfying

$$\sum_{j=1}^{k} x_{1j} = \xi_1;$$
$$\sum_{j=1}^{k} x_{2j} = \xi_2; \qquad (11\text{–}33)$$
$$\sum_{j=1}^{k} x_{3j} = \sum_{j=1}^{k} b_j - \xi_1 - \xi_2,$$
$$x_{1j} + x_{2j} + x_{3j} = b_j,$$
$$j = 1, \ldots, k.$$

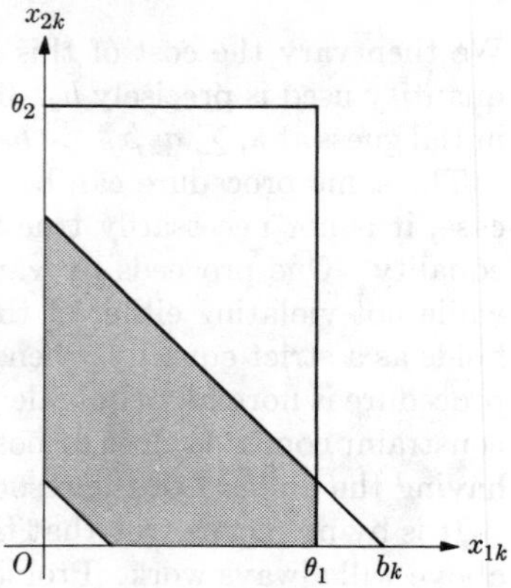

FIGURE 11–5

The recurrence relations become

$$\Lambda_k(\xi_1, \xi_2) = \min_{x_{1k}, x_{2k}} [C_{1k}(x_{1k}) + C_{2k}(x_{2k}) + C_{3k}(b_k - x_{1k} - x_{2k}) + \Lambda_{k-1}(\xi_1 - x_{1k}, \xi_2 - x_{2k})], \qquad (11\text{–}34)$$

where the minimization is taken over x_{1k}, x_{2k} satisfying

$$0 \le x_{1k} \le \min(\xi_1, b_k) = \theta_1; \quad 0 \le x_{2k} \le \min(\xi_2, b_k) = \theta_2;$$
$$x_{1k} + x_{2k} \le b_k,$$
$$x_{3k} = b_k - x_{2k} - x_{1k} \le \sum_{j=1}^{k} b_j - \xi_1 - \xi_2$$

or

$$x_{1k} + x_{2k} \ge \xi_1 + \xi_2 - \sum_{j=1}^{k-1} b_j.$$

The region over which the minimization was to be carried out might then look like the shaded area shown in Fig. 11–5. The $\Lambda_k(\xi_1, \xi_2)$ would be tabulated for all integers ξ_1, ξ_2 such that $\xi_1 + \xi_2 \le \sum_{j=1}^{k} b_j$.

To use the Lagrange multiplier approach, let us imagine that no constraint is placed on the quantity shipped from the second origin; instead a cost will be assigned to each unit shipped from origin 2. The quantity available at origin 1 will be specified. Since we are not stating how much is to be shipped from origin 2, we cannot specify the amount to be shipped from origin 3.

We then proceed to solve the problem

$$\sum_{j=1}^{n} x_{1j} = a_1; \quad x_{1j} + x_{2j} + x_{3j} = b_j, \quad j = 1, \ldots, n; \quad \text{all } x_{ij} \ge 0,$$

$$\min z = \sum_{j=1}^{n} [C_{1j}(x_{1j}) + C_{2j}(x_{2j}) + C_{3j}(x_{3j})] + \lambda \sum_{j=1}^{n} x_{2j} \qquad (11\text{–}35)$$

for various λ until we determine a λ such that the optimal solution satisfies $\sum_j x_{2j} = a_2$. It will then automatically follow that $\sum_j x_{3j} = a_3 = \sum_j b_j - a_1 - a_2$, and the solution so obtained will be an optimal solution to the three-origin problem.

To solve (11–35) we introduce the state functions

$$\Lambda_k(\xi) = \min_{\text{all } x_{ij}} \sum_{j=1}^{k} [C_{1j}(x_{1j}) + C_{2j}(x_{2j}) + \lambda x_{2j} + C_{3j}(x_{3j})], \qquad k = 1, \ldots, n, \tag{11-36}$$

where the minimization is carried out for non-negative x_{ij} satisfying

$$\sum_{j=1}^{k} x_{1j} = \xi; \qquad x_{1j} + x_{2j} + x_{3j} = b_j, \qquad j = 1, \ldots, n. \tag{11-37}$$

The recurrence relations then become

$$\Lambda_k(\xi) = \min_{x_{1k}, x_{2k}} [C_{1k}(x_{1k}) + C_{2k}(x_{2k}) + \lambda x_{2k} + C_{3k}(b_k - x_{1k} - x_{2k}) + \Lambda_{k-1}(\xi - x_{1k})], \qquad k = 2, \ldots, n, \tag{11-38}$$

where x_{1k} and x_{2k} must satisfy

$$0 \le x_{1k} \le \min(\xi, b_k), \qquad x_{1k} + x_{2k} \le b_k. \tag{11-39}$$

The $\Lambda_k(\xi)$ would be tabulated for every integer $\xi = 0, 1, \ldots, \sum_{j=1}^{k} b_j$.

Thus the problem involving three origins and n destinations can be reduced to solving a sequence of n-stage problems in which there is only a single state parameter needed to describe the state functions. For strictly linear problems, the method could not possibly compete in computational efficiency with other techniques which have been developed for solving transportation problems. However, it could be useful in cases where the costs were nonlinear.

11–8 Equipment replacement. In Section 10–16 we showed that dynamic programming could be used to solve certain types of equipment replacement problems. We would now like to study two somewhat more complicated cases. For the situations studied in Section 10–16, each time a decision was made, the only alternatives were to keep the present machine or buy a new one. Let us now allow one additional alternative, that of overhauling the current machine. With this added degree of freedom all functions which enter into the analysis of Section 10–16 will depend not only on the age of the machine and the year in which it was purchased, but also on the time since the last overhaul. Two state parameters are now needed to describe the state functions; one for the age of the machine currently in use, and the other for the number of periods since it was last overhauled. Then, as in Section 10–16, let I_u be the installed cost of a machine purchased at the beginning of period u; $C_u(j, v)$ the expected operating and maintenance cost of a machine (purchased at the beginning of period u), in the jth period of use when it last had an overhaul at the beginning of period v (we ignore the time required to make the overhaul); and $S_u(j, v)$ will be the salvage value of a machine (purchased at the beginning of period u) after j periods of use when it last had an overhaul at the beginning of period v. Let us denote by $H_u(j, v)$ the overhaul cost of a machine purchased at the beginning of period u after j periods of use when it last had an overhaul at the beginning of period v. If the machine has never had an overhaul, v will refer to the period in which the machine was purchased. Then, if $\Lambda_k(\xi_1, \xi_2)$ is the cost over the planning horizon, discounted to the beginning of period k when an optimal decision is made at the beginning of period k and at the beginning of all future periods, and the current machine has been used for ξ_1 periods and had its last overhaul at the beginning of period ξ_2, the recurrence relations become

$$\Lambda_k(\xi_1, \xi_2) = \min \begin{cases} C_{k-\xi_1}(\xi_1 + 1, \xi_2) \\ \qquad + \alpha\Lambda_{k+1}(\xi_1 + 1, \xi_2)\text{: keep—no overhaul;} \\ C_{k-\xi_1}(\xi_1 + 1, k) + H_{k-\xi_1}(\xi_1, \xi_2) \\ \qquad + \alpha\Lambda_{k+1}(\xi_1 + 1, k)\text{: overhaul;} \\ I_k + C_k(1, k) - S_{k-\xi_1}(\xi_1, \xi_2) \\ \qquad + \alpha\Lambda_{k+1}(1, k)\text{: buy new machine.} \end{cases} \tag{11–40}$$

This problem is much more difficult to solve than the problems discussed in Section 10–16 because of the appearance of the two state parameters. However, since very little work needs to be done to carry out the minimization, and since ξ_2 will never be too large, it can be solved readily on a digital computer. Again, of course, in practice, one might, in attempting to determine the costs, encounter considerable difficulties.

The other generalization we shall consider is that where the decision maker has the choice of selecting one of several competing makes of new machines. The only possible alternatives will be assumed to be to keep the current machine or buy one of the new machines. We shall not allow for the possibility of overhaul. Let I_{uv}, $C_{uv}(j)$, and $S_{uv}(j)$ have their usual meanings except that the additional subscript v refers to a particular make of machine. We shall illustrate the case where there are only two competing makes, but as we shall see, any number of competing makes can be handled without undue difficulty.

It is convenient to imagine that the state functions are characterized by two parameters. One of the parameters gives the age of the current machine if it is of make 1, and the other gives the same information if it is of make 2. Both parameters cannot be positive simultaneously, since at any given time we possess a machine of one make or the other, but not both. Then let $\Lambda_k(\xi_1, \xi_2)$ be the cost discounted to the beginning of period k when we end period $k - 1$ with a machine of a given make and age, and an optimal decision is made at the beginning of period k and of all future periods. If at the end of period 1, we have a machine of make 1, ξ_1 will give its age, and we set $\xi_2 = 0$ to indicate that we do not have a machine of make 2. Conversely, if we have a machine of make 2, ξ_2 will give its age, and $\xi_1 = 0$. Note that for this problem, if ξ_1 and ξ_2 can have n values, $\Lambda_k(\xi_1, \xi_2)$ can have only $2n - 1$ values and not n^2 as in the case where every combination of ξ_1 and ξ_2 must be considered. Indeed, we could describe the state of the system with only one state parameter. To see how we proceed, suppose that we knew that a machine of make 1 would never be kept for more than 10 periods. Then we define ξ so that if ξ had one of the values $1, \ldots, 10$, this would tell that we had a machine of make 1 of age ξ. If $\xi > 10$, we have a machine of make 2, and its age is $\xi - 10$. However, it is convenient to use two parameters instead of this approach. To illustrate the form of the recurrence relations, assume that we end period $k - 1$ with a machine of make 1 which is ξ_1 periods old. Then the recurrence relations have the form

$$\Lambda_k(\xi_1, 0) = \min \begin{cases} C_{k-\xi_1,1}(\xi_1 + 1) + \alpha\Lambda_{k+1}(\xi_1 + 1, 0): & \text{keep;} \\ I_{k1} - S_{k-\xi_1,1}(\xi_1) + C_{k1}(1) & \\ \qquad + \alpha\Lambda_{k+1}(1, 0): & \text{buy make 1;} \\ I_{k2} - S_{k-\xi_1,1}(\xi_1) + C_{k2}(1) & \\ \qquad + \alpha\Lambda_{k+1}(0, 1): & \text{buy make 2.} \end{cases} \tag{11-41}$$

If the computations were to be carried out on a computer, choices between ten or more competing makes could easily be allowed for.

In Problem 11-8 we ask the reader to formulate the case where two machines are in use and are considered simultaneously. The possible decisions are to keep both, replace one or the other, or replace both. For this kind of problem, two state parameters are needed, and it is necessary to consider all combinations of values which the two state parameters may assume. Problem 11-9 requires that the formulation for this situation be generalized to allow for m machines.

11–9 Other problems in the calculus of variations. In Section 10–19 we showed how dynamic programming can be used to find numerical solutions to problems in the calculus of variations which seek a function $y(x)$ minimizing the integral

$$I = \int_{\alpha}^{\beta} F(y, y', x)\, dx$$

when $y(\alpha) = a$, $y(\beta) = b$. Let us now consider a more complicated problem in which it is desired to determine m functions $y_j(x)$ which minimize the integral

$$I = \int_{\alpha}^{\beta} F(y_1, \ldots, y_m, y'_1, \ldots, y'_m, x)\, dx \tag{11–42}$$

when it is specified that $y_j(\alpha) = a_j$, $y_j(\beta) = b_j$, $j = 1, \ldots, n$. In other words, we wish to determine a curve in the $(m + 1)$-dimensional space of points $[x, y_1, \ldots, y_n]$, beginning at the point $\mathbf{a} = [\alpha, a_1, \ldots, a_m]$ and terminating at $\mathbf{b} = [\beta, b_1, \ldots, b_m]$ which minimizes the integral I in (11–42).

In principle, we can use precisely the same sort of computational scheme that was developed in Section 10–19. The interval $\alpha \leq x \leq \beta$ is divided by $n + 1$ grid points $x_u = \alpha + u\,\Delta x$, $u = 0, 1, \ldots, n$, into n subintervals of length Δx. For any admissible arc, let $y_j(x_u) = y_{uj}$, and approximate $y'_j(x_u)$ by

$$\frac{y_{u+1,j} - y_{uj}}{\Delta x}.$$

The given problem can then be replaced by an approximating problem which seeks to determine values for $m(n - 1)$ variables y_{uj} minimizing

$$I = \sum_{u=0}^{n} F\left(y_{u1}, \ldots, y_{um}, \frac{y_{u+1,1} - y_{u1}}{\Delta x}, \ldots, \frac{y_{u+1,m} - y_{um}}{\Delta x}, x_u\right) \Delta x \tag{11–43}$$

and satisfying $y_{0j} = a_j$, $y_{nj} = b_j$, $j = 1, \ldots, m$.

The approximating problem can be formulated as a dynamic programming problem. In order to do so m state parameters are needed as arguments in the state functions. Let

$$\Lambda_k(\xi_1, \ldots, \xi_m) =$$
$$= \min_{\text{all } y_{uj}} \sum_{u=k}^{n} F\left(y_{u1}, \ldots, y_{un}, \frac{y_{u+1,1} - y_{u1}}{\Delta x}, \ldots, \frac{y_{u+1,m} - y_{um}}{\Delta x}, x_u\right) \Delta x, \tag{11–44}$$

where $y_{kj} = \xi_j$ and $y_{nj} = b_j$, $j = 1, \ldots, m$. Then the recurrence relations take the form

$$\Lambda_k(\xi_1, \ldots, \xi_m) =$$

$$= \min_{y_{k+1,1},\ldots,y_{k+1,m}} \left[F\left(\xi_1, \ldots, \xi_m, \frac{y_{k+1,1} - \xi_1}{\Delta x}, \ldots, \frac{y_{k+1,m} - \xi_m}{\Delta x}, x_k\right) \Delta x + \Lambda_{k+1}(y_{k+1,1,\ldots,}y_{k+1,m}) \right], \tag{11-45}$$

$$k = 0, \ldots, n-2,$$

and

$$\Lambda_{n-1}(\xi_1, \ldots, \xi_m) = F\left(\xi_1, \ldots, \xi_m, \frac{b_1 - \xi_1}{\Delta x}, \ldots, \frac{b_m - \xi_m}{\Delta x}, x_{n-1}\right) \Delta x.$$

Note that in this problem we must minimize over m variables at each stage; moreover m state parameters are required. If $m \geq 3$, it would be completely out of the question to solve such a problem numerically by dynamic programming. However, the case of $m = 2$ would usually be feasible.

Sometimes problems are encountered which seek to minimize an integral (11-42) when the $y_j(x)$ are not independent, but for each x, must satisfy the following set of $r(r < m)$ differential equations:

$$G_i(y_1, \ldots, y_m, y_1', \ldots, y_m', x) = 0, \qquad i = 1, \ldots, r. \tag{11-46}$$

The equations (11-46) represent constraints on the problem. Consider then how the problem can be solved when the $y_j(x)$ must satisfy (11-46). We proceed as above and consider the approximating problem (11-43), where (11-46) now becomes

$$G_i\left(y_{u1}, \ldots, y_{um}, \frac{y_{u+1,1} - y_{u1}}{\Delta x}, \ldots, \frac{y_{u+1,m} - y_{um}}{\Delta x}, x_u\right) = 0,$$

$$i = 1, \ldots, r, \qquad u = 0, \ldots, n-1, \tag{11-47}$$

so that the differential equations (11-46) are converted into a set of ordinary equations relating the y_{uj}. Define the state functions Λ_k as above, except that the y_{uj} must now also satisfy (11-47). Then the recurrence relations become (11-45) again, except that the minimization is to be carried out over $y_{k+1,j}$ which satisfy

$$G_i\left(\xi_1, \ldots, \xi_m, \frac{y_{k+1,1} - \xi_1}{\Delta x}, \ldots, \frac{y_{k+1,m} - \xi_m}{\Delta x}, x_k\right) = 0,$$

$$i = 1, \ldots, r. \tag{11-48}$$

Hence the problem is more easily solved by the dynamic programming approach when constraints of the form (11–46) are present, since these constraints do nothing but restrict the range of variation of the $y_{k+1,j}$ at each stage. Of course, unless the functions G_i have a simple form, it may be difficult to determine precisely what the region is over which the $y_{k+1,j}$ are allowed to vary.

Another type of problem that can arise is that of finding a curve which begins on some surface $g(x, y_1, \ldots, y_m) = 0$, ends at the point **b**, and minimizes (11–42), where the lower limit is no longer specified. Here the curve does not begin at a given point. All that is required is that it begin at some point on the given surface. For this problem, we can, in principle, obtain an approximate solution by the dynamic programming technique. We would proceed precisely as we did for the unconstrained problem above except that when we reached Λ_k for which there existed y_j satisfying $g(x_k, y_1, \ldots, y_k)$, we would evaluate Λ_k for a set of such $y_1, \ldots, y_k$, and this would be repeated for all appropriate x_k. Then the smallest of all these Λ_k could be selected to be I^*, and the solution would therefore be obtained.

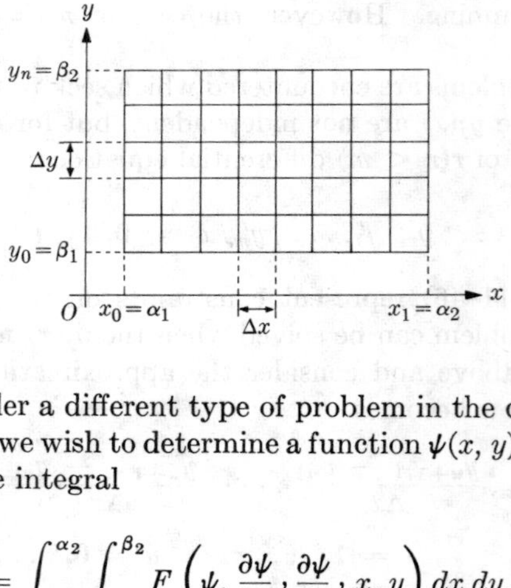

FIGURE 11–6

Let us now consider a different type of problem in the calculus of variations. Suppose that we wish to determine a function $\psi(x, y)$ of two variables which minimizes the integral

$$I = \int_{\alpha_1}^{\alpha_2} \int_{\beta_1}^{\beta_2} F\left(\psi, \frac{\partial \psi}{\partial x}, \frac{\partial \psi}{\partial y}, x, y\right) dx\, dy, \tag{11–49}$$

where $\psi(x, y)$ is specified on the boundaries of the rectangle $\alpha_1 \leq x \leq \alpha_2$, $\beta_1 \leq y \leq \beta_2$ shown in Fig. 11–6. We wish to find the surface $\psi(x, y)$ which is specified on the boundaries of the rectangle and which minimizes the integral of F over the rectangle.

This is again a problem that can approximately be represented as a dynamic programming problem. To obtain this representation, let us divide the rectangle of Fig. 11–6 by a set of grid points (x_i, y_j), $i = 0, 1, \ldots, m$, $j = 0, 1, \ldots, n$. The value of ψ will be determined only at these grid points. Write $\psi_{ij} = \psi(x_i, y_j)$. We shall approximate $\partial\psi/\partial y$ and $\partial\psi/\partial y$, using

$$\frac{\partial\psi}{\partial x} \doteq \frac{\psi_{i+1,j} - \psi_{ij}}{\Delta x}; \quad \frac{\partial\psi}{\partial y} \doteq \frac{\psi_{i,j+1} - \psi_{ij}}{\Delta y}.$$

The given problem can then be replaced by the approximating problem which seeks ψ_{ij} minimizing

$$I = \sum_{i=0}^{m-1} \sum_{j=0}^{n-1} F\left(\psi_{ij}, \frac{\psi_{i+1,j} - \psi_{ij}}{\Delta x}, \frac{\psi_{i,j+1} - \psi_{ij}}{\Delta y}, x_i, y_j\right) \Delta x \, \Delta y, \quad (11\text{–}50)$$

where the values of ψ_{ij} on the boundaries are specified.

This can be thought of as a multistage decision problem where at stage j, we assign values to the $m - 1$ values of ψ_{ij}. In other words, at stage j, we assign values to an entire row of grid points in Fig. 11–6. If this interpretation is used, we can imagine that we start at $y_n = \beta_2$ and then work our way down to $y_0 = \beta_1$, assigning all ψ_{ij}-values in the row at stage j. To do this, $m - 1$ state parameters will be needed. Let us define the state functions as follows:

$$\Lambda_k(\xi_1, \ldots, \xi_{m-1}) =$$
$$= \min_{\text{all } \psi_{ij}} \sum_{i=0}^{m-1} \sum_{j=k}^{n-1} F\left(\psi_{ij}, \frac{\psi_{i+1,j} - \psi_{ij}}{\Delta x}, \frac{\psi_{i,j+1} - \psi_{ij}}{\Delta y}, x_i, y_j\right) \Delta x \, \Delta y, \quad (11\text{–}51)$$

where $\psi_{ik} = \xi_i$ and ψ is also specified as is required on the boundaries included. The recurrence relations then take the form

$$\Lambda_k(\xi_1, \ldots, \xi_{m-1}) =$$
$$= \min_{\text{all } \psi_{i,k+1}} \left\{\sum_{i=0}^{m-1} F\left(\xi_i, \frac{\xi_{i+1} - \xi_i}{\Delta x}, \frac{\psi_{i,k+1} - \xi_i}{\Delta y}, x_i, y_k\right) \Delta x \, \Delta y \right.$$
$$\left. + \Lambda_{k+1}(\psi_{1,k+1}, \ldots, \psi_{m-1,k+1})\right\},$$
$$k = 0, \ldots, n - 2, \quad (11\text{–}52)$$

where $\psi_{0,k}, \psi_{m,k}, \psi_{0,k+1}, \psi_{m,k+1}$ are specified. Also

$$\Lambda_{n-1}(\xi_1, \ldots, \xi_{m-1}) =$$
$$= \sum_{i=0}^{m-1} F\left(\xi_i, \frac{\xi_{i+1} - \xi_i}{\Delta x}, \frac{\psi_{in} - \xi_i}{\Delta y}, x_i, y_{n-1}\right) \Delta x \, \Delta y, \quad (11\text{–}53)$$

where the ψ_{in}, as well as $\psi_{0,n-1}$, $\psi_{m,n-1}$, are specified. Clearly, it is not actually possible to solve such a problem numerically by dynamic programming because of the large number of state parameters and the large number of variables over which the minimization must be made at each stage. However, it is interesting to note that the problem can be converted to a dynamic programming problem.

11–10 Combined production scheduling and inventory control problems. An important class of sequential decision stochastic programming problems is concerned with scheduling production of a product over some planning horizon in a way that will minimize the combined expected costs of production and of carrying inventory when the demand for the product in any time interval must be treated as a random variable. We shall imagine that production decisions are made only periodically. Each time these decisions are to be made, a planning horizon of n periods is used. The demand v_j for the product in period j will be assumed to be a random variable with density function $\phi_j(v_j)$. Demands in different periods will be imagined to be independent random variables.

One can develop a variety of models of widely varying complexity depending on how many decisions are assumed to be required at the beginning of each period. We shall illustrate with two cases. In the first, the only decision which needs to be made is how much of the product will be produced for the period. It will be assumed that this decision automatically determines the size of the work force, the number of hours to be worked, raw materials requirements, and any other pertinent parameters.

It will be imagined that the only inventory of concern is the one in the factory warehouse. Let y_j be the net inventory at the beginning of period j. This is defined to be the on-hand inventory net of unfilled orders. If y_j is negative, the unfilled orders exceed the on-hand inventory. If x_j is the quantity produced in period j and v_j is the demand, then

$$y_{j+1} = y_j + x_j - v_j. \tag{11–54}$$

Consider now the costs incurred in period j. First there will be the cost of producing the goods. This includes wages, raw materials, etc. It is a function only of x_j and will be denoted by $C_j(x_j)$. Next there is a cost incurred when the level of production is changed; this includes hiring, transfer, layoff, modification costs, etc. It is a function of $x_j - x_{j-1}$ and will be written $D_j(x_j - x_{j-1})$. Finally, there will be a cost of carrying inventory or a cost associated with unfilled orders. We shall assume that this depends only on $y_j + x_j$. The expected cost of carrying inventory and of backorders for period j will be denoted by $F_j(y_j + x_j)$.

Let Λ_k be the expected cost for periods k through n discounted to the beginning of period k when an optimal decision is made at the beginning of period k and of all future periods. Note that Λ_k will depend on both y_k and x_{k-1}. Thus two state parameters are needed as arguments in the state functions. Then it is clear that the recurrence relations take the form

$$\Lambda_k(\xi_1, \xi_2) = \min_{x_k} \Big[C_k(x_k) + D_k(x_k - \xi_1) + F_k(\xi_2 + x_k) + \alpha \int_0^\infty \Lambda_{k+1}(x_k, \xi_2 + x_k - v_k)\phi_k(v_k)\, dv_k \Big], \quad k = 1, \ldots, n-1, \tag{11-55}$$

where α is the discount factor. Also

$$\Lambda_n(\xi_1, \xi_2) = \min_{x_n} [C_n(x_n) + D_n(x_n - \xi_1) + F_n(\xi_2 + x_n)]. \tag{11-56}$$

We would determine the optimal value for x_1 on computing $\Lambda_1(x_0, y_1)$. Since only x_1 would be of interest, we would not need to record the tables $\hat{x}_k(\xi_1, \xi_2)$, $k \geq 2$. Since two state parameters are required, it could be quite time consuming to solve a problem of this type. However, if there were only ten or twenty periods in the planning horizon and ξ_1, ξ_2 could each take on only about thirty values, the problem could be solved quite easily and very quickly on a large-scale digital computer.

As our second case, let us suppose that the quantity to be produced does not uniquely determine the work force. For any given production, we might have several alternatives regarding the size of the work force. This could be possible because a smaller work force might be compensated for by more overtime. Let w_j be the size of the work force in period j. Consider then the costs that will be incurred in period j. There will be the cost $C_j(x_j)$ of raw materials, etc., the cost $S_j(w_j)$ of wages, the cost $D_j(w_j - w_{j-1})$ of changing the size of the labor force, the cost $E_j(w_j, x_j)$ of having the labor force deviate from the size established as ideal for an output x_j, and the expected cost $F_j(y_j + x_j)$ of carrying inventory and of backorders. We shall assume that there are no costs which depend on $x_j - x_{j-1}$.

As in the previous case, two state parameters are needed. Here though they are w_{k-1} and y_k. Now, however, two control variables must be determined at each stage. Let $\Lambda_k(\xi_1, \xi_2)$ be defined as for the previous case. For the present situation, the recurrence relations become

$$\Lambda_k(\xi_1, \xi_2) = \min_{x_k, w_k} \Big[C_k(x_k) + S_k(w_k) + D_k(w_k - \xi_1) + E_k(w_k, x_k) + F_k(\xi_2 + x_k) + \alpha \int_0^\infty \Lambda_{k+1}(w_k, \xi_2 + x_k - v_k)\phi_k(v_k) dv_k \Big], \quad k = 1, \ldots, n-1. \tag{11-57}$$

The numerical solution of the present version of the problem would require much more time than in the previous case, because of the necessity of minimizing over two variables at each stage. However, it could be handled on a large digital computer.

11–11 Case of quadratic costs. An interesting case arises when in (11–57) we attempt to approximate all the costs by a combination of linear and quadratic functions in the control variables. The reason that this case is especially interesting will emerge in the discussion below. To begin, let us consider the simplified form of the cost terms. First we shall write

$$C_k(x_k) = C_0 + C_1x_k; \qquad S_k(w_k) = S_0 + S_1w_k. \tag{11–58}$$

It should be obvious why have chosen to represent C_k, S_k in the form (11–58). For $D_k(w_k - w_{k-1})$, we shall use

$$D_k(w_k - w_{k-1}) = D_0(w_k - w_{k-1} - D_1)^2 + D_2. \tag{11–59}$$

The reasoning underlying our approach is based on Fig. 11–7. The correct form of D_k might look like the solid curve shown. However, we shall approximate it by the dashed parabola whose equation has the form (11–59). Clearly, the representation is crude, and is only approximately correct when $|w_k - w_{k-1}|$ is not too large. A better approximation might be obtained by having the axis of symmetry inclined rather than parallel to the D_k-axis, but then D_k would no longer be a combination of a linear and a quadratic function of $w_k - w_{k-1}$.

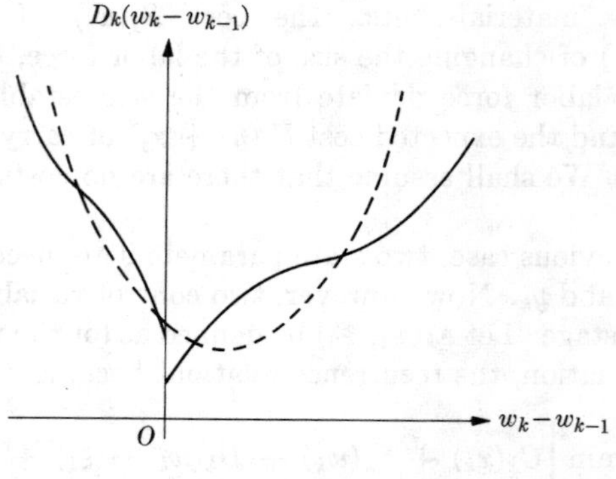

FIGURE 11–7

We shall assume that for a given work force, there is an ideal output quantity E_1w_k, and if x_k increases above E_1w_k, overtime costs are incurred. The function $E_k(w_k, x_k)$ might then be roughly approximated by $E_0(x_k - E_1w_k)^2$. We shall do this, and add terms proportional to x_k, w_k

to allow for improving the fit to empirical data. Thus we shall write

$$E_k(w_k, x_k) = E_0(x_k - E_1w_k)^2 + E_2x_k + E_3w_k. \tag{11-60}$$

This formula has the unfortunate feature that E_k increases when $x_k < E_1w_k$, which we would not normally expect to happen. The approximation therefore becomes poorer and poorer as x_k moves to values less than E_1w_k.

Consider finally the representation of F_k. Instead of approximating the expected cost of carrying inventory and of backorders for period k, let us approximate the actual cost when the demand is v_k. Now, the situation will be quite similar to that represented in Fig. 11–7; the cost here will depend on $y_k + x_k - v_k$ and will be approximated by

$$F_0(y_k + x_k - v_k - F_1)^2 + F_2 = F_0(y_{k+1} - F_1)^2 + F_2. \tag{11-61}$$

Let us imagine that in the above expressions, the constants have been determined so that each cost is non-negative regardless of what values the x_k, w_k, and v_k have, and that for any set of v_k, the total cost over the planning horizon is positive. We have made all the constants independent of k, that is, of the particular period in the planning horizon, because in practice this would be the typical procedure. On expanding the various cost terms set down above, we see that the cost K_k in period k can be written

$$K_k = G_0 + G_1x_k + G_2w_k + G_3x_k^2 + G_4w_k^2 + G_5w_kx_k + G_6w_kw_{k-1} + G_7w_{k-1}^2 + G_8w_{k-1} + G_9y_{k+1} + G_{10}y_{k+1}^2. \tag{11-62}$$

In Problem 11–11 the reader is asked to determine the G_j as functions of the other parameters introduced above. For a given set of v_j, the discounted cost over the planning horizon will then be

$$K = \sum_{j=1}^{n} \alpha^{j-1}K_j, \tag{11-63}$$

where w_0 and y_1 are specified and

$$y_{j+1} = y_j + x_j - v_j = y_1 + \sum_{i=1}^{j} x_i - \sum_{i=1}^{j} v_i. \tag{11-64}$$

Let us now write

$$\mathbf{x} = [x_1, \ldots, x_n], \qquad \mathbf{w} = [w_1, \ldots, w_n],$$
$$\mathbf{u} = [\mathbf{x}, \mathbf{w}], \qquad \mathbf{y} = [y_2, \ldots, y_{n+1}]. \tag{11-65}$$

Then the K of (11–63) can be written

$$K = \beta + \mathbf{hu} + \mathbf{u'Hu} + \mathbf{qy} + \mathbf{y'Qy}, \tag{11-66}$$

where $\mathbf{h}$ and $\mathbf{q}$ are row vectors, and $\mathbf{H}$ and $\mathbf{Q}$ are symmetric matrices. In Problem 11–12, it is required that $\mathbf{h}$, $\mathbf{q}$, $\mathbf{H}$, $\mathbf{Q}$, and β be expressed in terms of the G_j. Note that w_0 appears in $\mathbf{h}$. Also observe from the definitions of the various cost terms that $\mathbf{u'Hu}$ and $\mathbf{y'Qy}$ are positive definite quadratic forms.

Let us next introduce the vector $\mathbf{r} = [r_1, \ldots, r_n]$, where

$$r_j = y_1 - \sum_{i=1}^{j} v_i. \tag{11–67}$$

Then by (11–64)

$$\mathbf{y} = \mathbf{r} + \mathbf{Tx}, \tag{11–68}$$

where

$$\mathbf{T} = \begin{bmatrix} 1 & 0 & 0 & 0 & \cdots & 0 \\ 1 & 1 & 0 & 0 & \cdots & 0 \\ 1 & 1 & 1 & 0 & \cdots & 0 \\ \vdots & & & & & \\ 1 & 1 & 1 & 1 & \cdots & 1 \end{bmatrix} \tag{11–69}$$

is a triangular matrix containing all ones on and below the main diagonal. The matrix $\mathbf{T}$ is nonsingular, since none of the elements on the main diagonal is zero. By the introduction of the vector $\mathbf{r}$ we have separated the v_j from the control variables. Substitution of (11–68) into (11–66) yields

$$K = \beta + \mathbf{hu} + \mathbf{u'Hu} + \mathbf{qr} + \mathbf{qTx} + \mathbf{r'Qr} + 2\mathbf{r'QTx} + \mathbf{x'T'QTx}. \tag{11–70}$$

The quadratic form $\mathbf{x'T'QTx}$ is positive definite, since $\mathbf{y'Qy}$ was, and $\mathbf{T}$ is nonsingular.

Let us now introduce the matrix of order $2n$,

$$\mathbf{M} = \begin{bmatrix} \mathbf{T'QT} & \mathbf{0} \\ \mathbf{0} & \mathbf{0} \end{bmatrix}. \tag{11–71}$$

Then $\mathbf{u'Mu} = \mathbf{x'T'QTx}$, and $\mathbf{u'Mu}$ is positive semidefinite. Also write

$$2\mathbf{r'QTx} = (2\mathbf{r'QT}, \mathbf{0})\mathbf{u}, \tag{11–72}$$

$$\mathbf{qTx} = (\mathbf{qT}, \mathbf{0})\mathbf{u}. \tag{11–73}$$

If $\mathbf{h} = (\mathbf{h}_1, \mathbf{h}_2)$, where $\mathbf{h}_1$ contains the first n components of $\mathbf{h}$, (11–71) can be written

$$K = \beta + \mathbf{qr} + \mathbf{r'Qr} + (\mathbf{h}_1 + \mathbf{qT} + 2\mathbf{r'QT}, \mathbf{h}_2)\mathbf{u} + \mathbf{u'Ru}, \tag{11–74}$$

where $\mathbf{R} = \mathbf{H} + \mathbf{M}$. Note that $\mathbf{u'Ru}$ is positive definite because the sum of a positive definite and a positive semidefinite form is positive definite.

After going through a great deal of manipulation we are now ready to consider the reason for studying the case of quadratic costs in so much detail. We shall prove in the next section that when the discounted cost over the planning horizon for a given set of v_j has the form (11–74), and $\mathbf{r'Qr}$ and $\mathbf{u'Ru}$ are positive definite quadratic forms, then so far as the decision for the first period is concerned, i.e., for the selection of w_1 and x_1, we can find w_1^* and x_1^* by minimizing K of (11–74) when the v_j are replaced by their expected values μ_j. In other words, if we ignore the fact that the demands are random variables and instead simply use the expected demands, the optimal values of x_1 and w_1 obtained by solving this problem will be precisely the same as would be obtained by treating the demands as random variables and solving (11–57). We can replace the stochastic sequential decision problem by a deterministic sequential decision problem, and the optimal decisions for the first period will be the same in either case. This result is not true in general, of course. It is true only because we restricted our attention to costs which were combinations of linear and quadratic forms. We noted in Chapter 5 that to make an optimal decision for the first period, one must usually compute the complete policy functions for the other periods in the planning horizon. Here we have encountered a situation where this is not necessary.

To determine w_1^* and x_1^*, we can, for quadratic costs, solve the deterministic dynamic programming problem for which the recurrence relations are

$$\Lambda_k(\xi_1, \xi_2) = \min_{x_k, w_k} [C_k(x_k) + S_k(w_k) + D_k(w_k - \xi_1) + E_k(w_k, x_k) + F_k(\xi_2 + x_k) + \alpha\Lambda_{k+1}(w_k, \xi_2 + x_k - \mu_k)],$$
$$k = 1, \ldots, n - 1. \qquad (11\text{–}75)$$

This problem would be somewhat easier to solve than (11–57). However, in the present case, the problem can be solved much more simply by direct methods of the calculus. All we need to do is to set the partial derivative of the K of (11–74) with respect to each x_j and w_j equal to zero. In the resulting system of linear equations in the x_j and w_j, we then eliminate the x_j and w_j, $j > 1$, and solve explicitly for x_1 and w_1 in terms of w_0, y_1, and the μ_j. The set of equations obtained by setting the partial derivatives equal to zero has a simple form, and explicitly solving for x_1 and w_1 is not too difficult. In Problem 11–13 the reader is asked to obtain the structure of $\mathbf{R}$ in (11–74) and the set of equations to be solved. The optimal values for x_1 and w_1 then have the form

$$x_1^* = \rho_1 y_1 + \rho_2 w_0 + \sum_{j=1}^{n} \gamma_j \mu_j; \quad w_1^* = \delta_1 y_1 + \delta_2 w_0 + \sum_{j=1}^{n} \epsilon_j \mu_j. \qquad (11\text{–}76)$$

Once the coefficients $\rho_1, \rho_2, \gamma_j, \delta_1, \delta_2, \epsilon_j$ have been determined (these never change), it is only necessary to forecast the expected demand for each period in the planning horizon and then use (11–76) to obtain x_1^* and w_1^*. In the derivation of (11–76), no attempt was made to impose the requirements that all $x_j, w_j \geq 0$. For most practical situations, this is no problem, and x_1^*, w_1^* automatically turn out to be positive. Neither was any attempt made to require that w_j be an integer. Again in practice this is seldom a serious drawback. The decision rules (11–76) are frequently referred to as *linear decision rules*, since the optimal values of x_1 and w_1 depend linearly on the other relevant parameters. This production scheduling model, based on quadratic costs and hence linear decision rules, was developed by Holt, Modigliani, Muth, and Simon and is discussed in detail in [6]. These authors have actually implemented this model in several different industrial firms, and they claim that the applications were successful, although it was not possible to obtain any clear-cut estimates of what sort of cost reductions were made.

11–12 Proof of certainty equivalence for quadratic costs. We would like to prove that if $\mathbf{r}'\mathbf{Qr}$ and $\mathbf{u}'\mathbf{Ru}$ are positive definite quadratic forms in (11–74), then, if we determine x_1^* and w_1^* by minimizing (11–74) when the v_j are replaced by their expected values μ_j, these values of x_1^* and w_1^* will be precisely the same values that would be obtained if we minimized the expected discounted cost over the planning horizon. In the proof we do not even need to assume that the v_j are independent random variables. If $\phi(v_1, \ldots, v_n)$ is the joint density function for the v_j, the expected discounted cost for a given set of x_j and w_j is

$$z = \int_0^\infty \cdots \int_0^\infty K\phi(v_1, \ldots, v_n)\, dv_1 \cdots dv_n. \tag{11–77}$$

Let us first show how to find the optimal decisions for the first period which are obtained by minimizing (11–77). For this problem, we wish to allow x_k and w_k, $k > 1$, to be functions of y_k and w_{k-1}. Let $\mathbf{u}^*$ contain the optimal policy functions. Then $\mathbf{u}^*$ will have the form

$$\mathbf{u}^* = [x_1^*, \hat{x}_2(y_2, w_1), \ldots, \hat{x}_n(y_n, w_{n-1}), w_1^*, \hat{w}_2(y_2, w_1), \ldots, \hat{w}_n(y_n, w_{n-1})]. \tag{11–78}$$

To avoid integrating over the random variables in a number of formulas, we shall simply denote by $E\{f\}$ the expected value of any function f of the random variables. Let $\mathbf{u}$ contain any other set of policy functions and write $\boldsymbol{\delta} = \mathbf{u} - \mathbf{u}^*$. Let z be the expected discounted cost corresponding to the policy functions $\mathbf{u}$, and z^* be the minimum cost. From (11-77),

$$z - z^* = E\{(\mathbf{h}_1 + \mathbf{qT} + 2\mathbf{r}'\mathbf{QT}, \mathbf{h}_2)\mathbf{u}\} - E\{(\mathbf{h}_1 + \mathbf{qT} + 2\mathbf{r}'\mathbf{QT}, \mathbf{h}_2)\mathbf{u}^*\} + E\{\mathbf{u}'\mathbf{Ru}\} - E\{(\mathbf{u}^*)'\mathbf{Ru}^*\}, \qquad (11\text{-}79)$$

or using $\mathbf{u} = \mathbf{u}^* + \boldsymbol{\delta}$, we have

$$\begin{aligned} z - z^* &= E\{(\mathbf{h}_1 + \mathbf{qT} + 2\mathbf{r}'\mathbf{QT}, \mathbf{h}_2)\boldsymbol{\delta}\} + 2E\{(\mathbf{u}^*)'\mathbf{R}\boldsymbol{\delta}\} + E\{\boldsymbol{\delta}'\mathbf{R}\boldsymbol{\delta}\} \\ &= E\{[(\mathbf{h}_1 + \mathbf{qT} + 2\mathbf{r}'\mathbf{QT}, \mathbf{h}_2) + 2(\mathbf{u}^*)'\mathbf{R}]\boldsymbol{\delta}\} + E\{\boldsymbol{\delta}'\mathbf{R}\boldsymbol{\delta}\}. \end{aligned} \qquad (11\text{-}80)$$

Since z^* is the minimum cost, it must be true that $z - z^* \geq 0$, that is,

$$E\{[(\mathbf{h}_1 + \mathbf{qT} + 2\mathbf{r}'\mathbf{QT}, \mathbf{h}_2) + 2(\mathbf{u}^*)'\mathbf{R}]\boldsymbol{\delta}\} + E\{\boldsymbol{\delta}'\mathbf{R}\boldsymbol{\delta}\} \geq 0 \qquad (11\text{-}81)$$

for *all* $\boldsymbol{\delta}$. Let us now derive a necessary condition for $\mathbf{u}^*$ to contain an optimal set of policy functions. Because (11-81) holds for all $\boldsymbol{\delta}$, it must hold for $\boldsymbol{\delta} = \pm\epsilon\mathbf{e}_1$ where ϵ is small. Then $E\{\boldsymbol{\delta}'\mathbf{R}\boldsymbol{\delta}\} = \epsilon^2 r_{11} > 0$, while the other term is proportional to ϵ. Now write

$$E\{[(\mathbf{h}_1 + \mathbf{qT} + 2\mathbf{r}'\mathbf{QT}, \mathbf{h}_2) + 2(\mathbf{u}^*)'\mathbf{R}]\mathbf{e}_j\} = s_j.$$

Thus for ϵ small enough, the sign of the left-hand side of (11-81) will depend only on $\delta_1 s_1$. If $s_1 \neq 0$, the left-hand side of (11-81) can have either sign, which is not permissible. Therefore it is necessary that $s_1 = 0$. We can repeat the argument, using $\boldsymbol{\delta} = \pm\epsilon\mathbf{e}_2, \ldots, \pm\epsilon\mathbf{e}_n$. This then implies that a necessary condition for $\mathbf{u}^*$ to contain an optimal set of policy functions is that $\mathbf{s} = \mathbf{0}$, that is,

$$E\{[(\mathbf{h}_1 + \mathbf{qT} + 2\mathbf{r}'\mathbf{QT}, \mathbf{h}_2) + 2(\mathbf{u}^*)'\mathbf{R}]\} = \mathbf{0}, \qquad (11\text{-}82)$$

or, since $\mathbf{h}_1$, $\mathbf{q}$, $\mathbf{T}$, $\mathbf{Q}$, $\mathbf{h}_2$, and $\mathbf{R}$ are independent of the random variables,

$$(\mathbf{h}_1 + \mathbf{qT} + 2E\{\mathbf{r}'\}\mathbf{QT}, \mathbf{h}_2) + 2E\{(\mathbf{u}^*)'\}\mathbf{R} = \mathbf{0}. \qquad (11\text{-}83)$$

But $\mathbf{R}$ is nonsingular because $\mathbf{u}'\mathbf{Ru}$ is positive definite. Thus we can solve (11-83) for a unique $E\{\mathbf{u}^*\}$, which is

$$E\{(\mathbf{u}^*)\} = -\tfrac{1}{2}\mathbf{R}^{-1}(\mathbf{h}_1 + \mathbf{qT} + 2E\{\mathbf{r}'\}\mathbf{QT}, \mathbf{h}_2)'. \qquad (11\text{-}84)$$

However, x_1 and w_1 are not functions of any of the random variables. Therefore, the first and $(n + 1)$-components of (11-84) will be the optimal values of x_1 and w_1 for the first period.

Suppose, now, that we determine x_1 and w_1 by minimizing (11-74), where the v_j in $\mathbf{r}$ are replaced by the μ_j so that $\mathbf{r}$ is replaced by $E\{\mathbf{r}\}$. A set of necessary conditions for $\mathbf{u}$ to minimize K is that $\nabla_{\mathbf{u}} K = \mathbf{0}$:

$$\nabla_{\mathbf{u}} K = 2\mathbf{u}'\mathbf{R} + (\mathbf{h}_1 + \mathbf{q}\mathbf{T} + 2E\{\mathbf{r}'\}\mathbf{Q}\mathbf{T}, \mathbf{h}_2) = \mathbf{0},$$

or

$$\mathbf{u} = -\tfrac{1}{2}\mathbf{R}^{-1}(\mathbf{h}_1 + \mathbf{q}\mathbf{T} + 2E\{\mathbf{r}'\}\mathbf{Q}\mathbf{T}, \mathbf{h}_2)'. \tag{11-85}$$

But the right-hand sides of (11–84) and (11–85) are identical, so that the first and $(n+1)$-components of $\mathbf{u}$ computed from (11–85) are precisely the same as those computed from (11–84). Therefore we have proved what we wished to show. It is rather surprising that the optimal decision for the first period should be independent of the distributions of the demands v_j, but depend only on their means. This peculiarity is brought about by the fact that the costs are quadratic in both the control variables and the v_j. Theil [10] seems to have been the first to point out that when for a single-stage problem, the cost is quadratic in the random variables, the optimal value of the decision variable depends only on the expected value of the random variables. Simon [9] generalized this to n-stage problems, and his result was in turn generalized by Theil [11].

11–13 Treatment of stochastic sequential decision problems with an infinite planning horizon as Markov processes. Most of our previous studies of stochastic sequential decision problems were concerned with cases where the density function for the stochastic variable(s) and the costs could change from one period to the next. In such situations only a finite planning horizon could be used. However, if the density function for the random variable(s) and the costs do not change from period to period, then it is possible to use an infinite planning horizon; i.e., we can imagine that the system will continue to operate for all future time, and allow the influence of decisions at all future times to be felt in the current decision. We shall continue to assume that the random variables associated with different periods are independent. In Section 10–18 we did consider a situation of this type in the form of an inventory problem. We noted then that dynamic programming can be applied to determine the structure of an optimal policy. The methods of analysis used there did not, however, provide a direct way of determining an optimal policy, although we did note that there existed the possibility of solving explicitly for $\Lambda(\xi)$ and that the parameters R and r for an optimal policy could be determined by minimizing $\Lambda(\xi)$ with respect to them—a procedure which could be employed only when an optimal policy had a very simple form. We would now like to consider another approach for determining optimal policies for stochastic sequential decision problems with an infinite planning horizon. We shall see that the task of finding an optimal policy may be simpler than in the case where only a finite planning horizon is used. As usual, the method is limited to cases where there are only very few state parameters. Indeed, the restrictions will be somewhat more stringent here than in the previous cases considered.

Instead of examining a particular type of practical problem, we shall now consider a rather general type of stochastic sequential decision problem. We shall imagine that decisions are made only at discrete, equally spaced points in time, with the time between two successive decisions being referred to as a period. At the beginning of any one period, the system will be assumed to be in one of M different states. We shall not introduce any specific state parameters. If there was only one state parameter, the M different states referred to would correspond to the M different values which the state parameter could take on. If there were two state parameters, the M states would correspond to all possible combinations of values which the state parameters could assume, and a given state i would refer to a particular combination of the two state parameters.

Denote by $\Lambda(i)$ the expected profit over all future time, discounted to the beginning of a period when the state of the system is i before a decision is made, and an optimal decision is made at the beginning of the period and at the beginning of all future periods. $\Lambda(i)$ is independent of which period we are concerned with, since an infinite planning horizon is being used. In addition to not introducing explicitly any state parameters, we shall not introduce explicitly any control variables either. What we are seeking is a rule which tells us what to do if we begin a period in state i. This rule will not change from period to period. If we are considering an inventory system, this rule might have the following form: order 5 units if you start in state 1, 4 units if in state 2, and 0 otherwise. Let us now imagine that we have enumerated all possible actions that can be taken if we begin a period in a particular state i. There will, in general, be a very large number N_i of such actions. Our task then for a given i is to select an optimal action out of all the N_i possible ones. An optimal policy which tells us what to do for every i will simply be the collection of the optimal rules for each individual i. If we are not going to introduce any control variables, then we must provide another method of relating a given policy to the costs. We shall do this as follows: Once we have selected an action, say u, and we know that we begin a period in state i, then it will be assumed that $f(i, u)$, the expected profit or return from the period, is determined. Furthermore, it will be assumed that once i and u are specified, the probability $p_{ij}(u)$ that the system will be in state j at the beginning of the next period is also determined. This has always been a characteristic of the problems previously considered. In inventory problems, for example, if the inventory position is i before the placement of any order, and u units are ordered, then the probability that the inventory position will be j at the beginning of the next period is determined and is

$$p_{ij}(u) = \begin{cases} 0 & \text{if } j > i + u, \\ p(i + u - j), \end{cases}$$

where $p(v)$ is the probability that v units are demanded in a period.

With these definitions, the functional equation for $\Lambda(i)$ becomes

$$\Lambda(i) = \max_u \left[f(i, u) + \alpha \sum_{j=1}^{M} p_{ij}(u)\Lambda(j) \right], \qquad i = 1, \ldots, M, \tag{11-86}$$

where $\sum_{j=1}^{M} p_{ij}(u) = 1$, all u, and u takes on the values $1, \ldots, N_i$, with u referring to a particular action and not necessarily to the magnitude of a variable. As usual, $\alpha < 1$ is the discount factor.

The type of problem which we are considering has the property that at the beginning of each period we will be in one of M states. Furthermore once we have selected a rule for making decisions, we have determined a set of *transition probabilities* p_{ij} which have the property that if the system is in state i at the beginning of one period, the probability that it will be in state j at the beginning of the next period is p_{ij}. Note that p_{ij} is completely independent of how the system got into state i. Let $q_k(i)$ be the probability that the system is in state i at the beginning of period k. Then

$$q_{k+1}(j) = \sum_{i=1}^{M} q_k(i)p_{ij}, \qquad j = 1, \ldots, M. \tag{11-87}$$

When the stochastic behavior of a system can be described in this manner, the stochastic process is called a Markov process. Each of the stochastic sequential decision problems which we have previously treated by dynamic programming has the Markovian property.

Let us now select any one of $\prod_{i=1}^{M} N_i$ policies for operating the system obtained by selecting for each state i one of the N_i possible decisions which can be made for this i. For this (not necessarily optimal) policy, let $h(i)$ be the expected profit over all future time discounted to the beginning of a period when this policy is used and when we are in state i at the beginning of the period. Then by analogy with (11-86), if $f(i)$ is the expected return for a period using this policy when we begin the period in state i, we see that $h(i)$ must satisfy

$$h(i) = f(i) + \alpha \sum_{j=1}^{M} p_{ij}h(j), \qquad j = 1, \ldots, M, \tag{11-88}$$

where the p_{ij} are the transition probabilities appropriate to this policy.

Suppose that we now write $\mathbf{P} = ||p_{ij}||$ and define the column vectors

$$\mathbf{h} = [h(1), \ldots, h(M)]; \qquad \mathbf{f} = [f(1), \ldots, f(M)]. \tag{11–89}$$

The vector form of (11–88) can then be written

$$\mathbf{h} = \mathbf{f} + \alpha\mathbf{P}\mathbf{h}, \tag{11–90}$$

or

$$(\mathbf{I} - \alpha\mathbf{P})\mathbf{h} = \mathbf{f}, \tag{11–91}$$

or

$$\mathbf{h} = (\mathbf{I} - \alpha\mathbf{P})^{-1}\mathbf{f}. \tag{11–92}$$

We are certain that $\mathbf{I} - \alpha\mathbf{P}$ has an inverse, since each row of $\mathbf{P}$ sums to unity, and thus each row of $\alpha\mathbf{P}$ sums to a number which is greater than 0 but less than 1. From the results of {LA 3–22} we know that this fact guarantees the existence of the inverse. Therefore, by solving the set of M simultaneous linear equations (11–92) we can determine uniquely the $h(i)$ for the given policy. As we shall show below, this observation can be used to assist us in determining an optimal policy.

Before going on to discuss the methods of determining an optimal policy, let us digress for a moment to illustrate the way in which the return for a k-stage process converges as the number of stages becomes infinite. Imagine that we have selected some, not necessarily optimal, policy and that we let $h_k(i)$ be the profit discounted to the beginning of the first period when there are k stages and we begin the first stage in state i. Then

$$\mathbf{h}_k = \mathbf{f} + \alpha\mathbf{P}\mathbf{h}_{k-1} \qquad \text{and} \qquad \mathbf{h}_1 = \mathbf{f}. \tag{11–93}$$

Hence

$$\mathbf{h}_2 = \mathbf{f} + \alpha\mathbf{P}\mathbf{f}, \qquad \mathbf{h}_3 = \mathbf{f} + \alpha\mathbf{P}\mathbf{h}_2 = \mathbf{f} + \alpha\mathbf{P}\mathbf{f} + \alpha^2\mathbf{P}^2\mathbf{f},$$

or

$$\mathbf{h}_k = \left(\sum_{j=0}^{k-1} \alpha^j\mathbf{P}^j\right)\mathbf{f}, \quad \mathbf{P}^0 = \mathbf{I}. \tag{11–94}$$

Now from {LA 3–22}, we know that since each row of $\alpha\mathbf{P}$ sums to a number greater than 0 but less than 1,

$$\sum_{j=0}^{\infty} \alpha^j\mathbf{P}^j = (\mathbf{I} - \alpha\mathbf{P})^{-1}. \tag{11–95}$$

Therefore, $\mathbf{h}_k$ does approach a unique limit as $k \to \infty$, which is $(\mathbf{I} - \alpha\mathbf{P})^{-1}\mathbf{f}$, that is, $\mathbf{h}$.

Let us now return to the problem of determining an optimal policy for operating the system under consideration, and of obtaining $\Lambda(i)$. Assume that we have selected an arbitrary policy, call it 0, and denote by $\mathbf{h}(0)$, $\mathbf{f}(0)$, and $\mathbf{P}_0$ the values of $\mathbf{h}$, $\mathbf{f}$ and $\mathbf{P}$ corresponding to this policy. Then (11–92) reads

$$\mathbf{h}(0) = (\mathbf{I} - \alpha\mathbf{P}_0)^{-1}\mathbf{f}(0).$$

Suppose then that we begin the first period in state i and agree to use policy 0 for all periods after the first, but not necessarily at the first period. For the first period we shall determine the decision which will maximize the discounted profit, given that we are going to use policy 0 after the first period. Thus we arrive at the decision to be made at the beginning of the first period by determining the u which maximizes

$$f(i, u) + \alpha \sum_{j=1}^{M} p_{ij}(u)h(j; 0),$$

where $h(j; 0)$ is the jth component of $\mathbf{h}(0)$. We do this for each i. This provides us with a new policy, call it 1, to be used at the first period and also with a set of $f(i, u)$ and $p_{ij}(u)$, which in vector and matrix notation we shall denote by $\mathbf{f}(1)$ and $\mathbf{P}_1$. Suppose now that we decide to use policy 1 for all periods. We can then compute the discounted profit corresponding to this policy by computing

$$\mathbf{h}(1) = (\mathbf{I} - \alpha\mathbf{P}_1)^{-1}\mathbf{f}(1).$$

We shall show that policy 1 is better than (or at least as good as) policy 0, that is, $\mathbf{h}(1) \geq \mathbf{h}(0)$. We can now repeat the procedure just outlined and assume that policy 1 will be used from period 2 onward; given this assumption, we determine the best policy for period 1, call it policy 2. Then $\mathbf{h}(2) \geq \mathbf{h}(1)$, and policy 2 is at least as good as policy 1. We shall also show that this iterative procedure must converge to an optimal policy in a finite number of steps.

Let us now provide the proofs of the two facts referred to in the previous paragraph. Assume that we have carried out r iterations of the process outlined above. We would like to show that $\mathbf{h}(r) \geq \mathbf{h}(r-1)$. From the method used to determine policy r, we know that

$$\mathbf{f}(r) + \alpha\mathbf{P}_r\mathbf{h}(r-1) \geq \mathbf{f}(r-1) + \alpha\mathbf{P}_{r-1}\mathbf{h}(r-1). \tag{11–96}$$

However,

$$\mathbf{h}(r-1) = \mathbf{f}(r-1) + \alpha\mathbf{P}_{r-1}\mathbf{h}(r-1);$$
$$\mathbf{h}(r) = \mathbf{f}(r) + \alpha\mathbf{P}_r\mathbf{h}(r). \tag{11–97}$$

Let $\mathbf{s} \geq \mathbf{0}$ be

$$\mathbf{s} = \mathbf{f}(r) - \mathbf{f}(r-1) + \alpha(\mathbf{P}_r - \mathbf{P}_{r-1})\mathbf{h}(r-1). \tag{11–98}$$

The fact that $\mathbf{s} \geq \mathbf{0}$ follows directly from (11–96). Next

$$\begin{aligned} \boldsymbol{\delta} = \mathbf{h}(r) - \mathbf{h}(r-1) &= \mathbf{f}(r) - \mathbf{f}(r-1) + \alpha \mathbf{P}_r \mathbf{h}(r) - \alpha \mathbf{P}_{r-1} \mathbf{h}(r-1) \\ &= \mathbf{s} + \alpha \mathbf{P}_r [\mathbf{h}(r) - \mathbf{h}(r-1)] \\ &= \mathbf{s} + \alpha \mathbf{P}_r \boldsymbol{\delta}, \end{aligned} \qquad (11\text{–}99)$$

or

$$\begin{aligned} \boldsymbol{\delta} &= (\mathbf{I} - \alpha \mathbf{P}_r)^{-1} \mathbf{s} = (\mathbf{I} + \alpha \mathbf{P}_r + \alpha^2 \mathbf{P}_r^2 + \cdots) \mathbf{s} \\ &= \mathbf{s} + \alpha \mathbf{P}_r \mathbf{s} + \alpha^2 \mathbf{P}_r^2 \mathbf{s} + \cdots \end{aligned} \qquad (11\text{–}100)$$

by (11–99). However, $\mathbf{s} \geq \mathbf{0}$, and every element of $\mathbf{P}_r$ is non-negative. Thus $\boldsymbol{\delta} = \mathbf{h}(r) - \mathbf{h}(r-1) \geq \mathbf{0}$, which is what we wished to show. We have thus proved that policy r is at least as good as policy $r - 1$. We shall now show that if there is no improvement in going from iteration r to iteration $r+1$, then policy r (and $r+1$) is an optimal policy. We can prove this by contradiction. Suppose that there is a policy r^* such that $\mathbf{h}(r^*) \geq \mathbf{h}(r)$, with the strict inequality holding for at least one component. Then

$$\mathbf{h}(r^*) - \mathbf{h}(r) = \boldsymbol{\delta}^* = (\mathbf{I} - \alpha \mathbf{P}_*)^{-1} \mathbf{s}^* = \mathbf{s}^* + \alpha \mathbf{P}_* \mathbf{s}^* + \cdots, \qquad (11\text{–}101)$$

where

$$\mathbf{s}^* = \mathbf{f}(r^*) - \mathbf{f}(r) + \alpha(\mathbf{P}_* - \mathbf{P}_r)\mathbf{h}(r).$$

Since at least one component of $\boldsymbol{\delta}^*$ is positive, it follows from (11–101) that at least one component of $\mathbf{s}^*$ is positive. Assume $s_i^* > 0$. However, this contradicts the fact that in choosing policy $r + 1$, we made the best decision when starting out in state i, because in going from r to $r+1$, we concluded that $\mathbf{s} = \mathbf{0}$. Therefore the iterative procedure must converge on an optimal policy. Since we have assumed that there is only a finite number of different policies, convergence must occur in a finite number of steps.

The iterative technique just described for finding an optimal policy suffers from the same limitations concerning the number of state parameters as the other techniques considered previously that applied to a finite number of stages. If there were two state parameters, each of which could take on 100 values, then there would be 10,000 different states i in which the system could find itself at the beginning of a period. Recall that at each step in the iterative procedure, it is necessary to solve a set of linear equations (11–92) having a number of variables equal to the number of states. With 10,000 states, it would be necessary to solve sets of equations involving 10,000 variables. There could be as many as 100 million nonzero coefficients in the matrix of the coefficients $\mathbf{I} - \alpha \mathbf{P}$. It would be an extremely difficult task to solve such a set of equations even on the largest computer presently available. If there were three state parameters, each of which could take on 100 values, it would be necessary to solve a set of linear equations containing one million variables. This is totally impossible at the present time.

The material discussed in this section was originally developed by Howard [7].

11–14 An example. By solving a trivial example in which there are only two states, and two decisions for each state, we shall illustrate how the iterative technique introduced in the previous section can be used to find an optimal policy for an infinite-stage process.

Once each year, a particular automobile manufacturer must make a decision on model changes for the next year. Imagine that at the time the decision is made, he can be considered to be in only one of two states: (1) the current model is selling well, (2) the current model is not doing well. If he has a successful model, then for the coming year, he can (a) keep essentially the same model or (b) try something new. If he does not have a successful model, he can (c) copy the competitor's successful model, or (d) try something new.

Assume that the transition probabilities for each state and each possible action are

$$p_{11}(a) = 0.6, \quad p_{12}(a) = 0.4, \quad p_{11}(b) = 0.7, \quad p_{12}(b) = 0.3,$$
$$p_{21}(c) = 0.4, \quad p_{22}(c) = 0.6, \quad p_{21}(d) = 0.5, \quad p_{22}(d) = 0.5.$$

In the above, $p_{11}(a)$ is the probability that the manufacturer will remain in state 1 if he is in state 1 and selects action (a), i.e., "keep essentially the present model." Denote by $R_{ij}(u)$ the profit for the coming year if he starts in state i, takes action u and is in state j for the next model year. Assume that

$$R_{11}(a) = 7, \quad R_{12}(a) = 1, \quad R_{11}(b) = 5, \quad R_{12}(b) = -1,$$
$$R_{21}(c) = 6, \quad R_{22}(c) = 0, \quad R_{21}(d) = 5, \quad R_{22}(d) = -2,$$

where the profits are in millions of dollars. If $f(i, u)$ is the expected profit for the coming year when he is currently in state i and takes action u, then

$$f(1, a) = 0.6(7) + 0.4(1) = 4.6, \quad f(1, b) = 0.7(5) + 0.3(-1) = 3.2,$$
$$f(2, c) = 0.4(6) + 0.6(0) = 2.4, \quad f(2, d) = 0.5(5) + 0.5(-2) = 1.5.$$

Let the discount factor be $\alpha = 0.90$.

We would like to determine the optimal action to take for each state so as to maximize the present worth of all future profits. We begin by selecting one of the (four) possible policies. Let us say that he uses action b if in state 1 and action c if in state 2. This is policy 0 in the notation of the previous section. For this policy

$$\mathbf{f}(0) = [3.2, 2.4], \qquad \mathbf{P}_0 = \begin{bmatrix} 0.7 & 0.3 \\ 0.4 & 0.6 \end{bmatrix}; \qquad \mathbf{I} - \alpha\mathbf{P}_0 = \begin{bmatrix} 0.37 & -0.27 \\ -0.36 & 0.46 \end{bmatrix}.$$

Now we compute $h(1;0)$ and $h(2;0)$, the present worth of all future profits if we use this policy and begin in states 1 and 2, respectively. These are found by solving the set of equations (11–92), which in this case become

$$0.37h(1;0) - 0.27h(2;0) = 3.2; \qquad -0.36h(1;0) + 0.46h(2;0) = 2.4.$$

The solution is $h(1;0) = 29.1$, $h(2;0) = 27.9$.

We next determine another policy which is at least as good as the current one. We do this by assuming that policy 0 will be used for the periods from 2 onward, but given this information we select an optimal policy for period 1. If we start out period 1 in state 1 and use action a for the first period, the discounted profit is

$$\begin{aligned} 4.6 + 0.9[0.6h(1;0) + 0.4h(2;0)] &= 4.6 + 0.9[0.6(29.1) + 0.4(27.9)] \\ &= 30.35, \end{aligned}$$

whereas if action b is used, the discounted profit is simply $h(1;0) = 29.1$. Thus, if we begin in state 1, action a is the action to adopt for policy 1. When we begin in state 2 and use action c, the discounted profit is $h(2;0) = 27.9$. If action d is used, the discounted profit is

$$1.5 + 0.9(0.5)[h(1;0) + h(2;0)] = 27.2.$$

Therefore action c is still preferred. The new policy, policy 1, then says to take action a if we are in state 1 and action c if we are in state 2.

Next we determine the present worth of all future profits given that policy 1 is used at all times and we begin in states 1 and 2, respectively. These are found by solving the set of equations

$$\begin{aligned} 0.46h(1;1) - 0.36h(2;1) &= 4.6, \\ -0.36h(1;1) + 0.46h(2;1) &= 2.4, \end{aligned}$$

which yields $h(1;1) = 36.25$ and $h(2;1) = 33.6$. Now we imagine that policy 1 will be used for the periods from 2 onward, but, given this information, an optimal policy is to be chosen for period 1. If we start in state 1 and use action a, the discounted profit is simply $h(1;1) = 36.25$, and if we use action b, the discounted profit is

$$3.2 + 0.9[0.7(36.25) + 0.3(33.6)] = 35.43.$$

Thus action a is preferred. If we begin in state 2 and use action c, the discounted profit is $h(2; 1) = 33.6$, and if we use action d, the discounted profit is

$$1.5 + 0.9(0.5)[36.25 + 33.6] = 33.0.$$

Therefore action c is preferred, and the new policy, policy 2, says to take action a if in state 1, and action c if in state 2. This is precisely the same as policy 1. An optimal policy has, then, been found, and it says that if the automobile manufacturer currently has a good model, he should keep the same model next year, and if he has a poor model, he should copy the competitor's model which is doing well. Note that here the optimal policy has the property that, for each state, it maximizes the gain in the coming year.

11–15 Optimality of pure strategies. In our discussion of stochastic sequential decision problems in the previous section we assumed that at the beginning of a period, knowing the state of the system at that time, the decision maker would select from a finite number of alternatives the optimal action to take. Note that the decision maker actually chooses the action to take. In game theory and statistical decision theory, one often considers more general types of *strategies*. Suppose that instead of actually selecting an action, the decision maker chooses a game of chance which will determine the action to take. The game of chance might, for example, correspond to the random selection of a ball from an urn. Assume that if the system is in state i at the beginning of a period, the game of chance will select action u with a probability v_{iu}, where

$$v_{iu} \geq 0, \qquad \sum_u v_{iu} = 1.$$

With this procedure, the decision maker lets the game of chance select the action to take, and does not know himself what action it will be until after playing the game of chance. The problem now becomes that of selecting the probabilities v_{iu} for the game so as to maximize the discounted expected profits. When a game of chance selects the action to take, we say that the decision maker is using a *mixed* strategy. Note that a *pure* strategy which says to take action u_1 is a special case of a mixed strategy for which $v_{iu_1} = 1$, $v_{iu} = 0$, $u \neq u_1$. We now wish to prove that there will always be at least one pure strategy which is optimal for the model of Section 11–13. In other words, it is not possible to increase the expected discounted profits by generalizing things so that mixed strategies are allowed.

The proof is easy. When mixed strategies are allowed, we specify a policy by selecting a set of $\sum_{i=1}^{m} N_i$ numbers v_{iu}, $v_{iu} \geq 0$, $\sum_u v_{iu} = 1$, which give the probability that action u will be taken if the system is in state i. Let the set v_{iu}^* constitute an optimal policy. If this policy has the property that for each i, only one v_{iu}^* is positive (and hence equal to unity), we have a pure strategy. We shall next show that if for at least one i, two or more $v_{iu}^* > 0$, so that we do not have a pure strategy, there nonetheless exists a pure strategy which is just as good.

When we use the policy characterized by the v_{iu}^*, the expected return in the first period is

$$\hat{f}(i) = \sum_u f(i, u)v_{iu}^*, \tag{11-102}$$

and the probability that the system will be in state j at the beginning of the second period, given that it begins in state i, is

$$\hat{p}_{ij} = \sum_u p_{ij}(u)v_{iu}^*. \tag{11-103}$$

Then the set of $h^*(i)$, $h^*(i)$ being the discounted profit over all future time when we begin in state i and use the optimal policy, is found by solving the set of equations

$$(\mathbf{I} - \alpha\hat{\mathbf{P}})\mathbf{h}^* = \hat{\mathbf{f}}. \tag{11-104}$$

Let us now turn to the iterative procedure introduced in Section 11-13 and imagine that the policy characterized by the v_{iu}^* will be used from period 2 onward, but that we are free to choose the policy for period 1. If we begin in state i, then for any set of v_{iu} used for the first period, the discounted expected profit becomes

$$\sum_u f(i, u)v_{iu} + \alpha \sum_{u,j} p_{ij}(u)v_{iu}h^*(j) = \sum_u \left[f(i, u) + \alpha \sum_j p_{ij}(u)h^*(j)\right] v_{iu}.$$

Let us write

$$\gamma_{it} = \max_u \left[f(i, u) + \alpha \sum_j p_{ij}(u)h^*(j)\right] = f(i, t) + \alpha \sum_j p_{ij}(t)h^*(j).$$

Then, since $v_{iu} \geq 0$, we have for any set of $v_{iu} \geq 0$, $\sum_u v_{iu} = 1$,

$$\sum_u \left[f(i, u) + \alpha \sum_j p_{ij}(u)h^*(j)\right] v_{ij} \leq \sum_u \gamma_{it}v_{iu} = \gamma_{it}.$$

Therefore, if we start out in state i, the pure stategy $v_{it} = 1$; $v_{iu} = 0$, $u \neq t$, is as good as any other. For each state i, we reach the same conclusion, that a pure strategy is as good as any mixed strategy. Thus we have obtained a new policy which is a pure strategy. However, by what we proved in Section 11-13 (the reader should check that the proof carries through to the case of mixed strategies), the new policy is at least as good as the original one. But the original mixed strategy was optimal. Hence the new pure strategy must be optimal also. Thus there will always be at least one pure strategy which is optimal.

11–16 Reduction to a linear programming problem. We shall now show that the problem formulated in Section 11–13 can be solved as a linear programming problem. That is, the $\Lambda(i)$ are the solutions to a linear programming problem which has the property that its solution can also be used to obtain an optimal policy. The basis for deriving the linear programming problem is the functional equation (11–86), which can be written

$$\Lambda(i) \geq f(i, u) + \alpha \sum_{j=1}^{M} p_{ij}(u)\Lambda(j), \qquad \text{all } u, \qquad i = 1, \ldots, M, \tag{11–105}$$

and, of course, the strict equality holds only for the optimal action (or actions if the optimal action is not unique). The inequalities of (11–105) can be rearranged to read

$$\Lambda(i) - \alpha \sum_{j=1}^{M} p_{ij}(u)\Lambda(j) \geq f(i, u), \qquad \text{all } u, \qquad i = 1, \ldots, M. \tag{11–106}$$

There are $\sum_{i=1}^{M} N_i$ of these inequalities. Consider then any set of x_j satisfying

$$x_i - \alpha \sum_{j=1}^{M} p_{ij}(u)x_j \geq f(i, u), \qquad \text{all } u, \qquad i = 1, \ldots, M. \tag{11–107}$$

Note that the $\Lambda(i)$ are a solution to (11–107) with the property that for each i, the strict equality will hold for at least one u. Then write $\mathbf{x}^* = [\Lambda(1), \ldots, \Lambda(M)]$. Let $\mathbf{x}$ be any other solution to (11–107). Let $\mathbf{x} = \mathbf{x}^* + \boldsymbol{\delta}$. Then

$$\Lambda(i) + \delta_i - \alpha \sum_{j=1}^{M} p_{ij}(u)\Lambda(j) - \alpha \sum_{j=1}^{M} p_{ij}(u)\,\delta_j \geq f(i, u), \qquad \text{all } i, u. \tag{11–108}$$

However, for each i, there is at least one u, call it u_i, for which

$$\Lambda(i) - \alpha \sum_{j=1}^{M} p_{ij}(u_i)\Lambda(j) = f(i, u_i).$$

If we subtract this from (11–108) evaluated at u_i, we obtain

$$\delta_i - \alpha \sum_{j=1}^{M} p_{ij}(u_i)\, \delta_j \geq 0, \qquad i = 1, \ldots, M,$$

or

$$\delta_i - \alpha \sum_{j=1}^{M} p_{ij}(u_i)\, \delta_j = d_i, \qquad d_i \geq 0, \qquad i = 1, \ldots, M.$$

On writing $\mathbf{P} = ||p_{ij}(u_i)||$, we obtain

$$(\mathbf{I} - \alpha\mathbf{P})\boldsymbol{\delta} = \mathbf{d}$$

or

$$\boldsymbol{\delta} = (\mathbf{I} - \alpha\mathbf{P})^{-1}\mathbf{d} = \mathbf{d} + \alpha\mathbf{P}\mathbf{d} + \alpha^2\mathbf{P}^2\mathbf{d} + \cdots \geq \mathbf{0},$$

since $\mathbf{d} \geq \mathbf{0}$ and each element of $\mathbf{P}$ is non-negative. Thus we have proved that $\boldsymbol{\delta} \geq \mathbf{0}$, or, equivalently, if $\mathbf{x}^*$ is a vector whose components are the $\Lambda(i)$, then $\mathbf{x} \geq \mathbf{x}^*$ for *every* other solution $\mathbf{x}$ to (11–107). Therefore, if we can find a solution $\mathbf{x}^*$ to (11–107) with the property that $\mathbf{x} \geq \mathbf{x}^*$ for any other solution $\mathbf{x}$, we will have found the $\Lambda(i)$. All we now need to observe is that if we solve the linear programming problem which seeks to minimize the objective function

$$z = \sum_{j=1}^{M} \epsilon_j x_j = \boldsymbol{\epsilon}\mathbf{x} \tag{11–109}$$

subject to the constraints (11–107), where each ϵ_j can be an arbitrary positive number, then an optimal solution will be $\mathbf{x}^*$. Denote an optimal solution by $\mathbf{x}_0$. Then $\mathbf{x}_0 = \mathbf{x}^*$ if $\mathbf{x} \geq \mathbf{x}_0$ for all other solutions $\mathbf{x}$. This will follow immediately if we can show that for each i, there will be at least one u such that $\mathbf{x}_0$ satisfies (11–107) as a strict equality, since we can then consider any other solution $\mathbf{x}_0 + \boldsymbol{\delta}$ and use the argument given previously to demonstrate that it must be true that $\boldsymbol{\delta} \geq \mathbf{0}$. To prove that for each i there is at least one u such that $\mathbf{x}_0$ satisfies (11–107) as a strict equality, suppose that for $i \in I_>$, $I_>$ not empty, the strict inequality holds for every u. We shall then show that one can find a new solution $\mathbf{x}_1 = \mathbf{x}_0 - \boldsymbol{\rho}$, $\boldsymbol{\rho} \geq \mathbf{0}$, with at least one component of $\boldsymbol{\rho}$ positive. To do this, select for each $i \notin I_>$ one constraint which is satisfied as a strict equality by $\mathbf{x}_0$. This must also be satisfied as a strict equality by $\mathbf{x}_1$. Thus it must be true that

$$\rho_i - \alpha \sum_{j=1}^{M} p_{ij}(u_i)\rho_j = 0, \qquad i \notin I_>.$$

Next select any u_i for each $i \in I_>$. Assume that

$$x_i^0 - \alpha \sum_{j=1}^{M} p_{ij}(u_i)x_j^0 = f(i, u_i) + g_i, \qquad g_i > 0, \qquad i \in I_>.$$

We shall attempt to find ρ_j so that these constraints hold as strict equalities, i.e.,

$$x_i^0 - \rho_i - \alpha \sum_{j=1}^{M} p_{ij}(u_i)(x_j^0 - \rho_j) = f(i, u_i), \qquad i \in I_>,$$

or

$$\rho_i - \alpha \sum_{j=1}^{M} p_{ij}(u_i)\rho_j = g_i, \qquad i \in I_>.$$

Thus if we can determine ρ_j satisfying

$$\rho_i - \alpha \sum_{j=1}^{M} p_{ij}(u_i)\rho_j = 0, \qquad i \notin I_>,$$

$$\rho_i - \alpha \sum_{j=1}^{M} p_{ij}(u_i)\rho_j = g_i, \qquad i \in I_>,$$

we shall have a new solution where for each i, there is at least one u such that (11–107) is satisfied as a strict equality. This is possible since the above set of equations has the unique solution

$$\boldsymbol{\rho} = (\mathbf{I} - \alpha\mathbf{P})^{-1}\mathbf{g} \geq \mathbf{0},$$

where $\mathbf{g}$ has all components zero except those for $i \in I_>$, which have the value g_i. Thus we have a new solution $\mathbf{x}_1 = \mathbf{x}_0 - \boldsymbol{\rho}$, with $\boldsymbol{\rho} \geq \mathbf{0}$ and at least one component of $\boldsymbol{\rho}$ positive. But this is a contradiction, since

$$z_1 = \boldsymbol{\epsilon}\mathbf{x}_1 = z_0 - \boldsymbol{\epsilon\rho} < z_0 = \boldsymbol{\epsilon}\mathbf{x}_0,$$

and the original solution $\mathbf{x}_0$ was not optimal. Thus for each i, $\mathbf{x}_0$ must satisfy (11–107) as a strict equality for at least one u, and therefore $\mathbf{x} \geq \mathbf{x}_0$ for every solution $\mathbf{x}$. Hence $\mathbf{x}_0 = \mathbf{x}^*$, which is what we wished to show.

We have proved that the $\Lambda(i)$ are an optimal solution to the linear programming problem with constraints (11–107) and objective function (11–109), where the objective function is to be minimized and the variables are unrestricted. To determine an optimal policy, all we need to do is observe which of the constraints (11–107) hold as strict equalities for the optimal solution. The u for which a constraint for state i holds as a strict equality is an optimal action if we start a period in state i.

11-17 The dual linear programming problem. It will be noted that the linear programming problem discussed in the preceding section has $\sum_{i=1}^{M} N_i$ constraints, i.e. a number which is usually much larger than the number of variables (which is equal to M, the number of states). This suggests that we should solve the problem by solving the dual. There are $\sum N_i$ dual variables w_{iu}, and the dual problem is

$$\sum_u w_{ju} - \alpha \sum_{i,u} p_{ij}(u) w_{iu} = \epsilon_j, \qquad j = 1, \ldots, M,$$

$$w_{iu} \geq 0, \qquad \text{all } i, u, \tag{11-110}$$

$$\max Z = \sum_{i,u} f(i, u) w_{iu}.$$

In the dual the constraints hold as strict equalities because the primal variables are unrestricted in sign. By the complementary slackness principle, we know that the only w_{iu} which can be positive in an optimal solution to the dual are those for which the corresponding primal constraint holds as a strict equality for the corresponding optimal solution to the primal. Therefore only those w_{iu} can be positive for which u is an optimal action when we begin in state i.

It is possible to give an interesting interpretation to the dual problem (11-110) by reinterpreting the original one. We have viewed the original problem as representing a process which will continue to operate for all future time, and at the beginning of each period, will always be in one of M states. The factor α discounts costs known at the end of a period to the beginning of the period. Let us now consider a different problem in which there are $M + 1$ states, M of the states are as before, but the $(M + 1)$-state has the property that if the system gets into this state, call it state 0, the process terminates, and hence the system can never leave this state. Assume that if the system gets into state 0 the profit over all future time is zero, that is, $\Lambda(0) = 0$. Let $1 - \alpha$ be the probability that the process will terminate during the period if it begins the period in one of the states $i = 1, \ldots, M$; α is the probability that the process will not terminate. Then $p_{ij}(u)$ will be the conditional probability that if we begin the period in state i and use action u, then the system will be in state j at the beginning of the next period, given that the process does not terminate. The probability that the system will be in state j at the end of the period if we begin the period in state i and use action u is therefore $\alpha p_{ij}(u)$, since α is the probability that the process does not terminate. If we begin the period in state i, the probability that the process will terminate, i.e., end in state 0, is $1 - \alpha$, regardless of what action is taken. If the $\Lambda(i)$ are defined to be the expected profit over all future time (*not discounted*) when we begin a period in state i and make an optimal decision at the beginning of this and all future periods, the functional equation for $\Lambda(i)$ becomes

$$\Lambda(i) = \max_u \left[f(i, u) + \alpha \sum_j p_{ij}(u)\Lambda(j) + (1 - \alpha)\Lambda(0) \right]$$

$$= \max_u \left[f(i, u) + \alpha \sum_j p_{ij}(u)\Lambda(j) \right], \quad i = 1, \ldots, M. \tag{11–111}$$

These are precisely the same equations as in (11–86). Thus the new problem is mathematically equivalent to the original one.

Let us now interpret (11–110) in terms of the new problem for which there is no discounting, but a probability $1 - \alpha$ of terminating the process in each period. We have shown previously that even if we allow the use of mixed strategies, at least one pure strategy will be optimal. Let us consider the case where mixed strategies are allowed, and let v_{iu} be the probability that action u will be taken if we begin a period in state i. Let $q_k(i)$ be the probability that we begin period k in state i (this will depend on the state in which we began the first period). Then in accordance with (11–87),

$$q_{k+1}(j) = \alpha \sum_{i,u} q_k(i)v_{iu}p_{ij}(u) = \alpha \sum_i q_k(i)\hat{p}_{ij},$$

$$j = 1, \ldots, M, \tag{11–112}$$

$$\hat{p}_{ij} = \sum_u v_{iu}p_{ij}(u), \qquad \sum_j \hat{p}_{ij} = \sum_u v_{iu}\left[\sum_j p_{ij}(u)\right] = 1. \tag{11–113}$$

Since $\alpha \sum_j \hat{p}_{ij} = \alpha < 1$, it follows that as $n \to \infty$, $(\alpha\hat{\mathbf{P}})^n \to \mathbf{0}$\{LA 3–22\}, and hence, if $\mathbf{q}_k = (q_k(1), \ldots, q_k(M))$,

$$\lim_{n \to 0} \mathbf{q}_{k+n} = \mathbf{q}_k(\alpha\hat{\mathbf{P}})^n = \mathbf{0}, \tag{11–114}$$

and the probability that the system is in any one of the states $i = 1, \ldots, M$ at the beginning of a period approaches zero. The reason for this, of course, is that in each period there is a probability $1 - \alpha$ that the process will terminate, so that the probability that the process has terminated (is in state 0) approaches unity as $k \to \infty$.

Let us try to modify the situation so that the $q_k(i)$ approach unique limits (not zero) as $k \to \infty$. To do this we must counteract the fact that the process can terminate during any period. We shall do this by imagining that if the process terminates during a period, we shall start it again at the beginning of the next period. Let ρ_i be the conditional probability that we start the process in state i, given that it terminated during the previous period. Since we wish to require that the process be started up again if it terminates in the previous period, it must be true that $\sum_i \rho_i = 1$. The probability that the process will terminate in a period is $1 - \alpha$. Thus $\epsilon_i = (1 - \alpha)\rho_i$ is the unconditional probability that we shall start the process in state i at the beginning of a period.

With this assumption, i.e. if the process terminates during some period, it will be started again at the beginning of the next period, we find that at the beginning of any period, the system will always be in one of the states i, $i = 1, \ldots, M$. We shall attempt to determine a set of $q(i)$, $q(i)$ being the probability that the system is in state i at the beginning of a period, which are independent of k. The system is said to be in a steady-state mode of operation or in statistical equilibrium if the probabilities that the system is in any state i, $i = 1, \ldots, M$, at the beginning of a period are independent of time. If the process is in state i at the beginning of a period, it was either operating previously or was started at the beginning of the period in state i. Thus it must be true that

$$q(j) = \alpha \sum_{i=1}^{M} q(i)\hat{p}_{ij} + \epsilon_j \tag{11-115}$$

or

$$\mathbf{q} = \mathbf{q}(\alpha\hat{\mathbf{P}}) + \boldsymbol{\epsilon};$$

that is,

$$\mathbf{q} = \boldsymbol{\epsilon}(\mathbf{I} - \alpha\hat{\mathbf{P}})^{-1}, \tag{11-116}$$

since the inverse of $\mathbf{I} - \alpha\hat{\mathbf{P}}$ exists. Thus with our interpretation of the process, the steady-state $q(i)$-values do exist. If they are to be probabilities and it is to be true that the system will always be in one of the states i, $i = 1, \ldots, M$, at the beginning of a period, it must be true that $\sum_{i=1}^{M} q(i) = 1$. If we sum (11-115) over j, we obtain

$$\sum_{j=1}^{M} q(j) = \alpha \sum_{i=1}^{M} q(i)\left[\sum_{j=1}^{M} \hat{p}_{ij}\right] + \sum_{j=1}^{M} \epsilon_j, \tag{11-117}$$

or by (11-113),

$$\sum_{i=1}^{M} q(i) = \frac{1}{1-\alpha} \sum_{i=1}^{M} \epsilon_i. \tag{11-118}$$

However, we previously defined ϵ_i to be $(1 - \alpha)\rho_i$. Thus

$$\sum_{i=1}^{M} \epsilon_i = (1 - \alpha) \sum_{i=1}^{M} \rho_i = (1 - \alpha),$$

and $\sum_{i=1}^{M} q(i) = 1$, as desired. Now write

$$w_{iu} = q(i)v_{iu}, \tag{11-119}$$

so that w_{iu} is the joint steady-state probability that we begin a period in state i and take action u. Because $\sum_u v_{iu} = 1$ and because of (11–113), (11–115), we can write

$$\sum_u w_{ju} - \alpha \sum_{i,u} w_{iu} p_{ij}(u) = \epsilon_j, \tag{11–120}$$

$$w_{iu} \geq 0, \qquad \text{all } i, u,$$

$$\sum_{i,u} w_{iu} = 1. \tag{11–121}$$

We are now ready to return to the dual problem (11–110), and interpret it physically. Let us assume that in the dual problem (11–110), we have chosen the $\epsilon_j > 0$ in such a way that $\sum \epsilon_j = 1 - \alpha$. Then the dual variables w_{iu} can be interpreted in the sense outlined above as the steady-state probabilities that we will be in state i at the beginning of a period and will take action u. The dual problem indicates that the optimal values of the w_{iu} are found by maximizing the expected profit per period.

11–18 Additional developments. The dual problem suggests several other things that are of interest. Consider a process in which there is no discounting and which never terminates, but is always in one of the M states i, $i = 1, \ldots, M$, at the beginning of a period. Then for this system, all the $\Lambda(i)$ as defined above would be infinite since $\alpha = 1$. Suppose, however, that instead of attempting to maximize the profit over all future time, we agree to maximize the expected profit per period (or equivalently, the average annual profit). We shall also assume that the $\hat{p}_{ij}$ of (11–113) have the property that even though for a given i and j, it may be true that $\hat{p}_{ij} = 0$, it is nonetheless true that if we start a period in state i, we can ultimately reach any other state j (although perhaps not at the next period). Mathematically this means that for every i and j, there is an n (which may depend on i and j) such that the jth component of $\mathbf{e}_i'\hat{\mathbf{P}}^n$ is positive. (A Markov process with this characteristic is called *ergodic*.) In this event, there exists a unique set of steady-state probabilities $q(i)$, each of which is positive, which satisfies

$$\mathbf{q} = \mathbf{q}\hat{\mathbf{P}}, \qquad \sum_{i=1}^{M} q(i) = 1. \tag{11–122}$$

(We ask the reader to prove this in Problem 11–15.) It then follows that the process can never terminate, and hence we do not need to introduce probabilities of starting up the process to ensure that positive steady-state probabilities $q(i)$ will exist.

Let us then define w_{iu} to be the steady-state probability that the system is in state i at the beginning of a period and the decision maker will choose action u. Let us determine an optimal policy (i.e., the w_{iu}) so as to maximize the expected profit per period. This then gives rise to the linear programming problem

$$\begin{aligned} \sum_u w_{ju} - \sum_{i,u} w_{iu}p_{ij}(u) &= 0, \qquad j = 1, \ldots, M, \\ \sum_{i,u} w_{iu} &= 1 \\ w_{iu} \geq 0, &\qquad \text{all } i, u, \\ \max z &= \sum_{i,u} f(i, u)w_{iu}. \end{aligned} \tag{11-123}$$

An optimal policy will be characterized by the positive w_{iu}. Usually, for a given i, only one $w_{iu} > 0$, and then u is the action to be taken if we begin a period in state i.

For a system in which there are only 100 possible states, the linear programming problem (11-110) would have 100 constraints and perhaps 1000 or more variables, whereas problem (11-123) would have 101 constraints and perhaps 1000 variables. Although linear programming problems of this size can readily be solved, they are rather large. For more realistic situations in which there are 1000 or more states, the resulting linear programming problems would have the same number of constraints. At present we are not able to handle problems of this size. The linear programming formulation of the problem involving discounting (or equivalently a process which might terminate) was originally developed by d'Epenoux [4], and form (11-123) for the case without discounting was developed by Manne [8].

The procedures introduced above can easily be generalized to handle dynamic situations with a finite number of periods in which the transition probabilities and possibly the actions which can be taken change from one period to the next. An example of the sort of situation we have in mind is the dynamic inventory model studied in Section 10-18. We shall suppose that at the beginning of period k, the system will be in one of M_k states. The number of states may change from one period to the next. If period k is begun in state i, we shall assume that there are N_{ik} actions which may be taken; a particular action will be denoted by u. Let $f_k(i, u)$ be the expected profit from period k if we begin in state i and take action u, and let $p_{ij}(u, k)$ be the probability that the system will be in state j at the beginning of period $k + 1$ if it is in state i at the beginning of period k and action u is taken at the beginning of this period. We shall allow mixed strategies. Again it is true that at least one pure strategy will be optimal.

We ask the reader to prove this in Problem 11–16. Denote by w_{kiu} the probability that the system will be in state i at the beginning of period k and that action u will be taken. We shall imagine that there are a total of n periods in the planning horizon, and that we wish to maximize the discounted expected profit over the planning horizon. We assume that we know the state that the system is in at the beginning of the first period; it will be denoted by r, and v_{ru} will denote the probability that action u will be taken at the beginning of the first period. Then the w_{kiu}, v_{ru} must satisfy the constraints

$$\sum_u w_{2ju} - \sum_u v_{ru}p_{rj}(u, 1) = 0, \qquad j = 1, \ldots, M_1, \tag{11–124}$$

$$\sum_u w_{k+1,ju} - \sum_{i,u} w_{kiu}p_{ij}(u, k) = 0,$$

$$k = 2, \ldots, n-1, \quad j = 1, \ldots, M_k, \tag{11–125}$$

$$\sum_u v_{ru} = 1, \tag{11–126}$$

$$\sum_{i,u} w_{kiu} = 1, \qquad k = 2, \ldots, n, \tag{11–127}$$

$$v_{ru} \geq 0, \quad \text{all } u; \qquad w_{kiu} \geq 0, \quad \text{all } k, i, u. \tag{11–128}$$

We wish to maximize the discounted profit subject to the above constraints. The discounted profit is

$$z = \sum_u f_1(r, u)v_{ru} + \sum_{k,i,u} \alpha^{k-1}f_k(i, u)w_{kiu}. \tag{11–129}$$

Here we have a linear programming problem, which unfortunately will, in general, be a very large one. For example, if there were 10 periods, with 100 states possible each period, and 10 actions per state, the problem would have about 1000 constraints and 10,000 variables. As noted above, a problem of such size could not be solved with standard linear programming codes. The constraints have a simple form which makes it possible to solve the problem by using special techniques, such as the decomposition principle. However, one is still confronted with a very large linear programming problem. The computational technique of dynamic programming is a much more efficient technique of solving problems of this type. Although we have not found a better computational technique than dynamic programming, we have at least shown that the type of sequential decision problem introduced in Section 5–3 can be formulated as a linear programming problem if the variables are treated as discrete.

11–19 Final remarks on the dimensionality problem. In this chapter we have been concerned mostly with the application of dynamic programming to the solution of multistage problems in which more than a single state parameter is needed in the state functions and/or more than a single control variable must be determined at each stage. We have found that the computational difficulties increase very fast with the number of state parameters, and most cases involving four or more parameters exceed the capacity of present-day computers. Problems with three state parameters can sometimes be solved—but not always. The problem is made much worse, of course, if more than a single control variable must be determined at each stage. The difficulties are due to two facts: (1) the demands made on the computer memory become huge as the number of state parameters increase, and (2) for each possible combination of parameters, one must determine Λ_k by carrying out an optimization over one or more variables. In certain cases, we saw that optimal policies could be obtained by iterative methods or that alternative formulations such as linear programming were possible. None of these removed or appreciably reduced the difficulties brought about by the dimensionality problem.

Very little progress has been made in the direction of overcoming the dimensionality problem. The basic problem is a combinatorial one—it is necessary to consider all possible combinations of the state parameters. Now it is, in general, true that a very large fraction of the combinations of the state parameters have no real influence on the problem, since either the probability of their occurrence is sufficiently small to be ignored or they represent situations so unprofitable that they are irrelevant. Thus one might hope that a procedure could be developed that would eliminate a great number of these combinations and solve the problem either exactly or approximately by considering only a very small percentage of the possible combinations. In a few situations, special techniques have been developed to exploit this aspect. The simplex method of linear programming is one example. Little has been accomplished, however, except in these few very special cases.

References

1. Beckmann, M. J., "Production Smoothing and Inventory Control," *Operations Research*, **9**, 1961, pp. 456–476. This paper illustrates how the functional equations of dynamic programming can be used to characterize the nature of an optimal policy when there are two state parameters.

2. Bellman, R., *Dynamic Programming*. Princeton, N. J.: Princeton University Press, 1957.

3. Bellman, R., and S. Dreyfus, *Applied Dynamic Programming*. Princeton, N. J.: Princeton University Press, 1962.

4. D'EPENOUX, F., "Sur un probleme de production et de stockage dans l'aléatoire," *Revue Française de recherche opérationnelle*, **4,** 1960, pp. 3–15. "A Probabilistic Production and Inventory Problem," *Management Science*, **10,** 1963, pp. 98–108. (A translation with some modifications of the French original.)

5. GUILBAUD, G. TH., "Programmes dynamiques et programmes linéaires. Note sur un modèle de R. Bellman," *Cahiers du Bureau universitaire de recherche opérationnelle*, **2,** 1957.

6. HOLT, C., F. MODIGLIANI, J. MUTH, and H. SIMON, *Planning Production, Inventories, and Work Force.* Englewood Cliffs, N. J.: Prentice-Hall, 1960.

7. HOWARD, R., *Dynamic Programming and Markov Processes.* Cambridge, Mass.: Technology Press, 1960.

8. MANNE, A. S., "Linear Programming and Sequential Decisions," *Management Science*, **6,** 1960, pp. 259–267.

9. SIMON, H. A., "Dynamic Programming Under Uncertainty with a Quadratic Function," *Econometrica*, **24,** 1956, pp. 74–81.

10. THEIL, H., "Econometric Models and Welfare Maximisation," *Weltwirtschaftliches Archiv*, **72,** 1954, pp. 60–83.

11. THEIL, H., "A Note on Certainty Equivalence in Dynamic Planning," *Econometrica*, **25,** 1957, pp. 346–349.

12. WAGNER, H., "On the Optimality of Pure Strategies," *Management Science*, **6,** 1960, pp. 268–269.

PROBLEMS

11–1. For the problems studied in Sections 11–2 and 11–3, prove that if the $f_j(x_j)$ or $f_j(x_j, y_j)$ are continuous functions, then the $\Lambda_k(\xi_1, \xi_2)$ are continuous functions of ξ_1 and ξ_2.

11–2. Consider the programming problem $\mathbf{Ax} \leq \boldsymbol{\xi}$, $\mathbf{0} \leq \mathbf{x} \leq \mathbf{d}$, $\max z = f(\mathbf{x})$, where $f(\mathbf{x})$ is a concave function. Prove that the optimal value of z is a concave function of $\boldsymbol{\xi}$. Of what relevance is this result for Sections 11–5 and 11–6?

11–3. For the problem studied in Section 11–3, prove that if the $f_j(x_j, y_j)$ are convex (concave) functions, the $\Omega_k(x_k, y_k; \xi_1, \xi_2)$ and $\Lambda_k(\xi_1, \xi_2)$ are also convex (concave) functions.

11–4. Consider the following problem:

$$x_1 - x_2 = 0; \quad x_1 + x_2 \leq 3; \quad x_1, x_2 \geq 0, \quad x_1, x_2 \text{ integers};$$
$$\max z = 2x_1 + 3x_2.$$

Show that there does not exist a Lagrange multiplier λ such that one can find an optimal solution by minimizing

$$2x_1 + 3x_2 + \lambda(x_1 - x_2)$$

subject to the constraint $x_1 + x_2 \leq 3$. [*Hint:* Note that for any specified λ, an optimal solution to the latter problem is either (0, 3) or (3, 0), but never (1, 1), which is the optimal solution to the given problem.]

11–5. Show that if the variables in the problem referred to in Problem 11–4 are allowed to vary continuously, then there is a λ with the desired properties. Plot $S = x_1 - x_2$ as a function of λ and note the very peculiar behavior of this curve. Would convergence difficulties be encountered in an attempt to find the proper λ?

11–6. For the problem of Section 11–2, prove that if the variables x_j are continuous and the $f_j(x_j)$ are concave, then the Lagrange multiplier technique can be used. [*Hint:* Apply the theory of Chapter 6 to show that there exist two Lagrange multipliers with the property that the Lagrangian function has a saddle point.] Next use the same theory to show that the same Lagrangian function is obtained for a proper choice of λ_1 as one applies the theory to the problem of maximizing $z + \lambda_1(b_1 - \sum_j a_{1j}x_j)$ subject to $x_j \geq 0$, $\sum_j a_{2j}x_j \leq b_2$.

11–7. Consider a transportation problem with two origins and five destinations. The availability at origin 1 is 10 and at origin 2 is 15. The destination requirements are 7, 3, 5, 8, and 2, respectively. The transportation costs as a function of the number of units x_{ij} shipped are shown in the following tableau. Find the x_{ij}^*.

1	$3x_{11}^2$	$4x_{12}$	$2x_{13}^2$	$5x_{14}^{1/2}$	$3x_{15}$
2	$4x_{21}$	$2x_{22}^2$	$5x_{23}^{1/2}$	$3x_{24}$	$2x_{25}^2$

11–8. Given: an equipment replacement problem which involves the simultaneous consideration of two machines when the possible decisions are to keep both, replace one or the other, or replace both. Formulate this problem in terms of the recurrence relations of dynamic programming.

11–9. Generalize the situation considered in Problem 11–8 to the case where there are m machines and the required output expressed as a function of time is known (for example, the required output may be specified to increase at 5 percent per year).

11–10. Consider a problem in the calculus of variations which seeks to find a function $y(x)$ minimizing

$$I = \int_\alpha^\beta F(y, y', x)\, dx$$

when it is also required that $y(x)$ satisfy the constraint

$$\int_\alpha^\beta G(y, y', x)\, dx = \gamma.$$

Show that the problem can be solved by dynamic programming with the introduction of two state variables. Also show the introduction of a Lagrange multiplier will reduce the problem to one in a single state variable.

11–11. In Eq. (11–62) determine the G_j in terms of the other parameters introduced in the cost functions.

11–12. Express the $\mathbf{h}$, $\mathbf{q}$, $\mathbf{H}$, $\mathbf{Q}$ and β introduced in Eq. (11–66) in terms of the G_j.

11–13. Determine the structure of $\mathbf{R}$ in Eq. (11–74) and obtain the set of equations to be solved for $\mathbf{u}$.

11–14. Show how the inventory model of Section 10–18 can be cast into the form of the problem studied in Section 11–12. What are the states? How does one decide how many to include? What are the actions? Determine the $p_{ij}(u)$ and $f(i,u)$.

11–15. Prove that for an ergodic Markov process, the steady-state probabilities $q(i)$ exist, are unique, and each $q(i) > 0$. [*Hint:* The vector $\mathbf{q}$ must satisfy $\mathbf{q}(\mathbf{I} - \hat{\mathbf{P}}) = \mathbf{0}$, where $\mathbf{I} - \hat{\mathbf{P}}$ is singular.] Show, however, that it is possible to solve uniquely for all the $q(i)$, $i = 1, \ldots, M - 1$, in terms of $q(M)$, and that the matrix obtained by crossing off the last row and column of $\mathbf{I} - \hat{\mathbf{P}}$ is indeed nonsingular and can be expanded in a power series.

11–16. Prove that for the dynamic problem with n periods studied in Section 11–18, at least one pure strategy will be optimal. [*Hint:* Do this one stage at a time, working backward, just as we would proceed in solving the problem numerically.]

11–17. Consider the problem discussed in Section 11–3. Suppose that we guess initially that x_j^0 is the optimal value of x_j. Then we solve the problem

$$\max z_0 = \sum_{j=1}^{n} f_j(x_j^0, y_j),$$

$$\sum_{j=1}^{n} a_{2j} y_j \leq b_2; \qquad y_j \geq 0, \qquad j = 1, \ldots, n; \qquad y_j \text{ integers},$$

to obtain a set of values y_j^0. Next we solve the problem

$$\max z_1 = \sum_{j=1}^{n} f_j(x_j, y_j^0),$$

$$\sum_{j=1}^{n} a_{1j} x_j \leq b_1; \qquad x_j \geq 0, \qquad j = 1, \ldots, n; \qquad x_j \text{ integers},$$

to yield a set of values x_j^1. Next we use the x_j^1 to compute a set of y_j^1. Show that this iterative procedure is such that $z_0 \leq z_1 \leq z_2 \leq \cdots$ Thus demonstrate that the iterative procedure converges to a relative maximum of z. Show geometrically by a one-stage example that the procedure need not converge to the absolute maximum of z.

11–18. Show that if we were using a Lagrange multiplier to solve the problem of Section 11–2 as described in Section 11–7, then we would expect $\sum_j a_{2j} x_j$ to increase monotonically as λ is varied from $-\infty$ to ∞, where the x_j are an optimal solution to the problem of Eq. (11–29).

11–19. Show how one might use a Lagrange multiplier as an aid in solving a cargo-loading problem of the type discussed in Section 10–6 when there is in addition a constraint on the total weight.

11–20. Show how one could use a Lagrange multipler as an aid in solving a reliability problem of the type discussed in Problem 10–6 when there is in addition a weight constraint.

11–21. Solve the example of Section 11–14 by the linear programming formulation introduced in Section 11–17.

11–22. Suppose that it is known that the constraint involving the y_j will hold as a strict equality for an optimal solution to the problem of Eq. (11–9). Show how we can use a Lagrange multiplier as an aid in solving the problem. Note that after introducing the multiplier one obtains a problem in which there is only a single state parameter, but it is necessary to maximize over two variables at each stage. What, then, is the interval over which y_j can range?

11–23. Explain why the problem of Section 11–3 cannot be considered to be a dynamic programming problem with $2n$ stages.

11–24. What sort of an economic interpretation can be given to the linear programming problem of Eqs. (11–107) and (11–109)?

11–25. Prove that the iterative method of finding an optimal policy which was developed in Section 11–13 can be used without modification if mixed strategies are allowed.

11–26. In Section 10–18, we studied an inventory problem in which it was assumed that the density function $\phi_k(v_k)$ for the demand in period k was known for each k in the planning horizon. Consider now a different situation where the density function for the demand in period k may be one of a finite number of different functions $\phi_{ik}(v_k)$. If the density function turns out to be $\phi_{ik}(v_k)$, we shall say that the system is in demand state i in period k. Let us assume that the demand state cannot be predicted with certainty ahead of time. However, if the system is in demand state i at the beginning of period k, the probability that it will be in demand state j at the beginning of period $k + 1$ is $p_{ij}(k)$. The remainder of the problem is assumed to be as described in Section 10–18. Show how dynamic programming can be used to solve such a problem when the demand state for the first state is known. [*Hint:* Two state parameters are needed in this case. Assume that at the beginning of a period the decision maker knows the demand state.] Problems of this sort have been considered by Iglehart and Karlin, Chapter 8 of *Studies in Applied Probability and Management Science*, edited by Arrow, Karlin, and Scarf, and published by Stanford University Press.

11–27. Work out explicitly in terms of the relevant parameters the form of the linear decision rules discussed in Section 11–11, given (a) that there is only one period in the planning horizon, and (b) that there are two periods.

INDEX

INDEX

Printed in Japan CDE6987

A, B on shelf